COMPARATIVE ENDOCRINOLOGY

Volume I
Glandular Hormones

COMPARATIVE ENDOCRINOLOGY

A Treatise in Two Volumes

VOLUME I
GLANDULAR
HORMONES

VOLUME II

Part One

INVERTEBRATE
HORMONES

Part Two

TISSUE
HORMONES

COMPARATIVE ENDOCRINOLOGY

EDITED BY

U. S. von Euler

Fysiologiska Institutionen, Karolinska Institutet, Stockholm, Sweden

H. Heller

Department of Pharmacology, University of Bristol, Bristol, England

VOLUME I

GLANDULAR
HORMONES

1963

ACADEMIC PRESS
NEW YORK AND LONDON

ACADEMIC PRESS INC.
111 Fifth Avenue, New York 3, New York

United Kingdom Edition published by
ACADEMIC PRESS INC. (LONDON) LTD.
Berkeley Square House, London W.1

LIBRARY OF CONGRESS CATALOG CARD NUMBER: 63–16982

PRINTED IN THE UNITED STATES OF AMERICA

CONTRIBUTORS

Numbers in parentheses indicate pages on which the authors' contributions begin.

D. BELLAMY, Department of Zoology, University of Sheffield, Sheffield, England (208)

J. BERTHET, Laboratory of Physiological Chemistry, University of Louvain, Belgium (410)

U. S. VON EULER, Fysiologiska Institutionen, Karolinska Institutet, Stockholm, Sweden (258)

CLAUDE FORTIER, Faculté de Médecine, Université Laval, Québec, P.Q., Canada (1)

A. GORBMAN, Barnard College, Columbia University, New York, New York (291)

ROY O. GREEP, Harvard School of Dental Medicine, Boston, Massachusetts (325)

H. HELLER, Department of Pharmacology, University of Bristol, Bristol, England (25)

J. N. KARKUN, Central Drug Research Institute, Chattar Manzil Palace, Lucknow, India (81)

E. KNOBIL, Department of Physiology, The University of Pittsburgh School of Medicine, Pittsburgh, Pennsylvania (447)

F. W. LANDGREBE, Department of Materia Medica and Pharmacology, Welsh National School of Medicine, The Parade, Cardiff, Wales (81)

CHOH HAO LI, Hormone Research Laboratory, University of California, Berkeley, California (428)

J. G. PHILLIPS,* Department of Zoology, University of Sheffield, Sheffield, England (208)

R. SANDLER, Department of Physiology, The University of Pittsburgh School of Medicine, Pittsburgh, Pennsylvania (447)

G. J. VAN OORDT,† Department of Zoology, University of Utrecht, Utrecht, The Netherlands (154)

WEIERT VELLE, Department of Reproductive Physiology and Pathology, The Veterinary College of Norway, Oslo, Norway (111)

F. G. YOUNG, Department of Biochemistry, University of Cambridge, Cambridge, England (371)

---

* Present address: Department of Zoology, University of Hong Kong, Hong Kong.
† Deceased April 22, 1963.

PREFACE

The aim of this book is to give readers with some basic knowledge of animal morphology, physiology, and chemistry, a systematic and comprehensive account of endocrine principles from the comparative point of view. It has been written by men who are actively engaged in research in the field which their contribution covers. It can therefore be hoped to present a critical and up-to-date picture of the comparative aspects of endocrinology to the medical scientist and zoologist generally and to furnish an adequately documented background to the research worker who is beginning to take an interest in one of the many endocrine systems described.

The subject matter has been divided into three sections. The largest — which forms the contents of the first volume — deals with hormones originating in well-defined glandular organs and tissues and also reviews the relationships between the central nervous system and these endocrine complexes. The second section (Volume II, Part 1) discusses hormonal systems of invertebrates, and the third (Volume II, Part 2) contains a description of neurohormones and tissue hormones.

This arrangement is based on the following considerations. As originally conceived, an endocrine organ was a discrete anatomical entity which elaborates and stores active principles that are then discharged into the blood to act as chemical messengers or hormones. This definition has the advantage of dividing the two main systems of intercellular communication — the endocrine apparatus and the nervous system — into two neat categories. However, it is doubtful whether this definition can now be maintained in its original simplicity. One of the "glands" involved, the neurohypophysis, has turned out to be only one part of a complex hormone-producing system, consisting of secretory neurons (otherwise undistinguishable from neurons in the central nervous system) which in higher vertebrates deliver their products either to the neural lobe — where they are stored and then released to act as long-range hormone in line with the classical concept — or to the median eminence from which they enter the hypophyseal portal circulation to act as releasers of "tropic" hormones of the adenohypophysis. Thus this compound organization functions not only as a bridge between the two systems of communication but bears also a suggestive resemblance to processes in peripheral nerves. The chemical transmitters of peripheral nerve impulses, whether acetylcholine or noradrenaline, appear also to be formed in the cell bodies of the relevant neurons, to be transported along the corresponding axons, and to be concentrated and stored at the endings of these axons, either at their synaptic endings in ganglia or their neuroeffector junctions. Since evidence is accumulating that similar mechanisms of chemical transmission also take place at most of the synaptic junctions of the central nervous systems, a division into "true hormones" and "neurohormones" seems somewhat arbitrary.

There exists a further — and rather varied — group of chemical messengers whose "systematic" position is not quite clearly defined. The substances in this group, which may be said to contain such biologically active principles as 5-hydroxytryptamine, heparin, and angiotensin, are apparently in some instances also produced by or stored in specific cells but their "physiological range" may or may not be restricted to the organ or tissue in which they originate. The distinction between these tissue factors and the more conventional hormones is again somewhat tenuous, and it was therefore felt that a discussion of their occurrence and properties should not be excluded from the present survey.

Initially, and due no doubt to the endeavor to link this new branch of physiology to human endocrine disease, hormone research was almost exclusively concerned with mammals. During recent years, however, the comparative aspect has come very much to the fore. The morphology of endocrine organs throughout the vertebrate phylum has been intensively studied and a good beginning has been made with the chemical identification of hormones of lower vertebrates. The results to date suggest an astonishing constancy in the chemistry of the endocrine principles: the adrenal hormones, both "medullary" and "cortical," for example, do not seem to vary from fish to man, though subtle differences in the composition of protein or peptide hormones have recently come to light. It has also been shown that endocrine mechanisms in certain groups of invertebrates are as important as in vertebrates. Moreover, there are distinct resemblances in organization, as manifested for example by neurohormonal interaction. But the chemistry of invertebrate hormones is very much in its infancy.

We wish to thank the contributors and the publishers for their patient collaboration. Our thanks are also due to the authors, societies, and publishers for permission to use illustrations and tables which have appeared in previous publications.

U.S. von Euler

April 1963

H. Heller

CONTENTS

~1~

Hypothalamic Control of Anterior Pituitary

CLAUDE FORTIER

~2~

Neurohypophyseal Hormones

H. HELLER

~3~

Pituitary Hormones Affecting the Chromatophores

J. N. KARKUN AND F. W. LANDGREBE

~12~

Comparative Biochemistry of Adenohypophyseal Hormones

Choh Hao Li

~13~

The Physiology of the Adenohypophyseal Hormones

E. Knobil and R. Sandler

CONTENTS OF VOLUME II

xiii

Hypothalamic Control of Anterior Pituitary[*]

CLAUDE FORTIER

Faculté de Médecine, Université Laval, Québec, P.Q., Canada

---

[*] This review was aided in part by grants from the Office of Scientific Research, U. S. Air Force (AF–AFOSR–61–15), and from the National Institutes of Health, U. S. Public Health Service (B–2827). The author is indebted to Drs. W. F. Ganong, J. D. Green, M. A. Greer, G. W. Harris, and D. M. Hume, and to their publishers for permission to adapt or reproduce the illustrative material used in Figs. 1, 2, and 3.

I. INTRODUCTION

A. Indirect Evidence of Nervous Control

Exteroceptive stimuli acting upon the nervous system are known to induce important functional changes mediated by the tropic hormones of the adenohypophysis (Harris, 1948, 1955a, 1960). Thus the sexual rhythm of many birds and mammals are conditioned by environmental factors such as light, temperature, or the presence of a mate (Marshall, 1936, 1942, 1956). The photosexual reflex, among others, is an essential mechanism in the control of birds' gonadotropic activity (Benoit and Assenmacher, 1955, 1959, and 1960). As shown by Benoit and his associates (1955, 1956) in the duck, the variation of environmental lighting, in all likelihood, accounts for the seasonal sexual cycle characteristic of this species and of birds in general, since this cyclicity is abolished by exposing the animals to either constant lighting or darkness. The same applies to a number of mammals, among which the ferret has been studied most extensively (Harris, 1960). It is common knowledge, on the other hand, that ovulation in many species is normally triggered by coitus (Heape, 1905, in the rabbit) or other forms of sexual excitation (Matthews, 1939, in the pigeon), implying a neural substratum. The involvement of the central nervous system in the adrenocorticotropic response to environmental change is also suggested by the rapidity of its occurrence after the onset of stimulation (Gray and Munson, 1951; Sydnor and Sayers, 1954), and by the activating effect of such emotional and sensory stimuli as intense light, sound, restraint, handling, room transfer, changes in the level of environmental activity, and, in general, any condition resulting in anxiety, frustration, pain, or anger (Fortier, 1956; Mason, 1959). Conversely, the same stimuli were shown to result in depressed thyroid activity (Brown-Grant et al., 1954; Brown-Grant, 1956). In agreement with these findings are clinical observations on menstrual cycle changes commonly associated with emotional upsets (Theobald, 1936), or the frequent incidence of psychic trauma at the onset of Graves' disease (see Harris, 1960) which emphasize the role of nervous factors in the control of endocrine activity.

B. Hypothalamo-Adenohypophyseal Complex

The hypothalamus, in view of its numerous afferent connections and close anatomical relationship with the pituitary, appeared to be a likely center for the integration of the impulses which arise from the periphery or from higher cerebral regions and result in activation or depression of the adenohypophyseal functions. This part of the diencephalon occupies a central position in a network of complex neural circuits involving the brain stem, cerebral hemispheres, and other components of the diencephalon. However, in spite of early claims to the contrary, direct neural connections between the hypothalamus and adenohypophysis were found to be practically nonexistent (Harris, 1960). A search for alternative pathways led Green and Harris (1947) to suggest that the pituitary portal system might serve as a functional link between the two structures.

C. Hypophyseal Portal Vessels

This system, first described by Popa and Fielding (1930), was studied in detail by Green and Harris (1947) in a variety of mammals. It originates (Fig. 1) from small branches of the internal carotid and posterior communicating arteries which supply a large vascular plexus between the pars tuberalis and median eminence. From this plexus arises a multitude of capillary loops which penetrate into the median eminence where they come into close contact with the nerve terminals of the region and coalesce

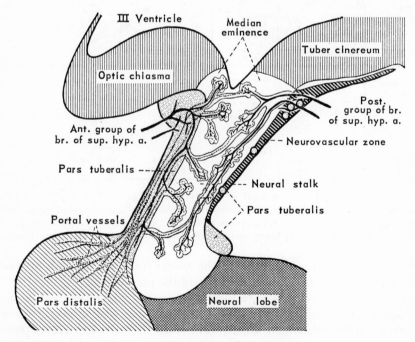

FIG. 1. Diagrammatic representation of the hypophyseal portal vessels (from Green, 1948).

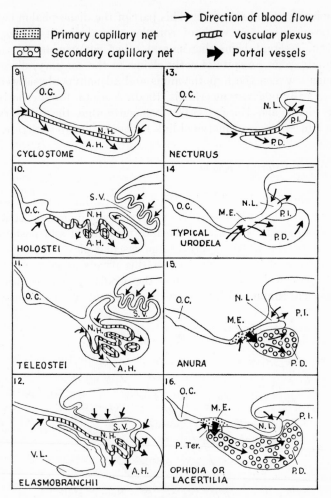

Fig. 2. Phylogenetic development of the hypophyseal portal vessels in the vertebrates. A.H., adenohypophysis; M.E., median eminence; N.L., neural lobe; O.C., optic chiasma; P.D., pars distalis; S.V., saccus vasculosus; V.L., ventral lobe. Arrows indicate direction of blood flow; heavy arrows indicate portal vessels (from Green, 1951).

to form the large portal trunks of the neural stalk which break up and redistribute the blood into the sinusoids of the pars distalis.

According to Green (1951), a hypophyseo-portal circulation is constant in vertebrates from the anura to the primates, and similar vessels occur in cyclostomes, fishes, and salamanders (Fig. 2). This phylogenetic constancy suggested functional significance and lent support to the view that the hypothalamus could influence adenohypophyseal activities through humoral effects mediated by these vessels.

D. Experimental Approaches

In order to ascertain the extent, nature, and modalities of the postulated hypothalamic control of pituitary functions, alterations of these functions were studied by a variety of procedures which involved separating the gland from overlying nervous structures, destroying these structures, or selectively inducing by electrical stimulation the release of specific tropic hormones. In addition, pharmacological studies were devoted to the identification of suspected neurohumors and, more recently, *in vivo* and *in vitro* systems were developed to detect the hypophyseotropic activity of various principles, extracts, or purified fractions of neurohypophyseal or hypothalamic origin. The rest of this chapter is an attempt to sift the resulting evidence.

II. ADRENOCORTICOTROPIN

A. Adrenocorticotropin (ACTH) Field

A large and convincing literature has confirmed the original observation of de Groot and Harris (1950) that ACTH release could be induced by electrical stimulation of the floor of the third ventricle, and that, conversely, the adrenocorticotropic response to stress can be prevented by electrolytic lesions in the same area. There is as yet no general agreement, however, on the exact localization of the ACTH field or center, which roughly extends, with possible species differences, from the rostral aspect of the infundibulum to the mammillary bodies (Fig. 3). In view of the scarcity of its cellular components this funnel-like area may represent, instead of a center in the usual sense, a sort of relay or end-station for the nerve fibers of diverse origins which terminate in the vicinity of the primary portal plexus.

If the involvement of the hypothalamus in the control of adrenocorticotropic activity is established beyond doubt, several points which will presently be considered, remain to be clarified.

B. Basal ACTH Activity

Assessment of the pituitary's inherent ability to maintain the morphological and functional integrity of the adrenal cortex necessitates deafferentiation of the gland by transplantation to a distant site, section of its stalk, or localized destruction of the ventral hypothalamus. Since all of these procedures interfere, to some extent, with the portal vascular supply,

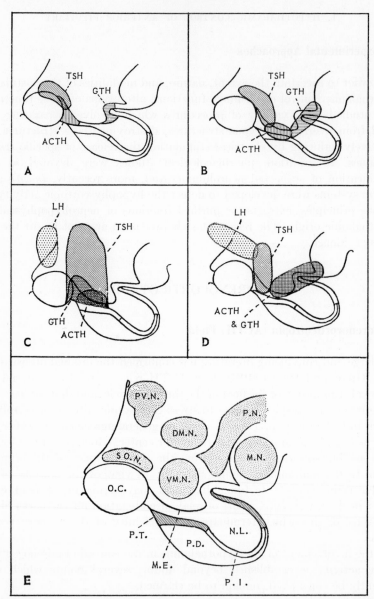

FIG. 3. Hypothalamic areas involved in the control of adrenocorticotropin (ACTH), thyrotropin (TSH), gonadotropins (GTH:FSH, and LH), and ovulation (LH): A, according to Hume (1958) and B, to Ganong (1959a) from observations in the dog; C, according to Greer (1957) from observations in the rat; D, according to Harris (1955b) from composite observations in mammals. E (after Harris, 1955b and Hume, 1958) shows projections of main hypothalamic nuclei (PV.N., paraventricular nucleus; SO.N., supraoptic nucleus; DM.N., dorsomedial nucleus; VM.N., ventromedial nucleus; P.N., posterior nucleus; M.N., mammillary nuclei) on diagrammatic frame of reference (O.C., optic chiasma; M.E., median eminence; N.L., neural lobe; P.T., pars tuberalis; P.I., pars intermedia; P.D., pars distalis).

it has proved difficult to differentiate the effects of ischemia from the consequences of deprivation of a specific hypothalamic influence.

Atrophy of the adrenal cortex, less marked than atrophy after hypophysectomy, was generally observed as a result of heterotopic transplantation of the pituitary (Cheng *et al.*, 1949; McDermott *et al.*, 1950; Schweizer and Long, 1950; Fortier, 1951; Harris and Jacobsohn, 1952), or section of its stalk with adequate prevention of portal revascularization (Donovan and Harris, 1956; Fortier *et al.*, 1957). On the other hand, no consensus has been achieved regarding the effects of lesions in the median eminence which, according to some (Hume, 1953; McCann, 1953; Ganong and Hume, 1954; Laqueur *et al.*, 1955), are compatible with normal adrenal weight maintenance, and, according to others (Bogdanove *et al.*, 1955; Greer and Erwin, 1956; Slusher, 1958; Fortier and de Groot, 1959a; McCann and Haberland, 1960), result in some adrenal atrophy. These differences probably pertain to varying involvement of the primary portal plexus with the site of the lesion. From a concurrent study of the changes in adenohypophyseal ACTH and adrenal corticosteroidogenesis consequent to destruction of the bulbus of the median eminence, it was inferred by Fortier and de Groot (1959a) that suppression of hypothalamic influence, probably associated with impairment of the adenohypophyseal blood supply, results in a marked depression of both synthesis and release of ACTH. The specific role of the portal vessels in the maintenance of basal ACTH activity was elegantly illustrated by Nikitovitch-Winer and Everett (1958) who observed that retransplantation of the pituitary from a well-vascularized heterotopic site to its original location under the median eminence is followed by partial restoration of the adrenal weight.

C. Steroid Feedback

Recent observations on the changes in pituitary corticotropin concentration and cortical secretory activity associated with regeneration of the enucleated adrenal cortex in the rat (Fortier and de Groot, 1959b) reinforce the conclusion reached from previous studies (Fortier, 1959a, b) that, although both release and synthesis of ACTH are accelerated by hypo- and depressed by hypercorticoidism, the predominant effect of steroids is exerted on synthesis. The site of this regulation has yet to be clarified.

Since lesions in the median eminence or its immediate vicinity result in abolition or marked depression of the compensatory hypertrophy of the remaining gland induced by unilateral adrenalectomy (Ganong and Hume, 1954; Fulford and McCann, 1955), and also block the secondary increase of pituitary ACTH concentration consequent to removal of the two glands (Fortier and de Groot, unpublished), it appears that the activating effect of hypocorticoidism is exerted through the hypothalamus. Hypothalamic lesions, on the other hand, do not interfere with the adrenal atrophy which results from the prolonged administration of cortical hormones (Ganong and Hume, 1955). This suggests a hypophyseal site for steroid-induced inhibition which, however, may be overcome, according to some reports (Porter and Jones, 1956; McCann, 1957; de Garilhe et al., 1958; Casentini et al., 1959), by principles of hypothalamic or neurohypophyseal origin.

D. Response to Stress

Whether the hypothalamus is the necessary mediator of the adrenocorticotropic response to all types of stress stimuli has been the object of some controversy. The pituitary, isolated from the hypothalamus by heterotopic transplantation or transection of its stalk with interposition of a plate between the cut ends, was shown to retain its ability to release ACTH in response to tissue trauma or metabolic disturbances (Cheng et al., 1949; McDermott et al., 1950; Fortier, 1951; Fortier et al., 1957), but not to emotional or sensory types of stimulation (Fortier 1951; Fortier et al., 1957). On that basis, stresses were tentatively divided into two groups, neural and systemic, according to whether they activated ACTH release solely by the mediation of the nervous system or could act on the pituitary through the systemic circulation (Fortier, 1951, 1952). Results of lesions of the median eminence provide little support for this viewpoint, since under certain conditions (vide infra) the response to both types of stimuli is allegedly prevented by this procedure (R. W. Porter, 1953; McCann, 1953; Ganong and Hume, 1954; Hume and Nelson, 1955). It thus appears more likely that all stress stimuli act through the nervous system, and that intense stimuli can cause the liberation of enough chemotransmitter from the median eminence to excite the isolated pituitary. The blocking effect of pentobarbital–morphine administration on the ACTH response to a wide range of stimuli was also interpreted by Briggs and Munson (1955) to support the view that the hypothalamus is an essential component of the mechanism of acute stimulation of ACTH secretion. Many gaps persist, however, in our understanding of this mechanism whose complexity is illustrated by the following observations:

Adrenal ascorbic acid (AAA) depletion, which normally parallels corticosteroidogenesis, has been used extensively as an indicator of adrenocorticotropic activity. In the light of Slusher's (1958) data, it now appears that separate zones of the hypothalamus may be involved in the mediation of the AAA and corticosterone responses to a given stimulus.

According to Nowell (1959) and Smelik (1959), separate zones of the hypothalamus may likewise be involved in the mediation of the AAA response to different stimuli.

This response has been ascertained, in most studies, one hour after the onset of the stress stimulus. It appears that lesions in the anterior, middle or posterior hypothalamus, though effective in preventing the 1-hour response to unilateral adrenalectomy, do not affect the 2–4-hour response to the same stimulus (Brodish, 1960).

According to Hume and Jackson (1959), in the dog the corticoidogenic response to trauma is not immediately suppressed by lesions in the anterior median eminence or by removal of the ventral hypothalamus, but may persist for a few days after surgery.

Thus, particular attention should be paid to choice of criteria, duration of response, time interval after lesion, and nature and intensity of the stimuli before general conclusions can be drawn regarding the extent of hypothalamic involvement in the mediation of the stress response.

E. Afferent Pathways

The wide variety of sensory and emotional stimuli which result in adrenocorticotropic activation suggests that many pathways contribute to the afferent input of the hypothalamus. Of these, the limbic and reticular activating systems have received special notice.

Evidence has been presented that two limbic structures may be involved in the control of ACTH secretion. From lesion and stimulation experiments in the monkey, it was inferred by Mason (1958) that the amygdaloid nucleus and the hippocampus–fornix system respectively exert facilitating and suppressive influences on pituitary–adrenocortical activity, and contribute to the maintenance of the normal diurnal rhythm in ACTH secretion. Speculating on the significance of his findings, recently confirmed in the dog by Japanese workers (Okinaka et al., 1960), Mason considers the possibility of "a cyclical mechanism from reticular formation and hypothalamus up to limbic system and back again, in which the hippocampus would be reciprocally related to these lower areas, acting as a negative feed-back or damping influence on the hypothalamus and reticular formation, in proportion to the stimulation received via ascending fibers."

The results of electrophysiological studies indicating similarities between the hypothalamus and midbrain reticular formation (Feldman et al., 1959) are in keeping with recent anatomical and endocrinological findings which underline the relationship between the two structures. Thus, reticular projections from the medial regions of the caudal midbrain to the posterior, dorsal, and infundibular zones of the hypothalamus have been described by Nauta and Kuypers (1958). Increased adrenocortical activity was observed as a result of electrical stimulation of the midbrain reticular formation (Okinaka *et al.*, 1960) or of fibers ascending therefrom through the dorsal longitudinal fasciculus (Mason, 1958). Transection of the midbrain, though compatible with high levels of corticosteroids (Newman *et al.*, 1958; Davis *et al.*, 1960; Slusher, 1960), allegedly prevents the adrenocorticotropic response to a number of stress stimuli (Anderson *et al.*, 1957; Sayers, 1957; Giuliani *et al.*, 1960). Egdahl (1960a) observed notwithstanding persistence of the response to sciatic nerve stimulation in midbrain-transected dogs. Furthermore, according to this investigator isolation of the pituitary by complete removal of the brain (hypothalamus included) down to the level of the inferior colliculus, in the dog results in high "resting" corticosteroid outputs, and in most animals does not interfere with a further response to burn trauma (Egdahl, 1960b), sciatic nerve stimulation (Egdahl, 1961b), or caval constriction (Egdahl, 1961a). Thus, it is inferred that higher regions of the brain tonically inhibit lower areas, including one in the hindbrain, which produce and release ACTH-stimulating neurohumors. The elaboration by the hindbrain of an ACTH-releasing principle of its own (Hindbrain Factor or HBF, Egdahl, 1960b) appears unlikely in the light of subsequent experiments in which high resting corticosteroid levels were observed following total removal of the brain down to the cord (Egdahl, 1962, Ganong, in press), or even following excision of the entire spinal cord in addition (Egdahl, 1962). The elevated corticosteroid levels and persistent response to stress of the isolated pituitary preparation would be more plausibly ascribed to the abnormal permeability of relatively ischemic pituitary cells, resulting in chronic leakage of ACTH liable to be further enhanced by peripheral factors released by trauma.

F. Corticotropin-Releasing Factor

Substantial progress has been made in the identification of the chemotransmitter presumably conveyed through the portal circulation from the median eminence to the pars distalis. After experimental elimination of known neurohumors (adrenaline, acetylcholine, histamine) as possible candidates for this role (see Guillemin, 1955), interest has centered on peptides of neurohypophyseal or hypothalamic origin.

McCann was, until recently, the chief proponent of the thesis that vasopressin, as distinct from other neurohypophyseal peptides, is the postulated Corticotropin-Releasing Factor (CRF). Commercial (Pitressin)

or synthetic vasopressin has been shown by McCann and others to break
through the blockade of the adrenal ascorbic acid response to stress induced in the rat by treatment with pentobarbital and morphine (McCann,
1957; McCann and Fruit, 1957; Guillemin et al., 1959), hydrocortisone
(McCann, 1957; de Garilhe et al., 1958; Mialhe-Voloss, 1958), neurohypo-
physectomy (Nowell, 1959), production of hypothalamic lesions (McCann,
1957; McCann and Fruit, 1957; Royce and Sayers, 1958a; Guillemin et al.,
1959), transection of the midbrain (Sayers, 1957; Giuliani et al., 1960;
Martini et al., 1960), or heterotopic transplantation of the pituitary
(Martini and de Poli, 1956; Casentini et al., 1959). Royce and Sayers
(1958a) confirmed the adrenal ascorbic acid depleting effect of Pitressin in
rats with lesions of the median eminence, but concluded that only part of
this effect could be explained by release of ACTH from the anterior pituitary, since Pitressin also depleted adrenal ascorbic acid and potentiated
the action of ACTH in hypophysectomized and decapitated rats.

Some parallelism between antidiuretic activity and ACTH release is
implied by the claim that vasopressin is the mediator of the adrenocorticotropic response to stress. In this connection, the alleged correlation between
high water intake and inhibition of stress-induced release of ACTH in rats
with hypothalamic lesions (McCann and Brobeck, 1955) was not corroborated by further reports (Greer and Erwin, 1956; Daily and Ganong,
1958; Slusher, 1958; Ganong et al., 1959). Neither was any constant correlation noted in a number of studies (see Fortier and de Groot, 1959c;
Ganong and Forsham, 1960; Fortier, 1962) between alterations of diuresis
and ACTH secretion in intact animals.

If distinct from vasopressin, the physiological mediator of ACTH release
appears to be closely related to this polypeptide, as judged by the difficulty
involved in their separation. Progress in this field should be specially
credited to Saffran, Guillemin and their co-workers (Saffran et al., 1955;
Guillemin et al., 1957, 1959; Saffran, 1959; Schally and Guillemin, 1959,
1960) who independently isolated from material of neurohypophyseal or
hypothalamic origin the first ACTH-releasing principle (CRF) relatively
free of pressor activity. Similar claims have since been made by others
(de Garilhe et al., 1958; Royce and Sayers, 1958b; McCann and Haberland, 1959; Rumsfeld and Porter, 1959; Royce and Sayers, 1960; Sayers,
1960).

The in vitro activity of CRF in Saffran and Schally's (1955) pituitary
incubation system, which served as the basis of its isolation, was shown to
be specifically related to enhanced release of ACTH (Guillemin and
Schally, 1959), as opposed to alternative modes of action (Barrett and
Sayers, 1958; Fortier and Ward, 1958). The secretory nature of the process
was further intimated by the concurrent increase in the incorporation of

radioactive phosphorus into the phospholipid fraction of the incubated pituitary, observed by Hokin *et al.* (1958). CRF appears to be equally active *in vivo*; like stress, it has the ability to deplete pituitary ACTH in rats (Rochefort *et al.*, 1959), and to elicit its release in human subjects (Clayton *et al.*, 1957). Furthermore, according to Guillemin *et al.* (1959), a small dose of their original and relatively crude chromatographic fraction D, inactive in the hypophysectomized animal, can overcome the blockade of the plasma corticosteroid response to stress induced in the rat by median eminence lesions or pentobarbital–morphine administration, whereas equipotent vasopressor amounts of vasopressin cannot.

Elaborate separative steps have recently yielded two active polypeptides of neurohypophyseal origin, termed α- and β-CRF, and respectively related by their physical characteristics and amino acid compositions to α-MSH and to vasopressin (Guillemin *et al.*, 1960; Schally *et al.*, 1960); α-CRF has a relatively low specific activity, and shares with a peptidic fraction isolated by de Garilhe *et al.* (1958), properties suggesting a possible role as a precursor of β-corticotropin, whereas β-CRF, in view of its high potency and presence in the hypothalamus (Guillemin *et al.*, 1962; Schally *et al.*, 1962), possibly represents the physiological mediator of ACTH release.

Direct evidence of portal chemotransmission was provided in 1956 by Porter and Jones' detection of ACTH-releasing activity in plasma (or extracts thereof) obtained from the portal vessels of stressed-hypophysectomized dogs. A recent claim (Porter and Rumsfeld, 1959) that the active substance can be dialyzed away from the proteins of lyophilized portal plasma suggests that a plasma protein, Cohn's Fraction IIIo (Porter and Rumsfeld, 1956), may serve as a carrier for the ACTH releaser in portal blood. Clarification of the relationship between Guillemin and Schally's β-CRF and Porter's dialyzable principle might bridge an important gap in our understanding of neuroendocrine processes.

III. THYROTROPIN

A. The Thyrotropin (TSH) Field

Hypothalamic involvement in the control of pituitary–thyroid activity may be inferred from reports that lesions in the anterior hypothalamus of the rat, dog, guinea pig, and other species result in depressed rates of radioactive iodine uptake and release by the thyroid, lower protein-bound iodine levels, and reduction of the pituitary stores and blood titer of TSH (see D'Angelo, 1958; Florsheim, 1959; Brown-Grant, 1960; Greer *et al.*,

1960; Bogdanove, 1962), that section of the pituitary stalk in the rabbit markedly interferes with I^{131} uptake and thyroid hormone release (Brown-Grant et al., 1957), and that, conversely, thyroid activity can be increased by stimulation of the hypothalamus (Harris and Woods, 1958).

The precise location of the TSH-regulating area remains controversial, though most investigators would agree that it lies in or near the midline, behind the optic chiasma (Fig. 3). Regarding its posterior limit, Harris and Woods (1958) in studying the effects of prolonged electrical stimulation of the hypothalamus on thyroid activity in the rabbit, noted that the effective zone of stimulation was restricted in the intact animal to the anterior portion of the median eminence adjacent to the supraoptico-hypophyseal tract, but extended posteriorly to this region in the bilaterally adrenalectomized rabbit maintained on a small daily dose of cortisone. It was suggested, therefore, that the ACTH and TSH fields of the hypothalamus overlap, and that, by raising the blood level of adrenal steroids, stimulation of the common zone in the intact animal might inhibit any TSH secretion that would otherwise have been elicited.

There is as yet no evidence that other areas of the brain significantly influence thyroid function; it is allegedly unaltered by amygdalectomy, (Yamada and Greer, 1960), decortication (Greer and Shull, 1957), destruction of the pineal and subcommissural organ (Greer et al., 1960), frontal lobectomy, or extensive lesions in the midbrain (Van Beugen and Van der Werff ten Bosch, 1960).

B. Site of Feedback

The negative feedback mechanism whereby thyrotropic activity adjusts to the level of circulating thyroid hormone appears to be largely independent of the hypothalamus, since lesions in the anterior hypothalamus (D'Angelo, 1958; D'Angelo and Traum, 1958; Florsheim, 1959; Reichlin, 1960b), stalk transection (Brown-Grant et al., 1957), or pituitary transplantation (Scow and Greer, 1955; C. von Euler and Holmgren, 1956b) failed to prevent the inhibition of thyroid activity consequent to the administration of thyroxine. However, the alterations of thyroid function observed after microinjections of systemically ineffective amounts of thyroxine into either the pituitary gland (C. von Euler and Holmgren, 1956a; Yamada, 1959; Yamada and Greer, 1959) or the anterior hypothalamus (Yamada, 1959; Yamada and Greer, 1959) suggest that the inhibitory effect of this hormone may be exerted at both sites.

Several reports (Bogdanove and Halmi, 1953; Bogdanove and D'Angelo, 1959; Florsheim, 1958) have confirmed Greer's (1951, 1952) original observation that interference with hypothalamo-hypophyseal connections prevents the goitrogenic response to propylthiouracil (PTU) without significantly altering the elevation of the Thyroid/Serum (T/S) concentration ratio induced by this agent. Similar evidence of dissociation between thyroid growth and iodide trapping was obtained by Reichlin (1957) who studied the effect of hypothalamic lesions on the thyroid response of the rat to partial thyroidectomy. That quantitative differences in pituitary secretion of TSH can account for this dichotomy is suggested by evidence (Bogdanove and Bogdanove, 1957; Greer, 1959; Reichlin, 1960a) that the T/S ratio responds to very slight thyrotropic stimulation, and achieves virtually maximal values with levels of secretion insufficient to affect thyroid structure. Florsheim (1959) concludes from his findings in rats with hypothalamic lesions that the smaller elevation of circulating TSH, shown by these animals in response to PTU, is not related to interference with the normal releasing mechanism, but to depressed synthesis resulting in lower pituitary stores of available TSH.

C. Response to Cold and Other Types of Stress

The well-known increase in thyroid activity associated with exposure to cold apparently requires the integrity of the hypothalamo-adenohypophyseal complex, since it is suppressed by the classic procedures aimed at excluding hypothalamic influence (see Brown-Grant, 1960, D'Angelo, 1962). Other environmental stimuli known to induce the release of ACTH were generally shown, however, to depress pituitary-thyroid activity (Brown-Grant et al., 1954; Brown-Grant and Pethes, 1960). Since the thyroid response to stress persists in adrenalectomized animals (Brown-Grant, 1956), it is probably independent of an elevated adrenal steroid output, and could be ascribed to a decrease in TSH secretion associated with an increased secretion of ACTH (Brown-Grant, 1960). Brown-Grant et al. (1957) reported, in this connection, that the decrease in thyroid activity which normally follows surgical trauma, was not abolished in the rabbit by transection of the pituitary stalk, whereas the thyroid response to emotional stress (forced immobilization) was prevented. It may be inferred therefrom that the inhibitory response is effected at different levels (hypothalamic or hypophyseal) according to the nature of the stimulus.

D. Mediation of Hypothalamic Influence

In contrast to the pituitary's intrinsic ability to alter thyroidal activity in response to trauma or to changed blood levels of thyroxine, the hypothalamus apparently mediates TSH responsivity to cold or to emotional stimulation, but little is known of the underlying mechanism, and attempts to identify a hypothetical TSH-releasing factor have been, so far, inconclusive (see Greer *et al.*, 1960; Bogdanove, 1962; D'Angelo, 1962). Brown-Grant (1957) suggested, as an ingenious alternative, that the role of the hypothalamus in TSH regulation may be to remove thyroxine from the arterial blood which supplies the primary plexus of the portal system, and thus expose the pituitary to blood of a modified thyroid hormone content. According to this view, the suppressive effect of thyroxine or triiodothyronine on pituitary TSH secretion should be appreciably greater after destruction of the hypothalamus. Yet the amount of thyroid hormone needed to inhibit thyroidal I^{131} discharge (Florsheim, 1959; Reichlin, 1960b), or to lower adenohypophysial TSH stores (D'Angelo, 1958), is about the same in hypothalamic-lesioned as in intact rats.

IV. GONADOTROPINS

A. Follicle-Stimulating Hormone (FSH) and Luteinizing Hormone (LH)

In clinical reports, testicular atrophy in the male and amenorrhea in the female have long been associated with lesions of the ventral hypothalamus without demonstrable involvement of the pituitary (see Ganong, 1959b; Harris, 1960). Aschner (1912), Camus and Roussy (1920), and Bailey and Bremer (1921) were among the first to reproduce these effects experimentally. Since then, gonadal atrophy in association with lesions of the tuber cinereum has been observed in rats, dogs, rabbits, and cats (see Harris, 1960, Greep, 1961). The diffuseness of the atrophy, which involves all parts of the gonads, suggests a curtailment of both FSH and LH secretion by the adenohypophysis. This is consistent with the depletion of pituitary FSH and LH observed as a result of destruction of the posterior median eminence in the dog (Davidson *et al.*, 1960). The term "gonadotropin field or center" (Fig. 3) may still not properly apply to the median eminence which possibly represents only a final common pathway, collecting afferents from other areas specifically concerned with the regulation of one or the other gonadotropin.

In contrast to median eminence lesions, selective destruction of the preoptic and anterior hypothalamic areas produces persistent estrus, uterine hypertrophy, and inhibition of corpus luteum formation in the ovary (see D'Angelo, 1960, Van Rees *et al.*, 1962). These effects are generally ascribed, to a primary deficiency in LH secretion. From a comparison of the pituitary and serum LH contents in rats with prolonged vaginal

estrus due to a lesion in the anterior hypothalamus, and in rats with
regular cycles, it appears that the pituitary of the persistently estrous rat
releases little LH into the blood, although the storage of this hormone by
the gland is unimpaired (Van der Werff ten Bosch *et al.*, 1962). On the
other hand, the findings of Flerko (1957a, b) are interpreted to suggest
that destruction of the hypothalamic site governing reproductive rhythmicity in the rat (Fig. 3) abolishes an estrogen-sensitive area through which
pituitary FSH secretion is cyclically restrained. In support of this interpretation, D'Angelo and Kravatz (1960) reported that the adenohypophysis of the lesioned rat with persistent estrus loses its ability to augment
secretion of FSH under conditions of enhanced demand (unilateral öopho-
rectomy). They concluded therefore that the integrity of the rostral
hypothalamus is necessary for both cyclic release of LH and normal
estrogen-FSH interaction.

Retrochiasmatic lesions involving Flerko's estrogen-sensitive area were
shown to result in premature secretion of FSH in the anestrous ferret
(Donovan and Van der Werff ten Bosch, 1959b), and in precocious puberty
in the immature rat (Bogdanove and Schoen, 1959; Donovan and Van der
Werff ten Bosch, 1959a). It was inferred that the onset of estrus or puberty
had been hastened by release of the pituitary gland from an inhibition
exerted by the central nervous system through the mediation of the rostral
hypothalamus, and that the release was possibly brought about by blockade
of the action of gonadal hormones upon the hypothalamus (Donovan and
Van der Werff ten Bosch, 1959a).

Studies have indicated that the ovulatory mechanism in rats can be explained by a progressive rise in the estrogen (Markee *et al.*, 1952) and
progesterone (Everett, 1948) levels which, by lowering the response
threshold of a hypothalamic "timing center," trigger off at cyclic intervals
a neurohumoral process involving, at yet undetermined levels, adrenergic
and cholinergic components, and resulting in the release of LH from the
pars distalis. Under controlled conditions of lighting, the critical period of
stimulation was between 2:00 and 4:00 P.M. of the day of proestrus.
Electroencephalographic studies in proestrous animals have shown that
during this period marked spontaneous electric changes take place in the
preoptic area and anterior hypothalamus, to the exclusion of other parts
of the brain (Critchlow and Sawyer, 1955). Pharmacological blockade of
spontaneous ovulation in the rat may be overcome by electrical stimulation
of the tuberal (Critchlow, 1958a) or preoptic (Everett and Christian, 1959)
regions and, according to a recent report (Everett and Harp, 1960), adequate stimulation can thus be achieved in as little as 90 seconds, in contrast to Everett and Sawyer's (1953) estimate of 30 minutes for the duration of the natural neurogenic stimulus coextensive with LH release.

In a spontaneously ovulating form such as the rat the neural elements essential to ovulation are presumably encephalized and relatively insulated from environmental influences conveyed through ascending sensory pathways. Critchlow's (1958b) observations on the effect of mesencephalic lesions in this species point to the involvement of the mammillary peduncle in the cyclic mechanism of ovulation, since interruption of a portion of this tract (rostrad to the interpeduncular nucleus) selectively interfered with the process. The occurrence of ovulation in rats made somnolent and unresponsive to nociceptive stimuli by massive midbrain destruction sparing the mammillary peduncle (Critchlow, 1958b) implies, however, that the mechanisms which underlie behavioral arousal are not essential to the release of pituitary ovulating hormone. The effectiveness of amygdaloid stimulation in the induction of ovulation in several species (Koikegami et al., 1954; Shealy and Peele, 1957; Bunn and Everett, 1957) suggests a facilitatory role for this structure in the regulation of LH release. By contrast, an inhibitory influence of the amygdaloid complex on FSH secretion is suggested by reports that lesions in this area as well as in the anterior hypothalamus are associated with precocious sexual development of prepubertal rats (Elwers and Critchlow, 1960), and that, conversely, electrical stimulation of the corticomedial part of the amygdala delays the onset of puberty in these animals (Elwers-Bar-Sela and Critchlow, 1962).

The role of the portal vessels in the regulation of FSH and LH secretion appears well established in the light of pituitary transplantation experiments in mammals (Harris and Jacobsohn, 1952; Nikitovitch-Winer and Everett, 1958, 1959, in the rat), birds (Assenmacher and Benoit, 1958, in the duck), and amphibians (Jørgensen and Larsen, 1960, in the frog; Vivien and Schott, 1958, in a urodele), in which normal gonadotropic function was shown to depend upon vascularization of the transplants by these vessels. Recent evidence points to the existence in the median eminence of the rat (McCann et al., 1960; McCann and Taleisnik, 1961; Nikitovitch-Winer, 1962) and rabbit (Campbell et al., 1961) of a humoral substance capable of directly releasing the ovulating hormone from adenohypophyseal cells. The nature of this releasing factor is unknown but, according to McCann et al. (1960), it differs from histamine, serotonine, substance P, epinephrine, vasopressin, or oxytocin.

B. Luteotropin (LTH)

Several observations suggest that the hypothalamus exerts an inhibitory influence on the secretion of LTH. Thus, LTH activity, shown by lactation, maintenance of corpora lutea, or deciduoma formation, is reportedly maintained and even enhanced in various species by procedures known to

Campbell, H. J., Feuer, G., Garcia, J., and Harris, G. W. (1961). *J. Physiol. (London)* **157**, 30P.

Camus, J., and Roussy, G. (1920). *Endocrinology* **4**, 507–522.

Casentini, S., de Poli, A., Hukovic, S., and Martini, L. (1959). *Endocrinology* **64**, 483–493.

Cheng, C. P., Sayers, G., Goodman, L. S., and Swinyard, C. A. (1949). *Am. J. Physiol.* **159**, 426–432.

Clayton, G. W., Bell, W. R., and Guillemin, R. (1957). *Proc. Soc. Exptl. Biol. Med.* **96**, 777–779.

Critchlow, V. (1958a). *Am. J. Physiol.* **195**, 171–174.

Critchlow, V. (1958b). *Endocrinology* **63**, 596–611.

Critchlow, V., and Sawyer, C. H. (1955). *Federation Proc.* **14**, 32.

Daily, W. J. R., and Ganong, W. F. (1958). *Endocrinology* **62**, 442–454.

D'Angelo, S. A. (1958). *J. Endocrinol.* **17**, 286–299.

D'Angelo, S. A. (1960). *Am. J. Physiol.* **199**, 701–706.

D'Angelo, S. A. (1962). *In* "N.I.H. Symposium on Neuroendocrinology" (A. V. Nalbandov, ed.). Univ. Illinois Press, Urbana, Illinois. In press.

D'Angelo, S. A., and Kravatz, A. S. (1960). *Proc. Soc. Exptl. Biol. Med.* **104**, 130–133.

D'Angelo, S. A., and Traum, R. E. (1958). *Ann. N. Y. Acad. Sci.* **72**, 241–270.

Davidson, J. M., Contopoulos, A. N., and Ganong, W. F. (1960). *Endocrinology* **66**, 735–740.

Davis, J. O., Anderson, E., Ayers, R., Carpenter, C. C. J., Haymaker, W., and Spence, W. T. (1960). *1st Intern. Congr. Endocrinol. Copenhagen, Abstr. Communs.* p. 77.

de Garilhe, M. P., Gros, C., Chauvet, J., Fromageot, Cl., Mialhe-Voloss, C., and Benoit, J. (1958). *Biochim. et Biophys. Acta* **29**, 603–611.

De Groot, J., and Harris, G. W. (1950). *J. Physiol. (London)* **111**, 335–346.

Desclin, L. (1956). *Compt. rend. soc. biol.* **150**, 1489–1491.

Donovan, B. T., and Harris, G. W. (1956). *J. Physiol. (London)* **131**, 102–114.

Donovan, B. T., and van der Werff ten Bosch, J. J. (1959a). *J. Physiol. (London)* **147**, 78–92.

Donovan, B. T., and van der Werff ten Bosch, J. J. (1959b). *J. Physiol. (London)* **147**, 93–108.

Eckles, N. E., Ehni, G., and Kirschbaum, A. (1958). *Anat. Record* **130**, 295.

Egdahl, R. H. (1960a). *1st Intern. Congr. Endocrinol. Copenhagen Abstr. Communs.* p. 35.

Egdahl, R. H. (1960b). *Endocrinology* **66**, 200–216.

Egdahl, R. H. (1961a). *Endocrinology* **68**, 226–232.

Egdahl, R. H. (1961b). *Endocrinology* **68**, 574–581.

Egdahl, R. H. (1962). *Abstr. Endocrine Soc., 44th Meeting, Chicago* p. 20–21.

Elwers, M., and Critchlow, V. (1960). *Am. J. Physiol.* **198**, 381–385.

Elwers-Bar-Sela, M., and Critchlow, V. (1962). *Abstr. Endocrine Soc., 44th Meeting, Chicago* p. 19.

Everett, J. W. (1948). *Endocrinology* **43**, 389–405.

Everett, J. W. (1954). *Endocrinology* **54**, 685–690.

Everett, J. W. (1956). *Endocrinology* **58**, 786–797.

Everett, J. W., and Christian, C. D (1959). *Abstr. Endocrine Soc. 41st Meeting, Atlantic City* pp. 48–49.

Everett, J. W., and Harp, J. R. (1960). *1st Intern. Congr. Endocrinol. Copenhagen, Abstr. Communs.* p. 7.

Everett, J. W., and Sawyer, C. H. (1953). *Endocrinology* **52**, 83–92.

Feldman, S., Van der Heide, C. S., and Porter, R. W. (1959). *Am. J. Physiol.* **196**, 1163–1167.

Flerko, B. (1957a). *Arch. anat. microscop. et morphol. exptl.* **46**, 159–172.

Flerko, B. (1957b). *Endokrinologie* **34**, 202–208.

Florsheim, W. H. (1958). *Endocrinology* **62**, 783–790.

Florsheim, W. H. (1959). *Proc. Soc. Exptl. Biol. Med.* **100**, 73–75.

Fortier, C. (1951). *Endocrinology* **49**, 782–788.

Fortier, C. (1952). *Acta Neuroveget. (Vienna)* **5**, 55–131.

Fortier, C. (1956). *20th Intern. Congr. Physiol. Brussels, Abstr. Rev.* pp. 490–508.

Fortier, C. (1959a). *Proc. Soc. Exptl. Biol. Med.* **100**, 13–16.

Fortier, C. (1959b). *Proc. Soc. Exptl. Biol. Med.* **100**, 16–19.

Fortier, C. (1962). *Ann. Rev. Physiol.* **24**, 223–258.

Fortier, C., and de Groot, J. (1959a). *21st Intern. Congr. Physiol. Sci. Buenos Aires, Abstr. Communs.* p. 96.

Fortier, C., and de Groot, J. (1959b). *Am. J. Physiol.* **196**, 589–592.

Fortier, C., and de Groot, J. (1959c). *Progr. in Neurol. and Psychiat.* **14**, 256–269.

Fortier, C., and Ward, D. N. (1958). *Can. J. Biochem. and Physiol.* **36**, 111–118.

Fortier, C., Harris, G. W., and McDonald, I. R. (1957). *J. Physiol. (London)* **136**, 344–364.

Fulford, B. D., and McCann, S. M. (1955). *Proc. Soc. Exptl. Biol. Med.* **90**, 78–80.

Ganong, W. F. (1959a). *In* "Comparative Endocrinology" (A. Gorbman, ed.), pp. 187–201. Wiley, New York.

Ganong, W. F. (1959b). *In* "Reproduction in Domestic Animals" (H. H. Cole, and P. T. Cupps, eds.), Vol. I, pp. 185–221. Academic Press, New York.

Ganong, W. F. (1962). *In* "N.I.H. Symposium of Neuroendocrinology" (A. V. Nalbandov, ed.). Univ. Illinois Press, Urbana, Illinois. In press.

Ganong, W. F., and Forsham, P. H. (1960). *Ann. Rev. Physiol.* **22**, 579–615.

Ganong, W. F., and Hume, D. M. (1954). *Endocrinology* **55**, 474–483.

Ganong, W. F., and Hume, D. M. (1955). *Proc. Soc. Exptl. Biol. Med.* **88**, 528–533.

Ganong, W., Lieberman, A., Daily, W., Yuen, V., Mulrow, P., Luetscher, J., and Bailey, R. (1959). *Endocrinology* **65**, 18–28.

Giuliani, G., Martini, L., and Pecile, A. (1960). *1st Intern. Congr. Endocrinol. Copenhagen, Abstr. Communs.* p. 37.

Gray, W. D., and Munson, P. L. (1951). *Endocrinology* **48**, 471–481.

Green, J. D. (1948). *Anat. Record* **100**, 273–276.

Green, J. D. (1951). *Am. J. Anat.* **88**, 225–312.

Green, J. D., and Harris, G. W. (1947). *J. Endocrinol.* **5**, 136–146.

Greep, R. O. (1961). *In* "Sex and Internal Secretions" (W. C. Young, ed.), Vol. I, pp. 240–301. Williams & Wilkins, Baltimore, Maryland.

Greer, M. A. (1951). *Proc. Soc. Exptl. Biol. Med.* **77**, 603–608.

Greer, M. A. (1952). *J. Clin. Endocrinol. and Metabolism* **12**, 1259–1268.

Greer, M. A. (1957). *Recent Progr. in Hormone Research* **13**, 67–98.

Greer, M. A. (1959). *Endocrinology* **64**, 724–729.

Greer, M. A., and Erwin, H. L. (1956). *Endocrinology* **58**, 665–674.

Greer, M. A., and Shull, H. F. (1957). *Proc. Soc. Exptl. Biol. Med.* **94**, 565–566.

Greer, M. A., Scow, R. O., and Grobstein, C. (1953). *Proc. Soc. Exptl. Biol. Med.* **82**, 28–30.

Greer, M. A., Yamada, T., and Iino, S. (1960). *Ann. N. Y. Acad. Sci.* **86**, 667–675.

Guillemin, R. (1955). *Endocrinology* **56**, 248–255.

Guillemin, R., and Schally, A. V. (1959). *Endocrinology* **65**, 555–562.

Guillemin, R., Hearn, W. R., Cheek, W. A., and Householder, D. W. (1957). *Endocrinology* **60**, 488–506.

Guillemin, R., Dear, W. E., Nichols, B., and Lipscomb, H. S. (1959). *Proc. Soc. Exptl. Biol. Med.* **101**, 107–111.

Guillemin, R., Schally, A. V., Andersen, R., Lipscomb, H., and Long, J. (1960). *Compt. rend. acad. sci.* **250**, 4462–4464.

Guillemin, R., Schally, A. V., Lipscomb, H. S., Andersen, R. N., and Long, J. (1962). *Endocrinology* **70**, 471–477.

Harris, G. W. (1948). *Physiol. Revs.* **28**, 139–179.

Harris, G. W. (1955a). "Neural Control of the Pituitary Gland," Arnold, London.

Harris, G. W. (1955b). *Bull. Johns Hopkins Hosp.* **97**, 358–375.

Harris, G. W. (1960). *In* "Handbook of Physiology," Section 1: "Neurophysiology" (J. Field, H. W. Magoun, and V. E. Hall, eds.), Vol. II, pp. 1007–1039. American Physiological Society, Washington, D. C.

Harris, G. W., and Jacobsohn, D. (1952). *Proc. Roy. Soc.* **B139**, 263–276.

Harris, G. W., and Woods, J. W. (1958). *J. Physiol. (London)* **143**, 246–274.

Haun, C. K., and Sawyer, C. H. (1960). *Endocrinology* **67**, 270–273.

Heape, W. (1905). *Proc. Roy. Soc.* **B76**, 260–286.

Hokin, M. R., Hokin, L. E., Saffran, M., Schally, A. V., and Zimmermann, B. U. (1958). *J. Biol. Chem.* **233**, 811–814.

Hume, D. M. (1953). *Ann. Surg.* **138**, 548–557.

Hume, D. M. (1958). *In* "Reticular Formation of the Brain" (H. H. Jasper, L. D. Proctor, R. S. Knighton, W. C. Noshay, and R. T. Costello, eds.), pp. 231–249. Little, Brown, Boston, Massachusetts.

Hume, D. M., and Jackson, B. T. (1959). *Abstr. Endocrine Soc. 41st Meeting Atlantic City* p. 31.

Hume, D. M., and Nelson, D. H. (1955). *J. Clin. Endocrinol. and Metabolism* **15**, 839–840.

Jørgensen, C. B., and Larsen, L. O. (1960). *Ergeb. Biol.* **22**, 1–29.

Koikegami, H., Yamada, T., and Usui, K. (1954). *Folia Psychiat. Neurol. Japon.* **8**, 7–31.

Laqueur, G. L., McCann, S. M., Schreiner, L. H., Rosenberg, E., Rioch, D. McK., and Anderson, E. (1955). *Endocrinology* **57**, 44–54.

McCann, S. M. (1953). *Am. J. Physiol.* **175**, 13–20.

McCann, S. M. (1957). *Endocrinology* **60**, 664–676.

McCann, S. M., and Brobeck, J. R. (1955). *Proc. Soc. Exptl. Biol. Med.* **88**, 318–324.

McCann, S. M., and Friedman, H. (1959). *Federation Proc.* **18**, 101.

McCann, S. M., and Fruit, A. (1957). *Proc. Soc. Exptl. Biol. Med.* **96**, 566–567.

McCann, S. M., and Haberland, P. (1959). *Proc. Soc. Exptl. Biol. Med.* **102**, 319–325.

McCann, S. M., and Haberland, P. (1960). *Endocrinology* **66**, 217–221.

McCann, S. M., and Taleisnik, S. (1961). *Endocrinology* **68**, 1071–1073.

McCann, S. M., Mack, R., and Gale, C. (1959). *Endocrinology* **64**, 870–889.

McCann, S. M., Taleisnik, S., and Friedman, H. M. (1960). *Proc. Soc. Exptl. Biol. Med.* **104**, 432–434.

McDermott, W. V., Fry, E. G., Brobeck, J. R., and Long, C. N. H. (1950). *Proc. Soc. Exptl. Biol. Med.* **73**, 609–610.

Markee, J. E., Everett, J. W., and Sawyer, C. H. (1952). *Recent Progr. in Hormone Research* **7**, 139–165.

Marshall, F. H. A. (1936). *Phil. Trans. Roy. Soc. London* **B226**, 423–456.

Marshall, F. H. A. (1942). *Biol. Revs. Cambridge Phil. Soc.* **17**, 68–90.

Marshall, F. H. A. (1956). "Physiology of Reproduction" 3rd ed. Longmans, Green, New York.

Martini, L., and De Poli, A. (1956). *J. Endocrinol.* **13**, 229–234.

Martini, L., Pecile, A., Saito, S., and Tani, F. (1960). *Endocrinology* **66**, 501–507.

Mason, J. W. (1958). *In* "Reticular Formation of the Brain" (H. H. Jasper, L. D. Proctor, A. S. Knighton, W. C. Noshay, and A. T. Costello, eds.), pp. 645–662. Little, Brown, Boston, Massachusetts.

Mason, J. W. (1959). *Recent Progr. in Hormone Research* **15**, 345–378.

Matthews, L. H. (1939). *Proc. Roy. Soc.* **B126**, 557–560.

Meites, J., Talwalker, P. K., and Ratner, A. (1962). *Abstr. Endocrine Soc., 44th Meeting, Chicago* p. 39.

Mialhe-Voloss, C. (1958). *Acta Endocrinol. Suppl.* **35**, 1–96.

Nauta, W. J. H., and Kuypers, J. M. (1958). *In* "Reticular Formation of the Brain" (H. H. Jasper, L. D. Proctor, A. S. Knighton, W. C. Noshay, and A. T. Costello, eds.), pp. 3–30. Little, Brown, Boston, Massachusetts.

Newman, A. E., Redgate, E. S., and Farrell, G. (1958). *Endocrinology* **63**, 723–737.

Nicoll, C. S., Talwalker, P. K., and Meites, J. (1960). *Am. J. Physiol.* **198**, 1103–1107.

Nikitovitch-Winer, M. B. (1962). *Endocrinology* **70**, 350–358.

Nikitovitch-Winer, M., and Everett, J. W. (1958). *Endocrinology* **63**, 916–931.

Nikitovitch-Winer, M., and Everett, J. W. (1959). *Endocrinology* **63**, 357–368.

Nowell, N. W. (1959). *Endocrinology* **64**, 191–202.

Okinaka, S., Ibayashi, H., Motohashi, K., Fujita, T., Yoshida, S., Ohsawa, N., and Murakawa, S. (1960). *1st Intern. Congr. Endocrinol. Copenhagen. Abstr. Communs.* p. 35.

Popa, G. T., and Fielding, U. (1930). *J. Anat.* **65**, 88–91.

Porter, J. C., and Jones, J. C. (1956). *Endocrinology* **58**, 62–67.

Porter, J. C., and Rumsfeld, H. W. (1956). *Endocrinology* **58**, 359–364.

Porter, J. C., and Rumsfeld, H. W. (1959). *Endocrinology* **64**, 948–954.

Porter, R. W. (1953). *Am. J. Physiol.* **172**, 515–519.

Reichlin, S. (1957). *Endocrinology* **60**, 567–569.

Reichlin, S. (1960a). *Endocrinology* **66**, 306–308.

Reichlin, S. (1960b). *Endocrinology* **66**, 327–339.

Rochefort, G. J., Rosenberger, J., and Saffran, M. (1959). *J. Physiol. (London)* **146,** 105–116.

Rothchild, I. (1960). *Endocrinology* **67,** 9–42.

Rothchild, I., and Quilligan, E. J. (1960). *Endocrinology* **67,** 122–125.

Royce, P. C., and Sayers, G. (1958a). *Proc. Soc. Exptl. Biol. Med.* **98,** 70–74.

Royce, P. C., and Sayers, G. (1958b). *Proc. Soc. Exptl. Biol. Med.* **98,** 677–680.

Royce, P. C., and Sayers, G. (1960). *Proc. Soc. Exptl. Biol. Med.* **103,** 447–450.

Rumsfeld, H. W., and Porter, J. C. (1959). *Arch. Biochem. Biophys.* **82,** 473–477.

Saffran, M. (1959). *Can. J. Biochem. and Physiol.* **37,** 319–331.

Saffran, M , and Schally, A. V. (1955). *Can. J. Biochem. and Physiol.* **33,** 408–405.

Saffran, M., Schally, A. V., and Benfey, B. G. (1955). *Endocrinology* **57,** 439–445.

Sayers, G. (1957). *CIBA Foundation Colloqia on Endocrinol.* **11,** 138–149.

Sayers, G. (1960). *1st Intern. Congr. Endocrinol. Copenhagen, Abstr. Symposia* pp. 25–33.

Schally, A. V., and Guillemin, R. (1959). *Proc. Soc. Exptl. Biol. Med.* **100,** 138–139.

Schally, A. V., and Guillemin, R. (1960). *1st Intern. Congr Endocrinol. Copenhagen, Abstr. Communs.* p. 63.

Schally, A. V., Andersen, R. N., Lipscomb, H. S., Long, J. M., and Guillemin, R. (1960). *Nature* **188,** 1192–1194.

Schally, A. V., Lipscomb, H. S., Long, J. M., Dear, W. E., and Guillemin, R. (1962). *Endocrinology* **70,** 478–480.

Schweizer, M., and Long, M. E. (1950). *Endocrinology* **47,** 454–457.

Scow, A. O., and Greer, M. A. (1955). *Endocrinology* **56,** 590–596.

Shealy, C. N., and Peele, T. L. (1957). *J. Neurophysiol.* **20,** 125.

Slusher, M. A. (1958). *Endocrinology* **63,** 412–419.

Slusher, M. A. (1960). *Endocrinology* **67,** 347–353.

Smelik, P. G. (1959). "Autonomic Nervous Involvement in Stress-Induced ACTH Secretion," Born, Assen, Netherlands.

Stutinsky, F. (1957). *Compt. rend. acad. sci.* **244,** 1537–1539.

Sydnor, K. L., and Sayers, G. (1954). *Endocrinology* **55,** 621–636.

Theobald, G. W. (1936). *Brit. Med. J.* **1,** 1038–1041.

Van Beugen, L., and Van der Werff ten Bosch. J. J. (1960). *1st Intern. Congr. Endocrinol. Copenhagen, Abstr. Communs.* p. 95.

Van der Werff ten Bosch, J. J., Van Rees, G. P., and Wolthuis, O. L. (1962). *Acta Endocrinol.* **40,** 103–110.

Van Rees, G. P., Van der Werff ten Bosch, J. J., and Wolthuis, O. L. (1962). *Acta Endocrinol.* **40,** 95–102.

Vivien, J. H., and Schott, J. (1958). *J. physiol. (Paris)* **50,** 561–563.

von Euler, C., and Holmgren, B. (1956a). *J. Physiol. (London)* **131,** 125–136.

von Euler, C., and Holmgren, B. (1956b). *J. Physiol. (London)* **131,** 137–146.

Yamada, T. (1959). *Endocrinology* **65,** 920–925.

Yamada, T., and Greer, M. A. (1959). *Endocrinology* **64,** 559–566.

Yamada, T., and Greer, M. A. (1960). *Endocrinology* **66,** 565–574.

Yokoyama, O., and Ota, K. (1959). *Endocrinol. Japan.* **6,** 14–20.

Neurohypophyseal Hormones

H. HELLER

Department of Pharmacology, University of Bristol, Bristol, England

I. INTRODUCTION

The pituitary gland was known to Galen but its division into a glandular and a nervous part seems to have been recognized first by the Venetian physician and anatomist G. D. Santorini who wrote in 1724: "Although the infundibulum seems to go straight down, as if into the gland below, and although the anterior part seems to be inserted into it, this is certainly not so. For where it touches the anterior gland, it curves back caudally. . . ."[1]

Typical neurohypophyseal tissue is found only in vertebrates. The neural complex of urochordates has been considered homologous to the vertebrate hypophysis and neurosecretory material has been found in the cerebral ganglion of ascidians (Dawson and Hisaw, 1956). Olsson and Wingstrand (1954) have suggested that the infundibular organ in *Amphioxus* may be "the functional and perhaps also the morphological counterpart of the hypothalamo-hypophysial neurosecretory system in vertebrates" but little attempt has so far been made to identify vertebrate-like hormones.

In the cyclostome *Petromyzon*, the neurohypophysis consists merely of a thin layer of epithelium and nerve endings in intimate contact with the meta-adenohypophysis (Scharrer, 1953; Green and Maxwell, 1959; van de Kamer and Schreurs, 1959). The pituitary gland of Myxinoidea is much reduced (Dodd, 1960), and the hypophyseal and neural elements do not come into close contact. Herlant (1954) has suggested this as the reason why the adenohypophysis in *Myxine* fails to differentiate. Elasmobranchs have a neuro-intermediate lobe, i.e., neural and intermediate lobe tissue interdigitate. Similarly, in teleosts the neurohypophysis usually takes the form of anastomosing strands which penetrate deeply into the adenohypophysis though there are exceptions (Kobayashi *et al.*, 1959). The pituitary of the Dipnoi is strongly reminiscent of that of amphibians. Wingstrand (1956), for example, has shown that the neurohypophysis of *Protopterus* is almost identical with that of the urodele *Necturus*. This lung fish is therefore the most primitive vertebrate with a true "neural lobe" but whether this morphological feature has functional significance (an interesting question in view of its estivating habit) remains to be seen.

In amphibians the neurohypophysis is differentiated into two parts in a manner which remains characteristic for all tetrapods. It consists of a median eminence which receives its blood supply from a hypophyseal portal circulation and a neural lobe (or infundibular process) with a separate arterial blood supply and venous drainage (Green, 1951). The neural lobe is relatively large in terrestrial amphibians and small in aquatic

---

[1] My sincere thanks are due to W. Beare, Professor of Latin, University of Bristol, who translated Santorini's remarks.

animals like *Necturus* (Green and Maxwell, 1959). The morphology of the pituitary gland varies somewhat in different groups of reptiles, birds, and mammals but the differences are superficial (de Beer, 1926; Hanström, 1957; Dodd, 1960).

All neurohypophyses contain the terminals of axons which originate in cell groups of the anterior hypothalamus and form the hypophyseal tract. In fishes and amphibians there is essentially only a single group of cells, the nucleus preopticus, situated on each side of the third ventricle. In reptiles and in the warm-blooded vertebrates there are two distinct cell groups, the paraventricular nucleus—which remains in much the same position as the preoptic nucleus and is probably phylogenetically the older structure (Meyer, 1935)—and the supraoptic nucleus.

Much effort has been expended on the problem of whether the pharmacological actions of mammalian posterior pituitary extracts are due to one or several hormones and whether these active principles occur in the pituitary of other vertebrate classes. Thanks mainly to the pioneer work of Herring (1913, 1915) and Hogben and de Beer (1925) it was soon established that neurohypophyseal extracts of "lower" vertebrates produce the same pharmacological effects as those of mammalian posterior pituitary preparations. Table I shows that this survey has since been almost completed in the sense that neurohypophyseal extracts of one or more representatives of all vertebrate classes have been investigated by a variety of qualitative biological tests. However, it was realized long ago (Heller, 1941b, 1942) that such results show at best only that related but not necessarily identical principles are present in these extracts. In fact, quantitative assays and calculations of potency ratios indicated (Heller, 1941b) that there are differences between the hormones of some vertebrate classes.

Important work during the second decade of the century had shown (Dudley, 1923; Kamm *et al.*, 1928) that mammalian posterior pituitary extracts can be separated into two active fractions. It culminated in the demonstration by du Vigneaud and his associated (1953a,b) that these activities were due to two cyclic octapeptides. Methods similar to his, together with a variety of pharmacological assays are now being applied to the analysis of nonmammalian neurohypophyseal extracts and have recently yielded important results.

Another subject which has much exercised the minds of investigators is that of the site of formation of the "neurohypophyseal" active principles. Earlier workers found it difficult to believe that the neural lobe which cytologically does not have the conventional structure of a gland elaborates endocrine principles. But this position was revolutionized by the discovery of Bargmann and Scharrer (1951) that the neural lobe is only a part of a neurosecretory system, and by their concept that it serves mainly as an organ of hormone storage and release.

TABLE I

Phyletic Distribution of Pharmacological Activities in Vertebrate Neurohypophysis[a]

Class	Oxytocic	Galactobolic	Mammalian pressor	Mammalian antidiuretic	Frog water balance
Cyclostomes	Lanzing (1954)	Sawyer et al. (1959)	Herring (1913)	Sawyer et al. (1959)	Lanzing (1954)
Elasmobranchs	Herring (1915)	Herring (1913)	Herring (1913)	Heller (1941a)	Heller (1941b)
Teleosts	Hogben and de Beer (1925)	Herring (1913)	Herring (1913)	Heller (1941a)	Boyd and Dingwall (1939)
Amphibians	Hogben and de Beer (1925)	Sawyer et al. (1959)	Herring (1913)	Heller (1941a)	Heller (1941b)
Reptiles	Hogben and de Beer (1925)	Sawyer et al. (1959)	Herring (1913)	Heller (1942)	Heller (1942)
Birds	Hogben and de Beer (1925)	Mackenzie (1911)	Herring (1915)	de Lawder et al. (1934)	Heller (1941b)
Mammals	Dale (1909)	Ott and Scott (1910)	Oliver and Schafer (1895)	von den Velden (1913)	Brunn (1921)

[a] The names refer to the first investigators.

II. MAMMALIAN NEUROHYPOPHYSEAL HORMONES

A. Standardization

The most recent (3rd) International Standard for Posterior Pituitary has been renamed International Standard for Oxytocic, Vasopressor, and Antidiuretic Substances. It consists of acetone-extracted dry powder prepared from fresh bovine posterior pituitary lobes. The unit of the oxytocic, vasopressor, and antidiuretic principles is defined as the activity of 0.5 mg of the dry powder, but it is recognized that the last two activities are properties of the same compound. Assay methods admitted by most national pharmacopoeias are those using the isolated rat uterus and the blood pressure-lowering effect in cockerels for the estimation of the oxytocic hormone (oxytocin), and the pressor or antidiuretic action in anesthetized rats for the estimation of the antidiuretic hormone (vasopressin).

The present standard has many drawbacks both for research and ther apy. For instance, the antidiuretic activity of the most commonly used commercial preparation of vasopressin may be due to a peptide which differs from that extracted from ox glands (Section II, B) and which may have a different ratio of pressor to antidiuretic potency when injected into human beings. Two preparations standardized by the pressor assay may therefore have very different antidiuretic activities. The adoption of the chemically pure hormones as standard preparations is undoubtedly desirable but seems at present to be difficult because of the relative instability of pure arginine vasopressin (du Vigneaud, 1955).

B. Chemistry

It was found quite early that the pressor–antidiuretic and oxytocic activities of mammalian posterior pituitary gland extracts can be differentially extracted and precipitated (Dudley, 1923; Schlapp, 1925; Draper, 1927), fractionally adsorbed (Schlapp, 1925), or separated by electrophoresis (du Vigneaud et al., 1938; Irving and du Vigneaud, 1938). However, although very active preparations were obtained and the strong suggestion emerged that the active substances were polypeptides, none of these methods led to the isolation of the pure hormones. This was achieved only when Craig's method of countercurrent distribution became available to du Vigneaud and his co-workers.

The oxytocic component (oxytocin) was found to be composed of eight amino acids and ammonia. Further studies of du Vigneaud and his associates (Mueller et al., 1953; Ressler et al., 1953; du Vigneaud et al., 1953c)

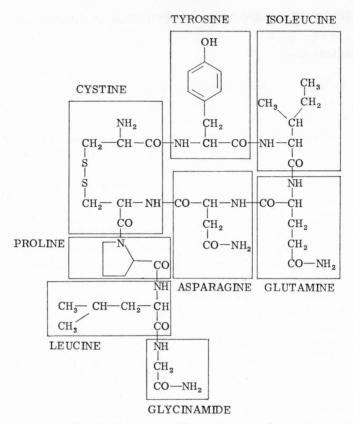

Fig. 1. The structural formula of oxytocin.

and Tuppy (1953) established the amino acid sequence of oxytocin as

CyS·Tyr·Ileu·Glu(NH₂)·Asp(NH₂)·CyS·Pro·Leu·Gly(NH₂)

and du Vigneaud (du Vigneaud *et al.*, 1953b) proposed the structural formula shown in Fig. 1 which was confirmed by the successful synthesis of the hormone (du Vigneaud *et al.*, 1953a, 1954a). When subjected to countercurrent distribution, the biological activity of the synthetic compound was found to be concentrated in a single peak. Its potency was indistinguishable from natural oxytocin when assayed by the chicken depressor method, it had the expected potency when tested on the isolated rat uterus, it was effective on the human uterus *in situ* and produced milk ejection in women when injected intravenously in a dose of 1 μg.

Chemically also, no difference could be detected between the synthetic and the natural polypeptide. Oxytocin synthetized by a different method

(Boissonnas *et al.*, 1955) and compared by further biological tests could likewise be shown to be identical with the natural product (Konzett *et al.*, 1956). Oxytocin is thus an octapeptide composed of a pentapeptide ring containing cystine, one-half of the cystine moiety possessing a free amino group, and the carboxyl group adjacent to the latter joined to the amino group of tyrosine. The other half of the cystine residue is connected through its amino group to aspartic acid and linked through its carboxyl group to a side chain consisting of the tripeptide Pro·Leu·Gly. It will be seen that all the other neurohypophyseal hormones whose structure is known at present follow the same pattern.

Purified by similar methods as the oxytocic compound, the pressor–antidiuretic fraction of ox pituitary extracts yielded a product with a potency of about 400 U/mg (Turner *et al.*, 1951). When analyzed by the technique of Moore and Stein the material yielded eight amino acids, six of which, namely cystine, tyrosine, proline, glutamic acid, aspartic acid, and glycine had also been found in oxytocin. In addition, the hydrolyzate contained phenylalanine and arginine. Further work on beef vasopressin revealed the amino acid sequence

$$CyS·Tyr·Phe·Glu(NH_2)·Asp(NH_2)·CyS·Pro·Arg·Gly(NH_2)$$

(du Vigneaud *et al.*, 1953a) a finding which was quickly confirmed by Acher and Chauvet (1954). A structure analogous to that of oxytocin could be postulated and was proved by synthesis (du Vigneaud *et al.*, 1954b).

Similar investigations on the pressor–antidiuretic factor in pig pituitary extracts showed however that this active principle differed chemically from beef vasopressin; it contained lysine instead of arginine in the penultimate position of the peptide chain (Popenoe *et al.*, 1952). A number of mammalian posterior pituitaries, including that of man, have been analyzed since. But although arginine vasopressin was found in some species and lysine vasopressin in others, it seems at present that these are the only vasopressins which mammals elaborate.

C. Pharmacological Activity of the Pure Mammalian Peptides

The exact potency of pure oxytocin and the vasopressins as measured by the appropriate bioassays cannot be stated at present since even the purest preparations available may contain contaminants. This is suggested by chromatographic results (Heller and Lederis, 1959) which showed often more than one "spot" when material like du Vigneaud's highly purified arginine vasopressin and commercially available synthetic oxytocin (Syntocinon) were investigated. The source of these contaminations may have been manifold. Du Vigneaud (1955) has commented on the instability of arginine vasopressin, and a solution of the highly purified hormone, particularly when heated before refrigeration, may therefore contain degradation products. Similarly, it cannot be excluded that preparations of a synthetic octapeptide contain traces of the nonapeptide from which it has been obtained by oxidative cyclization. Inactive dimers of the active monomeric molecule (Berde et al., 1961) may also be present.

It is obvious that, at least theoretically, any of the contaminating peptides may act as antagonists by receptor competition. Synthetic analogs of naturally occurring active peptides which have an inhibitory action in certain bioassays are in fact known (Guttmann et al., 1957; Konzett, 1957; Berde et al., 1961). It is, however, likely that more often than not, the small amounts of contaminating peptides are virtually inert. Berde et al. (1961) compared the potency of a crude solution of synthetic oxytocin with a more highly purified preparation obtained by 1095 transfers in countercurrent distribution and found little difference in the ratio of activities. This suggests that Table II, which summarizes the activities of oxytocin, arginine vasopressin, and lysine vasopressin, gives a fair approximation of the potencies of the pure hormones, although the potency ratios are probably more reliable than the absolute values.

It is not particularly surprising that compounds which are chemically as closely related as oxytocin and vasopressin share many qualitative actions. Thus oxytocin has some pressor and antidiuretic action in rats, and the vasopressins have a weak effect on the uterus. The pressor potency of lysine vasopressin assayed in the rat against the International Standard has been estimated (van Dyke, 1959) as 65–75% of that of arginine vasopressin. It could also be shown that in equipressor doses the antidiuretic effect of lysine vasopressin may differ from that of its arginine analog. Injected intravenously into dogs, lysine vasopressin exerts a much weaker inhibitory action in terms of both intensity and duration of response (van Dyke et al., 1956; Heller and Lederis, 1960). In man as well the antidiuretic effect of lysine vasopressin seems to be 3–4 times weaker than that of arginine vasopressin (Dicker and Eggleton, 1961). The difference in the antidiuretic potency of the two vasopressins in rats is more difficult to assess since antidiuresis measured as the maximum depression in urine flow may be much the same (Sawyer, 1958; Thorn, 1959). However, the duration of action of lysine vasopressin in this species is usually considerably shorter. The neurohypophysis of dog, man, and rat stores arginine vasopressin (van Dyke et al., 1957; Light and du Vigneaud, 1958). It is therefore of great interest that lysine vasopressin in the pig which synthesizes this peptide (Section II,H) is antidiuretically as potent, if not more potent, than the arginine compound (Munsick et al., 1958).

TABLE II

ACTIVITIES OF "HIGHLY PURIFIED" MAMMALIAN NEUROHYPOPHYSEAL HORMONES
(Units/mg peptide)

	Rat vaso-pressor	Rat anti-diuretic	Dog anti-diuretic	Isolated rat uterus	Rabbit milk ejection	Chicken depressor	Hen oviduct	Frog bladder
Arginine vasopressin	400[a,f]	400[a]	400[a]	12[e]	51[a]	56[a]	320[a]	~26[e]
Lysine vasopressin	270[a,b]	150[d]	50[a]	7.5[e]	42[a]	42[a]	15[a]–65[b]	<7.5[e]
Oxytocin	4–7[e]	4.5[c]	4[a,e]	420[a,c]	370[c]	430[c]	34[a]	420[e]

[a] Van Dyke (1959).
[b] Boissonnas and Guttmann (1960).
[c] Berde et al. (1961).
[d] Heller and Lederis (unpublished results).
[e] Munsick et al. (1960).
[f] Light et al. (1959).

D. Structure–Action Relationships of Neurohypophyseal Hormones and Some of Their Synthetic Analogs

The synthesis of oxytocin and of the vasopressins, and the advances in the methods of peptide synthesis generally, led to the preparation of a number of analogs of oxytocin and vasopressin with the hope of gaining some insight into the relationship between the chemical structure and the biological activities of the neurohypophyseal hormones. Apart from yielding some information of this kind these studies had also the surprising result that at least one oxytocin analog (8-arginine oxytocin or vasotocin) was synthesized (Katsoyannis and du Vigneaud, 1960) which was subsequently found to occur in nonmammalian pituitary glands.

With the rapid increase in the number of naturally occurring and synthetic octapeptides there is an obvious need for an agreed nomenclature for this group of substances. Berde and his associates (Konzett and Berde, 1959; Berde *et al.*, 1961) have proposed to number the amino acid residues of oxytocin from 1 to 9 (Table III). The number of the residue which is replaced is then indicated as a superscript to the "new" amino acid(s). In their terminology arginine vasopressin for example becomes phenylalanyl^3-arginyl^8-oxytocin, or phe^3-arg^8-oxytocin. Du Vigneaud and van Dyke (1960) however prefer to reserve the adjectival form of amino acids (e.g. glycyl) for compounds in which an amino acid has been added in peptide linkage. They also suggest that the number which defines the position of the substituent should be placed before the amino acid. Thus oxytocin in which the penultimate residue has been replaced by arginine, would be defined as 8-arginine oxytocin when expressed in the unabbreviated form. Since their procedure is more in line with common chemical usage, it has been adopted in the present article. The problem remains whether all the substances of this type should be expressed as derivatives of oxytocin or whether "laboratory" names like vasopressin, vasotocin, ichthyotocin, etc. should be used in parallel. In view of their historical connotations and failing the decision of an international body, it may be best to retain these terms for the present.

If the two cysteine moieties in the oxytocin or vasopressin molecule are not changed, but the position of the remaining amino acids in oxytocin and the two vasopressins is altered, 1,728,720 different polypeptides are possible (Konzett, 1960). The number becomes even more astronomical when iso-derivatives and amino acids not present in the naturally occurring mammalian hormones are introduced. But although the pharmacological activity of only about 30 synthetic analogs has been tested (Table III), certain tentative conclusions about relationships between chemical structure and biological activity can be drawn.

Replacement of one amino acid residue of oxytocin may result in compounds with considerable biological activity (e.g., 2-Phe-, 3-Phe-, 3-Leu-, 3-Val-, 8-Ileu-, 8-Val-, 8-Arg-, and 8-Lys- oxytocin) though none of these peptides have the potency (per molecule) of the naturally occurring mammalian hormone. Other peptides of this type (e.g., 2-Ser-, 3-Tyr-, 3-Try, 5-Glu-, 4-Isoglu-, and 5-Isoasp- oxytocin) have little if any oxytocic action and their other biological activities are also negligible (Table III). Note that substitution of isoleucine or valine for leucine in position 8 impairs oxytocic potency only little, and insertion of arginine or lysine decreases oxytocic activity per unit weight of peptide but enhances the pressor–antidiuretic activity in relation to the oxytocic activity, probably because the resulting compounds carry the same tripeptide side chain as do the naturally occurring vasopressins. Introduction of leucine or phenylalanine into position 3 has the effect of decreasing absolute oxytocic potency and increasing (relative) pressor–antidiuretic activity. In contrast, substitution of valine for isoleucine in position 3 leads probably to a "purer" oxytocic substance, 3-valine oxytocin apparently having relatively less pressor–antidiuretic activity than oxytocin. It also seems that positions 4 and 5 in the pentapeptide ring may be critical since the isoglutamine (Ressler and du Vigneaud, 1957) and isoasparagine (Lutz et al., 1959) isomers of oxytocin were found to be devoid of biological action. The pentapeptide ring of oxytocin itself, however, appears to have some slight pharmacological activity (Ressler and Rachele, 1958).

Inspection of Table III shows further that introduction of the same amino acid at different positions may produce very marked quantitative differences in action. A comparison of 2-phenylalanine oxytocin with 3-phenylalanine oxytocin, for example, demonstrates that it is not the presence of the phenylalanine residue in the disulfide ring as such which is mainly responsible for the vasopressin-like effects; the 3-phenylalanine compound is about 90 times as active as the 2-phenylalanine analog (Konzett, 1960). Jaquenoud and Boissonnas (1961) have shown quite recently that substitution of valine in position 8 of oxytocin impairs uterus-stimulating potency per molecule much less than substitution in position 3.

Berde et al. (1961) pointed out that in the group of synthetic oxytocin analogs in which two amino acids residues had been replaced, those which contain the tripeptide side chain of lysine vasopressin (Table III, nos. 20, 24, 25) have some vasopressin-like activity. Similarly, the triple-substituted oxytocins shown in Table III (nos. 26–30) may be regarded as lysine vasopressin with one amino acid replaced. The weak pressor action which these compounds exert is therefore likely to be due to their resemblance to the naturally occurring hormone.

TABLE III

STRUCTURE–ACTION RELATIONSHIPS OF NATURALLY OCCURRING AND SYNTHETIC ANALOGS OF OXYTOCIN[a]

Number	Compound	Potency (U/mg peptide)	Rat uterus (0.5 mM Mg++)	Potency relative to oxytocic activity[b]						
				Milk ejection	Avian depressor	Rat blood pressure	Rat anti-diuretic	Frog bladder	Frog natriferic
	Oxytocin[a]	360[d]	86	100	100	1.9	1.1	100	100
	Single substitution								
(1)	2-Phe	31.5	285	390	165	1.0	2.5	—	—
(2)	2-Ser	—	—	None	None	None	—	—	—
(3)	3-Leu	45	—	880	132	60[e]	60	—	—
(4)	3-Phe	16	138	550	340	19[e]	104	<125	—
(5)	3-Try	—	—	250	500	None	—	—	—
(6)	3-Tyr	0.1	—	390	280	11	—	—	—
(7)	3-Val	59	356	536	114	0.5[e]	1.4	—	—
(8)	4-Isoglu	None	—	—	None	—	—	—	—
(9)	5-Isoasp	None	—	—	None	None	—	—	—
(10)	5-Glu	None	—	Some	None	None	None	—	—
(11)	8-Arg[c]	37	192	297	—	177	177	19500	1470
(12)	8-Ileu	289	—	113	172	2.1	0.4	—	—
(13)	8-His	7	—	—	—	—	—	—	—
(14)	8-Lys	20	—	275	269	196	91	1250	1300
(15)	8-Val	200	—	155	140	4.5	0.4	—	—

Double substitution

(16)	2-His, 3-Phe	—	—	Some	Some	Some	—	—	—
(17)	2-Phe, 3-Phe	3.3	—	745	164	27	173	—	—
(18)	2-Phe, 3-Tyr	<0.01	—	None(?)	None(?)	None(?)	Some	—	—
(19)	2-Ser, 3-His	—	—	—	Some	None[b]	—	—	—
(20)	2-Ser, 8-Lys	—	—	None	None	Some	—	780	100
(21)	3-Phe, 8-Arg[d]	9	165	566	466	3330[e]	3330	—	—
(22)	3-Phe, 8-His	—	—	250	70	30[e]	125	—	—
(23)	3-Phe, 8-Lys[c]	5	255	680	560	4000	—	<100	160
(24)	3-Try, 8-Lys	—	—	None	Some	Some	—	—	—
(25)	3-Tyr, 8-Lys	0.01	—	1430	710	11600	1310	—	—

Triple substitution

(26)	2-His, 3-Phe, 8-Lys	Some	—	Some	Some	Some	—	—	—
(27)	2-His, 3-Ser, 8-Lys	—	—	None	—	Some	—	—	—
(28)	2-Phe, 3-Phe 8-Lys	0.06	—	5000	2330	131000	35700	—	—
(29)	2-Phe, 3-Tyr, 8-Lys	<0.01	—	—	<100	1400	130	—	—
(30)	2-Ser, 3-His, 8-Lys	—	—	—	Some	—	—	—	—

a Oxytocin: CyS·Tyr·Ileu·Glu(NH_2)·Asp(NH_2)·CyS·Pro·Leu·Gly(NH_2)

   1   2   3   4   5   6   7   8   9

The estimates of potencies are based on the papers of: Berde *et al.* (1961), Boissonnas and Guttmann (1960), van Dyke (1959), Heller and Pickering (1961), Jaquenoud and Boissonnas (1961), Lutz *et al.* (1959), Munsick *et al.* (1960), Ressler and du Vigneaud (1957) and Sawyer *et al.* (1960).

b Isolated rat uterus, little or no Mg^{++}.

c Naturally occurring active peptide.

d Activity in Munsick's (1960) solution (no Mg^{++}).

e Spinal cat.

An indication of the importance of the hydrogen atom on the imino nitrogen of the peptide bond between leucine and glycinamide (Fig. 1) has been obtained by substitution of sarcosinamide for glycinamide (Cash et al., 1962). The resulting compound 9-sarcosine oxytocin showed only a small fraction of the activity of oxytocin itself but the five biological actions tested were lowered to different extents.

Even more interesting is another recently prepared oxytocin analog, desamino-oxytocin—i.e., a peptide which lacks the free amino group on the cystine residue in position 1 (Hope et al., 1962). It was shown to have a considerably higher uterus-contracting activity (684 ± 32 U/mg) and avian depressor activity (733 ± 23 U/mg) than the purest preparation of oxytocin; its galactobolic potency was also high (400 ± 8 U/mg). The rat pressor activity was lower than that of oxytocin (Table II), namely 1.1 ± 0.1 U/mg, but the rat antidiuretic activity appears to be significantly higher (14.9 ± 2.1 U/mg). These results show clearly that the free amino group in oxytocin is not required for most of the biological activities tested.

Several analogs have recently been found which inhibit individual effects of the naturally occurring hormones. Thus 2-O-methyltyrosine oxytocin (Law and du Vigneaud, 1960; Jošt et al., 1961) strongly inhibits the uterus-stimulating effect of oxytocin in vitro (Beránková et al., 1961), the mode of action being that of a competitive antagonist (Rudinger and Krejči, 1962). Oxytocin analogs with the peptide chain extended at the amino end by an additional amino acid residue or peptide sequence, such as glycyl-oxytocin (du Vigneaud et al., 1960; Jošt et al., 1961) or leucyl-glycyl-glycyl-oxytocin (Jošt et al., 1961) also act as inhibitors of oxytocin in several preparations (du Vigneaud et al., 1960; Jošt et al., 1961; Bisset, 1962). Moreover, the avian depressor activity of these analogs is distinctly protracted (du Vigneaud et al., 1960; Jošt et al., 1961), as is their antidiuretic and oxytocic effect in vivo (Beránková-Ksandrová et al., 1962).

E. Neurosecretion and the Ultrastructure of the Hypothalamo-Neurohypophyseal System

Oxytocin and the vasopressins occur not only in the neural lobe but also in other parts of the hypothalamo-neurohypophyseal complex. Lederis (1961) has found that the active principles extracted from the hypothalamus of man, sheep, ox, rabbit, rat, and pig behave chromatographically like "glandular" oxytocin and vasopressin, and that the pressor–antidiuretic principle in pig hypothalamus extracts behaves like lysine vasopressin, whereas that in hypothalamic extracts from the other species behaves like the arginine compound. It is, however, by no means clear in what form the peptides are secreted and stored. Nor is it certain whether they circulate in the blood as free or bound compounds, or in what form they are excreted in the urine.

The granular material, demonstrable with selective stains (e.g., Gomori's chrome-alum-hematoxylin-phloxin) in the cell bodies, axons, and terminals of supraoptic and paraventricular neurons, is considered to contain the active peptides. This is suggested (a) by the parallel distribution of the neurosecretory material and biological activity, (b) by the observation that experimental conditions which deplete the neurohypophysis of hormones also empty the neurosecretory vesicles (Hild and Zetler, 1953; Sawyer and Roth, 1953; Palay, 1957), and (c) by the more recent findings (Lederis and Heller, 1960; Heller, 1961; Heller and Lederis, 1961) that subcellular particles can be isolated by differential centrifugation of rabbit posterior pituitary homogenates which, with regard to their size and other electron microscopical characteristics, resemble the neurosecretory vesicles seen *in situ*. The isolated subcellular elements were shown to contain 80% or more of the hormonal activities of the undifferentiated homogenate (Heller and Lederis, 1961).

The presence of protein in the neurosecretory granules was first stressed by Schiebler (1951). Barrnett and Seligman (1954) and Sloper (1954, 1955) found subsequently that material with the exact distribution of the chrome-alum-hematoxyphil granules could be demonstrated with methods devised to show protein-bound cystine or cysteine. This material could be removed by tryptic digestion. These histochemical results are in good agreement with evidence of another kind which suggests that the hormones in the neurohypophysis are bound to protein. Rosenfeld (1940) concluded from sedimentation experiments in the ultracentrifuge that the vasopressor and oxytocic activities in untreated press-juice of beef posterior lobes were large protein molecules. Van Dyke and his associates (1942) isolated a protein (molecular weight of about 30,000) from beef posterior pituitary glands which had pressor, antidiuretic, and oxytocic activities in the same ratio as an acetic acid extract of the gland. It appeared to be pure as judged by its solubility curve and its Schlieren patterns in the ultracentrifuge. When the oxytocin and the vasopressins had been isolated the question arose whether these peptides represented active fragments of a large molecule connected, for example, by disulfide linkages to longer peptide chains (Block and van Dyke, 1952), or whether they were bound to a protein carrier in a less intimate fashion, as e.g., by adsorption or electrostatic forces. Since the oxytocin in crude beef posterior extracts can be obtained by electrodialysis in a 100% yield (Haselbach and Piguet, 1952), and since this treatment does not involve the rupture of peptide or disulfide bonds, the latter possibility seems more likely.

Similarly, Acher and Fromageot (1957) could show that processes which do not involve hydrolysis, such as dialysis against dilute acetic acid, electrodialysis, precipitation with trichloracetic acid, and countercurrent distribution dissociate the oxytocic and pressor activities from "van Dyke's protein." Acher and his co-workers (Chauvet *et al.*, 1960a) have recently prepared a protein (neurophysin) from ox, pig, and horse posterior pituitaries which adsorbs oxytocin and vasopressin preferentially and which they therefore regard as the physiological carrier of these hormones.

Whether the active peptides reach the circulation bound to the specific carrier protein cannot be decided at present. Material stainable by Gomori's method has been found in the neurohypophyseal vessels of the giraffe (Hanström, 1952), the rat (Rothballer, 1953), and the dog (Scharrer and Frandson, 1954). Heller and Lederis (1962), in electronmicrographs of the rabbit pituitary, have recently noted structures within capillaries which look like the hormone-carrying vesicles or granules, but this was seen so rarely that it may well represent an artifact.

F. Storage in the Neural Lobe

Neurosecretory material and hormonal activity are present in several parts of the hypothalamo-neurohypophyseal system but in those forms which possess a neural lobe, this structure must be regarded as the main site of storage, both in terms of abundance of neurosecretory material and of hormone content. The amounts of active peptides relative to body weight vary considerably from one mammalian species to another and there is the strong suggestion (Enemar and Hanström, 1956) of a connection between the relative size of the neural lobe and the occurrence of hibernation or desert life. This would agree with the report (Ames and van Dyke, 1950) that the pituitary of the desert-living kangaroo rat (*Dipodomys merriami*) contains more antidiuretic hormone than that of normal laboratory rats although the latter are 5–6 times heavier.

The neural lobes of all mammalian species investigated may safely be regarded as storage organs since the quantities of active peptides which can be extracted are in all instances many times larger than the minimum active dose or the amounts which normally circulate. In the rat, for example, whose posterior pituitary may contain 1000 mU antidiuretic activity, about 3–15 μU vasopressin/100 gm body weight are secreted per minute (Dicker, 1954). It can be calculated from this estimate and from the constant obtained by Ginsburg and Heller (1953) in the equation for the plasma clearance of antidiuretic hormone that the corresponding concentration of the hormone in the blood would be 0.8–3.2 μU/ml or 5–19 μU in the total blood volume. The latter figure is of the same order as the minimum (intravenous) antidiuretic dose.

The ratio of vasopressor-antidiuretic to oxytocic activity in extracts of the International Standard powder is, by definition, one. But this ratio is not, strictly speaking, the same as the ratio of the amounts of pure peptides in the gland. First (as shown in Table II) because the vasopressins have some intrinsic oxytocic and oxytocin some pressor–antidiuretic activity, and secondly because it has been shown (Heller and Lederis, 1959) that the acetone treatment of ox posterior pituitary powder recommended by the pharmacopoeias extracts some of the oxytocin. Both corrections are small and may be neglected in adult males but not in very young (Heller and Lederis, 1959) or in lactating animals (Heller, 1961).

Table IV shows that, assayed against the International Standard, the ratio of activities (V/O ratio) approaches unity in many but by no means all mammalian species investigated. It may, in fact, be assumed that the V/O ratio in the mammalian infundibular process is to some degree a species characteristic.

G. Occurrence in the Hypothalamus

In terms of hormone content of the neural lobe, the amounts of hormonal activity found in the hypothalamus are small (Table V). The dog appears to be an exception; pressor activity amounting to up to 20% of the activity in the posterior lobe has been recorded (van Dyke *et al.*, 1957) but the oxytocic potency of dog anterior hypothalamus extracts is as low as that of other species or probably lower (Lederis, 1962). Indeed it is so low that Vogt (1961) has suggested that it may be accounted for by the intrinsic oxytocic activity of arginine vasopressin (Table II). However, Lederis (1962) has recently been able to demonstrate oxytocin chromatographically in extracts of dog hypothalami.

It is likely that in most species the nuclei contain both oxytocin and vasopressin although they may contain them in different proportions. Table VI, for example, shows the hormone content of the separated supraoptic and paraventricular nuclei of sheep (Lederis, 1961). Similar results, viz., a distinct preponderance of oxytocin over vasopressin in the paraventricular nucleus (V/O = 0.2) and the opposite in the supraoptic nucleus (V/O = 2.2) have also been shown in the Algerian camel (Adamsons *et al.*, 1956) and in the dog (van Dyke *et al.* 1957; Lederis, 1962).

These results suggest that estimations of V/O ratios in extracts of the whole hypothalamus are of limited importance since they may derive from the mean of two regions with very different hormone concentrations. Furthermore, they raise several possibilities: (a) that individual neurons produce both hormones but do so in different proportions; (b) that each neuron synthesizes one hormone only but that the proportion of oxytocin-producing neurons and of vasopressin-producing neurons varies in the

TABLE IV

RATIO OF HORMONAL ACTIVITIES AND DISTRIBUTION OF VASOPRESSINS IN THE NEURAL LOBE OF MAMMALS

Order	Species	Ratio of vasopressor to oxytocic activity	Authors	Type of vasopressin present	Authors
Monotremata	*Tachyglossus aculeatus*	—		AVP[b]	Sawyer et al. (1960)
Marsupialia	*Didelphys virginiana*	3.4–9.1	Heller and Lederis (unpubl.)	AVP	Sawyer et al. (1960)
	Setonix brachyurus	3.8–6.0	Ferguson and Heller (unpubl.)	—	
	Macropus rufus			—	
Edentata	*Dasypus novemcinctus*	~10.0	Oldham (1938)	—	
Glires	*Oryctolagus cuniculus*	2.9	Lederis (1961)	AVP	van Dyke et al. (1957), Lederis (1961)
	Cavia porcellus	2.1	Schlichtegroll (1954)	—	
	Mus rattus	1.0–1.4	Numerous	AVP	van Dyke et al. (1957), Lederis (1961)
Cetacea	*Physeter megalocephalus*	12.5	Geiling (1935)	—	
	Balaenoptera physalus	2.5	Geiling (1935)	—	
	Megaptera Grey	2.5–3.4	Geiling and Oldham (1937)	—	
	Balaenoptera gibbaldii	3.4	Geiling and Oldham (1937)	—	
	Tursiops truncatus	~1.0	Geiling et al. (1940)	—	
	Prodelphinus prajiodon	~1.0	Geiling et al. (1940)	—	
Sirenia	*Trichechus inunguis*	~1.0	Oldham et al. (1938)	—	

			Acher et al. (1959)	AVP[d]	Acher et al. (1959)
Mesaxonia	Equus caballus	1.0			
Paraxonia	Bos taurus	1.4[a]	Lederis (1961)	AVP[d]	du Vigneaud et al. (1953c)
	Ovis aries	1.8[a]	Lederis (1961)	AVP[d]	Chauvet et al. (1960a)
	Cervus elaphus	1.8	Heller and Lederis (unpubl.)	AVP	Heller and Lederis (unpublished)
	Capreolus capreolus	2.5	Heller and Lederis (unpubl.)	AVP	Heller and Lederis (unpublished)
	Camelus dromedarius	4.3	van Dyke et al. (1957)	AVP	van Dyke et al. (1957)
	Sus L.	1.6[a]	Lederis (1961)	LVP[c,d]	Popenoe et al. (1952)
	Dicotyles pecari	2.2	Ferguson et al. (1962)	LVP and AVP[3]	Ferguson et al. (1962)
	Hippopotamus amphibius	0.63	Heller and Lederis (unpubl.)	LVP	Heller and Lederis (1960)
Carnivora	Canis familiaris	1.1–1.5	van Dyke et al. (1957)	AVP	van Dyke et al. (1957)
	Felis catus	1.0–1.3	van Dyke et al. (1957)	AVP	van Dyke et al. (1957)
Primates	Homo sapiens	1.2	van Dyke et al. (1957)	AVP[d]	Light and du Vigneaud (1958)
	Macaca mulattus	1.5	van Dyke et al. (1957)	AVP	van Dyke et al. (1957)

[a] Referred to 3rd International Standard.
[b] AVP = Arginine vasopressin.
[c] LVP = Lysine vasopressin.
[d] By amino acid analysis.

TABLE V

HORMONE CONTENT AND VASOPRESSIN: OXYTOCIN RATIO (V/O) IN THE
MAMMALIAN HYPOTHALAMUS

| | Hormone content of hypothalamus[d] | | V/O in | |
Species	Vasopressin	Oxytocin	Hypothalamus	Neural lobe
Man[a]	4.6[e]	5.9[e]	1.9	1.6
Macaque[b]	0.4	—	—	—
Dog[b]	20.0	2.3	17.0	1.5
Cat[c]	—	—	1.0	1.3
Ox[a]	0.6	0.5	1.7	1.4
Camel[b]	0.4	1.2	1.1	3.3
Sheep[a]	0.5	0.6	1.9	1.8
Pig[a]	0.7	0.6	2.6	1.6
Rabbit[a]	1.9	1.4	4.0	2.9
Rat[a]	1.4	1.0	2.3	1.6

[a] Lederis (1961).
[b] van Dyke et al. (1957).
[c] Schlichtegroll (1954).
[d] As % of that of neural lobe.
[e] Two individuals only.

supraoptic and paraventricular nuclei; (c) that—perhaps in some species only—all the neurons of the supraoptic nucleus synthesize vasopressin and all the neurons of the paraventricular nucleus produce oxytocin, and that the oxytocin found in the former and the vasopressin in the latter are only contaminants present because of incomplete separation of the two nuclear regions at dissection.

H. Distribution in Mammals

The identification of neurohypophyseal hormones can be attempted by several methods. The only fully convincing procedure consists in the careful purification by chemical and physicochemical means of the unknown active peptide followed by amino acid analysis and establishment of the amino acid sequence. This method has the disadvantage that relatively large amounts of material are needed. Only the glands of a few large and easily obtainable mammals (ox, du Vigneaud et al. 1953c; Tuppy and Michl, 1953; Light and du Vigneaud, 1958; horse, Acher et al., 1958; sheep, Chauvet et al., 1960a) have therefore been analyzed in this manner.

Chromatography and comparison with pure reference substances offer a more limited but still very useful method of identification. It has been

TABLE VI

HORMONE CONTENT AND VASOPRESSIN: OXYTOCIN (V/O) RATIOS IN THE NEURAL LOBE, WHOLE ANTERIOR HYPOTHALAMUS, AND THE SEPARATED SUPRAOPTIC AND PARAVENTRICULAR NUCLEI OF SHEEP[a]

Tissue	Number of animals	Number of experiments	Hormone content in mU		
			Vasopressin	Oxytocin	V/O
Supraoptic nuclei	15	5	75 ± 20 (85)[b]	28 ± 6 (35)[c]	3.30 ± 0.57
Paraventricular nuclei	12	4	19 ± 3 (20)[b]	30 ± 6 (35)[c]	0.66 ± 0.08
Whole anterior hypothalamus	12	4	95 ± 12	59 ± 10	1.92 ± 0.26
Neural lobe	15	5	21,920 ± 920	12,390 ± 1,670	1.83 ± 0.32

[a] Lederis, (1961).
[b] Antidiuretic assays
[c] Milk ejection assays.

used widely and requires only small quantities of active material. With the method of Reindel and Hoppe (1954)—which is more suitable for staining of cyclopeptides than the more commonly used ninhydrin— Heller and Lederis (1958) were able to visualize less than 1 μg of the neurohypophyseal hormones on paper chromatograms. Considerably smaller quantities still (less than 1 mU or about 0.002 μg of oxytocin or arginine vasopressin) could be eluted from areas parallel to reference spots, and biologically assayed.

Chromatographic results, however, may not invariably differentiate between one active octapeptide and another. It was found, for instance(Heller and Lederis, 1958), that in the system n-butanol–acetic acid–water, oxytocin had the same R_f as one of its synthetic analogs, 3-phenylalanine oxytocin. Similarly, an oxytocic peptide found in teleost pituitaries, which was subsequently shown to differ substantially from oxytocin (Heller et al., 1961), appeared in the same position as the latter in both paper and column chromatograms (Heller and Pickering, 1961). It follows that the neurohypophyseal active peptides cannot be identified by R_f values only. But even when very small amounts of hormone are available, they can be further characterized, after chromatographic separation, by estimating the potency ratio in bioassays on several organs or tissues.

A combination of chromatography and multiple bioassays has proved very useful in determining the vasopressin elaborated by the hippopotamus (Heller and Lederis, 1960); only three glands were available. Vasopressin was separated from oxytocin by paper chromatography and was found in the region of highly purified pig lysine vasopressin. The action of eluates containing the hippopotamus vasopressin were then compared with that of arginine and lysine vasopressin on the isolated hen uterus. It was found that, like lysine vasopressin, the hippopotamus hormone had a much weaker effect. In assays on the water diuresis of unanesthetized dogs the hippopotamus hormone again behaved more like lysine vasopressin than like the arginine analog. Thus both pharmacological methods of comparison and the chromatographic findings showed that the vasopressor–antidiuretic principle in the posterior pituitary of the hippopotamus was not arginine vasopressin and was very probably lysine vasopressin.

Table IV shows that in mammals an antidiuretic hormone other than arginine vasopressin has thus far only been found in species belonging to the two surviving groups of the Suiformes which are a suborder of the Artiodactyla or even-toed ungulates. All other eutherian glands and the neural lobes of the three marsupials investigated apparently contained arginine vasopressin. It is of particular interest that the arginine compound has also been tentatively identified in the monotreme *Tachyglossus* since this may be taken to indicate (Sawyer et al., 1960) that "arginine vasopressin made its appearance very early in evolution, either in the reptilian stock from which mammals descended or in a very early mammalian ancestor common to monotremes, marsupials, and placental mammals." Since, so far as we know, in phylogenetically recent reptiles (Section IV,F) 8-arginine oxytocin (vasotocin) is the main antidiuretic hormone (Pickering and Heller, 1959; Sawyer *et al.*, 1959; Heller and Pickering, 1961) and vasopressin appears only in mammals and possibly in birds (Chauvet *et al.*, 1960b), it is tempting to connect its occurrence with the ability to produce a hypertonic urine, though the elongation of the loop of Henle was probably an equally or even more significant evolutionary step.

The oxytocic activity in mammalian neural lobe extracts can be accounted for by oxytocin and by the weak intrinsic uterus-stimulating effect of the vasopressins. There is at present no indication that mammalian glands contain an oxytocic hormone other than oxytocin in any considerable quantity.

I. Significance of Variation in the Chemical Composition of the Vasopressins

Whatever its mechanism, it appears that the process of peptide and protein biosynthesis allows a certain latitude in the incorporation of amino acids. Imprecision of peptide assembly is presumably determined and limited by the resemblance of some amino acids to each other. For example, the three-dimensional structure may be similar (as in the case of valine and isoleucine) or the similarity could include electrical properties (note e.g., the similarity of the pK_1 values for arginine and lysine, Alberty, 1953). The biological activity of new analogs may therefore be expected to vary according to the degree of alteration in their spatial structure, that is to say the new compound will have a better or worse fit to the receptors and will be a more effective or less effective "hormone."

There is much evidence available (Anfinsen, 1959) which suggests that the composition of proteins may be a relatively direct expression of gene structure. We may therefore infer the existence of one or several determining genes for each hormone and, in turn, that changes in the hormone molecule are basically due to gene mutation. Such mutations may be advantageous; it is, for example, conceivable that in the mammalian environment the vasopressins are more effective than the nonmammalian antidiuretic hormone(s). If so, the establishment of vasopressin in the heredity of the mammals would be easy to understand. However, recent studies of structure–action relationship in synthetic analogs of the neurohypophyseal hormones have shown that substitution of a single amino acid may deprive the hormone molecule completely or almost completely of one or more of its characteristic actions. A mutation of this type could obviously lead to extinction of the strain through the development of a lethal gene.

There seems to be a third possibility. A compound may be formed which is of no obvious adaptive value and which is in fact less active than the original molecule, but which permits the carrying organism to "get by"— it is known (Simpson, 1959) from other examples that a mutation which confers no benefit or may even be detrimental can become established. When applying this concept to the occurrence of lysine vasopressin in the pig and perhaps other Suiformes, it will be recalled (Section II, C) that lysine vasopressin was found to have a weaker antidiuretic action than the arginine compound in the three arginine vasopressin-producing species (man, dog, rat) which have so far been tested. The potency ratio (arginine vasopressin to lysine vasopressin) varies from test species to species but it may be assumed that lysine vasopressin was sufficiently potent to permit the survival of the first mutants of the Suiformes. That lysine vasopressin injected into pigs is antidiuretically as active or more active than arginine vasopressin (Munsick *et al.*, 1958) may be explainable by gradual adaptation of the receptors.

It has already been pointed out that not only the domestic pig but apparently also the hippopotamus synthesizes lysine vasopressin. On the other hand, all the other Artiodactyla so far investigated (ox, camel, sheep, deer) seem to carry the arginine analog. A systematic investigation of the main subdivisions of the Artiodactyla, i.e., of the Suiformes, the Tylopoda, and the Ruminantia is, however, highly desirable in order to put the distribution of the vasopressins, in this order at least, on a firmer experimental basis.

The surviving Suiformes or pig-like animals comprise the Suina or true pigs, the Tayassuinae or peccaries, and the Hippopotamidae. The relationship of these groups is controversial. Many paleontologists have considered the peccaries exclusively New World suids (Simpson, 1945); their evolution in North America is fairly well known from Oligocene times. But although some contest the strictly American origin of this group and assume a common ancestry of suids and tayassuids from the Eocene Dichobunoidea, others regard the peccaries as quite distinct from the Old World Suiformes constituting perhaps a third line in the evolution of artiodactyls, different from the true pigs and hippopotamus, and the ruminants. The origin of the Hippopotamidae is likewise debated (Thenius and Hofer, 1960). They are assumed either to stem from suids or from late Tertiary Anthracotheres, but the occurrence of lysine vasopressin in *Hippopotamus amphibius* somewhat favors the former assumption. Sawyer (1961) has recently investigated undifferentiated extracts of the pituitary of the collared peccary and has presented strong pharmacological evidence that these glands contained a mixture of arginine vasopressin and oxytocin. An investigation of the chromatographically separated and partially purified hormones obtained from the neurohypophyses of collared peccaries (*Pecari tajacu*) and white-lipped peccaries (*Tayassu pecari*), presently in progress in the writer's laboratory, shows further that both arginine vasopressin and lysine vasopressin may occur in the same neural lobe. Both vasopressins may also occur in a single gland of the African wart hog (*Phacochoerus aethiopicus*) or lysine vasopressin may be present alone.

Thus the investigation of the phyletic distribution of the vasopressins is not only likely to assist taxonomic problems from a rather unusual angle but it carries also the fascinating promise of gaining some insight into the paleontology of a large group of mammals by a biochemical study of recent forms.

III. PHYSIOLOGICAL SIGNIFICANCE OF THE NEUROHYPOPHYSEAL HORMONES IN MAMMALS

A. Water and Salt Metabolism

Differences in renal function between mammalian species are small but not unimportant. It is well known for example that the glomerular filtration rate (GFR) of dogs changes rapidly in response to alterations in diet or salt intake wheras that of human beings is remarkably stable. Strauss (1959) has tried to explain this difference on the basis of feeding habits. He points out that the ancestors of the dog "having hunted until they achieved a kill, gorged themselves to satiety thereby presenting the excretory mechanism with a large load of nitrogen and a surplus of sodium (the latter derived from the extracellular fluid of their prey). The ancestors of man, if they resembled present day anthropoids, were largely herbivorous and spent five or six hours daily in feeding, thus hardly ever ingesting more than a minimum of sodium." Unfortunately this attractive interpretation ceases to be acceptable when extended to other species. The GFR of the omnivorous rat responds to protein or salt loading in much the same manner as that of the dog (Dicker, 1949), and the variable glomerular function of the herbivorous rabbit has long been the bane of renal physiologists. It cannot, however, be excluded that species differences in the effects of the posterior pituitary hormones on electrolyte excretion are connected with the degree of lability of renal blood flow and filtration rate. But the main physiological effect of the pituitary on renal function, namely the increase of tubular water reabsorption under the influence of the antidiuretic hormone (vasopressin) appears to be the same in all mammalian species (see discussion later in this section).

Evidence for the physiological role of vasopressin in the regulation of the metabolism of water derives from several sources: (a) Severe interference with or destruction of the hypothalamo-neurohypophyseal complex gives rise to diabetes insipidus. (b) Injection of a small amount of vasopressin or inclusion of the head in a heart-lung-kidney preparation restores the concentrating ability of the diabetic kidney. (c) Dehydration increases the excretion in the urine of an antidiuretic substance which has the chemical and pharmacological characteristics of vasopressin.

Verney (1947) has shown that a small increase of plasma osmotic pressure, produced by the intracarotid injection of a hypertonic salt solution, causes release of vasopressin by stimulating "osmoreceptors" in the vascular bed of the internal carotid artery (Verney and Jewell, 1957). Direct proof that the same mechanism operates during the slow process of dehydration is still lacking but should probably only be regarded as a formality.

An exclusively renal site for the regulatory action of vasopressin on the water metabolism of mammals is generally accepted. There is also agreement that (a) water and electrolyte absorption in the proximal renal tubules are not affected by the antidiuretic hormone; (b) the essential effect of vasopressin on the distal segment of the nephron consists in an alteration of the epithelial permeability to water; (c) the production of a hypotonic urine (water diuresis) is mainly due to the decrease of the hormone concentration in the blood arising from the inhibitory effect of the diluted plasma on the osmoreceptors (Verney, 1947) and the very rapid inactivation (Ginsburg and Heller, 1953; Heller and Zaidi, 1957) of the still circulating vasopressin.

However, views on the role of the antidiuretic hormone in the elaboration of a hypertonic urine are to some degree still divided. The "classical" concept (H. W. Smith, 1956) may be summarized as: After osmotic equilibration in the thin part of the loop of Henle an iso-osmotic fluid is delivered to a virtually water impermeable segment of the distal tubule from which active absorption of sodium takes place leaving osmotically "free" water. Epithelial permeability to water is then increased under the influence of vasopressin so that water is passively absorbed until isotonicity is again established. The filtrate moves along, most likely to the collecting ducts where the removal of an additional amount of water without solute represents the last phase in the elaboration of a concentrated urine. Smith believed that this final step might be a continuous autonomous process, capable of being carried out in the complete absence of antidiuretic hormone.

The assumption that vasopressin is responsible for reducing the volume of filtrate by facilitating water absorption to isotonicity only, has a special appeal to the comparative endocrinologist since this concept of the renal action of neurohypophyseal hormones could be extended to lower vertebrates (e.g., amphibians) which are unable to prepare a hypertonic urine. Certain experimental results seem, at first glance, to support the independence of the concentrating mechanism from neurohypophyseal function. Shannon (1942) reported that dehydrated dogs with experimental diabetes insipidus and low filtration rates were able to excrete a hypertonic urine, and other workers (Berliner and Davidson, 1957; del Greco and de Wardener, 1956) found that in dogs in full water diuresis, urinary concentration could be raised above the plasma osmotic level when the GFR was markedly lowered. However, the concentrations observed in these experiments were never in excess of 475 milli-osm/liter whereas normal dogs are capable of elaborating a urine as concentrated as 2000 milliosm/liter. A lowered GFR may thus help in concentrating the urine—it is known that a higher concentration can be achieved by dehydration than by the injection of posterior pituitary extracts into a well hydrated animal— but the antidiuretic hormone remains the most important factor.

More recently the concept that vasopressin acts essentially by increasing the permeability of some tubular segment or segments has been fitted into the countercurrent multiplier theory of Wirz et al. (1951). By this interpretation (for details see Wirz, 1957; Lamdin, 1959; Wirz, 1960) the hormone increases the diffusion of water from the descending limb of Henle's loop and the collecting ducts. In other words, it permits the specific concentrating mechanism of the mammalian kidney (based on the spatial integration of the renal tubules and blood vessels) to operate in a more efficient manner. However, if the antidiuretic hormone acted simply by allowing diffusion of water, the medullary interstitial space would be progressively diluted and the purpose of the countercurrent mechanism would be ultimately defeated. It has therefore been suggested by Lamdin (1959) and Gottschalk (1960) that vasopressin facilitates not only the transport of water but also that of sodium.

The countercurrent theory of urinary concentration (which is receiving increasing experimental support (Gottschalk and Mylle, 1959; Jaenike and Berliner, 1960) may also aid in the understanding of certain comparative aspects of renal function: (a) the well known differences in the urinary concentration maxima of mammalian species may be based on anatomical divergences in the concentrating apparatus such as the number and length of the thin limbs of Henle's loop; (b) the inability of lower vertebrates to concentrate the urine beyond the iso-osmotic level may not be due to a difference in the mode of action of their antidiuretic hormone but to the morphological characteristics of their kidneys.

As to the "cellular" mechanism of action of the antidiuretic hormone in mammals, it has been suggested (Wirz, 1957; Sawyer, 1957) in analogy to the effect on the frog skin, that the neurohypophyseal active peptides increase the tubular absorption of water and enhance sodium transport from the lumen by increasing the pore size of the epithelial layer (Ussing, 1954, 1960). More recently, Ginetzinsky and his associates (Ginetzinsky and Ivanovna, 1958, Ginetzinsky et al., 1958; Ginetzinsky, 1958, 1961) have expressed the view that in the tubules vasopressin liberates hyaluronidase which depolymerizes the mucopolysaccharide complex of the intercellular cement so that more water passes through. The last word on this hypothesis has by no means been spoken (Berlyne, 1960; J. Heller and Lojda, 1960; Boss et al., 1961) but some suggestion that hyaluronidase is connected with the production of a concentrated, small volume of urine is provided by the interesting report of Dicker and Eggleton (1960) that after an injection of vasopressin, patients with nephrogenic diabetes insipidus fail to excrete hyaluronidase whereas normal subjects and patients with neurohypophyseal diabetes insipidus excrete large quantities.

High doses of pure oxytocin injected into rats in water diuresis produce a weak antidiuretic effect (Table II). Smaller doses may increase urine flow (Berde and Cerletti, 1956), but this diuretic effect is much more pronounced in rats without an extra water load or after the administration of 0.9% NaCl solution (Fraser, 1937; Kuschinsky and Bundschuh, 1939; Jacobson and Kellogg, 1956).

Vasopressin has usually a chloruretic and natriuretic effect in dogs and rats, but given in full antidiuretic doses it does not affect the excretion of these ions in man. The increase in the urinary excretion of Cl, Na, and K induced by oxytocin in rats (noted by numerous authors) appears to be influenced by the water and salt load of the animals. In dogs oxytocin has little effect on Na or K excretion during water diuresis but greatly increases Na (and sometimes also K) excretion at low rates of urine flow (Brooks and Pickford, 1957). In man oxytocin has no effect on electrolyte excretion (Chalmers et al., 1951; Thomson, 1959). Since the oxytocin doses which enhance electrolyte excretion have been shown to alter renal blood flow and glomerular filtration in rats (Dicker and Heller, 1946) and dogs (Brooks and Pickford, 1958; Ali, 1958) but not in human beings (Pickford, 1961), it may be conjectured that the effect of oxytocin (and probably also of vasopressin) on the urinary output of electrolytes is secondary to vascular changes. Species changes in renal "lability" may perhaps again be invoked. In summary, the conclusion expressed as long ago as 1950 (Heller, 1950) that in mammals the neurohypophyseal hormones play no role of importance in the physiological regulation of the metabolism of Cl, Na, and K can be maintained. It was pointed out at that occasion that the absence of electrolyte disturbances in diabetes insipidus strongly supports this contention.

B. Cardiovascular System

Administered in large doses, i.e., in quantities much in excess of the minimum antidiuretic dose, vasopressin is known to have a vasoconstrictor effect, including also the coronary and skin vessels. The physiological significance of these effects is doubtful but it cannot be excluded that vasopressin, even in very small doses, facilitates the operation of the renal countercurrent system by decreasing renal medullary blood flow (Gottschalk, 1960; Thurau, 1960). Brooks and Pickford have shown that minimal antidiuretic doses of vasopressin decrease renal plasma flow if it has first been raised by oxytocin. It may also be suspected that in certain pathological conditions, large enough amounts of vasopressin reach the systemic circulation to produce marked vascular effect. Ginsburg and Heller (1953) and Ginsburg and Brown (1956) showed, for example, that the concentration of antidiuretic activity in the external jugular blood of rats anesthetized with ether rose after severe hemorrhage from 10–25 mU to 700–2500 mU/100 ml blood. Similar results have been obtained by Weinstein et al. (1960) in dogs.

Pickford (1961), Lloyd and Pickford (1961a), and Lloyd (1959a, b) reported that in rats the vascular responses to oxytocin and vasopressin vary with the concentration of ovarian hormones in the body. Oxytocin was shown to have dilator effects during diestrus but in the estrous animal, during late pregnancy, or after the administration of ovarian hormone, oxytocin has a pressor and vasoconstrictor action. In normal men or women large doses of oxytocin produce dilatation of skin and striated muscle vessels and a transient fall in blood pressure (Woodbury et al., 1944; Schild et al., 1951; Wagner and Braunwald, 1956). However, in contrast to its action in rats, the vasodilation induced by the hormone is maintained in human pregnancy (Pickford, 1961; Bienarz, 1961). The pressor action of vasopressin is enhanced in estrous and probably also in pregnant rats.

Whether the changes in the vascular responses of rats to the posterior pituitary hormones are of physiological significance (and are connected with the phasic changes in neurohypophyseal function observed during the estrous cycle in the same species, Heller and Lederis, 1961) will have to be further investigated.

C. Reproductive Organs

Both mammalian neurohypophyseal hormones act on organs concerned with reproduction (uterus, mammary gland), but oxytocin is the more potent one (Table II). Present information suggests that oxytocin in mammals may be associated with three aspects of the viviparous habit, viz. internal fertilization, delivery of the young at term, and suckling of the offspring. It seems also to be concerned in the retardation of mammary involution (Benson and Folley, 1957; Meites and Hopkins, 1961). Firm evidence for the physiological importance of the hormone is available only for the last one of these functions. Beller *et al.* (1958) for example saw milk ejection in women after an intravenous dose of as little as 10 mU. The amounts of endogenous oxytocin released by suckling seem to be considerably higher. Cross (1961), for example, found in the rabbit that suckling evokes a milk ejection response which resembles the effect of an intravenous injection of 50 mU oxytocin. Inactivation of the posterior pituitary by an electrolytic lesion of the supraoptico-neurohypophyseal tract in the rabbit abolishes the milk ejection reflex (Cross and Harris, 1952); in this species therefore, and in the rat (Harris and Jacobsohn, 1952; Benson and Cowie, 1956; Gale and McCann, 1961) there can be little doubt that natural suckling stimulates the neurohypophysis. An increase in the oxytocic activity of the blood of sheep at the time of milk ejection has been recently reported by Fitzpatrick (1961).

Although an injection of oxytocin produced milk ejection in all mammals so far investigated, it has been pointed out (Cross, 1961) that its physiological significance is likely to vary from species to species. Oxytocin is primarily concerned with the removal of alveolar milk which in the goat, for example, with its capacious udder cisterns, is only a small fraction of the yield at a normal milking. This may account for the reports (Tverskoi, 1958; Denamur and Martinet, 1959) that goats give almost normal yields under conditions in which the neurohypophyseal milk ejection reflex is inoperative.

1. Parturition

A whole symposium (Caldeyro-Barcia and Heller, 1961) has recently been devoted to an inquiry into the role of oxytocin in parturition. The problem is befogged by reports that viable young can be delivered despite elimination of the neurohypophysis. In one of the latest papers on this subject Gale and McCann (1961) placed electrolytic lesions in the median eminence of rats at various stages of gestation, thus producing severe diabetes insipidus. In rats receiving lesions on days 7–9 and maintaining gestation to term, 32% experienced difficulty during delivery. Lesions placed after day 13 did not impair parturition. The authors conclude that in the rat oxytocin is not essential for parturition. Numerous other observers (for references see Fitzpatrick, 1957), however, have recorded prolonged labor and maternal and fetal death under similar conditions in other mammalian species including women. Caldeyro-Barcia and Poseiro (1959) have summarized some of the facts in favor of the assumption that oxytocin participates in the process of human labor. They point out that (a) all the characteristics of the contractions produced by the pregnant human uterus during an infusion of oxytocin are indistinguishable from those in spontaneous labor, (b) the doses of oxytocin needed to produce these effects are of the same order as the minimum antidiuretic dose of vasopressin; (c) a specific enzyme which inactivates oxytocin (oxytocinase) appears in the blood of primates in pregnancy. To be added to this is the demonstration in pregnant animals (Haterius and Ferguson, 1938; Ferguson, 1941) that stretching of the cervix produces a release of oxytocin, and that, in some mammals at least, the oxytocic activity of the blood increases substantially *intra partum* (Fitzpatrick, 1961; Fitzpatrick and Walmsley, 1962).

Whether, as some investigators hold, the essence of the role of the neurohypophysis in labor consists in an increase of the uterine reactivity to oxytocin at term or whether an increased release of the hormone is necessary, cannot be decided at present. It may be that species differences in the estrogen–progesterone equilibrium are involved. Likewise, it has yet to be decided whether oxytocin is material in the initiation of labor or whether it merely helps to expel the fetus.

2. FACILITATION OF SPERM TRANSPORT BY OXYTOCIN

This hypothesis which has been extensively discussed in a number of recent articles (Hartman, 1957; Noyes *et al.*, 1958; Cross, 1959) derives support from the demonstration in several species that at mating oxytocin is released and uterine motility increases. Massage of the seminal vesicles and ampullae of the ram also releases an oxytocic substance (Debackere *et al.*, 1961). The biological value of accelerating the transport of the spermatozoa has been questioned (Cross, 1961), and there seems little reason at present to suppose that fertility would be lower if all the spermatozoa were obliged to spend an hour or more in the uterus.

IV. NONMAMMALIAN NEUROHYPOPHYSEAL HORMONES

A number of early papers provided adequate evidence (Table I) that the neurohypophysis of all vertebrate classes contains principles which when tested by conventional assay methods resemble the mammalian hormones in their pharmacological activities. But some of these investigations (Heller, 1941b; Lazo-Wasem and Weisel, 1952) showed also that relative to their pressor and oxytocic potency, pituitary extracts of teleost fishes, amphibians, reptiles, and birds have a greater effect on the water metabolism of frogs than extracts of mammalian neural lobes. The conclusion was therefore drawn (Heller, 1941b, 1942) that the nonmammalian glands contained a principle which differs chemically from the mammalian hormones. Inadequacy of the techniques for the purification and analysis of peptides prevented further progress for a considerable period. The subject has, however, rapidly advanced in recent years thanks to application of methods pioneered by du Vigneaud, Sanger, Li, and other biochemists. It has also greatly profited from the introduction of new and more discriminating methods of bioassay. It will be attempted here to summarize the results of these recent investigations into the nature of the nonmammalian neurohypophyseal hormones, but it must be borne in mind that the subject is so much in flux that any conclusion as to the phyletic distribution and even the number of naturally occurring active peptides must be strictly provisional.

A. Urochordata

Butcher (1930) reported that extracts of the neural complex of *Molgula manhattensis* contains oxytocic activity, and Bacq and Florkin (1935) obtained both pressor and oxytocic effects with extracts of the neural complex of *Ciona intestinalis*. Pérès (1943) confirmed the occurrence of an oxytocic substance in the neural complex of *Ciona* but obtained similar effects with the extract of other tissues. He believed that the active principle resembled histamine. Sawyer (1959) found likewise that the oxytocic principle which could be extracted from the neural complex of *Chelyosoma productum* and *Pyura haustor* occurred in similar concentrations in extracts of other tissues of these ascidians. Moreover, the oxytocic activity did not disappear after treatment with NaOH or sodium thioglycollate. No antidiuretic or vasopressor activity could be detected in the extracts of *Chelyosoma* complexes; those of *Pyura* produced no pressor response but had a weak antidiuretic action.

These findings do not support the assumption that the neural complex of ascidians elaborates hormones which resemble the active peptides of the vertebrate neurohypophysis.

B. Agnatha (Cyclostomata)

Herring showed in 1913 that extracts of lamprey (*Petromyzon fluviatilis*) pituitary glands raise the blood pressure of the cat. Lanzing (1954) found subsequently that pituitary extracts of the same species increase the body water of frogs kept in water and stimulate the isolated guinea pig uterus. Similar "water balance" effects in *Bufo viridis* have been observed after the injection of pituitary extracts from *Myxine glutinosa* (Adam, 1961). Sawyer *et al.* (1959, 1961a) analyzed extracts from the pituitary of marine lampreys (*Petromyzon marinus*) by means of rat vasopressor, rat anti-diuretic, rat uterus, rabbit milk ejection, hen uterus, and bullfrog bladder assays and concluded that the results were compatible with the presence of 8-arginine oxytocin (arginine vasotocin) in these extracts. They could find no evidence for the occurrence of oxytocin. Since, however, recent work (Morel *et al.*, 1961; Heller *et al.*, 1961) has shown that the glands of lower vertebrates may contain peptides with activity ratios which differ from those of the known neurohypophyseal hormones, chromatographic and chemical work is needed to decide whether, in contrast to all other vertebrate classes, the neurohypophyses of the cyclostomes elaborate only one active principle.

C. Elasmobranchii

Herring (1913, 1915) was again the first who demonstrated that pitui-tary extracts of cartilaginous fishes exert similar actions as those of mam-malian glands; he found oxytocic and galactobolic activities in the pituitary of the skate (*Raja batis*) but was unable to obtain a pressor effect in mam-mals. Hogben and de Beer (1925) who used extracts of a much larger number of skate glands also failed to observe rises of blood pressure in spinal cats although with the same material they observed unmistakable depressor responses in birds. Heller (1941a, b) showed later that extracts of skate and dogfish pituitaries produce weak antidiuretic effects and influence the water balance of frogs. Sawyer *et al.* (1959, 1961a) subjected undifferentiated extracts of the neurohypophysis of the spiny dogfish (*Squalus acanthias*) to a variety of bioassays and came to the conclu-sion that the pharmacological profile obtained "was not that of arginine vasotocin (8-arginine oxytocin), oxytocin, or of any (synthetic) analog that we have studied." Essentially similar results were obtained by Perks *et al.* (1960) in an extensive investigation of the activities in the neuro-intermediate lobes of five species of elasmobranchs. These authors showed (Table VII) that the ratios of milk ejection activity, rat uterus activity and (mammalian) antidiuretic activity in the elasmobranch material ap-proximated 3.5:1:0.05 whereas the same ratios in the international (ox) posterior lobe pituitary powder are 1:1:1. They suggested therefore that elasmobranch glands contained no discrete vasopressor–antidiuretic principle, though an oxytocic substance not identical with oxytocin was undoubtedly present. Maetz *et al.* (1959) who estimated natriferic (active

TABLE VII

ACTIVITIES OF ELASMOBRANCH NEUROINTERMEDIATE LOBES[a]

Species	Oxytocic potency[b]	Galactobolic potency[c]	Antidiuretic potency[c]
Squalus acanthias (pregnant)	17.0	265	7.6
Scylliorhinus caniculus	13.2	450	3.8
Raja clavata	17.0	353	0.7
Raja batis	7.7	454	7.7
Raja naevus	10.0	—	5.0

[a] Expressed as mU/mg acetone-dried powder (modified from Perks *et al.*, 1960).
[b] Isolated rat uterus.
[c] Expressed as % of rat uterus activity.

sodium transport through frog skin, N) and oxytocic activity (O) in the pituitary glands of *Hexanchus griseus* and *Scylliorhinus caniculus* found N/O ratios of about 2 in both species. The ratio in teleosts was about 10 and that in amphibians about 12, suggesting again that little or no 8-arginine oxytocin (which has a very high natriferic potency, see Section IV,D) was present in the elasmobranch glands. When Heller and Pickering (1960) chromatographed pituitary extracts of *Squalus acanthias* and *Scylliorhinus caniculus* on paper in butanol–acetic acid–water, oxytocic activity could elute from two regions. One of these was at R_f 0.35–0.45 (8-arginine oxytocin in the same solvent system = 0.25–0.35), the R_f of the other (0.5–0.6) was much the same as that of oxytocin. However, an oxytocic substance (ichthyotocin) has been recently (Heller *et al.*, 1961) isolated from teleost pituitaries which behaves chromatographically much like oxytocin but which pharmacologically has an entirely different spectrum (Table VIII).

The very limited evidence just discussed may be interpreted as suggesting that the elasmobranch neurointermediate lobe elaborates at least two active peptides one of which has so far not been discovered or characterized in the pituitary of other vertebrate classes.

D. Actinopterygii and Choanichthyes

Only teleosts have so far been investigated. Early investigations (Herring, 1913; Hogben and de Beer, 1925; Boyd and Dingwall, 1939; Heller, 1941a) mainly on *Gadus morrhua* showed that the pituitary gland of this marine

TABLE VIII

POTENCY OF THE UNIDENTIFIED OXYTOCIC POLLACK PEPTIDE[a] (ICHTHYOTOCIN)

Assay method	Potency (U/ml)	Ratio of activity to rat uterus $(- Mg^{++})$ potency
Rat uterus without Mg^{++}	7	1
Rat uterus with 0.5 mM Mg^{++}/liter	~28	~4
Chicken blood pressure	~16.3	~2.3
Natriferic activity (isolated frog skin)	~0.35	~0.05
Water-balance activity (isolated frog skin)	~0.35	~0.05
Water-balance activity (isolated frog bladder)	~0.75	~0.11
Water-balance activity (intact frogs)	<1	<0.15

[a] Eluate from left-hand peak (see Section IV, D) assayed against oxytocin (Syntocinon, Sandoz). Note that, by definition, the activity ratios would be 1, had the unidentified substance been oxytocin (Heller et al., 1961).

teleost exerts all the activities of mammalian posterior lobe preparation but demonstrated also that the water balance activity of such extracts was far out of proportion to their (mammalian) antidiuretic and oxytocic potencies. Sawyer et al. (1959, 1961), using undifferentiated extracts of whole pollack (*Pollachius virens*) pituitaries found that the ratios of some of the pharmacological activities resembled those of synthetic 8-arginine oxytocin (vasotocin). The high N/O ratio in similar extracts obtained from *Scomber scombrus, Germo alalunga, Blennius gattorugine,* and *Trutta trutta* (Maetz et al., 1959) agrees with these results. The ratios of rat uterus to rat vasopressor activity in the assays of Sawyer and his associates was, however, significantly greater than the same ratio for vasotocin.

Further progress was only made by combining biochemical with pharmacological methods. Pickering and Heller (1959) applied the chromatographic procedure of Heller and Lederis (1958) which permits the separation of neurohypophyseal peptides in crude extracts, and were able to show that pituitary extracts of the trout (*Salmo irideus*), pollack, and cod contained at least two active principles both of which stimulated the rat uterus, produced milk ejection, and increased water uptake in frogs. Almost all the pressor and antidiuretic activities of the original extracts, however, was found in the eluate of which moved more slowly on paper.

Heller and Pickering (1960, 1961) subsequently separated the two active principles by ion-exchange chromatography. Figure 2 shows the elution curves. Eluates from the right-hand peak (maximum at tube 80)

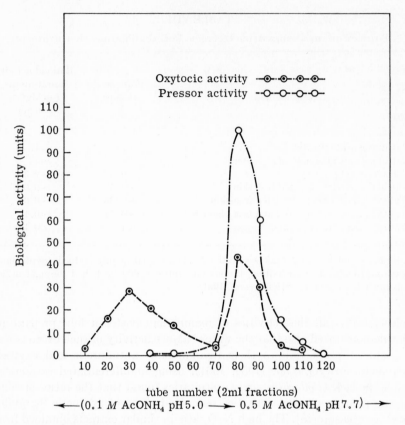

Fɪɢ. 2. Chromatography of pollack pituitary extracts on Amberlite CG–50.

gave both oxytocic and pressor effects. Eluates from the left-hand peak (maximum at tube 30) showed oxytocic activity but no pressor activity, and only traces of antidiuretic activity could be detected. The eluates in tubes 75–95 were then freeze-dried and further purified by paper chromatography. Comparison by four bioassay methods of the preparation of the pollock peptide so obtained with synthetic 8-arginine oxytocin gave mean potencies which were indistinguishable for each of the activities determined. It could also be shown that the highly purified pollack peptide and synthetic 8-arginine oxytocin when chromatographed side by side moved at the same rate in three different solvent systems. Lastly, when hydrolyzed and subjected to two-dimensional chromatography samples of the purified pollack peptide contained the same amino acid as 8-arginine oxytocin. Vasotocin has more recently also been isolated from the pituitary of the hake, *Merluccius vulgaris* (Rasmussen and Craig, 1961) and the whiting-pout, *Gordus luscus* (Acher *et al.*, 1961).

The eluates from the region of the left-hand peak were also purified as described above, and since this peak was in the position of mammalian oxytocin (Acher, Light and du Vigneaud, 1958) the resultant preparation was compared with this peptide by a variety of bioassays (Heller *et al.*, 1961). Table VIII shows the "pharmacological spectrum" obtained. The standard in each of the assays shown was synthetic oxytocin (Syntocinon). If, therefore, the unknown pollack peptide had been identical with oxytocin, the activity ratio would have been unity in all instances. Moreover, since all the assays on amphibians or amphibian tissues gave activity ratios very much below unity, oxytocin, if present at all, could only have been present in very small amounts. The new hormone (ichthyotocin) has recently also been isolated from the pituitary glands of the teleosts *Pollachius virens*, *Merluccius merluccius*, and *Gadus luscus* and has been identified as 4-serine, 8-isoleucine oxytocin (Acher *et al.*, 1962). The final proof of its identity with the naturally occurring teleost hormone, i.e., a pharmacological comparison of highly purified ichthyotocin with synthetic 4-Ser, 8-Ileu oxytocin, is still outstanding.

In one of Heller and Pickering's (1961) experiments in which pollack pituitary extracts were purified by ion-exchange chromatography the elution gradient was increased by the introduction of 0.75 M ammonium acetate to the mixing chamber, after the right-hand peak had emerged from the column. This procedure (Acher *et al.*, 1958) should have eluted arginine vasopressin but no evidence for its presence could be obtained. It therefore appears that the pollack, and probably the other marine and fresh-water teleosts investigated, synthesize in the main two neurohypophyseal hormones both of which differ from those found in the mammalian posterior pituitary lobe.

The endocrinology of the main order of the Choanichthyes, the Dipnoi or lungfishes, is of special interest since they form a link between fishes and tetrapods. The morphological similarity between the neurohypophysis of the African lungfish (*Protopterus*) and that of certain amphibians has been mentioned in the Introduction to this chapter. Investigation of pituitary extracts from *Protopterus aethiopicus* (Follett and Heller, 1962) showed that they contained one peptide with pharmacological characteristics of 8-arginine oxytocin (vasotocin). Another active component of these extracts was compared with ichthyotocin by several bioassay methods. A clear difference between ichthyotocin and the unidentified lungfish hormone could be established. However, the pharmacological spectrum of the latter resembled that of oxytocin very closely.

E. Amphibia

Heller showed in 1941 that in frogs kept in water the increase in body weight produced by the extract of a single frog pituitary gland is matched by about 1000 mU mammalian oxytocin but that assayed on a mammalian uterus a frog gland contains only about 40 mU of oxytocic activity. Since vasopressin has a much weaker "water balance effect" on *Rana* than oxytocin, it was concluded that frog glands contained an active principle which differed from the mammalian hormones. Sawyer (1957) found a similar disproportion in the ratio of activities in the bull frog, and Morel *et al.* (1958), concluded that the natriferic activity of extracts of frog (*Rana esculenta*) and toad (*Bufo bufo*) pituitary extract could not be accounted for by oxytocin or vasopressin. Further pharmacological investigations (Sawyer *et al.*, 1959; Sawyer, 1960; Uranga and Sawyer, 1960) of frog (*Rana catesbeiana*) and toad (*Bufo americanus*) neurohypophyseal extracts suggested that they contained 8-arginine oxytocin (arginine vasotocin) and the chromatographic results of Pickering and Heller (1959) supported this assumption. Finally, Acher and his co-workers (1960b) succeeded in isolating a peptide from the pituitary of *Rana esculenta* which on hydrolysis yielded the amino acids characteristic of 8-arginine oxytocin.

Arginine vasotocin has been shown to have a greater effect on the water metabolism of frogs (Sawyer, 1960; Heller and Pickering, 1961) and to have higher natriferic potency (Heller *et al.*, 1961) than any other neurohypophyseal hormone so far characterized. In that sense it can therefore be regarded as the "water balance principle" originally postulated (Heller, 1941b, 1942).

Arginine vasotocin is, however, not the only active peptide found in extract of anuran neurointermediate lobes. Chromatographically, extracts of *R. temporaria*, *R. esculenta*, and *B. bufo* contain at least one other oxytocic peptide (Pickering and Heller, 1959; Acher *et al.*, 1960a; Heller and Pickering, 1961; Morel *et al.*, 1961). The presence in the pituitary of an oxytocic principle other than vasotocin has also been suspected in *R. catesbeiana* and *B. americanus* on pharmacological grounds (Sawyer *et al.*, 1961b). This peptide behaves in chromatograms much like mammalian oxytocin but according to recent results of Morel *et al.* (1961), cannot be identical with it. They found that its natriferic activity was up to 15 times higher than that of oxytocin. Its water balance potency, as determined in assays on the frog bladder, was 90 times higher than that of oxytocin but still about 2.5 times smaller than that of 8-arginine oxytocin. Its relatively high natriferic activity would also differentiate it from the recently identified oxytocic peptide in teleost extracts (ichthyotocin). At present it therefore appears that anurans "share" one neurohypophyseal hormone, viz.,

8-arginine oxytocin with teleosts, reptiles, and birds, but the identification of the other amphibian peptide(s) requires further work.

It is well known that the water balance of frogs is more strongly affected by oxytocin than by vasopressin (Heller, 1930; Steggerda and Essex, 1934 Boyd and Brown, 1938 and others) whereas the reverse applies to toads (Jørgensen, 1950; Ewer, 1951). This led to the suggestion (Sawyer, 1957) that the neurohypophyses of these anuran groups contain different hormones. The results just reported, however, support the assumption that both suborders elaborate the same active peptides and that the difference in their response to the mammalian hormones is due to differences in the receptors.

F. Reptilia

As in most of the other vertebrate classes, chromatograms of pituitary extracts of reptiles (*Testudo graeca, Tropidonotus natrix*) showed the presence of two oxytocic principles (Heller and Pickering, 1961). One of these had much the same R_f as 8-arginine oxytocin and the presence of rat pressor and very high frog water balance activity in eluates from that region suggests also that this compound was present. Sawyer *et al.* (1959, 1961a) from their pharmacological studies of undifferentiated extracts of neurohypophyseal tissue of the green turtle (*Chelonia mydas*) and the caiman (*Caiman crocodilus*) concluded also that their material contained 8-arginine oxytocin. Whether the second oxytocic peptide in reptile pituitary extracts is oxytocin as Sawyer *et al.* (1961a) believe, or whether it is identical with one of the unknown oxytocic hormones found in the lower vertebrate classes, has still to be established.

G. Aves

The high activity of chicken posterior pituitary extracts in frog water balance (Heller, 1941b; Pickering and Heller, 1959), frog bladder, hen oxytocic, and chicken antidiuresis (Munsick *et al.*, 1958, 1960) assays relative to their (mammalian) pressor and oxytocic potencies supplied sufficient evidence for the conclusion that these effects could not be entirely due to a combination of the "mammalian" neurohypophyseal hormones. Pickering and Heller (1959) found in confirmation that one of the two oxytocic compounds obtained by paper chromatography from fowl pituitary extracts had an R_f which differed from those of arginine vasopressin, lysine vasopressin, and oxytocin. Its pharmacological spectrum was found to agree with that of 8-arginine oxytocin (Sawyer, *et al.*, 1959; Munsick *et al.*, 1960). The other peptide behaved chromatographically and pharmacologically like mammalian oxytocin and could be shown by Acher *et al.* (1960a) to contain the same amino acids. The same authors (Chauvet *et al.*, 1960b) also reported the isolation from fowl pituitary extracts (to which horse "neurophysin" has been added to facilitate precipitation of the active principles) of a pressor–oxytocic peptide with the amino acid composition of 8-arginine oxytocin (vasotocin) and of another compound with purely pressor activity which contained the same amino acids as arginine vasopressin. They believe therefore that the neurohypophysis of the chicken elaborates not only 8-arginine oxytocin like that of reptiles but also two of the peptides (oxytocin and arginine vasopressin) which occur in the posterior pituitary lobe of mammals.

Chauvet *et al.* (1960b) found that 80% of the oxytocic activity of chicken pituitary extracts was in the region usually occupied by mammalian oxytocin; it is difficult to reconcile this with the assessment of Munsick *et al.* (1960) that the chicken neurohypophysis contains about 10 times as much vasotocin as oxytocin. Moreover, neither the chromatographic and pharmacological studies of the American investigators (Munsick *et al.*, 1960) nor those of the English workers (Heller and Pickering, 1961; Pickering and Heller, 1959)—who used pigeon as well as chicken pituitary glands—provided any evidence for the presence of appreciable amounts of vasopressin in bird pituitary extracts. This may, however, have been due to the smaller quantities of glandular material used in their investigations. Moreover, the possibility cannot be excluded that some strains of chickens elaborate only vasotocin and others both vasopressin and vasotocin.

H. Tentative Survey of the Distribution of Neurohypophyseal Hormones in Vertebrates

Table IX reviews the presently known distribution of active peptides in the neurohypophysis of vertebrates. "Active peptides" should be understood to refer only to substances with pharmacological activities similar to those of oxytocin and vasopressin. Peptides whose main biological action, for example, consists in stimulating hormone release from the adenohypophysis, are not included.

It will be seen that five neurohypophyseal peptides occur in the phylum whose chemical composition has been established. Of these 8-arginine oxytocin (arginine vasotocin) seems to be most widely distributed. Another peptide occurs in elasmobranchs (peptide E). It has not been chemically identified but its chromatographic and pharmacological properties suggest that it differs from vasotocin, ichthyotocin, oxytocin, and the two vasopressins.

TABLE IX

TENTATIVE SCHEME OF DISTRIBUTION OF NEUROHYPOPHYSEAL ACTIVE PEPTIDES IN VERTEBRATES[a]

Class	Arginine vasopressin	Lysine vasopressin	Oxytocin	Vasotocin	Ichthyotocin[b]	Peptide E[c]
Agnatha	−	−	−	+	?	?
Elasmobranchii	−	−	−	−	?	+
Actinopterygii	−	−	−	+	+	−
Choanichthyes	−	−	?	+	−	−
Amphibia	−	−	?	+	−	−
Reptilia	−	−	?	+	−	−
Aves	?[d]	−	+	+	−	−
Mammalia						
(a) Suiformes[e]	+	+	+	−	−	−
(b) All others investigated	+	−	+	−	−	−

[a] Key: −, not found; +, presence demonstrated.
[b] See text Section IV, D.
[c] For characterization see Sawyer et al. (1959, 1961a), Heller and Pickering (1961).
[d] See text Section IV, G.
[e] See text Section II, I.

Table IX is quite provisional for at least two important reasons: (a) only a few species within each vertebrate class have been investigated; in some instances whole subclasses and orders have not been touched, and (b) the material for pharmacological and chromatographic analysis was in many cases so scanty that the presence of small amounts of known or unknown active peptides may well have escaped the investigators.

V. PHYSIOLOGICAL SIGNIFICANCE OF THE NEUROHYPOPHYSEAL HORMONES IN NONMAMMALIAN VERTEBRATES

A. Fishes

Insight into the physiology of neurohypophyseal function in this large group of vertebrates is complicated not only by the multiplicity of potential target organs (kidneys, gills, salt gland) but also by the variety of osmotic situations with which fishes are faced. In the latter respect a rough division can be made into (a) fishes whose blood is either isotonic with sea water (the Myxinoidea) or nearly so (the marine Elasmobranchii) and (b) fishes which maintain their blood electrolyte concentrations at a different level from that of their environment (the Petromyzontidae and the teleosts) (for reviews see Fontaine, 1956; D. C. W. Smith, 1956; Pickford and Atz, 1957; Jones et al., 1959; Morris, 1960). Participation of the neurohypophysis in osmoregulation in the latter group would not be unexpected, particularly in those species of teleosts which during their life cycle have to adapt to different salinities. The experimental evidence that the neurohypophyseal hormones influence the water and salt metabolism of stenohaline and euryhaline teleosts is, however, fragmentary and sometimes contradictory. This may be partly due to the fact that few workers used, in their investigations, fish pituitary extracts or the active peptides recently isolated from fish neurohypophyses. That the teleostean neurohypophysis is somehow concerned in osmoregulation is suggested by reports that changes in external salinity affect neurosecretion in the hypothalamo-neurohypophyseal system. Arvy et al., (1954, 1955), Arvy and Gabe (1954) and Rasquin and Stoll (1955) have shown in several teleosts (*Phoxinus phoxinus, Phoxinus laevis, Anguilla anguilla, Callionymus lyra,* and *Ammondytes lanceolatus*) that transfer to a hypertonic medium leads to pronounced depletion of Gomori-positive material during the first $1\frac{1}{2}$ hours and return to normal levels after 3 hours. Similar results have been reported by Tuurala (1957) and Fridberg and Olsson (1959).

In complementary experiments on the rainbow trout (*Salmo irideus*) Carlson and W. N. Holmes (1962) have recently determined that the antidiuretic activity in the pituitary decrease for several hours in fishes transferred to sea water. Since these authors showed also that handling of the fishes increases the pituitary hormone content, the objection that the exposure to a hypertonic medium acts as an unspecific stress loses much of its force. In apparent contrast to these findings is the report of D. C. W. Smith (1956) who found that neurohypophyseal extracts did not increase the salinity tolerance of *Salmo trutta*, and that of Burden (1956) who failed to promote the survival of hypophysectomized *Fundulus heteroclitus* in fresh water by injections of a mammalian posterior lobe preparation.

On the supposition that the neurohypophyseal hormones[2] of fish may act in analogy to those in other vertebrate classes, some of these effects have been investigated in fishes.

(a) *Antidiuresis*. Burgess *et al.* (1933) failed to find an antidiuretic action of vasopressin in a fresh-water species, *Ameiurus* which may be regarded as being in a natural state of diuresis. Pickford and Atz (1957) point out, however, that fresh-water fishes are under the constant necessity of excreting excess water and that the renal mechanism for water retention may therefore be in abeyance in such forms. Sexton (1955) has in fact reported that Pitressin produced an increased flow of urine in the goldfish. Marine teleosts have not been investigated. They are known to produce little urine and this may be due not only to poor glomerular development but also to a constant (and maximal?) release of neurohypophyseal hormone(s). An antidiuretic effect of exogenous neurohypophyseal principles would be difficult to demonstrate under these circumstances. However, R. M. Holmes (1962) in Cambridge has recently obtained most interesting results in studies on the rainbow trout. The urine flow of this euryhaline fish when fully adapted to sea water is only about 1/100 of that in fresh water. During the spawning season the fish appear to be unable to adapt to sea water. Holmes finds, however, that in such animals arginine vasopressin produces a marked antidiuresis in very small doses though it does not do so in nonspawning fishes adapted to fresh water.

(b) *Water balance effect* (the rise in body weight as a result of increased water intake and decreased water output). Neither Boyd and Dingwall (1939) who studied five species of fresh-water teleosts nor Fontaine and his associates (see Fontaine, 1957) who injected both marine and fresh-water teleosts with fish gland extracts observed an increase in body weight.

---

[2] To call a substance obtained from an endocrine gland a hormone may not be justifiable until its regulatory action has been demonstrated in the organism of its origin.

The cyclostome *Lampetra fluviatilis* (Heller, 1962) and the African lung-fish *Protopterus* (Heller, 1956) also failed to respond to several neuro-hypophyseal hormones. It must be remembered however, that it may not have been possible to demonstrate an increase of water uptake in the absence of an antidiuretic effect.

(c) *Effects on electrolyte metabolism.* Considering the pronounced effect of several neurohypophyseal peptides on active sodium transport in anurans (Section V,B) the scanty results on the effect of pituitary hor-mones on the salt metabolism of fishes are of special interest. In Sexton's (1955) experiments on goldfish vasopressin (Pitressin) had no effect on sodium uptake but prevented sodium loss from the gills. W. N. Holmes in the rainbow trout found that vasopressin did not modify sodium flux through the gills. It did, however, almost abolish renal sodium excretion. Maetz and Juien (1961) showed in the goldfish that oxytocin and extracts of *Carassius* neurohypophyses stimulate the influx of sodium through the gills leaving the outflux unchanged. Vasopressin had little effect. It seems then not unlikely that the teleost neurohypophysis contains one or several hormones which act on the gills in the same manner as extracts of anuran hypophyses affect frog skin. However, the interpretation of results of ex-periments in which an increase of sodium uptake follows the injection of neurohypophyseal hormones into intact fish is complicated by the possi-bility that this effect is indirect, i.e., mediated by the homologue of the adrenal cortex. This possibility can be ruled out in *Lampetra fluviatilis* in which several neurohypophyseal peptides increased the rate of sodium loss whereas aldosterone and corticotropin had the opposite effect (Bentley and Follett, 1962).

Whether neurohypophyseal hormones play a role in the water and salt metabolism of elasmobranchs (and perhaps also influence renal urea absorption) is not known.

B. Amphibians

The effect of neurohypophyseal hormones on anuran amphibians have been so thoroughly investigated that the existence of several target organs in this subclass can hardly be questioned. An increase of water uptake through the skin under the influence of mammalian posterior lobe extracts was suggested by the results of earliest investigators (Brunn, 1921; Biasotti, 1923 and others) and convincingly demonstrated by Novelli (1936) who, in toads, measured the water uptake of skin pouches with intact circulation. The hormonal effect can also be shown in isolated pieces of frog skin (Fuhrman and Ussing, 1951; Sawyer, 1951a; Capraro and Garampi, 1956).

To elucidate the action of the neurohypophyseal hormones on the anuran kidney has proved to be considerably more difficult. Taken as a whole, the reports suggest that vasopressin in quite small doses produces antidiuresis in toads (Jørgensen, 1950; Ewer, 1951) but that much larger doses of oxytocin and still larger doses of vasopressin have to be given to frogs to be effective. Since neither of these peptides appears to be present in the amphibian pituitary (Section IV,E), recent results of Jard et al. (1960) in *Rana esculenta* which suggest that 8-arginine oxytocin is much more potent than "mammalian" hormones are of considerable interest. The mode of action of the neurohypophyseal principles on the amphibian kidney is also to some extent controversial. A decrease in glomerular filtration has been observed in both frogs and toads (Sawyer, 1951b; Sawyer and Sawyer, 1952) but effects on tubular water reabsorption (Pasqualini, 1938; Jørgensen, 1950; Janczo, 1955; Sawyer, 1957) are probably of greater physiological importance. If so, there would be a remarkable similarity between the action of the neurohypophyseal hormones on the mesonephric kidney of anurans and the metanephric kidney of higher vertebrates.

The urinary bladder of toads (Ewer, 1952a; Uranga and Quintana, 1958) and frogs (Sawyer and Schisgall, 1956) reacts to mammalian posterior pituitary hormones by increased water absorption from the lumen. Bentley (1958) has analyzed the mechanism of the water transfer in the isolated bladder of *Bufo marinus* and has found that, as in the skin, neurohypophyseal peptides do not accelerate water movement in the absence of an osmotic gradient. The metabolis requirements for this effect are not clear. Bentley (1958) showed that the effect is reduced in the presence of various metabolic inhibitors but Rasmussen et al. (1960) believe that the increase in water transfer is partially independent of the oxidative metabolism of the epithelial cells.

Neurohypophyseal hormones have been shown to influence not only the movement of water but also the active transport of sodium through the skin (Jørgensen et al. 1946; Fuhrman and Ussing, 1951) and urinary bladder (Leaf et al., 1959; Bentley, 1960) of anurans. The two effects may be parts of the same mechanism. Bentley (1959a) has shown that the presence of sodium on the mucosal side of the toad bladder potentiates water transfer in response to posterior lobe extracts (Ussing, 1960), or they may be due to the action of the hormones on different tissue elements (Bourget and Maetz, 1961; Heller and Bentley, 1963).

It seems likely that these actions of neurohypophyseal hormones on water transfer are of physiological importance to anurans (urodele amphibians such as *Triturus* or *Ambystoma* fail to show a similar response; Heller and Bentley, 1963). The neurointermediate lobe of frogs and toads contains sufficient hormonal activity to affect water uptake through the skin (Heller, 1941b) and from the urinary bladder (Sawyer, 1960) and to produce antidiuresis (Jørgensen, 1950; Sawyer, 1957). Moreover, depletion of hormone(s) in the frog gland during dehydration has been demonstrated (Levinsky and Sawyer, 1953; Janczo, 1955). When *Bufo carens* (Ewer, 1952b) or *Rana pipiens* (Levinsky and Sawyer, 1953) are returned to water after desiccation, the rate of water uptake is much increased compared with nondehydrated animals suggesting that the "excess hormone" released during dehydration acts for a considerable time after liberation. Increased water uptake is not shown if the frogs are hypophysectomized before dehydration.

These results are consistent with the assumption that dehydration stimulates the release of 8-arginine oxytocin (shown to be the main "water-balance" hormone in the anuran neurohypophysis, Pickering and Heller, 1959; Heller and Pickering, 1961) from the anuran pituitary and that this hormone reduces water loss (Boyd and Whyte, 1938; Sawyer, 1951b) and accelerates recovery when the animal returns to water. Increased release of the hormone would also enable the amphibian to draw on the water in its urinary bladder which in frogs and toads is known to serve as an emergency water store (Darwin, 1839[3]; Overton, 1904; Steen, 1929; Ewer, 1952a, b). The osmoregulatory significance of the natriferic activity of the anuran hormones is less easy to understand. It is possible, however, that the ability to absorb sodium against the osmotic gradient on re-entry into water may help the animal to recover renal sodium losses.

Several authors (Steggerda, 1937; Jørgensen, 1950; Ewer, 1952b) have interpreted the composite water balance effect of the neurohypophyseal hormone in amphibians as an adaptation to partially terrestrial life. Indeed Steggerda (1937) and Ewer (1952b) have attempted to correlate the magnitude of the water balance effect obtainable with the habitat of a number of amphibian species. They point out, for example, that the injection of neurohypophyseal hormones does not increase the body weight of the wholly aquatic *Xenopus*, while the highest responses are obtained in *Bufo regularis* and *Bufo carens*, i.e., forms which can exist for long periods without access to ponds and streams. The evidence is suggestive although it has to be mentioned that effects on water retention have also been reported in larval *Ambystoma* (Bělehrádek and Huxley, 1927; Dow and Zuckerman, 1939; Schreiber and Schreiber, 1951), *Necturus* (Steggerda, 1937) and in the tadpoles of *Bufo bufo* (Howes, 1940) and of the Australian burrowing frog *Heleioporus eyrei* (Bentley, 1959b), all gill-breathing aquatic forms.

---

[3] Darwin, in *The Voyage of the Beagle*, wrote: "I believe it is well ascertained that the bladder of the frog acts as a reservoir for the moisture necessary to its existence."

C. Reptiles and Birds

Compared with the amphibians and mammals, studies of neurohypophyseal function in reptiles and birds are scanty. Some "pharmacological" effects of oxytocin, vasopressin, and vasotocin are known. Paton and Watson (1912) and Hogben and Schlapp (1924) found that unfractionated mammalian posterior pituitary extracts lowered the blood pressure in the duck and chicken. Gaddum (1928) showed subsequently that this effect was mainly due to oxytocin. A depressor action of oxytocin in birds seems to be the rule, irrespective of their habitat. It was also observed in the pigeon (Waring *et al.*, 1956), the emu (*Dromaius novae-hollandiae*, Wolley, 1959), penguins (*Endyptula minor*, Wolley, 1959), and the cormorant (*Phalocrocorax varius*, Wolley, 1959). Vasopressin (Pitressin) may have either a pressor or a depressor effect (Strahan and Waring, 1954; Waring *et al.*, 1956; Wolley, 1959). The duck-billed platypus (*Ornithorhynchus*) shows the avian response to oxytocin (Feakes *et al.*, 1950). Reptiles (*Alligator mississippiensis, Chelodina oblonga, Trachysaurus rugosus*) seem to react like birds (see Wolley, 1959). The mechanism of the depressor action of oxytocin in the fowl has been recently analyzed by Lloyd and Pickford (1961b). Vasotocin (8-arginine oxytocin), the other main active constituent of avian neurohypophyseal extracts depresses the blood pressure of the chicken (Munsick *et al.*, 1960) but is much less potent than oxytocin. It may be doubted whether any of the effects of these hormones on the systemic blood pressure of birds and reptiles is of physiological significance, though this cannot be ruled out in relation to renal vascular action. Relatively small doses of Pitressin have been shown (Burgess *et al.*, 1933; Sawyer and Sawyer, 1952) to decrease the glomular filtration rate in the chicken and the alligator, and the possibility of a vascular component in the neurohypophyseal regulation of the urine flow of reptiles and birds has therefore been considered by Heller (1950), Sawyer and Sawyer (1952), and Chew (1961). If it applies, it is likely to be more important in reptiles which cannot form a hypertonic urine then in birds in which the ability to raise the urine above the plasma osmotic level emphasizes the importance of the renal tubular apparatus for water reabsorption. The renal actions of the active peptides in the reptilian neurohypophysis (Section IV,F) have not as yet been studied in reptiles but vasotocin is likely to be their main antidiuretic hormone. It may, however, not be the only one since Bentley (1957) has shown in the lizard *Trachysaurus rugosus* that oxytocin and vasopressin produce approximately equal antidiuresis. Vasotocin in the fowl produces a pronounced decrease in urine flow by an unknown action (Munsick *et al.*, 1960). The role of oxytocin is still obscure.

There are some interesting suggestions that vasotocin may also play a

role in the reproductive physiology of birds and reptiles: Munsick *et al.*
(1960) have observed a marked "oxytocic" effect of this peptide on the
isolated uterine portion of laying hens and on the cloacal end of the oviduct
of the painted turtle (*Chrysemis picta*). The intravenous injection of 30
(rat pressor) mU in an intact hen induced oviposition within 90 seconds.
Arginine vasotocin and arginine vasopressin in equivalent hen oxytocic
doses caused equal intra-uterine pressure changes in a nonlaying hen;
oxytocin in the same dose had no effect. It is noteworthy in this connection
that Legait (1959) observed phasic changes in the hormone content of the
posterior lobe of hens during the egg-laying cycle and the incubation
period. Similarly, Tanaka and Nakajo (1960, 1962) have found that oviposition in the hen follows depletion of oxytocic activity in the neural lobe.

References

Acher, R., and Chauvet, J. (1954). *Biochim. et Biophys. Acta* **14**, 421–429.

Acher, R., and Fromageot, C. (1957). *In* "The Neurohypophysis" (H. Heller, ed.), pp. 39–48. Academic Press, New York.

Acher, R., Chauvet, J., and Lenci, M. T. (1958). *Bull. soc. chim. biol.* **40**, 2005–2018.

Acher, R., Chauvet, J., and Lenci, M. T. (1959). *Biochim. et Biophys. Acta* **31**, 545–548.

Acher, R., Chauvet, J., and Lenci, M. T. (1960a). *Biochim. et Biophys. Acta* **38**, 344–345.

Acher, R., Chauvet, J., Lenci, M. T., Morel, F., and Maetz, J. (1960b). *Biochim. et Biophys. Acta* **42**, 379–380.

Acher, R., Chauvet, J., Chauvet, M. T., and Crepy, D. (1961). *Biochim. et Biophys. Acta* **51**, 419–420.

Acher, R., Chouvet, J., Chauvet, M. T., and Crepy, D. (1962). *Biochim. et Biophys. Acta* **58**, 624–625.

Acher, R., Light, A., and du Vigneaud, V. (1958). *J. Biol. Chem.* **233**, 116–120.

Adam, H. (1961). *Naturwissenschaften* **48**, 75–76.

Adamsons, K., Jr., Engel, S. L., van Dyke, H. B., Schmidt-Nielsen, B., and Schmidt-Nielsen, K. (1956). *Endocrinology* **58**, 272–278.

Alberty, R. A. (1953). *In* "The Proteins" (H. Neurath and K. Bailey, eds.), Vol. I, Part A, pp. 461–548. Academic Press, New York.

Ali, N. M. (1958). *Brit. J. Pharmacol.* **13**, 131–137.

Ames, R. G., and van Dyke, H. B. (1950). *Proc. Soc. Exptl. Biol. Med.* **75**, 417–420.

Anfinsen, C. B. (1959). "The Molecular Basis of Evolution." Wiley, New York.

Arvy, L., and Gabe, M. (1954). *Compt. rend. assoc. anat.* **41**, 843–849.

Arvy, L., Fontaine, M., and Gabe, M. (1954). *Compt. rend. soc. biol.* **148**, 1759–1761.

Arvy, L., Fontaine, M., and Gabe, M. (1955). *Compt. rend. soc. biol.* **149**, 225–227.

Bacq, Z. M., and Florkin, M. (1935). *Arch. intern. physiol.* **40**, 422–428.

Bargmann, W., and Scharrer, E. (1951). *Am. Scientist* **39**, 255–259.

Barrnett, R. J., and Seligman, A. M. (1954). *J. Natl. Cancer Inst.* **14**, 769–803.

Bělehrádek, J., and Huxley, J. S. (1927). *J. Exptl. Biol.* **5**, 89–96.

Beller, F. K., Krumholz, K. H., and Zeininger, K. (1958). *Acta Endocrinol.* **29**, 1–8.

Benson, G. K., and Cowie, A. T. (1956). *J. Endocrinol.* **14**, 54–65.

Benson, G. K., and Folley, S. J. (1957). *J. Endocrinol.* **16**, 189–201.

Bentley, P. J. (1958). *J. Endocrinol.* **17**, 201–209.

Bentley, P. J. (1959a). *J. Endocrinol.* **18**, 327–333.

Bentley, P. J. (1959b). *Endocrinology* **64**, 609–610.

Bentley, P. J. (1960). *J. Endocrinol.* **21**, 161–170.

Bentley, P. J. (1957). *J. Physiol. (London)* **145**, 37–47.

Bentley, P. J., and Follett, B. K. (1962). *Gen. Comp. Endocrinol.* **2**, 329–335.

Beránková, Z., Rychlík, I., Jošt, K., Rudinger, J., and Šorm, F. (1961). *Collection Czechoslov. Chem. Communs.* **26**, 2673.

Beránková-Ksandrová, Z., Bisset, G. W., Jošt, K., Pliška, V., Rudinger, J., Rychlík, I., and Šorm, F. (1963). *Brit. J. Pharmacol.* In press.

Berde, B., and Cerletti, A. (1956). *Helv. Physiol. et Pharmacol. Acta* **14**, 129–134.

Berde, B., Cerletti, A., and Konzett, H. (1961). *In* "Oxytocin" (R. Caldeyro-Barcia and H. Heller, eds.), pp. 247–264. Pergamon Press, New York.

Berliner, R. W., and Davidson, D. G. (1957). *J. Clin. Invest.* **36**, 1416–1427.

Berlyne, G. M. (1960). *Clin. Sci.* **19**, 619–629.

Biasotti, A. (1923). *Compt. rend. soc. biol.* **88**, 361–362.

Bienarz, J. (1961). *In* "Oxytocin" (R. Caldeyro-Barcia and H. Heller, eds.), pp. 80–83. Pergamon Press, New York.

Bisset, G. W. (1963). *J. Physiol. (London)* In press.

Block, R. J., and van Dyke, H. B. (1952). *Arch. Biochem. Biophys.* **36**, 1–4.

Boissonnas, R. A., and Guttman, S. (1960). *Helv. Chim. Acta* **43**, 190–200.

Boissonnas, R. A., Guttmann, S., Jaquenoud, P. A., and Waller, J. P. (1955). *Helv. Chim. Acta* **38**, 1491–1501.

Boss, J. M. N., Breddy, P., and Cooper, G. F. (1961).*J. Physiol. (London)* **157**, 35–36P.

Bourget, J., and Maetz, J. (1961). *Biochim. et Biophys. Acta* (Preview) **1**, No. 3.

Boyd, E. M., and Brown, G. M. (1938). *Am. J. Physiol.* **122**, 191–200.

Boyd, E. M., and Dingwall, M. (1939). *J. Physiol. (London)* **95**, 501–507.

Boyd, E. M., and Whyte, D. W. (1938). *Am. J. Physiol.* **124**, 759–766.

Brooks, F. P., and Pickford, M. (1957). *In* "The Neurohypophysis" (H. Heller, ed.), pp. 141–153. Academic Press, New York.

Brooks, F. P., and Pickford, M. (1958). *J. Physiol. (London)* **142**, 468–493.

Brunn, F. (1921). *Z. ges. exptl. Med.* **25**, 170–175.

Burden, C. E. (1956). *Biol. Bull.* **110**, 8–28.

Burgess, W. W., Harvey, A. M., and Marshall, E. K. (1933). *J. Pharmacol. Exptl. Therap.* **49**, 237–249.

Butcher, E. O. (1930). *J. Exptl. Zool.* **57**, 1–11.

Caldeyro-Barcia, R., and Heller, H., eds. (1961). "Oxytocin." Pergamon Press, New York.

Caldeyro-Barcia, R., and Poseiro, J. J. (1959). *Ann. N. Y. Acad. Sci.* **75**, 813–830.

Capraro, V., and Garampi, M. L. (1956). *Mem. Soc. Endocrinol. No.* **5**, 60–66.

Carlson, J. H., and Holmes, W. N. (1962). *J. Endocrinol.* **74**, 23–32.

Cash, W. D., Mahaffey, L. M., Buck, A. S., Nettleton, D. E., Jr., Romas, C., and du Vigneaud, V. (1962). *J. Am. Chem. Pharm. Chem.* **5**, 413–423.

Chalmers, T. M., Lewis, A. A. G., and Pawan, G. L. S. (1951). *J. Physiol. (London)* **112**, 238–242.

Chauvet, J., Lenci, M. T., and Acher, R. (1960a). *Biochim. et Biophys. Acta* **38**, 266–272.

Chauvet, J., Lenci, M. T., and Acher, R. (1960b). *Biochim. et Biophys. Acta* **38**, 571–573.

Chew, R. M. (1961). *Biol. Revs. Cambridge Phil. Soc.* **36**, 1–31.

Cross, B. A. (1959). *In* "Endocrinology of Reproduction" (C. W. Lloyd, ed.), pp. 167–176. Academic Press, New York.

Cross, B. A. (1961). *In* "Oxytocin" (R. Caldeyro-Barcia and H. Heller, eds.), pp. 24–46. Pergamon Press, New York.

Cross, B. A., and Harris, G. W. (1952). *J. Endocrinol.* **8**, 148–161.

Dale, H. H. (1909). *Biochem. J.* **4**, 427–447.

Darwin, C. (1839). "The Voyage of the Beagle," Bantam, New York, 1958.

Dawson, A. B., and Hisaw, F. L., Jr. (1956). *Anat. Record* **125**, 582.

Debackere, M., Peters, G., and Tuyttens, N. (1961). *J. Endocrinol.* **22**, 321–334.

de Beer, G. R. (1926). "The Comparative Anatomy, Histology and Development of the Pituitary Body," Oliver & Boyd, Edinburgh.

De Lawder, A. M., Tarr, L., and Geiling, E. M. K. (1934). *J. Pharmacol. Exptl. Therap.* **51**, 142.

del Greco, F., and de Wardener, H. E. (1956). *J. Physiol. (London)* **131**, 307–316.

Denamur, R., and Martinet, J. (1959). *Compt. rend. acad. sci.* **248**, 743–746.

Dicker, S. E. (1949). *J. Physiol. (London)* **108**, 197–202.

Dicker, S. E. (1954). *J. Physiol. (London)* **124**, 464–475.

Dicker, S. E., and Eggleton, M. G. (1960). *J. Physiol. (London)* **154**, 378–385.

Dicker, S. E., and Eggleton, M. G. (1961). *J. Physiol. (London)* **157**, 351–362.

Dicker, S. E., and Heller, H. (1946). *J. Physiol. (London)* **104**, 353–360.

Dodd, J. M. (1960). *In* "Marshall's Physiology of Reproduction" (A. S. Parkes, ed.), Vol. 1, Part 2, pp. 417–582. Longmans, Green, New York.

Dow, D., and Zuckerman, S. (1939). *J. Endocrinol.* **1**, 387–398.

Draper, W. B. (1927). *Am. J. Physiol.* **80**, 90–99.

Dudley, H. W. (1923). *J. Pharmacol. Exptl. Therap.* **21**, 103–122.

du Vigneaud, V. (1955). *Proc. Intern. Congr. Biochem., 3rd Congr., Brussels, 1955,* p. 49.

du Vigneaud, V., and van Dyke, H. B. (1960). Private communication.

du Vigneaud, V., Irving, G. W., Dyer, H. M., and Sealock, R. R. (1938). *J. Biol. Chem.* **123**, 45–55.

du Vigneaud, V., Lawler, H. C., and Popenoe, A. (1953a). *J. Am. Chem. Soc.* **75**, 4880–4881.

du Vigneaud, V., Ressler, C., Swan, J. M., Roberts, C. W., Katsoyannis, P. G., and Gordon, S. (1953b). *J. Am. Chem. Soc.* **75**, 4879–4880.

du Vigneaud, V., Ressler, C., and Trippett, S. (1953c). *J. Biol. Chem.* **205**, 949–957.

du Vigneaud, V., Ressler, C., Swan, J. M., Roberts, C. W., and Katsoyannis, P. G. (1954a). *J. Am. Chem. Soc.* **76**, 3115–3121.

du Vigneaud, V., Gish, D. T., and Katsoyannis, P. G. (1954b). *J. Am. Chem. Soc.* **76,** 4751–4752.

du Vigneaud, V., Fitt, P. S., Bodanszky, M., and O'Connell, M. (1960). *Proc. Soc. Exptl. Biol. Med.* **104,** 653.

Enemar, A., and Hanström, B. (1956). *Kgl. Fysiograf. Sällskap. Lund Handl.* **67,** No. 17, 1–5.

Ewer, R. F. (1951). *J. Exptl. Biol.* **28,** 374–384.

Ewer, R. F. (1952a). *J. Exptl. Biol.* **29,** 173–177.

Ewer, R. F. (1952b). *J. Exptl. Biol.* **29,** 429–439.

Feakes, M. J., Hodgkin, E. P., Strahan, R., and Waring, H. (1950). *J. Exptl. Biol.* **27,** 50–58.

Ferguson, D. R., Heller, H., Lederis, K., and Pickford, M. (1962). Proc. Conf. European Comp. Endocrinologists, London 1962. *Gen. Comp. Endocrinol.* **2,** 605.

Ferguson, J. K. W. (1941). *Surg. Gynecol. Obstet.* **73,** 359–366.

Fitzpatrick, R. J. (1957). *In* "The Neurohypophysis" (H. Heller, ed.), pp. 203–217. Academic Press, New York.

Fitzpatrick, R. J. (1961). *In* "Oxytocin" (R. Caldeyro-Barcia and H. Heller, eds.), pp. 360–376. Pergamon Press, New York.

Fitzpatrick, R. J., and Walmsley, C. F. (1962). *J. Physiol. (London)* **163,** 13–14P.

Follett, B. K., and Heller, H. (1962). Proc. Conf. European Comp. Endocrinologists, London 1962. *Gen. Comp. Endocrinol.* **2,** 606.

Fontaine, M. (1956). *Mem. Soc. Endocrinol. No.* **5,** 69–81.

Fraser, A. M. (1937). *J. Pharmacol. Exptl. Therap.* **60,** 80–95.

Fridberg, G., and Olsson, R. (1959). *Z. Zellforsch. u. mikroskop. Anat.* **49,** 531–540.

Fuhrman, F. A., and Ussing, H. H. (1951). *J. Cellular Comp. Physiol.* **38,** 109–130.

Gaddum, J. H. (1928). *J. Physiol. (London)* **65,** 434–440.

Gale, C. C., and McCann, S. M. (1961). *J. Endocrinol.* **22,** 107–117.

Geiling, E. M. K. (1935). *Bull. Johns Hopkins Hosp.* **57,** 123–142.

Geiling, E. M. K., and Oldham, F. K. (1937). *Trans. Assoc. Am. Physicians* **52,** 132–137.

Geiling, E. M. K., Vos, B. J., and Oldham, F. K. (1940). *Endocrinology* **27,** 309–316.

Ginetzinsky, A. G. (1958). *Nature* **182,** 1218–1219.

Ginetzinsky, A. G. (1961). *In* "The Development of Homeostasis" (P. Hahn, ed.), pp. 63–70. Czechoslovak Academy of Science, Prague.

Ginetzinsky, A. G., and Ivanovna, L. N. (1958). *Doklady Akad. Nauk S.S.S.R.* **119,** 1043–1045.

Ginsburg, M., and Brown, L. M. (1956). *Brit. J. Pharmacol.* **11,** 236–244.

Ginsburg, M., and Heller, H. (1953). *J. Endocrinol.* **9,** 274–282.

Gottschalk, C. W. (1960). *In* "Nierensymposion Göttingen" (K. Kramer and K. J. Ullrich, eds.), pp. 111–118. Thieme, Stuttgart.

Gottschalk, C. W., and Mylle, M. (1959). *Am. J. Physiol.* **196,** 927–936.

Green, J. D. (1951). *Am. J. Anat.* **88,** 225–312.

Green, J. D., and Maxwell, D. S. (1959). *In* "Comparative Endocrinology" (A. Gorbman, ed.), pp. 368–392. Wiley, New York.

Guttmann, S., Jaquenoud, P. A., Boissonnas, R. A., Konzett, H., and Berde, B. (1957). *Naturwissenshaften* **44**, 632–633.

Hanström, B. (1952). *Kgl. Fisiograf. Sällskap. Lund. Forh.* **22**, 1–5.

Hanström, B. (1957). *In* "Handbook of Primatology" (H. Hofer, A. H. Schultz, and D. Starck, eds.), Vol. III-1, pp. 705–755. S. Karger, Basel.

Harris, G. W., and Jacobsohn, D. (1952). *Proc. Roy. Soc.* **B139**, 263–276.

Hartman, C. G. (1957). *Fertility and Sterility* **8**, 403–427.

Haselbach, C. H., and Piguet, A. R. (1952). *Helv. Chim. Acta* **35**, 2131–2135.

Haterius, H. O., and Ferguson, J. K. W. (1938). *Am. J. Physiol.* **124**, 314–321.

Heller, H. (1930). *Arch. exptl. Pathol. Pharmakol. Naunyn-Schmiedeberg's* **157**, 323–329.

Heller, H. (1941a). *J. Physiol. (London)* **99**, 246–257.

Heller, H. (1941b). *J. Physiol. (London)* **100**, 125–141.

Heller, H. (1942). *J. Physiol. (London)* **101**, 317–326.

Heller, H. (1950). *Experientia* **6**, 368–376.

Heller, H. (1956). *Mem. Soc. Endocrinol. No. 5.* 25–37.

Heller, H. (1961). *In* "Oxytocin" (R. Caldeyro-Barcia and H. Heller, eds.), pp. 3–22. Pergamon Press, New York.

Heller, H. (1962). Unpublished results.

Heller, H., and Bentley, P. J. (1963). *Mem. Soc. Endocrinol. No. 13.* In press.

Heller, H., and Lederis, K. (1958). *Nature* **182**, 1231–1232.

Heller, H., and Lederis, K. (1959). *J. Physiol. (London)* **147**, 299–314.

Heller, H., and Lederis, K. (1960). *J. Physiol. (London)* **151**, 47–49P.

Heller, H., and Lederis, K. (1961). *J. Physiol. (London)* **158**, 27–29P.

Heller, H., and Lederis, K. (1962). *In* "Neurosecretion" (H. Heller and R. B. Clark, eds.), pp. 35–46. Academic Press, New York.

Heller, H., and Pickering, B. T. (1960). *J. Physiol. (London)* **152**, 56–57P.

Heller, H., and Pickering, B. T. (1961). *J. Physiol. (London)* **155**, 98–114.

Heller, H., and Zaidi, S. M. A. (1957). *Brit. J. Pharmacol.* **12**, 284–292.

Heller, H., Pickering, B. T., Maetz, J., and Morel, F. (1961). *Nature* **191**, 670–671.

Heller, J., and Lojda, Z. (1960). *Physiol. bohemosloven.* **6**, 504–507.

Herlant, M. (1954). *Bull. soc. zool. France* **79**, 256–281.

Herring, P. T. (1913). *Quart. J. Exptl. Physiol.* **6**, 73–108.

Herring, P. T. (1915). *Quart. J. Exptl. Physiol.* **8**, 245–274.

Hild, W., and Zetler, G. (1953). *Arch. ges. Physiol. Pflüger's* **257**, 169–201.

Hogben, L. T., and de Beer, G. R. (1925). *Quart. J. Exptl. Physiol.* **15**, 163–176.

Hogben, L. T., and Schlapp, W. (1924). *Quart. J. Exptl. Physiol.* **14**, 229–258.

Holmes, R. M. (1962). Proc. Conf. European Comp. Endocrinologists, London 1962. *Gen. Comp. Endocrinol.* In press.

Hope, D. B., Murti, V. V. S., and du Vigneaud, V. (1962). *J. Biol. Chem.* **237**, 1563–1566.

Howes, N. H. (1940). *J. Exptl. Biol.* **17**, 128–138.

Irving, G. W., and du Vigneaud, V. (1938). *J. Biol. Chem.* **123**, 485–489.

Jacobson, H. N., and Kellogg, R. H. (1956). *Am. J. Physiol.* **184**, 376–389.

Jaenike, J. R., and Berliner, R. W. (1960). *J. Clin. Invest.* **39**, 481–490.

Janczo, N. (1955). "Speicherung." Académiai Kiado, Budapest.

Jaquenoud, P. A., and Boissonnas, R. A. (1961). *Helv. Chim. Acta* **44**, 113–122.

Jard, S., Maetz, J., and Morel, F. (1960). *Compt. rend. acad. sci.* **251**, 788–790.

Jones, I. C., Phillips, J. G., and Holmes, W. N. (1959). *In* "Comparative Endocrinology" (A. Gorbman, ed.), pp. 582–612. Wiley, New York.

Jørgensen, C. B. (1950). *Acta Physiol. Scand.* **22**, Suppl. No. 78, pp. 7–79.

Jørgensen, C. B., Levi, H., and Ussing, H. H. (1946). *Acta Physiol. Scand.* **12**, 350–371.

Jošt, K., Rudinger, J., and Šorm, F. (1961). *Collection Czechoslov. Chem. Communs.* **26**, 2496.

Kamm, O., Aldrich, T. B., Grote, T. W., Rowe, L. W., and Bugbee, E. P. (1928). *J. Am. Chem. Soc.* **50**, 573–601.

Katsoyannis, P. G., and du Vigneaud, V. (1960). *J. Biol. Chem.* **233**, 1352–1354.

Kobayashi, H., Ishii, S., and Gorbman, A. (1959). *Gunma J. Med Sci.* **8**, 301–321.

Konzett, H. (1957). *Helv. Physiol. Acta* **15**, 419–425.

Konzett, H. (1960). *In* "Polypeptides Which Affect Smooth Muscles and Blood Vessels" (M. Schachter, ed.), pp. 20–35. Pergamon Press, New York.

Konzett, H., and Berde, B. (1959). *Brit. J. Pharmacol.* **14**, 133–136.

Konzett, H., Berde, B., and Cerletti, A. (1956). *Schweiz. med. Wochschr.* **86**, 226–229.

Kuschinsky, G., and Bundschuh, H. E. (1939). *Arch. exptl. Pathol. Pharmakol. Naunyn-Schmiedeberg's* **192**, 683.

Lamdin, E. (1959). *A.M.A. Arch. Internal Med.* **103**, 644–671.

Lanzing, W. J. R. (1954). *Acta Endocrinol.* **16**, 277–283.

Law, H. D., and du Vigneaud, V. (1960). *J. Am. Chem. Soc.* **82**, 4579.

Lazo-Wasem, E. A., and Weisel, G. F. (1952). *Biol. Bull.* **102**, 25–29.

Leaf, A., Anderson, J., and Page, L. B. (1959). *J. Gen. Physiol.* **41**, 657–668.

Lederis, K. (1961). *Gen. Comp. Endocrinol.* **1**, 80–89.

Lederis, K. (1962). In "Neurosecretion" (H. Heller and R. B. Clark, eds.), pp. 227–236. Academic Press, New York.

Lederis, K., and Heller, H. (1960). *Proc. 1st. Intern. Congr. Endocrinol., Copenhagen 1960* pp. 115–116.

Legait, H. (1959). Thèse d'Agrégation de l'Enseignment superior. Louvain.

Levinsky, N. G., and Sawyer, W. H. (1953). *Proc. Soc. Exptl. Biol. Med.* **82**, 272–274.

Light, A., and du Vigneaud, V. (1958). *Proc. Soc. Exptl. Biol. Med.* **98**, 692–696.

Light, A., Studer, R. D., and du Vigneaud, V. (1959). *Arch. Biochem. Biophys.* **83**, 84–87.

Lloyd, S. (1959a). *J. Physiol. (London)* **148**, 625–632.

Lloyd, S. (1959b). *J. Physiol. (London)* **149**, 586–592.

Lloyd, S., and Pickford, M. (1961a). *J. Physiol. (London)* **155**, 161–174.

Lloyd, S., and Pickford, M. (1961b). *Brit. J. Pharmacol.* **16**, 129–136.

Lutz, W. B., Ressler, C., Nettleton, D. E., and du Vigneaud, V. (1959). *J. Am. Chem. Soc.* **81**, 167–173.

Mackenzie, K. (1911). *Quart. J. Exptl. Physiol.* **4**, 305–330.

Maetz, J., and Juien, M. (1961). *Nature* **189**, 152–153.

Maetz, J., Morel, F., and Lahlouh, B. (1959). *Nature* **184**, 1236–1237.

Meites, J., and Hopkins, T. F. (1961). *J. Endocrinol.* **22**, 207–213.

Meyer, W. C. (1935). *Z. Nervenheilk* **138**, 65–74.

Morel, D., Maetz, J., and Lucarain, C. (1958). *Biochim. et Biophys. Acta* **28**, 619–626.

Morel, F., Maetz, J., Acher, R., Chauvet, J., and Lenci, M. T. (1961). *Nature* **190**, 828–829.

Morris, R. (1960). *Symposia Zool. Soc. London* **1**, 1–15.

Mueller, J. M., Pierce, J. G., and du Vigneaud, V. (1953). *J. Biol. Chem.* **204**, 857–860.

Munsick, R. A. (1960). *Endocrinology* **66**, 451–457.

Munsick, R. A., Sawyer, W. H., and van Dyke, H. B. (1958). *Endocrinology* **63**, 688–693.

Munsick, R. A., Sawyer, W. H., and van Dyke, H. B. (1960). *Endocrinology* **66**, 860–871.

Novelli, A. (1936). *Rec. soc. arg. biol.* **12**, 163.

Noyes, R. W., Adams, C. E., and Walton, A. (1958). *J. Endocrinol.* **18**, 165–174.

Oldham, F. K. (1938). *Anat. Record* **72**, 265–287.

Oldham, F. K., McCleery, D. P., and Geiling, E. M. K. (1938). *Anat. Record* **71**, 27–32.

Oliver, G., and Schafer, E. A. (1895). *J. Physiol. (London)* **18**, 277–279.

Olsson, R., and Wingstrand, K. G. (1954). *Univ. Bergen Arbok Naturvitenskap. Rekke No.* **14**, 1–14.

Ott, I., and Scott, J. C. (1910). *Proc. Soc. Exptl. Biol. Med.* **8**, 48–49.

Overton, E. (1904). *Verhandl. physik. med. Ges. Würzburg* **36**, 277–295.

Palay, S. L. (1957). *In* "Ultrastructure and Cellular Chemistry of Neural Tissue" (H. Waelsch, ed.), pp. 31–44. Cassell, London.

Pasqualini, R. Q. (1938). *Rev. soc. arg. biol.* **14**, 260–274.

Paton, D. N., and Watson, A. (1912). *J. Physiol. (London)* **44**, 413–424.

Pérès, J. M. (1943). *Ann. inst. océanog. (Paris)* **21**, 229. Cited by Sawyer, W. H. (1959).

Perks, A. M., Dodd, M. H., and Dodd, J. M. (1960). *Nature* **185**, 850–851.

Pickering, B. T., and Heller, H. (1959). *Nature* **184**, 1463–1465.

Pickford, G. E., and Atz, J. W. (1957). "The Physiology of the Pituitary Gland of Fishes," New York Zoological Society, New York.

Pickford, M. (1961). *In* "Oxytocin" (R. Caldeyro-Barcia and H. Heller, eds.), pp. 68–78. Pergamon Press, New York.

Popenoe, E. A., Lawler, H. C., and du Vigneaud, V. (1952). *J. Am. Chem. Soc.* **74**, 3713.

Rasmussen, H., and Craig, L. (1961). *Endocrinology* **68**, 1051–1055.

Rasmussen, H., Schwartz, I. L., Schoessler, M. A., and Hochster, G. (1960). *Proc. Natl. Acad. Sci. U.S.* **48**, 1278–1287.

Rasquin, P., and Stoll, M. L. (1955). *Anat. Record.* **122**, 452–453.

Reindel, F., and Hoppe, W. (1954). *Chem. Ber.* **87**, 1103–1107.

Ressler, C., and du Vigneaud, V. (1957). *J. Am. Chem. Soc.* **79**, 4511–4515.

Ressler, C., and Rachele, J. R. (1958). *Proc. Soc. Exptl. Biol. Med.* **98**, 170–174.

Ressler, C., Trippett, S., and du Vigneaud, V. (1953). *J. Biol. Chem.* **204**, 861–869.

Rosenfeld, M. (1940). *Bull. Johns Hopkins Hosp.* **66**, 398–403.

Rothballer, A. B. (1953). *Anat. Record* **115**, 21–41.

Rudinger, J., and Krejčí, I. (1962). *Experentia.* In press.

Santorini, G. D. (1724). "Observationes Anatomicae," p. 70. Gysberg Langerak, Leyden.

Sawyer, W. H. (1951a). *Am. J. Physiol.* **164**, 44–48.

Sawyer, W. H. (1951b). *Am. J. Physiol.* **164**, 457–466.

Sawyer, W. H. (1957). *In* "The Neurohypophysis" (H. Heller, ed.), pp. 171–178. Academic Press, New York.

Sawyer, W. H. (1958). *Endocrinology* **63**, 644.

Sawyer, W. H. (1959). *Endocrinology* **65**, 520–523.

Sawyer, W. H. (1960). *Endocrinology* **66**, 112–120.

Sawyer, W. H., and Roth, W. D. (1953). *Federation Proc.* **12**, 125.

Sawyer, W. H., and Sawyer, M. K. (1952). *Physiol. Zoöl.* **25**, 84–98.

Sawyer, W. H., and Schisgall, R. M. (1956). *Am. J. Physiol.* **187**, 312–314.

Sawyer, W. H., Munsick, R. A., and van Dyke, H. B. (1959). *Nature* **184**, 1463–1465.

Sawyer, W. H., Munsick, R. A., and van Dyke, H. B. (1960). *Endocrinology* **67**, 137–138.

Sawyer, W. H., Munsick, R. A., and van Dyke, H. B. (1961a). *Endocrinology* **68**, 215–225.

Sawyer, W. H., Munsick, R. A., and van Dyke, H. B. (1961b). *Gen. Comp. Endocrinol.* **1**, 30–36.

Scharrer, E. (1953). *Verhandl. anat. Ges. Mainz.* **51**, 5–28.

Scharrer, E., and Frandson, R. D. (1954). *Anat. Record.* **118**, 350–351.

Schiebler, T. H. (1951). *Acta Anat.* **13**, 233–255.

Schlapp, W. (1925). *Quart. J. Exptl. Physiol.* **15**, 327–347.

Schlichtegroll, A. (1954). *Naturwissenschaften* **41**, 188–189.

Schreiber, V., and Schreiber, O. (1951). *Compt. rend. soc. biol.* **145**, 619–620.

Sexton, A. W. (1955). *Dissertation Abstr.* **15**, 2270. Cited from I. C. Jones *et al.* (1959).

Shannon, J. A. (1942). *J. Exptl. Med.* **76**, 387–399.

Simpson, G. G. (1945). *Bull. Am. Museum Nat. Hist.* **85**, 1–350.

Simpson, G. G. (1959). "The Meaning of Evolution." New American Library, New York.

Sloper, J. C. (1954). *J. Anat.* **88**, 576–577.

Sloper, J. C. (1955). *J. Anat.* **89**, 301–316.

Smith, D. C. W. (1956). *Mem. Soc. Endocrinol.* **No. 5**, 83–98.

Smith, H. W. (1956). "Principles of Renal Physiology," Oxford Univ. Press, London and New York.

Steen, W. B. (1929). *Anat. Record* **43**, 215–220.

Steggerda, F. R. (1937). *Proc. Soc. Exptl. Biol. Med.* **36**, 103–106.

Steggerda, F. R., and Essex, H. E. (1934). *Proc. Soc. Exptl. Biol. Med.* **32**, 425–428.

Strahan, R., and Waring, H. (1954). *Australian J. Exptl. Biol. Med. Sci.* **32**, 193–206.

Strauss, M. B. (1959). *A.M.A. Arch. Internal Med.* **103**, 489–494.

Tanaka, K., and Nakajo, S. (1960). *Nature* **187**, 245.

Tanaka, K., and Nakajo, S. (1962). *Endocrinology* **70**, 453–458.

Thenius, E., and Hofer, H. (1960). "Stammesgeschichte der Säugetiere." Springer, Berlin.

Thomson, W. B. (1959). *J. Physiol.* (*London*) **145**, 12–13P.

Thorn, N. A. (1959). *Acta Endocrinol.* **32**, 134–141.

Thurau, K. (1960). *In* "Nierensymposium Göttingen" (K. Kramer and K. J. Ullrich, eds.), pp. 121–135. Thieme, Stuttgart.

Tuppy, H. (1953). *Biochim. et Biophys. Acta* **11**, 449–450.

Tuppy, H., and Michl, H. (1953). *Monatsh.* **84**, 1011–1020.

Turner, R. A., Pierce, J. G., and du Vigneaud, V. (1951). *J. Biol. Chem.* **191**, 21–28.

Tuurala, O. (1957). *Ann. Acad. Sci. Fennicae Ser. A. IV No.* **36**, 1–9. Quoted from Arvy *et al.* (1959).

Tverskoi, G. B. (1960). *Nature* **186**, 782–784.

Uranga, J., and Quintana, G. (1958). *Rev. soc. arg. biol.* **34**, 75–81.

Uranga, J., and Sawyer, W. H. (1960). *Am. J. Physiol.* **198**, 1287–1290.

Ussing, H. H. (1954). *In* "Recent Developments in Cell Physiology" (J. A. Kitching, ed.), pp. 33–41. Butterworths, London.

Ussing, H. H. (1960). *In* "Heffter's Handbuch der experimentellen Pharmakologie," Ergänzungswerk 13, pp. 1–576. Springer, Berlin.

van de Kamer, J. C., and Schreurs, A. F. (1959). *Z. Zellforsch. u. mikroskop. Anat.* **49**, 605–630.

van Dyke, H. B. (1959). *21st Intern. Congr. Physiol. Sci., Buenos Aires, 1959 Symposia Spec. Lectures*, pp. 61–70.

van Dyke, H. B., Chow, B. F., Greep, R. O., and Rothen, A. (1942). *J. Pharmacol. Exptl. Therap.* **74**, 190–209.

van Dyke, H. B., Engel, S. L., and Adamsons, K. (1956). *Proc. Soc. Exptl. Biol. Med.* **91**, 484–486.

van Dyke, H. B., Adamsons, K., and Engel, S. L. (1957). *In* "The Neurohypophysis" (H. Heller, ed.), pp. 65–73. Academic Press, New York.

Verney, E. B. (1947). *Proc. Roy. Soc.* **B135**, 25–106.

Verney, E. B., and Jewell, P. A. (1957). *Phil. Trans. Roy. Soc. London* **B240**, 197–324.

Vogt, M. (1961). Personal communication.

von den Velden, R. (1913). *Klin. Wochschr.* **50**, 2083–2086.

Wagner, H. N., and Braunwald, E. (1956). *J. Clin. Invest.* **35**, 1412–1418.

Waring, H., Morris, L., and Stephens, G. (1956). *Australian J. Exptl. Biol. Med. Sci.* **34**, 235–238.

Weinstein, H., Berne, R. M., and Sachs, H. (1960). *Endocrinology* **66**, 712–718.

Wingstrand, K. G. (1956). *Vidensk. Medd. Dansk naturh. Foren.* **118**, 193–210.

Wirz, H. (1957). *In* "The Neurohypophysis" (H. Heller, ed.), pp. 157–266. Academic Press, New York.

Wirz, H. (1960). *In* "Nierensymposium Göttingen" (K. Kramer and K. J. Ullrich, eds.), pp. 101–108. Thieme, Stuttgart.

Wirz, H., Hargitary, B., and Kuhn, W. (1951). *Helv. Physiol. Pharmacol. Acta* **9**, 196–207.

Wolley, P. (1959). *J. Exptl. Biol.* **36**, 453–458.

Woodbury, R. A., Hamilton, W. F., Volpitto, P. P., Abreu, B. E., and Harper, H. T. (1944). *J. Pharmacol. Exptl. Therap.* **81**, 95.

~ 3 ~

Pituitary Hormones Affecting the Chromatophores

J. N. KARKUN

Central Drug Research Institute, Chattar Manzil Palace, Lucknow, India

AND

F. W. LANDGREBE

Department of Materia Medica and Pharmacology, Welsh National School of Medicine, The Parade, Cardiff, Wales

I. INTRODUCTION

Many species of cold-blooded vertebrates belonging to the classes Pisces, Amphibia, and Reptilia exhibit a striking dermal pigmentary response to changes of illumination, temperature, humidity, etc. The color change observed results from the dispersion or concentration of "pigment granules" in dermal and epidermal chromatophores (Fig. 1). This is commonly

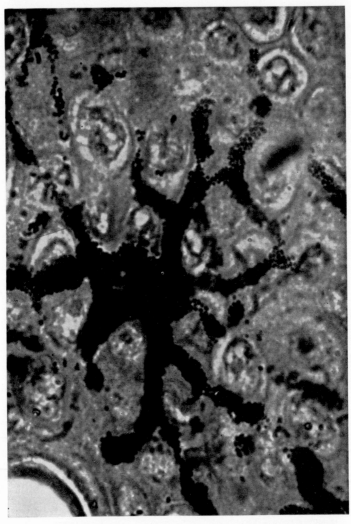

Fig. 1. Epidermal melanophore of *Xenopus laevis*. Photographed under a Crooke apochromatic oil immersion objective N.A. 1.32 and eyepiece 8 times compensating. 1440×.

and conveniently referred to as expansion or contraction of chromatophores. These are distinguished as melanophores, xanthophores, or erythrophores according to whether they contain black, yellow, or red pigment. Melanophores are the most important of the chromatophores and are usually more abundant than the others.

When the pigment granules in the chromatophores are concentrated, the skin appears pale and when dispersed throughout the chromatophores, the skin appears dark. Broadly speaking, light is the most important physical stimulus and commonly predominates over all others, and the eye is the most important receptor for the response.

The time required for these color changes differs among different lower vertebrates. For example, some fish can change color completely in a few minutes whereas certain amphibia take a few days. This fast color change is under nervous control and this direct nervous control of the melanophore in most species of fish is largely replaced by a humoral one in the amphibian.

Over 40 years ago, Atwell (1919) showed that larval amphibians from which the embryonic rudiments of the pituitary gland had been removed always developed into pale individuals. Two years later Swingle (1921) found that amphibian pituitary implants caused darkening of pale tadpoles. These findings led to an extensive investigation of the role of the pituitary in the chromatic behavior of lower vertebrates by Hogben and his collaborators (Hogben and Winton, 1922; Hogben, 1924, 1936; Hogben and Gordon, 1930; Hogben and Slome, 1936; Hogben and Landgrebe, 1940; Waring, 1942). By careful experimentation involving nerve transection, hypophysectomy, and removal and implantation of the various pituitary lobes, these workers established beyond doubt that color change in amphibians does not involve direct innervation of the melanophore but depends upon fluctuating amounts of pituitary secretion. They showed that the hormone which expands melanophores (MEH)[1] in such animals is secreted by the pituitary gland. They also obtained indirect evidence for the existence of a melanophore-contracting hormone which Hogben called "W". Later work discussed in an excellent review by Pickford (1957) provides further evidence for its existence. It is interesting to note that Lerner et al. (1960) have recently extracted from ox pineal glands a substance which will contract expanded melanophores in isolated frog skin. It does this in a concentration similar to that required for expansion of contracted melanophores by pure MSH. This substance is a 5-hydroxytryptamine derivative which the authors have labeled "melatonin" (see also Lerner and Case, 1959).

Early workers attempted to purify the pituitary substance which was responsible for expanding the melanophores. In view of the paucity of material present in amphibian glands, they turned their attention to ex-

---

[1] Several purified pituitary extracts expand amphibian melanophores, e.g., MSH and ACTH. This article is concerned solely with MSH.

tracts of the pituitaries of domestic animals (Zondek and Krohn, 1932b; Stehle, 1933, 1936; Landgrebe and Waring, 1941, 1944). These were found to be active in expanding the melanophores of amphibians and this action was used in the methods of assay developed at that time (Landgrebe and Waring, 1941, 1944). Assay techniques used by workers in this field still rely on this action of extracts on their test objects or animals (Landgrebe and Waring, 1962). This activity of mammalian pituitary extracts is in fact, therefore, defined by its action on amphibian melanophores. The melanophore-expanding substance extractable from human pituitaries, for instance, is almost certainly not the same substance as the hormone present in, say, frog pituitaries, and we have as yet no evidence that the former substance is a true hormone in human beings. It is therefore with some hesitation that we adhere to the current practice of using the term "melanophore-stimulating hormone" (MSH) when discussing the various extracts of higher vertebrate pituitaries. When dealing with extracts of blood from higher vertebrates, we are even less certain that the activity found is hormonal and we prefer to call it "melanophore-expanding substance" (MES).

For many years interest in this activity was only lukewarm and only a few workers were engaged in the field. This was due to the prevailing belief that, apart from its effect on color change of lower animals, the active principle had no function in higher vertebrates.

During recent years, however, the matter has acquired renewed interest in view of the report of Sprague et al. (1950) on the effects of adrenocorticotropin (ACTH) extracts in the treatment of rheumatoid conditions in humans. After prolonged administration of these pituitary extracts the patients' skin became pigmented. Since these extracts were found to contain large quantities of material active on the melanophores of hypophysectomized amphibians, this effect was believed by some to be due to the presence of MSH as an impurity in the relatively crude preparations of ACTH. Interest in the activity was further increased by the claim that the ACTH and MSH were identical (Sulman, 1952a; Johnsson and Hogberg, 1952), but this has since been proved incorrect (Morris, 1952; Karkun et al., 1953, 1954a, 1956).

Attempts to isolate the different melanophore-expanding substances obtained from various sources and to elucidate their nature, chemical constitution, and physiological function have been made in many laboratories (Landgrebe and Mitchell, 1954; Porath et al., 1955; Li, 1957, 1959; Harris, 1959a, 1960; Acher, 1960). Work has also been done on human material particularly by Lerner and his school and attempts have been made to elucidate the function of the activity in human pigmentation. Since in this problem they were concerned with the effect of the material

on the melanocytes[2] of human skin, Lerner and Takahashi (1956) refer
to it as melanocyte-stimulating hormone (MSH).

A great deal of information is now available and makes possible a comparative study of the chemistry and physiology of this activity present in
the pituitaries of different vertebrates. More recent work will be emphasized, since earlier work has already been exhaustively reviewed (Stehle,
1944; Landgrebe et al., 1955; Pickford, 1957).

II. SITE OF ORIGIN OF MELANOPHORE-STIMULATING HORMONE

As early as 1930, Allen showed that in frogs a hormone secreted by the
pars intermedia (intermedin) is responsible for the darkening observed
during the normal chromatic behavior of the animal.

It is now well-established that MSH is found in the intermediate lobe of
the pituitary of higher vertebrates where this exists as a separate morphological entity. The latter, however, occurs in only a few species, e.g., cat
and mouse. In the majority of animals, e.g., ox, pig, dog, rat, and frog the
intermediate portion of the gland remains in close association with the
neural lobe and is differentiated therefrom only by its cellular structure.

In some other animals, such as fowl, whale, and porpoise, etc., no morphologically distinct intermediate lobe is seen (Geiling, 1943).

In the adult human pituitary, there is no definitive pars intermedia. Up
to late fetal life a narrow zone, two or three cells deep, appears to be
analogous to the pars intermedia of lower vertebrates. This zone undergoes regression after birth and disappears during childhood.

Evidence for the location of the active substance comes from a variety
of experiments. Geiling and Lewis (1935) observed that tissue cultures of
neural lobe admixed with intermediate lobe have both pressor and melanophore-expanding activity but those of the intermediate lobe alone have
only the latter property. Anderson and Haymaker (1935) found that when
rat posterior pituitary is cultured in vitro, only the pars intermedia cells
of the posterior lobe thrive and elaborate the substance. In cattle, Van
Dyke (1926) observed that the pars intermedia contained much greater

---

[2] The term "melanophore" refers to a pigmentary effector cell and should not be con-
fused with that of "melanocyte" which is generally accepted to denote a pigment-pro-
ducing cell present in mammalian and other vertebrate tissues. There is no evidence that
the pigment granules present in some melanocytes disperse and concentrate in response
to external stimuli. In amphibians and fishes it is probable that a melanophore is later
and special development of a melanocyte (Chavin, 1959). In view of Lerner and
McGuire's (1961) findings (see p. 102) it may be that melanophores exist in human
skin.

amounts of MSH than does any other part of the pituitary. More recent work of Miahle-Voloss (1953) also supports this finding. Geschwind et al. (1952) showed that in the rat pituitary, the posterior lobe (including pars intermedia) contained about 75% of the total activity. In the dog, Sulman and Eviator (1956) observed that the amount of MSH in the neuro-inter-mediate lobe was double that present in the anterior lobe.

In species in which a discrete pars intermedia is lacking, the anterior lobe produces MSH (Oldham, 1938; Kleinholtz and Rahn, 1940; Geiling and Oldham, 1941). According to Roth (1932), and Jores and Glogner (1933), it also originates in the anterior lobe of the human gland. Recent studies by Morris et al. (1956) support this. The authors divided human pituitaries into three parts: (1) anterior lobe, (2) posterior lobe, and (3) intermediate zone (areas of basophil cell invasions) and found that of these three parts the anterior lobe contained the highest concentration of melanophore-expanding activity.

Our knowledge of the type of cell in the pars intermedia (or anterior lobe) which elaborates the substance is incomplete. Detailed information in different vertebrates is lacking. In the cat, Karkun et al. (1954b) under-took a cytological study of the pars intermedia and found that the cellular parenchyma comprised mostly basophils, which constituted 95% of the tissue, whereas the chromophobes and the macrophages constituted re-spectively 0.5 and 4.5% of the gland. Since chromophobes are regarded either as pre-secretory or post-secretory cells, and macrophages are not known to have any secretory function, it was argued that basophils were the cells elaborating intermedin. In the rat, the pars intermedia has a similar preponderance of basophil cells (Karkun and Kar, 1954, unpublished data). In sheep, Herlant (1954) obtained pure suspensions of acidophils from sheep hypophyses by homogenization and repeated washing and centrifugation, and found MSH in extracts completely freed of acidophils. In the ox pituitary, Giroud and Martinet (1947) found that the basophils contained much more MSH than the acidophils.

In humans, Jores and Glogner (1933) found that a basophil adenoma of the pituitary contained large amounts of MSH activity and believed that the basophil cells of the human pituitary are the site of origin. Morris et al. (1956) observed that the anterior lobe and the basophil cell invasion of the "intermediate zone" yielded significantly high levels of the activity and suggested that it is produced by delta type basophil cells.

Little work is recorded regarding the time at which the activity first appears in different vertebrate pituitaries. Rahn and Drager (1941) studied the amount present in the anterior lobe of the chicken pituitary during its embryonic and postnatal development. The activity first appeared on the fifth day of incubation (see also Chen et al., 1940) and could be assayed quantitatively on the seventh day. The concentration rose rapidly during the second half of incubation and did not change significantly during post-natal development. Etkin (1941) found that in the *Xenopus tadpole* the activity could be detected 48 hours after fertilization, even though the pituitary is undifferentiated at this stage. Mussio-Fournier *et al.* (1947) found MSH in the pituitary body of the human fetus, 4–6 months old. Perhaps future research will explore this important field more thoroughly.

Other Sources

Apart from the pituitary, MSH has also been found in the hypothalamus of the catfish *Parasilurus agotus* (Enami, 1955) and in the hypothalamus and cerebral cortex of the rat (Miahle-Voloss and Stutinsky, 1953). In normal rats, the latter authors observed that the amount of activity in the hypothalamus is 3–5 times that in the cerebral cortex. The activity also appeared in the corresponding tissues of hypophysectomized rats after administration of MSH. MSH has been found in the hypothalamus of the duck (Miahle-Voloss and Benoit (1954), in the pig (Guillemin *et al.*, 1962), and in the dog (Schally *et al.*, 1962). Only further work can clarify whether the presence of MSH in the hypothalamus of different species can be explained by migration and storage in this tissue after elaboration from the pituitary.

The activity has also been detected in the placenta of domestic animals (Jöchle, 1955) and in the liver and gastrointestinal tract of warm- and cold-blooded animals (Jöchle, 1957). The recent observation of Varon (1959) that a melanophore-expanding substance is present in the human placenta is worthy of note. Eschbach (1959) examined hydatiform mole and chorioepithelioma tissue and found MES. Karkun and Sen (1963) have recently shown that extracts of human placentas contained only a small amount of MES. The quantity present is not related to either age of the placenta or color of the mother. Whether these substances are true hormones or nonspecific substances remains to be seen.

III. PURIFICATION AND CHEMISTRY OF MELANOPHORE-STIMULATING HORMONE

A. Biological Assay

Any discussion on the purification of the substance must be preceded by an appraisal of the assay methods used to assess its potency. Only biological methods are employed. The literature has been well documented

(Landgrebe and Waring, 1950; Landgrebe et al., 1955; Landgrebe and Waring, 1962). Broadly, the methods fall into two categories: in vivo and in vitro methods.

For in vivo assay, amphibians (usually frogs or toads), adapted to a white background, are injected with the extract to be tested. With active extracts the animals change color by darkening. The melanophores in the skin change shape from punctate to reticulate with various intermediate stages (Fuchs, 1906; Spaeth, 1913). Hogben and Slome (1936) graded these changes on a scale of 1–5, as shown in Fig. 2.

FIG. 2. Melanophore Index. (From Landgrebe and Waring, 1944.)

By microscopic examination of the web of the foot (or the skin) of an amphibian, one can follow the changes and record the "Melanophore Index" every half hour or so, both before and after administration of the active substance. The response evoked by an unknown preparation is thus assessed and compared with that obtained with a standard preparation.

Different species of frogs (Rana temporaria, Rana pipiens, Rana esculenta) can be used for assay purposes. Rana are fairly sensitive but the intact animal often responds to nonspecific substances (Fuchs, 1906; Hogben and Winton, 1922; Houssay and Unger, 1925). The use of hypophysectomized frogs was therefore advocated by many workers. Teague et al. (1939) made an extensive study of the influence of different substances on the color changes of normal and hypophysectomized frogs (Rana pipiens) and concluded that the response of the latter was very specific, "provided that a very dark gross appearance of the skin with complete expansion of melanophores to the reticular phase is obtained before referring the result as a positive test." According to Thing (1952a), "the sensitivity of the frog (Rana esculenta) to MES increases after hypophysectomy and becomes stationary 4 to 5 months hence. However, if such animals are used repeatedly they become unreliable 3 to 4 months after hypophysectomy."

Sulman (1952b, c) and Edgren (1954) used the tree frogs Hyla arborea and Hyla cinerea respectively, and found a very specific and sensitive response. Both investigators used the gross color changes in the body of the animal as criteria. We have examined *Hyla arborea* and can confirm the unpublished finding of one of our co-workers (Main) that the melanophore change in the skin of the leg of *Hyla* is a better indicator than macroscopic color change of the whole animal. *Hyla* are smaller than the *Xenopus* usually used and, partly for this reason, they are more sensitive (about × 3).

Houssay and Unger (1924) used the toad *Bufo arenarum* Hensel as a test animal. The same species has recently been used by Stoppani (1942) and Stoppani *et al.* (1953). Hogben and his collaborators preferred the South African clawed toad (*Xenopus laevis*) for biological assay of the activity and their method has been developed by Landgrebe and Waring (1944). In several respects, the animal is an ideal one. Being completely aquatic, it can easily be kept under standard conditions of temperature, light, and background necessary for the use of nonhypophysectomized animals. With simple pituitary extracts similar results were obtained using either normal or hypophysectomized *Xenopus* (Landgrebe and Waring, 1944). According to Thing (1952b) "results obtained with intact *Xenopus* are just as reliable as that obtained with hypophysectomized green frogs (*Rana esculenta*) provided standard conditions are maintained."

Karkun (1962, unpublished) has recently observed that the Indian pond frog (*Rana cyanophlyctis*) is comparable to *Xenopus* in several respects. It is also an aquatic animal and can be reared under laboratory conditions. The response of the animal compares with that of *Xenopus laevis* as indicated by statistical analysis of responses to different doses, though its specificity has still to be examined.

The *in vitro* method is based on the same effect of the activity, i.e., the expansion of melanophores in pieces of amphibian skin, which are mounted in a frame and immersed in saline containing the active principle. As a result of this, the transmission or reflection of incident light on the skin is reduced. This change can be studied by photoelectric means. On immersing the skin in fresh saline, the melanophores contract again and the skin may be used repeatedly.

Hill *et al.* (1935) were the first to use such a method and it has been developed by a number of investigators (Frieden *et al.*, 1948; Wright, 1948; Shizume *et al.*, 1954; Long and Guillemin, 1961). The *in vitro* methods are objective and are more sensitive than the *in vivo* methods. Hudson and Bentley (1957) using *Xenopus laevis* claimed that the sensitivity of the method using isolated skin is 150 times that using the whole animal. It seems, however, that the *in vitro* method is at best only 30 times more sensitive than *in vivo* assays (Landgrebe and Waring, 1962). The specificity of the response of isolated skin has not yet been fully investigated.

B. Partially Purified Preparations

Pituitary glands from various domestic animals are usually employed as starting material in the preparation of extracts. Table I shows the approximate amount of activity in the pituitaries of various vertebrates. MSH is more readily destroyed in badly prepared or stored posterior lobe powder than the other activities. The ratio between them, in fact, gives some measure of the condition of the powder, e.g., a commercial powder was found to contain 4.2% of water and the melanophore-expanding activity at room temperature was reduced from 40% of the international preparation to 16% in 1 year and to 9% in 2 years; both its oxytocic and pressor activities were only reduced from 65% to 55% (Waring and Landgrebe, 1949). Because of the difficulty in obtaining really fresh material some of the figures shown in Table I must be regarded as very approximate.

TABLE I

APPROXIMATE MSH CONTENT OF PITUITARIES OF DIFFERENT VERTEBRATES[a]

	Human	Horse	Pig	Ox	Sheep	Rat	Mouse	Frog
MSH content (IU/ whole gland)	350	300	180	80	25	0.6	0.7	0.1

[a] *Xenopus laevis* was used as the test animal.

It will be seen, however, that the pig pituitary gland is a very rich source of the activity. Lee and Lerner (1956) found only the equivalent of 2 IU/mg in their commercial pig posterior lobe powder. This low value is probably due to faulty collection of glands or deterioration during storage. When carefully collected and stored, pig posterior lobe powder contains 8–10 IU/mg (Waring and Landgrebe, 1949; Benfey and Purvis, 1955b). Ox glands, on the other hand, contain only one-fifth of this amount by weight (Landgrebe and Mitchell, 1954). Because of the greater availability and easier collection, ox posterior pituitary glands were used in early work on the purification of MSH.

Zondek and Krohn (1932a, b) were the first to produce a comparatively pure preparation of the activity. They extracted ox glands with dilute acetic acid, evaporated to dryness, and extracted the residue several times with absolute alcohol. In the dried alcoholic extract, pressor and oxytocic activities were destroyed by treating an aqueous solution with caustic soda. Further purification of MSH was achieved by precipitating the latter from alcoholic solution with acetone, ether, or ethyl acetate.

Subsequent investigators (Stehle, 1936, 1944; Fostvedt, 1940; Landgrebe and Waring, 1941; Landgrebe *et al.*, 1943, and others) retained the initial acetic acid extraction and acetone, ether, or ethyl acetate precipitation procedures of Zondek and Krohn (1932a), and adopted various devices for the removal of other activities without resorting to treatment with alkali. Landgrebe and Mitchell (1954) improved early methods (Landgrebe and Waring, 1941, Landgrebe *et al.*, 1943) considerably by substituting oxycellulose for carbon as an adsorbent, after an extraction procedure very similar to that adopted by Astwood *et al.* (1951) for the purification of ACTH. Pig posterior lobe powder was used as starting material and was extracted with glacial acetic acid at 70°C. Some inert protein was thrown down by adding half the volume of acetone to the acid extract in the presence of sodium chloride. The activity was precipitated from the clear solution with two volumes of ether and the precipitate was collected by centrifugation and then dried. The dried precipitate was dissolved and centrifuged again to remove the undissolved impurities. The activity was absorbed on oxycellulose and eluted with dilute hydrochloric acid. Further inert material was removed from the clear acid solution by adjusting the pH to 6.5 with ammonia and centrifuging. The activity was finally precipitated from the clear supernatant by addition of 5 volumes of ether.

The yield by this method is about 25 mg/100 gm of pig posterior lobe powder and the purification is approximately 100-fold.

The same authors obtained a similar degree of purity by applying their method to ox posterior lobe powder. Recently Karkun and Landgrebe (1961) assessed the stage to stage recovery of activity from pig posterior lobe powder using this procedure and observed that a recovery of 80–90% of the initial activity could easily be obtained up to the elution stage with hydrochloric acid, provided the initial posterior lobe powder is extracted twice with cold glacial acetic acid for approximately 1 hour and the subsequent steps of the method are rigorously followed. The recovery falls suddenly to 35–40% of the initial activity as soon as the final precipitation is made with acetone. The implication of this observation will be discussed later.

C. Electrophoretically Pure Peptides

The preparation of MSH obtained from pig posterior lobe powder by Landgrebe and Mitchell (1954) served as starting material for obtaining an electrophoretically pure polypeptide. Porath *et al.* (1955) subjected an acetic acid solution of the material to zone electrophoresis for 60 hours using a column packed with cellulose and employing pyridinium acetate as the conducting medium. Some inert material was separated in the process.

The active principle was collected in 4 ml fractions and pooled into 3 larger fractions: I, II, and III. Fraction II was found to contain more than 80% of the activity. It was subjected to a second run for 100 hours. A sharp peak containing most of the activity but only 65% of the solid matter was obtained. The product was found to be an electrophoretically pure polypeptide having an isoelectric point of 5.2 and a molecular weight of about 3000.

In the same year, Lerner and Lee (1955) independently isolated a homogenous MSH from pig posterior lobes. Their initial method of extraction and concentration did not differ fundamentally from that of Landgrebe and Mitchell (1954), except that they used petroleum ether in place of ether for precipitation of the hormonal activity at an initial stage and also employed 80% acetic acid in place of dilute hydrochloric acid for the elution of the hormone from oxycellulose. The eluate was lyophilized and then subjected to countercurrent fractionation (12 transfer) using secondary butanol and 0.5% aqueous trichloroacetic acid as solvents. The contents of tubes 4–6 were combined and lyophilized, and the substance was subjected to paper electrophoresis in barbiturate–acetic acid–hydrochloric acid buffer. Four components were visualized and the one moving fastest towards the cathode was extracted with 20% acetic acid and lyophilized. The substance, when subjected to re-electrophoresis in pyridine–acetic acid buffer behaved as a single component. The active area was extracted as before with 20% acetic acid and lyophilized. The product was homogeneous.

Benfey and Purvis (1955a) also obtained electrophoretically pure products from pig material by countercurrent procedures.

The isoelectric point of the preparations obtained by Porath et al. (1955) and Benfey and Purvis (1955a) is about 5.5, whereas that of the preparation obtained by Lerner and Lee (1955) is about 10.5. This was soon accounted for by Lee and Lerner (1956) who showed that pig posterior lobe powder contains two types of MSH, one more basic than the other. They called the former α-MSH and retained the term β-MSH for the component with the lower isoelectric point. There is no evidence for the hormonal nature of these polypeptides in higher vertebrates; they may well be protein fragments produced during extraction. Nonetheless, they may have pharmacological actions on the melanocytes of higher vertebrates (Section IV, A) as well as other effects. For example, Steelman and Guillemin (1959) believed corticotropic activity to be inherent in the molecule of α-MSH, but not in that of β-MSH.

Lee and Lerner (1956) and Lee (1958) tried to account for the inability of other workers to find α-MSH by pointing out that the substance is acetone soluble. They argued that in the method of Landgrebe and Mitchell

(1954) α-MSH was missed because it was dissolved in the acetone used for the final precipitation of β-MSH. The finding of Karkun and Landgrebe (Section III,B) that there is a sudden fall in recovery during that stage supports this argument, though other explanations are possible. However, Lee and Lerner (1956) actually obtained both α-MSH and β-MSH by initially extracting pig posterior lobe powder up to the stage of elution with hydrochloric acid by Landgrebe and Mitchell's method, and then submitting the eluate to countercurrent fractionation. Karkun (1961, unpublished) has also detected both substances in pig material by submitting this eluate to high voltage electrophoresis[3] by the method of Ryle et al. (1955). Lee (1958) showed that separation of α-MSH and β-MSH could be achieved by starch electrophoresis at pH 4.55 and pH 8.0 of the oxycellulose eluate.

In the last few years a great deal of work has been done on the purification and separation of the different active polypeptides by the application of countercurrent, electrophoretic, and chromatographic (ion-exchange) procedures. Geschwind et al. (1957a, b) obtained bovine β-MSH. Steelman et al. (1959) separated both α- and β-MSH from hog pituitaries as by-products in the preparation of corticotropin. They made use of ion-exchange chromatography with carboxymethyl cellulose (CMC) which after equilibration with 0.01 M ammonium acetate at pH 5.8 allowed β-MSH to pass through, and retained only α-MSH on the column. Both components were subsequently purified by re-chromatography on CMC with changes of pH and concentration of the buffer. Isolation of α- and β-MSH on a preparative scale from hog pituitary concentrates has been accomplished by Schally et al. (1960). They too made use of the differential absorptive properties of cellulose derivatives. Dixon (1960) obtained chromatographically pure material from human pituitaries by the use of Zeo-Karb 225 (2% cross linked, 200–400 mesh) as ion exchanger.

Recently, Lee et al. (1960) have also obtained human β-MSH. These investigators started with the oxycellulose eluate of human pituitary glands and separated ACTH and MSH from the crude eluate by adsorbing them on a diethylaminoethyl (DEAE) cellulose column equilibrated with 0.005 M ammonium acetate at pH 6.9, and separating them by gradient elution techniques. Final purification was attained by use of a CMC column equilibrated previously with 0.005 M ammonium acetate at pH 5.9, and by developing the column by stepwise elution with various concentrations of ammonium acetate at pH 6.9. Lee et al. believe that their human β-MSH is identical with that obtained by Dixon (1960). The

---

[3] One of the authors (J. N. K.) is indebted to Dr. J. I. Harris for kindly making his laboratory facilities available.

Yale workers have also claimed to have isolated both α- and β-MSH from human and monkey pituitaries (Lerner *et al.*, 1960, and Lee *et al.* (1961) have described details of the purification of α- and β-MSH from monkey pituitaries. Dixon and Li (1960, 1961) have also succeeded in isolating equine α- and β-MSH.

D. Structural Characteristics of Active Peptides

The structure of porcine β-MSH was first published by Harris and Roos (1956). This was confirmed independently by Geschwind *et al.* (1957a), who also published the structure of bovine β-MSH (Geschwind *et al.*, 1957b). Harris has since worked out the structures of porcine α-MSH (Harris and Lerner, 1957) and human MSH (Harris, 1959b) and has published details of the methods used to elucidate the structures (Harris and Roos, 1959; Harris, 1959a, 1960).

Dixon and Li (1960) have recently established the structure of equine α-MSH and Lerner *et al.* (1960) are believed to have completed their work on the structures of α- and β-MSH from human pituitaries.

Elucidation of the structure of monkey α- and β-MSH is now on record (Lee *et al.*, 1961), and Dixon and Li (1961) have worked out the structure of equine β-MSH.

Figure 3 shows the structures of α- and β-MSH from different pituitaries. In view of the partial similarity of these structures to those of cortico-tropins, the general structure of ACTH is also shown in the same figure.

Certain salient features can be seen:

(1) Both α- and β-MSH from all known sources (pig, ox, horse, and mon-key) are straight chain polypeptides and thus resemble the cortico-tropins.

(2) α-MSH is a tridecapeptide and has the same structure, whether ob-tained from ox, pig, horse, or monkey. The structures of human α-MSH are yet to be published (Lerner *et al.*, 1960).

(3) α-MSH is a polypeptide blocked both at the N- and C-terminal ends by acetyl (CH_3CO—) and amide (NH_2) groups respectively.

(4) β-MSH from ox, pig, horse, or monkey is an octadecapeptide which is open at both the N- and C-terminal ends.

(5) Human MSH (Dixon, 1960) is comprised of 22 amino acid residues and yet it is termed β-MSH for it is also open at both the ends like that from pig or ox.

(6) All peptides contain the heptapeptide sequence

—Met·Glu·His·Phe·Arg·Try·Gly—

I   H-His·Phe·Arg·Try·Gly·-OH

II   H-Glu·His·Phe·Arg·Try·Gly·-OH

III   H-Met·Glu·His·Phe·Arg·Try·Gly·-OH

IV   H-Ser·Met·Glu·His·Phe·Arg·Try·Gly·-OH

V   α-MSH (pig, ox, horse, monkey)   R-Ser·Tyr·Ser·Met·Glu·His·Phe·Arg·Try·Gly·Lys·Pro·Val-NH₂

VI   β-MSH (ox)   H-Asp·Ser·Gly·Pro·Tyr·Lys·Met·Glu·His·Phe·Arg·Try·Gly·Ser·Pro·Pro·Lys·Asp-OH

VII   β-MSH (pig)   H-Asp·Glu·Gly·Pro·Tyr·Lys·Met·Glu·His·Phe·Arg·Try·Gly·Ser·Pro·Pro·Lys·Asp-OH

VIII   β-MSH (horse)   H-Asp·Glu·Gly·Pro·Tyr·Lys·Met·Glu·His·Phe·Arg·Try·Gly·Ser·Pro·Arg·Lys·Asp-OH

IX   β-MSH (monkey)   H-Asp·Glu·Gly·Pro·Tyr·Arg·Met·Glu·His·Phe·Arg·Try·Gly·Ser·Pro·Pro·Lys·Asp-OH

X   β-MSH (human) H-Ala·Glu·Lys·Lys·Asp·Glu·Gly·Pro·Tyr·Arg·Met·Glu·His·Phe·Arg·Try·Gly·Ser·Pro·Pro·Lys·Asp-OH

XI   Corticotropin   H-Ser·Tyr·Ser·Met·Glu·His·Phe·Arg·Try·Gly·Lys·Pro·Val·Gly·Phe-OH

FIG. 3. Structures of MSH from various pituitaries and of corticotropin. I. 0.002 IU/mg (Hoffmann et al., 1958a). II. 0.015 IU/mg (Schwyzer et al., 1959). III. 0.02 IU/mg (Schwyzer et al. 1959). IV. 0.05 IU/mg (Hoffmann et al., 1958a). V. (Harris and Lerner, 1957) 1500 IU/mg (Landgrebe, 1962, unpublished). VI. (Geschwind et al., 1957) 300 IU/mg (Landgrebe, 1962, unpublished). VII. 1500 IU/mg (Porath et al., 1955). VIII. (Dixon and Li, 1961). Potency not yet certain but probably about 1500 IU/mg (Landgrebe, 1962, unpublished). IX. (Lee et al., 1961). Potency not yet known. X. (Harris, 1959b). Potency not yet known.

(7) The similarity between ox and pig β-MSH runs through the whole chain except that in position 2 a serine residue in the bovine material replaces a glutamic acid residue in the porcine substance.

(8) With corticotropin, the similarity of both the β-hormones from ox and pig extends to a sequence of 7 amino acid residues and but for the transposition of serine and lysine in positions 6 and 14 in β-MSH, the common sequence would extend to a group of 11 amino acid residues.

(9) α-MSH (ox, pig, monkey, or horse) reveals a close structural similarity with corticotropin which extends to a sequence of 13 amino acids.

(10) Human MSH (Dixon) resembles β-MSH (pig) very closely but has an additional sequence of 4 amino acids. The lysine residue in position 6 of the pig and ox substance is replaced by the arginine residue in position 10 of the human peptide.

(11) β-MSH (monkey) may be considered as a modification of porcine hormone with an interchange of lysyl and an arginyl residue at position 6. There is an indication that a trace amount of β-MSH may exist in the primate pituitary which is a modified bovine β-MSH with the same interchange at position 6.

(12) β-MSH (horse) is a modified porcine hormone where arginyl residue replaces prolyl residue of the latter in position 16.

E. Synthesis of MSH Peptides and Their Analogs

Guttmann and Boissonnas (1959) have recently synthesized α-MSH. They condensed

N-acetyl-L-seryl-L-tyrosyl-L-seryl-L-methionyl-y-benzyl-L-glutamate

(Guttmann and Boissonnas, 1958) with

L-histidyl-L-phenylalanyl-L-arginyl-L-tryptophenyl-glycyl-ε-N-

carbobenzoxy-L-lysyl-L-propyl-L-valylamide

(Boissonnas *et al.*, 1958) and then removed the carbobenzoxy and benzyl groups (as protecting groups) by hydrobromic acid in trifluoroacetic acid. The resulting peptide was then purified by application of countercurrent and electrophoretic methods. The product obtained resembled, both chemically and biologically, pure α-MSH (from pig pituitary glands).

Hofmann *et al.* (1957a,b, 1958a,b) also succeeded in preparing synthetic α-MSH. They condensed a pentapeptide carrying a carbobenzoxy group in the N-terminal position along with an octapeptide having a α-carboxyl amide group, and obtained the tridecapeptide. A substance resembling ox β-MSH (but with the amino and carboxyl groups blocked by protecting radicals) was synthesized by Schwyzer and his associates (Schwyzer *et al.*, 1959). The compound

$$Asp(NH_2) \cdot Ser \cdot Gly \cdot Pro \cdot Tyr \cdot Lys(Tos) \cdot Met \cdot Glu(NH_2) \cdot His \cdot Phe \cdot Arg$$

$$\cdot Try \cdot Gly \cdot Ser \cdot Pro \cdot Pro \cdot Lys(Tos) \cdot Asp(OMe)_2$$

however, possesses only about 1% of the activity of natural β-MSH.

In synthesizing these substances these workers prepared smaller peptides as intermediates and also prepared compounds similar to MSH but lacking a few amino acid residues or having them modified or blocked. The estimation of the biological activity of these compounds has given some insight into the structure-activity relationship (Flückiger, 1960; Hofmann, 1960; Schwyzer and Li, 1958; Schnabel and Li, 1960). The broader aspects of this relationship are (see also Fig. 3):

All the amino acids constituting α-MSH are levorotatory. The most reactive group of α-MSH seems to be the acetyl group at the N-terminus of the molecule. Removal of this group results in a fall of biological activity to about 7% of the original (Guttman and Boissonnas, 1961). The group can be replaced by a carbobenzoxy group or by peptides but the biological activity is then reduced. The free γ-carboxyl group of glutamic acid residue in position 5 and the free ϵ amino group of the lysine residue in position 11 of the α-MSH chain seem to be unreactive since their blocking by NH_2 and formyl (or tosyl) radicals respectively does not lower the biological activity of the hormone.

Reduction of α-MSH by removing two amino acid residues, viz: Ser· Tyr· from the N-terminus lowers the biological activity to $<1\%$ of the original value. Acetylation at the free Ser· end of the resulting monodecapeptide restores the activity only by 36%. Pentapeptides, hexapeptides, or octapeptides consisting of amino acid residues in the middle of the α-MSH molecule do not possess a marked biological activity. The synthesis and isolation of various MSH analogs are being continued with unabating zeal (Li *et al.*, 1960; Lo *et al.*, 1961).

F. Potency and Stability of the Active Polypeptides

Both *in vitro* and *in vivo* methods of assay have been used to assess the potency of the various polypeptides. Using the method of Shizume *et al.* (1954) on isolated skin, the results are expressed in terms of the authors' own reference powder and we find 1.33×10^4 of these equivalent to 1 International Unit (see Landgrebe and Waring, 1962), which is in fair agreement with the factor 1×10^4 found by Li (1957). The former result has been used to convert where necessary in Fig. 3.

The potency of α-MSH is variously stated as 2×10^{10} Shizume units/G., i.e., 1500 IU/mg (Li, 1959; Kappeler and Schwyzer, 1960) when measured on isolated skin and as 3300 Sandoz units/mg when assayed by both the *in vitro* method of Shizume *et al.* and Landgrebe and Waring's *in vivo* method (Flückiger, 1960). It is not known whether a Sandoz unit is equivalent to an International Unit but one may suspect that it is not. Undeteriorated pure α-MSH may not as yet have been available to us, but the most potent material so far seen is that kindly supplied by Dr. Dixon, which contained 1020 IU/mg.

The potency of β-MSH (pig) was stated to be 1500 IU/mg (Porath *et al.*, 1955) when measured by the *in vivo* technique and this result has since been confirmed by us and seems to have been accepted by others. It seems possible therefore that α-MSH and β-MSH are of similar potency.

One of the difficulties in assaying these materials is their limited stability unless certain precautions are taken. Guttmann and Boissonnas (1959) found that α-MSH in solution at pH 3.5 lost about half its original potency in 30 days even at 4°C.

Lerner (private communication) finds that solid α-MSH kept for several days at room temperature deteriorates considerably. We find that this applies also to solid β-MSH. The storage of the solid in evacuated and sealed ampoules also proved unsuccessful over a period of a few months, but samples of β-MSH carefully ampouled under nitrogen have retained their potency for over 6 years at room temperature. Solutions of β-MSH were carefully freeze-dried in ampoules and kept at a pressure of less than 20 μ Hg for 24 hours and then sealed, but the preparations were not active 3 months later. If, however, these freeze-dried preparations are kept under nitrogen they seem to retain their potency for at least a year. Solutions containing 0.1 mg/ml of β-MSH in 0.25% acetic acid retain their potency at room temperature for a few days, but if put in ampoules, placed in a boiling water bath for 3 minutes, and sealed while still hot, they usually, but not always, retain their potency for a year; one batch has retained some 40% of its potency after 6 years at room temperature. Weaker solutions are less stable.

IV. PHYSIOLOGICAL EFFECTS

A. Role of MSH in Pigmentation of the Skin

The term pigmentation is often loosely used to cover two distinct yet closely related phenomena:

(a) *Physiological color change.* The dispersion (or contraction) of pigment within the chromatophores present in the skin of some vertebrates.

(b) *Morphological color change.* The synthesis of pigments within specialized cells in the skin under certain physiological conditions.

The second of these is a relatively slow process; the first is more rapid in its manifestation and is reversible. In some vertebrates both changes may be provoked by the same agent (MSH) and in these cases physiological color change precedes the morphological color change.

Various types of pigment exist in the skin of different vertebrates. The one most commonly found is melanin. It is a polymerized product of hallochrome, an indole derivative which in its turn is produced within the skin from tyrosine through several intermediary stages (Raper, 1928; Mason, 1948). Propigment cells (melanoblasts) originate from the neural crest at an early embryonic stage and migrate to various parts of the skin where they become active as pigment producing cells (melanocytes). In warm-blooded animals melanocytes are found in the basal layer of the epidermis. Some may be traced deep down in the dermis (as nevi) or around the base of the hair bulbs. There may be some other cells which are not melanocytes but contain melanin, e.g., epithelial cells, macrophages, etc.

In cold-blooded animals such as amphibians and fishes, the pigment cells are distributed both in the epidermal and dermal layers of the integument. There is also one peculiar characteristic which distinguishes these pigment cells from those in warm-blooded animals. The former easily undergo physiological changes, which may be provoked by a variety of stimuli, e.g., temperature, humidity, light, etc.; of these, the photic stimuli are the predominant ones.

Hogben and his collaborators made a detailed study of the melanophore response of lower vertebrates to photic stimuli and have established the role of pituitary MSH in its production. For details, the reader is referred to the reviews by Waring (1942), Waring and Landgrebe (1950), and Hogben (1942). These workers distinguished four types of melanophore-response to photic stimuli. Two of these are called the "primary response." They are of little importance in the chromatic physiology of common vertebrates and need not be discussed here. The other two types of response are predominant and are termed "secondary" and "tertiary" responses, respectively. Both are coordinated phenomena in which the eye is the receptor.

Experimentally, the secondary response can be evoked by transferring an animal, e.g., an amphibian, from darkness to illumination in light-absorbing surroundings. The melanophores expand fully from a position about halfway between full contraction and full expansion. The change is slow and occurs only in animals which have their eyes open. The photic stimuli excite the floor (B area) of the retina and provoke a reflex liberation of pituitary hormone which, being blood-borne, reaches the effector organs, the melanophores, causing a change of shape and a dispersion of their pigment granules. Hypophysectomy (complete or partial) followed by administration of various hypophyseal extracts reveals that the excitant hormone originates in the pars intermedia. The speed of change is consistent with hormonal participation in the process and peripheral nerve transection has no effect.

The secondary response can be elicited in elasmobranchs, amphibians, and in most teleosts with the exception of *Fundulus*. Reptiles fall into two categories: *Anolis* and *Phrynosoma* behave more or less like amphibians and fishes, but *Chameleon* behaves differently—there is no significant pituitary control of its color change.

The tertiary response can be evoked in the melanophores of some vertebrates, e.g., elasmobranchs and amphibians by transferring them from a black to a white background. Light initiates this reaction also, but in this case both the floor and the periphery (W area) of the eye are excited. It is postulated that the W area sends impulses along the optic nerve which either inhibit the release of the B hormone, or cause the liberation of a W hormone with melanophore-contracting properties. The two-hormone hypothesis is preferred because according to Waring and Landgrebe (1950) it explains "all anomalies some of which receive no interpretation in terms of the one hormone theory." It is believed that the W hormone is liberated either from the pars tuberalis, the hypothalamus, or from some other gland under the influence of the pituitary. For this reason the results of Lerner *et al.* (1960) with pineal gland extracts are of particular interest. Such extracts cause contraction of melanophores in isolated frog skin, and this effect has been shown to be due to their content of a very active 5-hydroxytryptamine derivative.

In other lower vertebrates the tertiary response is not as typical as in elasmobranchs or in amphibians. Thus, in teleosts the response is considerably modified from *Anguilla* to *Fundulus*. The melanophores of these fishes are innervated, and the color changes are a result of direct neural action. This mechanism dominates the more primitive endocrine effect to a degree dependent upon the species. Thus in the eel, though the melanophores are innervated (unlike those of elasmobranchs and amphibians), the endocrine effect dominates the chromatic change. The nervous influence is not discernible, unless the animal is hypophysectomized. In *Phoxinus* and *Pleuronectides*, direct innervation of the melanophores is more important and supersedes any hormonal melanophore contracting mechanism, though melanophore expansion still seems to be under humoral control. In *Fundulus*, however, neural coordination of the chromatic response is completely dominant.

Where melanophore expansion is under humoral control the pituitary hormone responsible is MSH. It also provokes melanin synthesis in the skin, and physiological color change may precede and provoke morphological color change. Sumner and Wells (1933) observed that fish kept in darkness for prolonged periods developed an increase both in the number of melanophores and in the melanin content of the skin. Odiourne (1936, 1937) recorded a similar finding and suggested a common factor provoking both changes. Osborne (1941) concluded from his work on the catfish that the active principle is pituitary MSH (see review by Karkun and Mukerji, 1958). Dawes (1941) showed that the skin of dark-adapted frogs (*Rana pipiens*) contained more melanin than that of light-adapted ones. By perfusion of the hind legs with posterior pituitary extract (containing MSH) he showed that this increase was probably due to MSH. Further evidence was produced by Frieden and Bozer (1951) and Karkun and Mukerji (1953), who administered partially purified MSH to *R. pipiens* and *R. tigrina*, and found that the extract increased melanogenesis in the skin. This effect appeared only after many days of treatment.

Recent experiments indicate the possibility that in both types of color change MSH may not be the only pituitary hormone involved. Sulman (1952a) observed that impure extracts of ACTH darkened tree frogs (*Hyla arborea*). This finding has since been extended (see Thing, 1952b). Pickford and Kosto (1957) and Kosto *et al.* (1959) showed that in the killifish (*Fundulus heteroclitus*) MSH stimulates melanophore proliferation whereas prolactin promotes melanin synthesis within existing pigment cells. They found also that ACTH has no pigmentogenic effect in these animals. Chavin (1959) working on xanthic goldfish (*Crassius auratus* L.) and Hu and Chavin (1960) working on isolated skin of xanthic goldfish came to the conclusion that their extracts of ACTH stimulated melanin formation while extracts of α- and β-MSH (pig) did not do this. Since this activity of their ACTH preparations was not correlated with the ascrobic-acid-depleting, ketogenic, or melanophore-stimulating activity, they suggest that some portion of the ACTH molecule or contamination of the extract is responsible. Chavin (1959) found also that in salamanders a pituitary factor besides MSH was required for melanin synthesis (see also Dalton and Krassner, 1959). However, more work is needed to elucidate the role of MSH in the morphological color change of cold-blooded vertebrates.

In warm-blooded animals, physiological color changes are not observed. Morphological color changes too, are rarely striking and are usually seen only in certain pathological conditions. It was, in fact, the latter changes which started serious investigations in this field. The increased pigmentation of human skin in Addison's disease is well known. In 1952 Sulman, who believed MSH to be either identical (Sulman, 1952a) with, or a constituent of the ACTH complex (Sulman, 1952b) suggested that MSH was responsible for this increase in pigmentation and that observed in Cushing's syndrome and in pregnancy. In support he and others (Sulman, 1956; Johnsson and Högberg, 1953; Shizume and Lerner, 1954) claimed a high blood titer of MSH in such patients. Mussio-Fournier et al. (1943) had previously found that impure MSH stimulates pigmentation in vitiligous human skin, and Lerner et al. (1954) found that purified MSH stimulated melanin synthesis in human skin. The relevant literature has been extensively reviewed (Deutsch and Mescon, 1957a,b; Karkun and Mukerji, 1958). Lerner and McGuire (1961) have recently injected synthetic α-MSH and an extract of β-MSH (pig) into four negroes. Both preparations were of low potency and relatively impure. Nevertheless, a few milligrams injected daily produced skin darkening in three cases. This occurred within 24 hours, and the authors suggest that dispersion of melanin granules occurs inside the melanocytes similar to that seen in the melanophores of amphibia and fish.

Although all these studies suggest that MSH plays a role in the pigmentation of human skin, more work is needed to discover whether it is the only pituitary principle involved. Serious doubts have been raised about the validity of previous conclusions regarding MSH extractable from human blood and urine for several reasons:

(a) Pure ACTH has intrinsic MSH activity (Dixon 1959).
(b) Pure MSH and pure ACTH give the same slope in the dose–response curve by either of the usual methods for the assay of MSH (Karkun et al., 1960).
(c) Many fragments of the known polypeptides have MSH activity, and active degradation products of other pituitary polypeptides may be present in blood.

Research on the participation of MSH in melanin pigmentation is now being extended to include work on other mammals. Working on melanomas in hamsters, Foster (1959) found that MSH had a positive influence on the tissue. Snell (1961) injected guinea pigs daily with pure β-MSH (pig) and examined the effect on melanogenesis in the skin. The treatment produced an increase in the length, width, and complexity of the dendritic processes and an increase in the amount of melanin within the processes. The former phenomenon, however, did not appear to be due to a dispersion of the melanin such as occurs in amphibian melanophores.

The effect of MSH on mammals may be purely pharmacological although there is some evidence that it may also be of physiological significance.

Barbarossa and Pende (1950) found that estrogens injected into guinea pigs produced increased pigmentation in the nipples simultaneous with hyperplasia of the pituitary and signs of increased secretory activity in the pars intermedia. Hypothyroidism induced by goitrogens induces diminished pigmentation of the skin and Frieden (1951) noted that in rats which had been thyroidectomized or treated with thiouracil, there was a diminished amount of MSH in the pituitary. Shizume and Lerner (1954) estimated the melanophore-expanding activity of the blood in a large number of patients with abnormal skin pigmentation. They found a correlation between the amount of activity and the degree of skin pigmentation in pregnancy and in patients with Addison's disease and Cushing's syndrome, and similar findings have been reported by Johnsson and Högberg (1953) and by Sulman (1956). Karkun *et al.* (1960) also found blood from hyperpigmented patients to be potent in melanophore-expanding activity but point out the difficulties in identifying this activity with pituitary MSH. It is to be hoped that the application of modern physicochemical methods will lead to a solution of this problem.

B. Extrapigmentary Effect of MSH

Recent work indicates that MSH may have some extrapigmentary role. Ferrari (1958) observed certain behavioral changes in animals after intracisternal injection with MSH (or ACTH). A peculiar crisis of increasing muscular tonus resulting in a generalized act of stretching was observed in the dog after such treatment. Similar recurrent paroxysmal stretching movements were observed in rats, cats, and rabbits. Ferrari *et al.* (1961) have since evoked similar changes in dogs using a synthetic hexapeptide possessing melanophore-expanding activity.

Intravenous administration of β-MSH (0.25–2.0 μg/kg body weight) increased for a long time the amplitude of monosynaptic potentials in the spinal cord of the cat, although this did not occur with either α-MSH or ACTH. The effect was seen in the mid-collicular decerebrate or barbiturate-anesthetized animals (Krivoy and Guillemin, 1961). The recent findings that β-MSH is enzymatically inactivated by the brain is advanced as a supportive evidence for a physiological function of β-MSH (Long *et al.*, 1961). The authors opined that β-MSH probably maintains and modifies the central excitory state of some neuronal system in mammals, and suggest that during phylogeny the pigmentary activity of β-MSH in lower vertebrates is replaced by a neural function in higher animals. Alternatively it may be that the hormone in lower vertebrates has a dual function both neural and pigmentary.

Krivoy and Guillemin (1962) also found that β-MSH extracts antagonize the action of chlorpromazine and restore the positive intermediary potential lowered by the latter in decerebrate and decerebrate-spinal cats. They suggest the possibility that chlorpromazine acts to lower the central excitatory state by modifying the physiological action of β-MSH on the nervous system.

Novales and Novales (1961) have published findings that MSH produces melanin dispersion by increasing the sodium content of the melanophore. Melanophores and nerve cells show similar embryological and other properties. These authors suggest that in view of the established role of ionic fluxes in the origin of neural potentials, these effects of MSH are brought about by an effect on the ionic permeability of the nerve cell.

Other miscellaneous actions of extracts of MSH have also been reported. Krayer *et al.* (1961) observed an accelerating action of α-MSH on the heart lung preparation of the dog. Barbarossa and Di Ferrante (1950) found that MSH stimulated the maturation of ovarian follicles in normal rats but not in hypophysectomized ones. Cehovic (1960) observed that MSH injected into *Rana esculenta* diminished the fixation of I[131] by its thyroids, and Courier and Cehovic (1960) in rabbits and Cehovic (1962) in guinea pigs found that α-MSH produced histological changes in the thyroid which indicated hyperfunction of the gland. Karkun *et al.* (1963) found similar histological changes in the thyroids of albino rats.

It is difficult to evaluate the significance of many of these findings since pure MSH polypeptides were not used. Judging from the biological potency of some of the MSH extracts recorded by recent workers, many of them are content to use materials which are considered α-MSH or β-MSH and which often contain only 10–20% of the pure polypeptide on a weight basis. Miscellaneous effects such as these were reported by early workers using relatively crude extracts (see Landgrebe and Waring, 1950), and it is to be hoped that future workers will use the purer materials that are now available.

V. CONCLUDING REMARKS

The presence in pituitary extracts of two melanophore-stimulating polypeptides, α- and β-MSH, has been demonstrated. The structures of both have been established and corroborated by synthesis. Lerner believes that α-MSH is the physiologically active hormone, partly because he thinks that it is more potent on amphibian melanophores than β-MSH and partly because the structure of α-MSH is the same in different species of animals. However, the structure of β-MSH varies with the species and, by analogy with other hormones, it may indicate that β-MSH is the physiological hormone—if such exists. α-MSH is thought by some workers to be a degradation product of larger polypeptides. Burgers (1960, 1961) found that in a number of vertebrates there are at least three types of MSH; in mammals one resembles α-MSH; the other two are akin to ox β-MSH and pig β-MSH. In invertebrates also there may be several polypeptides with MSH activity.

Finally, several questions may be asked. Why are there so many substances in the pituitary gland with a similar action? Is it possible that each of them has some specific physiological function to perform and has melanophore-expanding activity in amphibian skin only because of the presence of a common amino acid sequence which is modified in different species? Do all these compounds arise from the same mother molecule either as artifacts due to chemical manipulation or as normal biogenetic products?

References

Acher, R. (1960). *Ann. Rev. Biochem.* **29**, 547–576.

Allen, B. M. (1930). *Proc. Soc. Exptl. Biol. Med.* **27**, 504–505.

Anderson, E., and Haymaker, W. (1935). *Proc. Soc. Exptl. Biol. Med.* **33**, 313–316.

Astwood, E. B., Raben, M. S., Payne, R. W., and Grady, A. B. (1951). *J. Am. Chem. Soc.* **73**, 2969–2970.

Atwell, W. J. (1919). *Science* **49**, 48–50.

Barbarossa, C., and Di Ferrante, N. (1950). *Arch. "E. Maragliano" patol. e clin.* **5**, 887.

Barbarossa, C., and Pende, T. (1950). *Arch. "E Maragliano" patol. e clin.* **5**, 27–31.

Benfey, B. G., and Purvis, J. L. (1955a). *Biochem. J.* **62**, 588–593.

Benfey, B. G., and Purvis, J. L. (1955b). *J. Am. Chem. Soc.* **77**, 5167–5168.

Boissonnas, R. A., Guttmann, S., Hugeunin, R. L., Jaquenoud, P.-A., and Sandrin, E. (1958). *Helv. Chim. Acta* **41**, 1867–1882.

Burgers, A. C. J. (1960). *Acta Endocrinol. Suppl.* **51**, 329–330.

Burgers, A. C. J. (1961). *Endocrinology* **68**, 698.

Cehovic, G. (1960). *Compt. rend. acad. sci.* **250**, 1114–1116.

Cehovic, G. (1962). *Compt. rend. rend. acad. sci.* **254**, 1872–1874.

Chavin, W. (1959). *In* "Pigment Cell Biology" (M. Gordon, ed.), p. 63. Academic Press, New York.

Chen, G., Oldham, F. K., and Geiling, E. M. K. (1940). *Proc. Soc. Exptl. Biol. Med.* **45**, 810–813.

Courrier, R., and Cehovic, G. (1960). *Compt. rend. acad. sci.* **251**, 832–834.

Dalton, H. C., and Krassner, Z. P. (1959). *In* "Pigment Cell Biology" (M. Gordon. ed.), pp. 51–61. Academic Press, New York.

Dawes, B. (1941). *J. Exptl. Biol.* **18**, 26–49.

Deutsch. S., and Mescon, H. (1957a). *New Engl. J. Med.* **257**, 222–226.

Deutsch, S., and Mescon, H. (1957b). *New Engl. J. Med.* **257**, 268–272.

Dixon, H. B. F. (1959). *Biochim. et Biophys. Acta* **34**, 251–253.

Dixon, H. B. F. (1960). *Biochim. et Biophys. Acta* **37**, 38–42.

Dixon, J. S., and Li, C. H. (1959). *Federation Proc.* **18**, 215.

Dixon, J. S., and Li, C. H. (1960). *J. Am. Chem. Soc.* **82**, 4568–4572.

Dixon, J. S., and Li C. H. (1961). *Gen. Comp. Endocrinol.* **1**, 161–169.

Edgren, R. A. (1954). *Proc. Soc. Exptl. Biol. Med.* **85**, 229–230.

Enami, M. (1955). *Science* **121**, 36–37.

Eschbach, J. (1959). *Bull. fedration soc. gynec. obstet. langue franc* **11**, 188–190.

Etkin, W. (1941). *Proc. Soc. Exptl. Biol. Med.* **47**, 425–428.

Ferrari, W. (1958). *Arch. ital. sci. farmacol.* **8**, 133–134.

Ferrari, W., Gessa, G. L., and Vargin, L. (1961). *Experientia* **17**, 90–91.

Flückiger, E. W. (1960). *Acta Endocrinol. Suppl.* **51**, 333–334.

Foster, M. (1959). In "Pigment Cell Biology" (M. Gordon, ed.), pp. 301–314. Academic Press, New York.

Fostvedt, G. A. (1940). *Endocrinology* **27**, 100–109.

Frieden, E. H. (1951). *Endocrinology* **49**, 557–564.

Frieden, E. H., and Bozer, J. M. (1951). *Proc. Soc. Exptl. Biol. Med.* **77**, 35–37.

Frieden, E. H., Fishbein, J. W., and Hisaw, F. L. (1948). *Arch. Biochem.* **17**, 183–189.

Fuchs, R. F. (1906). *Biol. Zentr.* **26**, 863–878.

Geiling, E. M. K. (1943). *Harvey Lectures Ser.* **37**, 269–312.

Geiling, E. M. K., and Lewis, M. R. (1935). *Am. J. Physiol.* **113**, 534–537.

Geiling, E. M. K., and Oldham, F. K. (1941). *J. Am. Med. Assoc.* **116**, 302–306.

Geschwind, I. I., Reinhardt, W. O., and Li, C. H. (1952). *Nature* **169**, 1061.

Geschwind, I. I., Li, C. H., and Barnafi, L. (1957a). *J. Am. Chem. Soc.* **79**, 620–625.

Geschwind, I. I., Li, C. H., and Barnafi, L. (1957b). *J. Am. Chem. Soc.* **79**, 1003–1004.

Giroud, A., and Martinet, M. (1947). *Compt. rend. soc. biol.* **141**, 1184–1185.

Guillemin, R., Schally, A. V., and Lipscomb, H. S. (1962). *Endocrinology* **70**, 471.

Guttmann, S., and Boissonnas, R. A. (1958). *Helv. Chim. Acta* **41**, 1852–1867.

Guttmann, S., and Boissonnas, R. A. (1959). *Helv. Chim. Acta* **42**, 1257–1264.

Guttmann, S., and Boissonnas, R. A. (1961). *Experientia* **17**, 265–267.

Harris, J. I. (1959a). *Biochem. J.* **71**, 451–459.

Harris, J. I. (1959b). *Nature* **184**, 167–169.

Harris, J. I. (1960). *CIBA Foundation Colloq. on Endocrinol.* **13**, 266–273.

Harris, J. I., and Lerner, A. B. (1957). *Nature* **179**, 1346–1347.

Harris, J. I., and Roos, P. (1956). *Nature* **178**, 90.

Harris, J. I., and Roos, P. (1959). *Biochem. J.* **71**, 445–451.

Herlant, M. (1954). *Ann. endocrinol. (Paris)* **15**, 1042–1045.

Hill, A. V., Parkinson, J. L., and Solandt, D. Y. (1935). *J. Exptl. Biol.* **12**, 397–399.

Hofmann, K. (1960). *Ann. N. Y. Acad. Sci.* **88**, 689–707.

Hofmann, K., Kappeler, H., Furlenmeier, A. E., Woolner, M. E., Schwartz, E. T., and Thompson, T. A. (1957a). *J. Am. Chem. Soc.* **79**, 1641–1644.

Hofmann, K., Thompson, T. A., and Schwartz, E. T. (1957b). *J. Am. Chem. Soc.* **79**, 6087–6088.

Hofmann, K., Woolner, M. E., Spühler, G., and Schwartz, E. T. (1958a). *J. Am. Chem. Soc.* **80**, 1486–1489.

Hofmann, K., Woolner, M. E., Yajima, H., Spühler, G., Thompson, T. A., and Schwartz, E. T. (1958b). *J. Am. Chem. Soc.* **80**, 6458–6459.

Hogben, L. T. (1924). "The Pigmentary Effector System" Oliver & Boyd, Edinburgh.

Hogben, L. T. (1936). *Proc. Roy. Soc.* **B120**, 142–158.

Hogben, L. T. (1942). *Proc. Roy. Soc.* **B131**, 111–136.

Hogben, L. T., and Gordon, C. (1930). *J. Exptl. Biol.* **7**, 260–285.

Hogben, L. T., and Landgrebe, F. W. (1940). *Proc. Roy. Soc.* **B128**, 317–342.

Hogben, L. T., and Slome, D. (1936). *Proc. Roy. Soc.* **B120**, 158–172.

Hogben, L. T., and Winton, F. R. (1922). *Proc. Roy. Soc.* **B93**, 318–329.

Houssay, B. A., and Ungar, I. (1924). *Compt. rend. soc. biol.* **91**, 318–320.

Houssay, B. A., and Ungar, I. (1925). *Compt. rend. soc. biol.* **93**, 253–255.

Hu, F., and Chavin, W. (1960). *J. Invest. Dermatol.* **34**, 377–379.

Hudson, B., and Bentley, G. A. (1957). *Australian J. Exptl. Biol. Med. Sci.* **35**, 45–55.

Jöchle, W. (1955). *Endokrinologie* **33**, 63–69.

Jöchle, W. (1957). *Acta Endocrinol.* **25**, 259–268.

Johnsson, S., and Högberg, B. (1952). *Nature* **169**, 286.

Johnsson, S., and Högberg, B. (1953). *Acta Endocrinol.* **13**, 325–342.

Jores, A., and Glogner, O. (1933). *Zentr. allgem. Pathol. u. pathol. Anat.* **54**, 234–242.

Kappeler, H., and Schwyzer, R. (1960). *Experientia* **16**, 415–417.

Karkun, J. N., and Mukerji, B. (1953). *Indian J. Med. Research* **41**, 467–471.

Karkun, J. N., and Mukerji, B. (1958). *Indian Physiol. Pharmacol.* **2**, 419–429.

Karkun, J. N., Kar, A. B., and Mukerji, B. (1953). *Acta Endocrinol.* **13**, 188–191.

Karkun, J. N., Kar, A. B., and Datta, S. N. (1954a). *Acta Endocrinol.* **16**, 187–192.

Karkun, J. N., Kar, A. B., and Mukerji, B. (1954b). *J. Endocrinol.* **10**, 124–128.

Karkun, J. N., Roy, S. K., and De, N. N. (1956). *J. Sci. Ind. Research (India)* **15C**, 63–66.

Kar un, J. N., Landgrebe, F. W., Main, R. A., and Mitchell, G. M. (1960). *J. Physiol. London)* **152**, 459–466.

Karkun, J. N., Kar, A. B., and Sen, D. P. (1963). *Ann. Biochem. Exptl. Med.* (In press).

Karkun, J. N., and Sen, D. P. (1963). *Ann. Biochem. Exptl. Med.* (in press).

Kleinholz, L. H., and Rahn, H. (1940). *Anat. Record* **76**, 157–172.

Kosto, B., Pickford, Grace E., and Foster, M. (1959). *Endocrinology* **65**, 869–881.

Krayer, O., Astwood, E. B., Wand, D. R., and Aeper, M. H. (1961). *Proc. Natl. Acad. Sci.* **47**, 1227–1235.

Krivoy, W. A., and Guillemin, R. (1961). *Endocrinology* **69**, 170–175.

Krivoy, W. A., and Guillemin, R. (1962). *Experientia* **18**, 20–20.

Landgrebe, F. W., and Mitchell, G. M. (1954). *Quart. J. Exptl. Physiol.* **39**, 11–16.

Landgrebe, F. W., and Waring, H. (1941). *Quart. J. Exptl. Physiol.* **31**, 31–62.

Landgrebe, F. W., and Waring, H. (1944). *Quart. J. Exptl. Physiol.* **33**, 1–18.

Landgrebe, F. W., and Waring, H. (1950). *In* "Hormone Assay" (C. W. Emmens, ed.), pp. 141–170. Academic Press, New York.

Landgrebe, F. W., and Waring, H. (1962). *In* "Methods in Hormone Research" (R. I. Dorfman, ed.), Vol. II, pp. 517–557. Academic Press, New York.

Landgrebe, F. W., Reid, E., and Waring, H. (1943). *Quart. J. Exptl. Biol.* **32**, 121–141.

Landgrebe, F. W., Ketterer, B., and Waring, H. (1955). *In* "The Hormones" (G. Pincus and K. V. Thimann, eds.), Vol. III, pp. 389–431. Academic Press, New York.

Lee, T. H. (1958). *J. Biol. Chem.* **233**, 917–919.

Lee, T. H., and Lerner, A. B. (1956). *J. Biol. Chem.* **221**, 943–959.

Lee, T. H., Lerner, A. B., and Buettner-Janusch, V. (1960). *CIBA Foundation Colloq. on Endocrinol.* **13**, 251–265.

Lee, T. H., Lerner, A. B., and Buettner-Janusch, V. (1961). *J. Biol. Chem.* **236**, 1390–1394.

Lerner, A. B., and Case, J. D. (1959). *J. Amer. Chem. Soc.* **81**, 6084–6085.

Lerner, A. B., and Lee, T. H. (1955). *J. Am. Chem. Soc.* **77**, 1066–1067.

Lerner, A. B., and McGuire, J. S. (1961). *Nature* **189**, 176–179.

Lerner, A. B., and Takahashi, Y. (1956). *Recent Progr. in Hormone Research* **12**, 303–313.

Lerner, A. B., Shizume, K., and Bunding, I. (1954). *J. Clin. Endocrinol. and Metabolism* **14**, 1463–1490.

Lerner, A. B., Lee, T. H., Wright, M. R., and McGuire, J. S. (1960). *Acta Endocrinol. Suppl.* **50**, 73.

Li, C. H. (1957). *Advances in Protein Chem.* **12**, 269.

Li, C. H. (1959). *Lab. Invest.* **8**, 574–587.

Li, C. H., Meinohofer, J., Schnabel, E., Chung, D., and Lo, J. B. (1960). *J. Amer. Chem. Soc.* **82**, 5760–5762.

Lo, T. B., Dixon, J. S., and Li, C. H. (1961). *Biochim. Biophys. Acta* **53**, 584–586.

Long, J. M., and Guillemin, R. (1961). *Experientia* **17**, 132–134.

Long, J. M., Krivoy, W. A., and Guillemin, R. (1961). *Endocrinology* **69**, 175–181.

Mason, H. S. (1948). *J. Biol. Chem.* **172**, 83–99.

Mialhe-Voloss, C. (1953). *J. physiol. (Paris)* **45**, 189–192.

Mialhe-Voloss, C., and Benoit, J. (1954). *Compt. rend. soc. biol.* **148**, 56–59.

Mialhe-Voloss, C., and Stutinsky, F. (1953). *Ann. endocrinol. (Paris)* **14**, 681–685.

Morris, C. J. O. R. (1952). *Lancet* i, 1210.

Morris, C. J. O. R., Russell, D. S., Landgrebe, F. W., and Mitchell, G. M. (1956). *J. Endocrinol.* **14**, 263–267.

Mussio-Fournier, J. C., Cervino, J. M., and Conti, O. (1943). *J. Clin. Endocrinol. and Metabolism* **3**, 353–356.

Mussio-Fournier, J. C., Conti, O., and Porta, I. (1947). *Ann. endocrinol. (Paris)* **8**, 363–363.

Novales, R. R., and Novales, Barbara J. (1961). *Gen. Comp. Endocrinol.* **1**, 134–144.

Odiourne, J. M. (1936). *J. Exptl. Zool.* **74**, 7–40.

Odiourne, J. M. (1937). *J. Exptl. Zool.* **76**, 441–466.

Oldham, F. K. (1938). *Anat. Record* **72**, 265–286.

Osborne, C. M. (1941). *Biol. Bull.* **81**, 341–351.

Pickford, Grace E. (1957). *In* "The Physiology of the Pituitary Gland of Fishes" (Grace Pickford and J. W. Atz, eds.). New York Zoologial Society, New York.

Pickford, Grace E., and Kosto, B. (1957b). *Endocrinology* **61**, 177–196.

Porath, J., Roos, P., Landgrebe, F. W., and Mitchell, G. M. (1955). *Biochim. et Biophys. Acta* **17**, 598–599.

Rahn, H., and Drager, G. A. (1941). *Endocrinology* **29**, 725–730.

Raper, H. S. (1928). *Physiol. Revs.* **8**, 245–282.

Roth, A. (1932). *Zentr. allgem. Pathol. u. pathol. Anat.* **54**, 234–242.

Ryle, A. P., Sanger, F., Smith, L. F., and Kitai, R. (1955). *Biochem. J.* **60**, 541–556.

Schally, A. V., Andersen, R. N., Long, J. M., and Guillemin, R. (1960). *Proc. Soc. Exptl. Biol. Med.* **104**, 290–293.

Schally, A. V., Lipscomb, H. S., Long, J. M., Dear, W. E., and Guillemin, R. (1962). *Endocrinology* **70**, 478.

Schnabel, E., and Li, C. H. (1960). *J. Am. Chem. Soc.* **82**, 4576–4579.

Schwyzer, R., and Li, C. H. (1958). *Nature* **182**, 1669–1670.

Schwyzer, R., Kappeler, H., Iselin, B., Rittel, W., and Zuber, H. (1959). *Helv. Chim. Acta* **42**, 1702–1708.

Shizume, K., and Lerner, A. B. (1954). *J. Clin. Endocrinol. and Metabolism* **14**, 1491–1510.

Shizume, K., Lerner, A. B., and Fitzpatrick, T. B. (1954). *Endocrinology* **54**, 553–560.

Snell, R. S. (1961). Private communication.

Spaeth, R. A. (1913). *J. Exptl. Zool.* **15**, 527–585.

Sprague, R. G., Power, M. H., Mason, H. L., Albert, A., Mathieson, D. R., Hench, P. S., Kendall, E. C., Slocumb, C. H., and Polley, H. F. (1950). *A.M.A. Arch. Internal Med.* **85**, 199–258.

Steelman, S. L., and Guillemin, R. (1959). *Proc. Soc. Exptl. Biol. Med.* **101**, 600–601.

Steelman, S. L., Andersen, R. N., and McGregor, R. M. (1959). *Biochim. et Biophys. Acta* **33**, 256–258.

Stehle, R. L. (1933). *J. Biol. Chem.* **102**, 573–590.

Stehle, R. L. (1936). *J. Pharmacol. Exptl. Therap.* **57**, 1–9.

Stehle, R. L. (1944). *Rev. can. biol.* **3**, 408–417.

Stoppani, A. O. M. (1942). *Rev. soc. arg. biol.* **18**, 215–224.

Stoppani, A. O. M., Pieroni, P. F., and Murrary, A. (1953). *Nature* **172**, 547–548.

Sulman, F. G. (1952a). *Nature* **169**, 588–589.

Sulman, F. G. (1952b). *Acta Endocrinol.* **10**, 320–332.

Sulman, F. G. (1952c). *Lancet* **ii**, 247–248.

Sulman, F. G. (1956). *J. Clin. Endocrinol. and Metabolism* **16**, 755–774.

Sulman, F. G., and Eviatar, A. (1956). *Acta Endocrinol.* **23**, 120–130.

Sumner, F. B., and Wells, N. A. (1933). *J. Exptl. Zool.* **64**, 377.

Swingle, W. W. (1921). *J. Exptl. Zool.* **34**, 119–141.

Teague, R. S., Noojin, R. O., and Geiling, E. M. K. (1939). *J. Pharmacol. Exptl. Therap.* **65,** 115–127.

Thing, E. (1952a). *Acta Endocrinol.* **11,** 74–90.

Thing, E. (1952b). *Acta Endocrinol.* **11,** 363–375.

Van Dyke, H. B. (1926). *Arch. exptl. Pathol. Pharmakol. Naunyn-Schmiedeberg's* **114,** 262.

Varon, H. H. (1959). *Proc. Soc. Exptl. Biol. Med.* **100,** 609–610.

Waring, H. (1942). *Biol. Revs. Cambridge Phil. Soc.* **17,** 120–150.

Waring, H., and Landgrebe, F. W. (1949). *Australian J. Exptl. Biol. Med. Sci.* **27,** 331–336.

Waring, H., and Landgrebe, F. W. (1950). *In* "The Hormones" (G. Pincus and K. V. Thimann, eds.), Vol. II, pp. 427–574. Academic Press, New York.

Wright, P. A. (1948). *J. Cellular Comp. Physiol.* **31,** 111–119.

Zondek, B., and Krohn, H. (1932b). *Klin. Wochschr.* **11,** 405–408.

Zondek, B., and Krohn, H. (1932a). *Klin. Wochschr.* **11,** 1293–1298.

Female Gonadal Hormones

WEIERT VELLE

Department of Reproductive Physiology and Pathology, The Veterinary College of Norway, Oslo, Norway

I. INTRODUCTION

On the basis of present knowledge regarding the biosynthesis and occurrence of gonadal hormones, the terms "male" and "female" hormones are somewhat misleading. Hormones of the gestogen and estrogen as well as those of the androgen group are now known to be produced normally in the gonads of both sexes. In some species estrogens are formed in the male gonad at rates far exceeding those considered normal for the female of the same species. On the other hand, androgen production in the female gonad is in all probability a normal event in estrogen biosynthesis, as is the production of gestogens as precursors for androgens in both ovary and testis.

The term "gonadal" in this connection is also not entirely correct. Gestogens, estrogens, androgens, and relaxin are admittedly produced by the female gonad. But other organs are also partly responsible for the formation of some or all of these hormones. Thus the adrenal cortex normally produces hormones of the steroid groups mentioned; during pregnancy the placenta, at least in some species, takes over the production of these hormones as well as that of relaxin.

Finally, the term "hormones" should also be considered critically as here applied. According to the classical definition hormones are biologically active compounds produced in endocrine glands or structures, from which they are released directly to the blood. This definition would exclude metabolites formed outside the glands of origin, many of which still possess biological activity. In many species a number of such substances related to the sex hormones are present in urine and feces. It is difficult, however, to distinguish sharply between "true" hormones and metabolites. According to the above definition metabolites may well arise in the blood and exercise important regulatory functions in tissue metabolism without being "true" hormones.

In this context the term "female gonadal hormones" will be taken to cover gestogenic, estrogenic, and androgenic hormones, as well as relaxin. Androgens will be dealt with only in connection with estrogen biosynthesis and gestogen metabolism, and only as far as it is necessary for the understanding of certain physiological phenomena related to this group of substances in the female.

In a short treatise like the present one, the coverage of all aspects of the subject is obviously impossible. Preference will be given to recent biochemical contributions in the comparative field. Physiological manifestations of hormone action in different species will be dealt with only briefly.

II. CHEMISTRY AND BIOSYNTHESIS OF FEMALE GONADAL HORMONES

Chemically the female gonadal hormones fall into two widely different categories. The gestogens, androgens, and estrogens belong to the class of compounds designated as steroids, but relaxin is a substance of protein-like nature.

A. The Steroid Hormones

The structural formulas of representatives of the gestogens, androgens, and estrogens are shown in Fig. 1. The gestogens (1) contain 21 carbon atoms, the androgens (2) 19, and the estrogens (3) have only 18 carbon atoms. The estrogens are distinguished from the two other groups of hormones by their aromatic character. Ring A and/or ring B may be unsaturated. The benzene character of ring A lends an acid function to the hydroxyl group at carbon 3. Very small alterations in chemical structure, such as a reduction of a keto group to a hydroxyl group, or the reverse, often results in marked changes in biological activity. Likewise, the orientation of hydroxyl groups in relation to the steroid nucleus often determines the degree of activity.

In the biosynthesis of steroid hormones in general, cholesterol seems to play an important role. Cholesterol itself is synthesized from acetate through a long series of intermediate reactions (Bloch, 1957). In addition to the liver, which is the main site of formation of endogenous cholesterol, all glands capable of synthesizing steroid hormones are also capable of cholesterol formation.

Progesterone can be produced *in vitro* from cholesterol via Δ^5-pregnene 3β-ol-20-one from organs like the adrenals, testis, ovary, and placenta (Samuels *et al.*, 1951). Since the two other naturally occurring gestogens may be considered as derivatives of progesterone, this observation explains the biosynthesis of the gestogens.

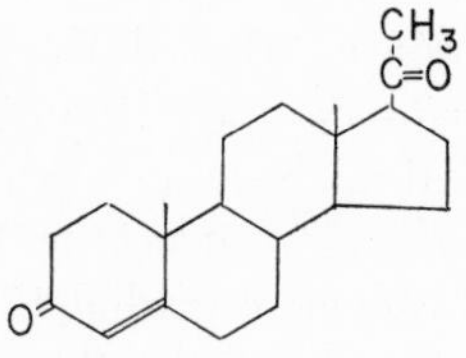

(1) PROGESTERONE

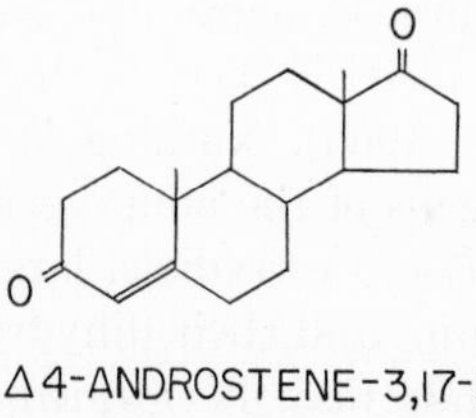

(2) Δ4-ANDROSTENE-3,17-DIONE 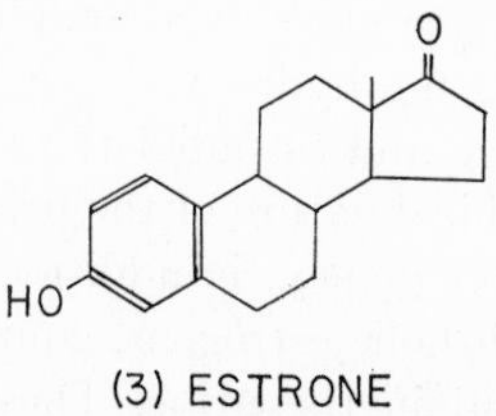   (3) ESTRONE

FIG. 1. Structural formulas of representatives of (1) gestogens, (2) androgens, and (3) estrogens.

The wide distribution of the enzymes necessary for the formation of progesterone from cholesterol indicated, however, that this hormone, in addition to its role as a gestogenic hormone, might also play a role as an intermediate in the biosynthesis of other steroid hormones. This has been shown experimentally. Incubation of tissue slices from mammalian testis resulted in the formation of Δ^4-androstene-3,17-dione, a potent androgen which is formed in testis together with testosterone (Slaunwhite and Samuels, 1956). Likewise, incubations of avian testicular tissue homogenates with progesterone gave rise to Δ^4-androstene-3,17-dione and testosterone (Fevold and Eik-Nes, 1961).

In 1955 Meyer showed that the bovine adrenal is able to transform Δ^4-androstene-3,17-dione to its 19-hydroxy derivative (Meyer, 1955b). 19-Hydroxy-Δ^4-androstene-3,17-dione yields estrone when incubated with human placenta and bovine follicular fluid (Meyer, 1955a). Later it was shown that testosterone gives rise to estradiol-17β when incubated with human ovarian slices (Baggett et al., 1955) and with human placental microsomes (Ryan, 1958). It thus seems to be quite firmly established that the biosynthesis of estrone and estradiol-17β goes via androgens. Additional support for this view comes from the recent detection of Δ^4-androstene-3,17-dione in both the human ovary (Zander, 1957) and placenta (Salhanick et al., 1956), and of testosterone in the bovine ovary (Short, 1962).

Another problem is the biosynthesis of estriol which in women is the major urinary estrogen in both the nonpregnant and pregnant state. This compound had been assumed to be a metabolite of estrone or estradiol-17β, but recent experiments indicate that during pregnancy estriol is formed by other routes. In in vitro studies Ryan (1959) showed that human placenta as well as placental microsomes are able to convert Δ^5-androstene-3β-16α-17β-triol, 16α-hydroxy-Δ^4-androstene-3,17-dione, and 16α-hydroxy-testosterone to estriol. However, estradiol-17β is not converted to estriol by this tissue (Ryan and Engel, 1953b). The observation lends support to the concept of estriol as a "true" hormone in women.

The horse presents a complicated picture. In mare follicular fluid a new estrogen, 6-α-hydroxyestradiol-17β has recently been found in addition to estrone and estradiol-17β (Bush et al., 1960). Nothing is known about the chemical nature of the urinary estrogens of the nonpregnant mare, but during pregnancy, in addition to estrone and estradiols, large amounts of the naphtholic estrogens, equilin, equilenin, and their dihydro derivatives, are found in the urine. These compounds may be formed from acetate (Heard et al., 1956). However, injection of C^{14}-labeled estrone to a pregnant mare did not lead to radioactive ring B unsaturated compounds

(Heard *et al.*, 1954), and testosterone gives rise to estrone, but not to ring B unsaturated estrogens (Heard *et al.*, 1955), indicating that these compounds originate through a separate pathway, not via estrone and/or estradiol-17β. As pointed out by Engel (1957) these experiments, although showing that the ring B unsaturated compounds are not peripheral metabolites of estrone, do not exclude the possibility that they are formed via estrone in endocrine tissues. However, this seems unlikely as far as the ovary is concerned, since neither of these compounds has been found in normal follicular fluid (Short, 1960a). It may well be that they are hormones of pregnancy, produced as such in the placenta, and are analogous to the production of estriol in human placenta.

B. Relaxin

Relaxin, a water-soluble, protein-like substance originally detected in the blood of various animals during pregnancy (Hisaw, 1926), possesses the ability to cause relaxation of the pelvis, the reaction being especially pronounced in ovariectomized, primed guinea pigs. The richest source of this hormone is ovaries from pregnant sows. It has not yet been isolated in pure form, and therefore its chemistry is not completely known. Purification of extracts from pregnant sows ovaries on carboxymethyl cellulose columns has recently been carried out by Paul and Wiquist (1960). Using the uterine relaxing activity as parameter, they found three peaks of which the second and third was active. When rechromatographed after heat treatment the second component appeared in the position of the third component. By this procedure the uterine relaxing activity was increased 8–10 times over that of the "crude preparation." Frieden *et al.* (1960) have shown that highly active relaxin fractions are associated with polypeptides of a molecular weight of 7500–9000 which contain most of the commonly occurring amino acids except histidine, methionine, and tryptophan.

III. THE GESTOGENS

A. Natural Sources

Progesterone which was isolated in pure form from pig corpora lutea in 1934 (Table I), was for a long time considered to be the only naturally occurring gestogen. However, discrepancies between results of biological and chemical progesterone determinations in biological material indicated that other gestogens might exist. Recently two previously unknown

TABLE I

SOURCES OF PROGESTERONE IN VARIOUS SPECIES

Tissue	Species	References
Corpus luteum	Human	Zander (1954)
	Horse	Short (1957)
	Cattle	Gorski (1958)
	Pig	Allen and Wintersteiner (1934); Butenandt *et al.* (1934); Hartmann and Wettstein (1934); Slotta *et al.* (1934)
	Elephant	Edgar (1952)
	Guinea pig	Rowlands and Short (1959)
	Rat	Wiest (1958)
	Whale	Prelog and Meister (1949)
	Seal	Short (1958)
Follicular fluid	Human	Zander (1954)
	Horse	Edgar (1952); Short (1960a)
	Cattle	Edgar (1952); Short (1962)
	Sheep	Edgar (1953)
	Pig	Edgar (1952)
Ovary	Hen	Layne *et al.* (1957)
	Starfish	Botticelli *et al.* (1960)
	Dogfish	Wotiz *et al.* (1960)
	Sea urchin	Botticelli *et al.* (1961)
	Mollusk	Botticelli *et al.* (1961)
Placenta	Human	Diczfalusy (1952); Noall *et al.* (1952); Pearlman and Cerceo (1952)
	Rhesus monkey	Short and Eckstein (1961)
	Horse	Short (1957)
	Sheep	Short and Moore (1959)
	Rat	Wiest (1958)
Adrenal	Cattle	Beall and Reichstein (1938)

gestogenic hormones have been isolated from human tissues by Zander *et al.* (1958). The substances, 20α-, and 20β-hydroxy-Δ^4-pregnene-3-one, are both active in the usual biological tests. The structural formulas of the three gestogens and their relative biological activities are given in Fig. 2.

COMPOUND	MOUSE (HOOKER – FORBES TEST)	RABBIT (CLAUBERG TEST)	MAN
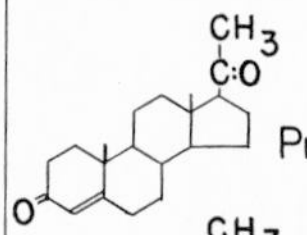 Progesterone	I	I	I
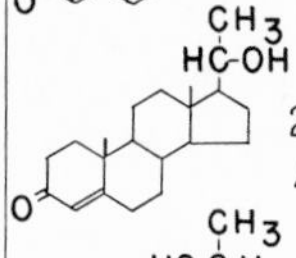 20α-Hydroxy-Δ4-pregnene-3-one	$\frac{1}{5}$	$\frac{1}{2}-\frac{1}{3}$	$< I^*$
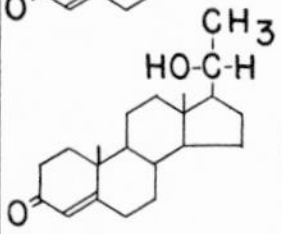 20β-Hydroxy-Δ4-pregnene-3-one	2	$\frac{1}{5}-\frac{1}{10}$	$< I^*$

FIG. 2. Structural formulas and biological activity of the naturally occurring gestogens (asterisk indicates that compound was administered as cyclopentylpropionate). (According to Zander, 1959.)

Although the significance of progesterone in reproductive physiology was early established, its isolation has only recently been accomplished from species other than the pig. Isolations so far achieved are given in Table I. Of special interest for comparative endocrinology is its presence in the ovaries of the sea urchin *Strongylocentrotus franciscanus* and the mollusk *Pecten hericius* (Botticelli *et al.*, 1961), the starfish *Pisaster ochraceus* (Botticelli *et al.*, 1960), the lungfish *Protopterus annectens* Owen (Dean and Chester Jones, 1959), the dogfish *Squalus suckleyi* (Wotiz *et al.*, 1960), and the hen (Layne *et al.*, 1957). Neither of these species has an established luteal function. The virtual absence of progesterone from the bovine, caprine, and porcine placenta (Short, 1957) indicates that in these species the ovaries represent the main source of the hormone throughout pregnancy. This is in accordance with results of ovariectomy during pregnancy.

Sources of the 20-hydroxy compounds are given in Table II. The occurrence of these hormones is subject to species variation. Although both isomers have been isolated from human tissues, rat and sheep tissues contain the 20α-isomer only. In other species so far examined, only the 20β-isomer is present in addition to progesterone. Their presence in gestogen producing tissues and in blood, as well as their high biological activities, seems to justify the inclusion of these substances in the category of "true" hormones.

TABLE II

Sources of 20α-Hydroxy-Δ⁴-pregnene-3-one and 20β-Hydroxy-Δ⁴-pregnene-3-one in Various Species and Chemical Identification

Tissue	Species	20α-Isomer	20β-Isomer	References
Corpus luteum	Human	+	+	Zander et al. (1958)
	Cattle	—	+	Gorski (1958)
	Rat	+	—	Wiest (1958)
	Whale	—	+	Kristoffersen et al. (1960)
Follicular fluid	Human	+	+	Zander et al. (1958)
Placenta	Human	+	+	Zander et al. (1958)
	Horse	—	+	Short (1957)
	Sheep	+	—	Short and Moore (1959)
	Rat	+	—	Wiest (1958)
Adrenal gland[a]	Calves	+	—	Balfour et al. (1959)

[a] The substance isolated from adrenal venous blood.

B. Levels in Tissues and Body Fluids

1. THE OVARY

In the nonpregnant female the ovary is the main source of gestogens. Of the ovarian components examined, the functional corpus luteum and the follicular fluid show the highest levels. For human follicular wall and/or fluid, Zander et al. (1958) reported values between 1.3 and 150 μg/gm. The average value for mare follicular fluid was 12.4 μg (Short, 1960a). Edgar (1952) reported values between 0.5 and 2 μg/ml fluid for sheep and 3 μg/ml for cattle.* For luteal tissue the following average progesterone values given in μg/gm wet tissue have been reported: human, 14.7 (Zander et al., 1958); horse, 37.7 (Short, 1958); cattle, 15.2 (Gorski et al., 1958), 20.2 (Kristoffersen, 1960). These determinations were not related to any stage of the sexual cycle. Such observations have been reported for the human by Zander et al. (1958) who found an increased level between 7 and 10 days after ovulation. In hysterectomized guinea pigs Rowlands and Short (1959) found ovarian progesterone levels to be above normal. This supports the hypothesis that the uterus influences ovarian functions.

---

* For normal follicular fluid from cattle, Short (1962) reported 0.23 μg/ml.

In the pregnant female the significance of the ovarian gestogen production varies considerably within the species. For the human Zander *et al.* (1958) reported an average value of 11 μg/gm luteal tissue. In cattle the level of progesterone in the corpus luteum tends to decrease during pregnancy. Average values of 12.2 and 10.8 μg/gm tissue during 30–120 days of gestation, and 5.0 and 8.2 μg/gm tissue during 150–280 days of gestation have been reported by Gorski (1958) and Kristoffersen (1960) respectively. In the guinea pig, however, permanently increased levels were observed after 21–23 days of gestation (Rowlands and Short, 1959). Evidence for significant ovarian gestogen production was found in late pregnancy in the goat by Raeside and Turner (1955) who found 2.3 μg progesterone/ml in ovarian vein blood, and in sheep by Edgar and Ronaldson (1958) who reported 1.8 μg/ml. In the blood which drains the ovary of the laying hen Lythle and Lorenz (1958) found 4–5 μg progesterone/100 ml.

2. THE ADRENAL GLAND

Evidence for a significant production of progesterone by the adrenal gland in cattle, pigs, and sheep of both sexes was presented by Balfour *et al.* (1957) who reported values ranging between 7.5 and 46.5 μg/100 ml plasma. A peculiar finding is the transient secretion of comparatively large amounts of 20α-hydroxy-Δ⁴-pregnene-3-one by the adrenal in the young calf (Balfour *et al.*, 1959). The significance of this finding is unknown.

3. THE PLACENTA

Great species variations are encountered with regard to gestogen levels in the placenta. Zander and von Münstermann (1956) found in the human placenta an average of 4.15 μg progesterone/gm tissue during the second and third month of gestation, with a subsequent decrease to 1.65 to 2.09 μg during the remaining months.* In the mare placenta 0.073 and 0.25 μg/gm tissue at 120 and 270 days of gestation respectively have been reported (Short, 1957), and the levels in sheep placenta are of the order of 0.004–0.009 μg/gm (Short and Moore, 1959). In the placenta of the cow, sow, goat, and bitch progesterone could not be detected by chemical methods (Short, 1956, 1957).

4. BLOOD

Reports on gestogen levels in the blood of the nonpregnant female are controversial. By bioassy, Forbes (1950) found cyclic variations in human blood gestogen levels with peaks of 1.7–5.2 μg progesterone equivalents/ml

---

* In the placenta of the rhesus monkey at term the levels are only about 1/40 of these values (Short and Eckstein, 1961).

plasma on days 19 and 22 of the cycle. Similar results were obtained in the monkey (Bryans, 1951). Using a chemical method Zander (1955) was able to detect progesterone in only 3 out of 16 women. The level was below 0.05 μg/ml. In the sheep Neher and Zarrow (1954) by bioassay found values equivalent to 0.3 to 2 μg progesterone/ml blood at estrus, rising to 6 μg in the luteal phase. In contrast, Short and Moore (1959) chemically determined a level of the order of 0.4 μg/100 ml plasma. The wide discrepancy between the results from biological and chemical assays will be noted.

The reports on the blood gestogen levels in the pregnant female are also controversial. Marked species variations seem to exist. According to Forbes (1951) who used bioassays the peripheral blood of humans and monkeys contained amounts of progesterone not exceeding 2–3 μg/ml. With chemical methods some values per 100 ml have been obtained during late human pregnancy: 14.2 μg (Zander, 1955), 12.2 μg (Aitken et al., 1958), and 10–30 μg (Short and Eton, 1959).* Short (1960b) has also identified 20α-hydroxy-Δ^4-pregnene-3-one in human peripheral blood during pregnancy. For the pregnant mare Short (1957) reported negative findings. However, the same author later detected progesterone in the peripheral blood of both nonpregnant and pregnant mares, but only in the presence of a functional corpus luteum. During the second half of gestation when the ovaries become fibrotic, progesterone is no longer found in peripheral blood. The level during the early period of gestation is 0.5–1.4 μg/100 ml plasma (Short, 1959). In cattle and sheep the progesterone levels in peripheral blood are very low, with averages of 0.8 and 0.5 μg/100 ml plasma respectively (Short, 1958; Short and Moore, 1959). The Hooker Forbes test indicates high levels of gestogens in peripheral blood during pregnancy in the ewe (Neher and Zarrow, 1954), rabbit (Zarrow and Neher, 1955) and mouse (Forbes and Hooker, 1957). A marked drop in the levels was observed after parturition. The large discrepancies between biological and chemical assay results indicate that other gestogens in addition to those known at present may exist during pregnancy.

In the species so far examined it appears that the gestogen levels in fetal blood are considerably higher than in maternal blood. On the basis of his findings in women, Zander (1959) concludes that toward the end of pregnancy about 75 mg progesterone passes from the placenta to the fetus in 24 hours. In human fetal cord blood Aitken et al. (1958) found a level of 45 μg progesterone/100 ml plasma. The corresponding value in the horse is 3.8–6.3 μg (Short, 1959). The biological significance of these findings is unknown at present.

---

* For the pregnant rhesus monkey the levels are less than 1 μg/100 ml plasma (Short and Eckstein, 1961).

C. Metabolism

In 1929 pregnanediol was isolated from human pregnancy urine (Marrian, 1929). Its relation to the metabolism of progesterone has since been shown repeatedly (Venning and Browne, 1936, 1937; Marrian, 1949; Dorfman, 1955; Davis and Plotz, 1957b). Investigations on the metabolism of progesterone have been carried out mainly in the human. However, according to data obtained from other species it seems safe to conclude that considerable species differences exist. The information available is partly based on isolation of the urinary steroids presumably related to progesterone, and partly on direct experimental results.

1. URINARY STEROIDS RELATED TO PROGESTERONE

None of the known gestogenic hormones has been isolated from urine. It is generally assumed that pregnanediols constitute the major part of gestogen metabolites in the human, 5β-pregnane-3α-20α-diol being the most important of the different isomers. The same applies to the rabbit. But as will be seen from Table III, other isomers have also been isolated. In addition, in some species other compounds have been shown to be metabolites of progesterone. The occurrence of the different metabolites is subject to species variation, as are the quantities in which the compounds are excreted. Thus in late pregnancy women excrete about 50 mg of pregnanediols in 24 hours, but the substances identified in the urine of cows (Klyne and Wright, 1959), goats (Klyne and Wright, 1957), and sheep (Robertson and Coulson, 1958), are present only in trace amounts. In the mare the picture is complicated; pregnanediols are present in high amounts during pregnancy, but the relative proportions of the different isomers change with the stage of gestation (Wright, 1958).

The very low amount of pregnanediols encountered in the urine of some species raises the question whether gestogens in these animals are mainly metabolized to other compounds and/or excreted by ways other than the renal route. This question seems to have been partly answered recently.

2. *In Vivo* EXPERIMENTS

Using C^{14}-labeled 21-progesterone, Riegel *et al.* (1950) showed that in rats and mice up to 25% of the injected radioactivity appeared in the expired air. Thus it appears that the side chain at C-17 is split off in the body. High activity was also found in feces. A similar pattern may obtain in ruminants. During pregnancy increased androgen activity in the feces has been reported for cattle (Gassner and Longwell, 1947; Gassner, 1952).

TABLE III

PREGNANEDIOLS IN THE URINE OF VARIOUS MAMMALIAN SPECIES

Compound	Human	Chimpanzee	Horse	Cattle	Sheep	Goat	Rabbit
5β-pregnane-3α-20α-diol	+	+	+	+	+	+	+
5α-pregnane-3α-20α-diol	+	−	+	+	−	−	−
5α-pregnane-3β-20α-diol	+	−	+	+	−	−	−
5α-pregnane-3β-20β-diol	−	−	+	−	−	−	−

Increased androgen activity in the feces of rams after progesterone injection has likewise been reported (Raeside, 1957). Pure androgens have also been isolated from the feces of cows after progesterone injections (Miller et al., 1956). In human subjects it has recently been shown that considerable radioactivity appears in the feces after injections of C^{14}-labeled progesterone (Davis and Plotz, 1957a). Sandberg and Slaunwhite (1958) have presented evidence for enterohepatic circulation of the hormone. Using C^{14}-labeled progesterone Taylor and Scratcherd (1961) showed that in the cat less than 1% of the injected dose appeared in the urine, whereas up to 67% was excreted in the bile, during the first 6 hours after the injection. Clearly, other compounds in addition to the urinary pregnanes must also be related to progesterone metabolism. This view is supported by the fact that only a low percentage of injected doses of progesterone can usually be accounted for by the metabolites recovered from the urine.

3. In Vitro EXPERIMENTS

The liver has for a long time been considered as a major site of gestogen metabolism, but until recently few investigations had been reported in which metabolites were identified. Using rabbit liver, Taylor (1956) showed that 5β-pregnane-3α-20α-diol was the major metabolite of progesterone. Rat liver homogenate has been shown to convert progesterone into 7 different pregnane compounds (see Atherden, 1959 for references). After incubation of progesterone with human liver slices Atherden (1959) isolated 6 pregnane compounds. This indicates that the main metabolic pathway is:

Progesterone → pregnanedione → pregnanolone → pregnanediol

Other tissues are also capable of metabolizing progesterone. Wiest (1959) showed that rat ovarian tissue rapidly transforms the hormone to 20α-hydroxy-Δ^4-pregnene-3-one, and Sweat et al. (1958) found that human uterine fibroblasts cultivated in vitro were able to metabolize progesterone to a variety of steroid products.

D. Biological Functions

Under physiological conditions gestogens and estrogens act synergistically in both the nonpregnant and pregnant female. The difficulties involved in ascribing certain effects to just one of the groups of hormones are therefore obvious, especially since both groups are also produced normally in extragonadal tissues which are not usually removed in most experiments.

This fact seems to be of significance when interpretations of ovary ablation experiments are attempted.

A full account of the physiological functions of gestogens is beyond the scope of this chapter. Only some of the important aspects will be dealt with.

1. EFFECTS ON THE REPRODUCTIVE SYSTEM

Ovarian function is significantly influenced by gestogens. Large doses of progesterone as well as persistent secretion of this hormone inhibit the release of luteinizing hormone and thereby inhibit ovulation. It may also inhibit the formation of follicles (Burrows, 1949). These effects have been demonstrated in the sow (Ulberg et al., 1951), the cow (Nellor and Cole, 1956), and the sheep (Dutt and Casida, 1948). However, as demonstrated in the cow, the time of administration of progesterone as well as the dose given is of decisive importance. In this animal small doses of progesterone given at the beginning of estrus hasten ovulation (Hansel and Trimberger, 1952). On the other hand, large doses can prevent estrus. On the basis of these observations and the fact that progesterone is normally present in follicular fluid, it is reasonable to assume that the hormone plays a role in the events leading up to ovulation. In the laying hen progesterone administration increases ovulation frequency (Neher and Fraps, 1950). Induction of ovulation in the hen can also be achieved by injection of less than 5 μg of progesterone into certain regions of the hypothalamus, whereas injections into the pituitary is without effect (Ralph and Fraps, 1960).

In growing chicks weekly injections of progesterone (2–16 mg) have been shown to cause decrease in size of the testes and comb in males, and delayed sexual maturity in females (Fox, 1955).

The uterus is affected by gestogens in several ways. In the endometrium progestational changes usually occur a short time after ovulation; these involve enlargement of stromal cells, growth of uterine glands, and increased secretory activity. It is generally accepted that the action of estrogens is necessary before the gestogens can exert their effects during this period. However, gestogen effects vary with the species. In the human female the glycogen content of the endometrium is at its maximum when the luteal function is at a maximum. In the cow it is at its lowest at this period (Skjerven, 1956). The changes in alkaline phosphatase levels in the endometrium are also different in the two species. The sow shows another pattern (Austad and Garm, 1959).

The avian oviduct is another target organ for the gestogens. Oviduct growth in young female birds is greatly stimulated by estrogens (see Parkes and Emmens, 1944). An additional effect is seen when either androgens or gestogens are given simultaneously. Maximal albumen production has been reported only when gestogen is given together with estrogen (Brant and Nalbandov, 1956). A peculiar situation exists with regard to gestogen action and the carbonic anhydrase level in the uterus or oviduct. In mammals the concentration of this enzyme is greatly increased by progesterone (Lutwak-Mann and Adams, 1957). In the chick no increase can be produced by progesterone or other steroid hormones tested (Marotta, cit. from Nalbandov, 1959).

In mammals the cervix shows diminished glycogen content and secretion during the luteal phase. In cattle it responds less to oxytocin during the luteal than during the follicular phase (Fitzpatrick, 1957). Progesterone causes marked increase in the consistency of the cervical mucus in the cow (Glover, 1960).

In the rat, mouse, and guinea pig after ovulation there is a transition from the cornified vaginal mucosa to a mucified condition. In spayed animals estrogens and gestogens in combination, but not singly, can cause mucification. In sheep the postovulatory leucocyte invasion and change in the consistency of the vaginal mucus depend probably upon a combined estrogen–gestogen action (Robinson and Moore, 1956; Moore and Robinson, 1957).

Normal pregnancy is dependent upon adequate gestogen supply. However, great species variations exist with regard to the quantities required. This is indicated by the great differences in gestogen levels in the placenta and blood in different animals, and by the differences in the requirements of progesterone after ovariectomy in different species in which ovarian gestogen production is normally necessary throughout pregnancy. The following daily doses have been reported necessary in the later stages of gestation: in the goat, 15 mg (Meites et al., 1951), in the cow, 75 mg (Raeside and Turner, 1951). In women progesterone production has been calculated to be about 250 mg per day during late pregnancy (Zander, 1959).

In this connection it is also interesting to note the gestogen effect on myometrial contractility. The stimulatory action of oxytocin is inhibited by progesterone in the rabbit (Harris, 1955) and the mouse (Steinetz et al., 1957). In the cow the myometrial response to oxytocin does not vary during the estrous cycle (Fitzpatrick, 1957). The cat is peculiar insofar as gestogens and estrogens act synergistically to sensitize the myometrium to oxytocin (Clary et al., 1951).

Interesting problems exist regarding the physiological significance of gestogens in lower vertebrates. The ovarian structure is similar in amphibians, reptiles, and birds (Miller, 1959). But the functional adaptation of the corpus luteum in relation to the reproductive patterns clearly points to variation in the significance of its secretions. Thus in the oviparous animals there is hardly an established luteal function, although gestogen production may be demonstrated. On the other hand, in viviparous amphibians like the toad *Nectophrynoides occidentalis* which is pregnant for 9 months, the corpora lutea persist and are believed to control gestation (Gallien, 1959). Earlier studies had indicated that the corpus luteum was necessary for normal gestation in viviparous snakes (Clausen, 1940; Fraenkel *et al.*, 1940). Later, however, observations on the viviparous garter snake (Bragdon, 1951) and on the ovoviviparous lizard (Panigel, 1956) have shown that ablation of the corpora lutea does not lead to abortion. That the corpora lutea nevertheless may have some endocrine function is indicated by the fact that in oviparous reptiles they regress shortly after egg laying, whereas in ovoviviparous and viviparous forms they persist for approximately $\frac{3}{4}$ of the gestation period (Miller, 1959). Progesterone-like activity has been detected by bioassay in the plasma of ovoviviparous snakes, with increased levels during pregnancy (Bragdon *et al.*, 1954). Progesterone has also been shown to stimulate oviduct growth of viviparous lizards (Panigel, 1956).

2. Extragenital Effects

For the normal development of the mammary gland, estrogens, gestogens, as well as pituitary, thyroid, and adrenal hormones, are currently considered to be necessary. In most species progesterone seems to be responsible for lobule–alveolar growth, but normally it acts in conjunction with estrogens. However, large doses of progesterone alone have been shown to cause lobule–alveolar growth in the rat, mouse, and monkey (Reece, 1958).

Body temperature in women increases at ovulation and after progesterone injections. The same phenomena has been recorded in cows (Wrenn *et al.*, 1958).

An important extragenital function of progesterone is its corticoid activity. It is able to keep adrenalectomized animals in good condition. This has been shown in the ferret (Gaunt and Hays, 1938), the cat (Corey, 1939), and rat (Greene *et al.*, 1939).

Progesterone also affects sexual receptivity. Injections into the lateral ventricles of the brain in hamsters causes estrus (Kent and Lieberman, 1949). Psychic signs of estrus have been shown to depend upon combined gestogen–estrogen action in the guinea pig (Dempsey *et al.*, 1936), rat (Boling and Blandau, 1939), mouse (Ring, 1944), and cow (Melampy *et al.*, 1957).

Numerous other extragenital effects of progesterone have been reported (Allen *et al.*, 1939; Pincus, 1955).

IV. THE ESTROGENS

A. Natural Sources

The structural formulas of some naturally occurring estrogens together with their relative biological activity are given in Fig. 3.

In 1936 MacCorquodale *et al.* isolated estradiol-17β from large batches of pig ovaries. Estrone was later isolated from the same source (Westerfeld *et al.*, 1938). Estradiol-17β, being the most biologically potent of the naturally occurring estrogens, has since been considered as the "true" estrogenic hormone of the ovary in spite of the fact that until 1958 it had not been isolated from the ovary of any other species. Recent investigations tend, however, to confirm this assumption since it has now been found to constitute the major ovarian estrogen in the cow (Velle, 1958a), women (Zander *et al.*, 1959; Smith, 1960), and mare (Short, 1960a; Knudsen and Velle, 1961). Estrone is probably present in small amounts in all species. In the horse a third estrogen, 6-α-hydroxyestradiol-17β is also present in follicular fluid (Bush *et al.*, 1960). Smith (1960) has also reported the presence of estriol in the human ovary. In a restricted sense these compounds might be considered as the genuine female gonadal estrogens.

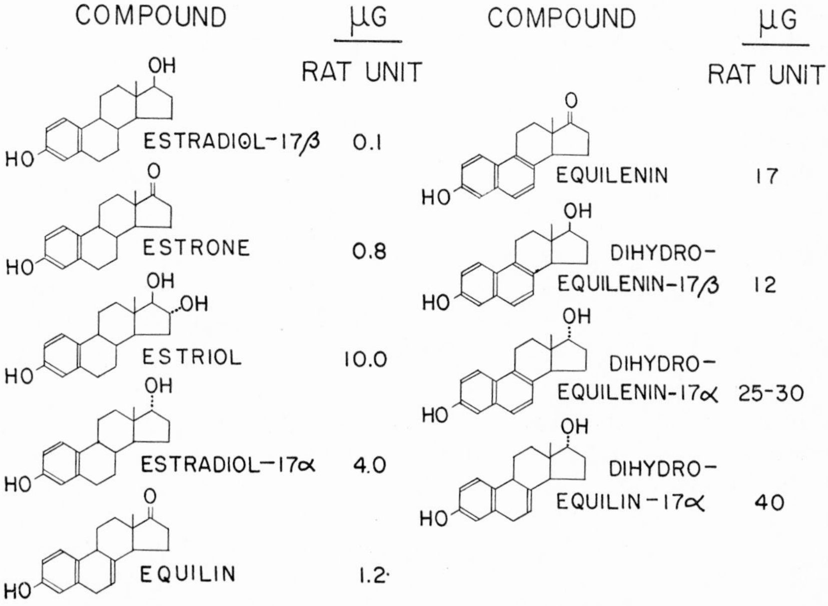

COMPOUND	μG RAT UNIT	COMPOUND	μG RAT UNIT
ESTRADIOL-17β	0.1	EQUILENIN	17
ESTRONE	0.8	DIHYDRO-EQUILENIN-17β	12
ESTRIOL	10.0	DIHYDRO-EQUILENIN-17α	25-30
ESTRADIOL-17α	4.0	DIHYDRO-EQUILIN-17α	40
EQUILIN	1.2·		

FIG. 3. Structural formulas and biological activity of some naturally occurring estrogens. (According to Shoppee, 1958.)

However, when the placental estrogen production is also taken into consideration, the picture becomes more complicated.

In the human placenta estradiol-17β, estrone, estriol (Diczfalusy, 1953), and 16-epiestriol (Diczfalusy and Halla, 1958) have been detected. The equine placental estrogens have not yet been characterized. But from the studies of the biosynthesis of estrogens in the pregnant mare it seems reasonable to assume a placental origin of the ring B unsaturated compounds as well as of the "ordinary" estrogens.

In the bovine placenta estrone, estradiol-17α, and estradiol-17β have been identified (Velle, 1958a; Gorski and Erb, 1959). Estradiol-17α seems to be the major placental estrogen in the goat (Velle, 1960) and sheep, but in the pig only estrone is present in measurable quantities (Velle, 1958a).

Estrogens isolated from ovary and placenta, as well as from testis and adrenal, are listed in Table IV. Recent work identified estradiol-17β in the ovaries of the sea urchin and the mollusk (Botticelli et al., 1961), the starfish (Botticelli et al., 1960), the dogfish (Wotiz et al., 1960), the cod *Gadus callarias* (Gottfried et al., 1962), and also estradiol-17β, estrone, and estriol in the ovary of the laying hen (Layne et al., 1958); these findings point to a possible functional significance of these hormones not only in vertebrates but also in some invertebrates.

B. Levels in Tissues and Body Fluids

1. THE OVARY

For pig ovaries Westerfeld et al. (1938) reported levels corresponding to 1.0 μg estrone and 1.4 μg estradiol-17β/100 gm tissue. For follicular fluid the following values (μg per 100 ml) have recently been reported for the two estrogens respectively: human, 50–198 and 10–91 (Zander et al., 1959), 6.4 and 32.5 (Smith, 1960); cattle, 0 and 10 (Velle, 1958a)*; horse, 3.4 and 46 (Short, 1960a); 2.8 and 34 (Knudsen and Velle, 1961). Although Zander et al. (1959) found no evidence of the presence of estriol in the human ovary, Smith (1960) reported 24 μg estriol/100 gm ovarian fluid sampled during the luteal phase, but found it absent in fluid collected during the follicular phase of the cycle.

For the pregnant animal few data are available on ovarian estrogen levels. Follicles in the ovaries of pregnant cows (Velle, 1960) and pregnant mares (Short, 1960c) have been found to be virtually free of estrogens. However, in the human, estrone and estradiol-17β were found in luteal tissue during pregnancy at concentrations of 24–89 and 7–64 μg/100 gm respectively (Zander et al., 1959).

* Values of 0.5 μg/100 ml estrone and 9.4 μg/100 ml estradiol-17β were reported by Short (1962).

TABLE IV

SOURCES OF ESTROGENIC HORMONES IN VARIOUS SPECIES

Tissue	Species	Estrone	Estradiol-17β	Estradiol-17α	Estriol	6-α-Hydroxy-estradiol-17β
Ovary	Human	+	−	−	+	−
	Horse	+	+	−	−	+
	Cattle	−	+	−	−	−
	Pig	+	+	−	−	−
	Hen	+	+	−	+	−
	Starfish	−	+	−	−	−
	Dogfish	+	+	−	−	−
	Sea urchin	−	+	−	−	−
	Mollusk	+	+	−	−	−
Ova	Dogfish	−	+	−	−	−
	Cod	+	+	−	−	−
Placenta	Human	+	+	−	+	−
	Cattle	+	+	+	−	−
	Sheep	−	−	+	−	−
	Goat	−	−	+	−	−
	Pig	+	−	−	−	−
Testis	Human	−	+	−	−	−
	Horse	+	+	−	−	−
	Pig	+	+	−	−	−
Adrenal	Cattle	+	−	−	−	−

2. The Adrenal Gland

Estrone has been isolated from bovine adrenal glands (Beall, 1939), and results obtained from ovariectomized animals indicate that this gland contributes to estrogen production.

3. The Placenta

For the full term human placenta Diczfalusy and Lindquist (1956) reported mean concentrations of 5.1 μg estrone, 17.0 μg estradiol-17β, and 31.5 μg estriol/100 gm wet tissue, with considerable individual variations. In bovine full term placenta Velle (1958a) found average values of 4.4 μg estrone and 12.4 μg estradiol-17α. In the same species Veenhuisen et al. (1960) reported 3.5 μg estrone, 5.6 μg estradiol-17β, and 9.7 μg estradiol-17α. In bovine placenta levels of 2 μg estradiol-17α, and in porcine placenta 8 μg estrone/100 gm tissue have been found (Velle, 1958a).

4. Blood

In nonpregnant animals the estrogen levels in peripheral blood are very low. Markee and Berg (1944) using bioassays, found two peaks during the human cycle: one between days 10 and 14 and another between days 18 and 22, corresponding to 0.58 μg estrone/100 ml blood. Svendsen (1960), using a chemical method, found levels of 0.01–0.075 μg/100 ml blood in normally menstruating women.

During pregnancy elevated levels are present in human peripheral blood. Estrone, estradiol-17β, and estriol have been identified in human blood (Oertel et al., 1959). Slaunwhite and Sandberg (1959) reported values of 3–9, 0–8, and 4–6 μg/100 ml plasma for the three estrogens respectively.

5. Bile

Biliary excretion of estrogens is indicated by the presence of estrone in the bile of pregnant cows (Pearlman et al., 1947), and by the experimental evidence for enterohepatic circulation of estrogens in human subjects (Sandberg and Slaunwhite, 1957).

6. Milk

Bovine colostrum has been reported to have estrogen levels comparable to those found in human and bovine pregnancy blood (Pope and Roy, 1953). Turner (1958) concludes from an extensive investigation that the mammary gland cells are relatively impermeable to the estrogens secreted during advanced pregnancy.

7. Feces

Experimental results obtained in man by the use of C^{14}-labeled estrogens show that 8–14% of injected doses are excreted in the feces (Sandberg and Slaunwhite, 1957; Migeon et al., 1959). In pregnant cows the fecal estrogen excretion exceeds the urinary excretion (El Attar and Turner, 1958). Thus species differences exist in the major routes of excretion of these compounds. Estrone, estradiol-17β, and estriol have been identified in avian droppings (Hurst et al., 1957; MacRae et al., 1959).

8. Urine

Most of the results of urinary estrogen determinations in the nonpregnant female have been obtained from humans. Among other recent investigators Brown (1955) reported average 24 hour values of 20, 9, and 27 μg for the ovulation peak, and 14, 7, and 22 for the luteal maximum for estrone, estradiol-17β, and estriol respectively in normal women. For other species little information is available about levels during the cycle. In the nonpregnant sow Velle (1958a) found peak values of estrone at the time of estrus, but no increase corresponding to maximal luteal activity. Values ranged between 2 and 28 μg/liter of urine.

Urine from pregnant animals has been the most important source of estrogens in most species investigated. In fact almost all naturally occurring estrogens were first isolated from pregnancy urine.

The estrogens isolated from human pregnancy urine are listed in Table V. Important contributions to our knowledge in this field have been made during very recent years.

Systematic quantitative studies on urinary estrogen excretion in human pregnancy have so far only been made for the three "classical" estrogens. Brown (1956) showed that the levels of estrone, estradiol-17β, and estriol increased continuously until parturition, after which a sudden decrease was observed. The amounts excreted per 24 hours in late pregnancy are in the range of 1–2, 0.3–0.8, and 20–40 mg respectively. More recent investigations indicate that other estrogens such as 2-methoxyestrone and 2-hydroxyestrone may contribute significantly to the total amount of estrogens excreted.

In the horse the picture is also complicated. Estrogens isolated from pregnant mares' urine are listed in Table VI. In the mare the urinary estrogen excretion increases markedly from the third month to the seventh or eighth month of gestation, and decreases before parturition. For months 7 to 8 Beall and Edson (1936) reported values of the order of 100 mg estrone per liter of urine. Recently the composition of the estrogen mixture

TABLE V

ESTROGENS PRESENT IN HUMAN PREGNANCY URINE

Compound	References
Estrone	Butenandt (1929); Doisy *et al.* (1929)
Estriol	Doisy *et al.* (1930)
Estradiol-17β	Smith *et al.* (1939)
16-ketoestrone	Serchi (1953)
16-epiestriol	Marrian and Bauld (1955)
16α-hydroxyestrone	Marrian *et al.* (1957)
2-methoxyestrone	Loke and Marrian (1958)
16β-hydroxyestrone	Layne and Marrian (1958)
18-hydroxyestrone	Loke *et al.* (1958)
16-ketoestradiol-17β	Layne and Marrian (1958)
2-methoxyestradiol-17β	Frandsen (1959)
17-epiestriol	Breuer (1960)
16,17-Epiestriol	Breuer and Pangels (1960)

TABLE VI

ESTROGENS PRESENT IN EQUINE PREGNANCY URINE

Compound	References
Estrone	De Jongh *et al.* (1931)
Equilin	Girard *et al.* (1932b)
Equilenin	Girard *et al.* (1932a)
Dihydroequilenin-17α	Schwenk and Hildebrandt (1932)
Estradiol-17β	Wintersteiner *et al.* (1935)
Dihydroequilenin-17β	Wintersteiner *et al.* (1936) Glen *et al.* (1956)
Dihydroequilin-17α	Wintersteiner and Hirschmann (1937)
Estradiol-17α	Wintersteiner and Hirschmann (1937)
3β-Hydroxy-$\Delta^{5,7,9}$-estratrien-17-one	Heard and Hoffman (1940)
3-Deoxyequilenin	Prelog and Führer (1945)

present in the urine in the fourth to ninth month of pregnancy has been investigated. Gaudry and Glen (1959) report the following relative figures as per cent of total estrogens present: estrone, 51; equilin, 22; dihydro-equilin-17α, 16; estradiol-17α, 6.4; equilenin, 2.6; and dihydroequilenin-17α, 1.3. The authors state that the relative amounts vary considerably with the stage of gestation.

In the pregnant cow the urinary estrogen level starts to increase markedly about 90 days after conception, and the increase continues until parturition, as shown by bioassay (Turner *et al.*, 1930) and by chemical determinations (El Attar and Turner, 1958; Velle, 1958a). In this species as well as in the goat estrone and estradiol-17α are the substances excreted (Wright and Klyne, 1955; Klyne and Wright, 1956a,b). In sheep even in late pregnancy only trace amounts are present in the urine, as shown by bioassay, (Beck, 1950; Bassett *et al.*, 1955), and by chemical determinations (Velle, 1958a).

The pig shows a unique urinary excretion pattern; estrogens are present in high amounts during two distinct periods during pregnancy, first during the fourth week and then from about the eightieth day until parturition (Küst, 1934). As recently shown, estrone is the major compound during both periods, being present at levels of 50–500 μg/liter during the early period and 2–8 mg toward the end of pregnancy (Velle, 1958a, 1959; Lunaas, 1962).

In the pregnant dog urinary estrogens are present in concentrations too low to be detected by chemical methods (Kristoffersen and Velle, 1960).

Estrone, estradiol-17β, and estradiol-17α were recently detected in rat urine (Ketz, 1961).

In other common laboratory animals, mouse, rabbit, and guinea pig, the chemical nature of the naturally occurring estrogens is still unknown.

Estrone was recently isolated from the urine of the laying hen in crystalline form (Ainsworth and Common, 1962).

9. ESTROGENS IN THE NEWBORN

Estriol has been identified in human fetal organs. The highest levels were found in the liver. Only small amounts of estrone and estradiol-17β were present (Diczfalusy and Magnusson, 1958). No information is available for other species.

Urine from newborn males contains approximately 7 mg estriol/liter on the second day of life, and decreases rapidly thereafter. Estrone is present in trace amounts; estradiol-17β could not be detected (Diczfalusy *et al.*, 1957). The excretion pattern is thus different from that of the adult.

In new born calves of both sexes estrone and estradiol-17α have been found in the urine at levels of 0.2 and 0.8 mg/liter of urine respectively; the levels decrease rapidly during the first days of life (Velle, 1958f). It is interesting that estriol and estradiol-17α are the major substances found in humans and cattle, respectively. Presumably these substances represent the major end products in estrogen metabolism in the two species.

The first estrogen isolated from meconium was estriol, found in the human (Francis and Kinsella, 1955); it contained approximately 100 mg/100 gm wet material (Diczfalusy *et al.*, 1959). Estradiol-17α has been isolated from bovine (Velle, 1957), ovine and caprine meconium (Velle, 1958a). The estrogens are present partly in free and partly in conjugated form. Total concentrations measured were of the order of 60, 10, and 650 mg/kg respectively. In equine meconium Velle and Pigon (1960) identified both estrone and estradiol-17α, in yields of approximately 10 and 50 mg/kg respectively. In addition six to eight other as yet incompletely identified phenolic compounds were found in this material. The biological significance of these findings is obscure. But the different proportions between the substances present in the maternal and the fetal excreta points to an active participation in the metabolism of estrogens by the fetus.

10. ESTROGENS IN THE MALE

Very high levels of estrogen activity were recorded in stallions' urine in the early thirties (Häussler, 1934; Zondek, 1934), and estrone was isolated in high yield (Häussler, 1934; Deulofeu and Ferrari, 1934). Zondek found only trace amounts present in the urine of castrates, indicating the testis as the site of origin. Both estrone and estradiol-17β were isolated from this gland (Beall, 1940), and the biosynthesis of estrogens in the stallion testis has been demonstrated experimentally (Baggett et al., 1959; Nyman et al., 1959). Estradiol-17β (Levin, 1945) and estradiol-17α (Pigon et al., 1961) also have been isolated from the urine of the stallion. Pigon et al. (1961) found levels of 20 mg of estrone and 2 mg of each of the two diols per liter of urine.

From 16,000 liters of human male urine Dingemanse et al. (1938) isolated 7 mg of estrone. Estrone and estradiol-17β have been isolated from human testis by Goldzieher and Roberts (1952).

In the testis of the boar estrone and estradiol-17β were detected by Velle (1958a) and the same hormones were isolated from the urine in levels of the order of 2 and 1 mg/liter respectively (Velle, 1958d,g). The urinary estrogen levels in the bull, ram, and male goat are extremely low. Estradiol-17β was recently isolated from the testes of a shark, Scylliorhinus stellaris, in quantities of 20 μg/kg tissue (Chieffi and Lupo, 1961). The extreme species variation in estrogen production in the male are remarkable, and the biological significance of the high estrogen production in some species remains to be elucidated.

C. Metabolism

1. In Vivo EXPERIMENTS

In the human species a variety of estrogen metabolites have been isolated from the urine after administration of estrone or estradiol-17β. Based mainly on the work of Marrian and his co-workers, and the investigations on the metabolism of C^{14}-labeled estrogens of Gallagher and his associates (for references see Brown, 1959), the metabolic scheme shown below may be indicated for the human being.

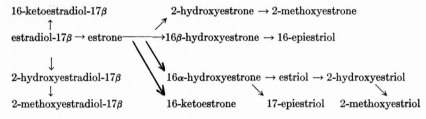

For cattle, goat, sheep, and rabbit the following pattern seems to be valid.

$$\text{Estradiol-17}\beta \rightarrow \text{estrone} \leftrightarrow \text{estradiol-17}\alpha$$

Evidence for these reactions in cattle have been presented by Velle (1958b, c,e).

The same pattern is probably valid for the horse. By analogy the following additional reactions may be suggested for the pregnant mare, assuming separate biosynthetic routes for the naphtholic estrogens.

$$\text{Dihydroequilin-17}\beta \rightarrow \text{equilin} \rightarrow \text{dihydroequilin-17}\alpha$$
$$\text{Dihydroequilenin-17}\beta \rightarrow \text{equilenin} \rightarrow \text{dihydroequilenin-17}\alpha$$

In vivo transformation of C^{14}-labeled dihydroequilenin-17β to equilenin has recently been demonstrated in the pregnant mare (Savard *et al.*, 1960).

The simplest picture seems to obtain in the pig in which the only reactions seem to be

$$\text{Estradiol-17}\beta \leftrightarrow \text{estrone}$$

with the equilibrium toward the right.

Recent investigations indicate a complicated metabolic pattern for estrogens in birds. Thus MacRae and Common (1960), after injection of C^{14}-labeled estradiol-17β to the laying hen, identified estrone, estriol, and 16-epiestriol in the excreta. In a similar study using estrone, Ainsworth *et al.* (1962) identified estriol, 16-epiestriol, 17-epiestriol, estradiol-17β, 16-ketoestradiol-17β, and 16-ketoestrone. The similarity in metabolic patterns between man and birds is remarkable.

In metabolism experiments with estrone or estradiol-17β in human subjects the recoveries of metabolites in the urine ranged from 13 to 38% (Brown, 1959) and from 43 to 63% (Migeon *et al.*, 1959). Even though some metabolites are excreted in the feces, a fraction of the injected doses remain unaccounted for, indicating that other metabolites may exist.

2. *In Vitro* EXPERIMENTS

In vivo experiments give little information about the tissues which are concerned with the metabolism of the hormones. The liver has long been considered the main site of estrogen metabolism, but only recently have the metabolites formed in the liver been chemically identified. Using rat liver, Ryan and Engel (1953a) demonstrated interconversions between estrone and estradiol-17β. The same authors found that these reactions also occur in a variety of human tissues (Ryan and Engel, 1953b). In these and similar studies, slices or homogenates have been used. Since erythrocytes also cause the interconversions (Repke and Markwardt, 1954; Gray and Bishoff, 1955), such studies may not be entirely conclusive. However, the same effects have now been demonstrated in cell cultures from different tissues grown in the absence of blood (Velle and Erichsen, 1960; Erichsen and Velle, 1960).

The interconversions of estrone and estradiol-17β take place in the presence of erythrocytes from a large number of species (Lunaas and Velle, 1960; Portius and Repke, 1960); but species differences exist. Bovine erythrocytes possess the unique ability to transform estrone to estradiol-17α (Axelrod and Werthessen, 1960; Lunaas and Velle, 1960), but erythrocytes from other ruminants such as sheep and goats do not, in spite of the fact that estradiol-17α is the major estrogen metabolite in all of these species.

In addition to the metabolic changes mentioned, a large number of other estrogen transformations have very recently been shown to take place in the liver of different species. These include reversible reduction of keto groups at carbon 17 and 16 to epimeric hydroxy compounds in liver from man, rat, and rabbit (Breuer and Knuppen, 1958, Breuer *et al.*, 1958a; Breuer and Nocke, 1959; Breuer *et al.*, 1959a,b,c,d,e; King, 1960), 6-hydroxylation in rat liver (Breuer *et al.*, 1958b; Breuer and Knuppen, 1960), and 2-hydroxylation in rat and rabbit liver (King, 1960). Using C^{14}-labeled estrone, Jellinck (1959) found evidence for the formation of nonsteroid, water soluble compounds after incubation with rat liver. Of special interest to comparative endocrinology is the recent demonstration of 16-hydroxylation of estradiol-17β to estriol in human fetal liver (Engel *et al.*, 1958), in rat liver (Hagopian and Levy, 1958), and in avian liver (Mitchell and Hobkirk, 1959).

The liver also actively participates in the conjugation of estrogens (Brown *et al.*, cit from Brown, 1959) and plays an important role in mediating estrogen-protein binding (Szego and Roberts, 1956). The latter phenomenon may have an important bearing on problems connected with the mechanism of action of estrogenic hormones (Villee *et al.*, 1960).

Recently attention has also been called to the intestinal wall as a major site of estrogen glucosiduronate formation in the rat (Lehtinen *et al.*, 1958) and in man (Diczfalusy *et al.*, 1961).

D. Biological Functions

𝒞The major property ascribed to the estrogenic hormones is the ability to cause estrus and characteristic changes in the female genital tract.⟩ In addition numerous other effects of estrogens have been reported. The literature in this field is overwhelming, and no attempt will be made to cover all aspects. The reader is referred to the reviews by Allen *et al.* (1939), Burrows (1949), Pincus (1955), Velardo (1958b), Young (1961), and Diczfalusy and Lauritzen (1961) for general information.

1. Effects on the Reproductive System

In experiments including a variety of species estrogenic hormones have been shown to possess the ability to influence sex differentiation and development. This is most clearly demonstrated in lower vertebrates. In the fish *Lebistes reticularis*, for example, feeding of Progynon tablets containing "estrogenic substances" to young, sexually undifferentiated males caused the suppression of secondary sex characteristics and of spermatogenesis (Berkowitz, 1937). Estrogens fed in large amounts to adult males of the same species caused no observable change (Hildemann, 1954). On the other hand, inclusion of estrone (1250 IU/gm) and stilbestrol (5000 IU/gm) in the diet to genotypic males of another fish *Oryzias latipes* from the time of hatching to about 8 months of age caused complete feminization and sex reversal: fully grown females of this male genotype produced offspring after mating with normal males (Yamamoto, 1953). In the brown trout (*Salmo trutta* L.) no sex reversal took place when estradiol-17β was added to the water in concentrations of 50–300 μg/liter, but there was strong inhibition of the development of germinal tissue (Ashby, 1957).

In amphibians estrogens exert marked effects on sex differentiation, but the responses vary considerably with species, time of administration, dose, and the nature of hormone administered. Thus, estradiol-17β has a feminizing effect in low doses and a masculinizing effect in high doses on *Rana*, whereas high doses will cause feminization in *Discoglossus*. Both estradiol-17β and testosterone cause feminization in *Pleurodeles waltlii* (Gallien, 1950).

Chang and Witschi (1955a) showed that *Xenopus* larvae of male genetic sex developed into phenotypic females when kept in water containing 25–1000 μg estradiol-17β per liter. Feminized genotypic males bred to normal males produced only male offspring, showing also that in *Xenopus* the males are the homozygous sex.

Another peculiar estrogen effect in amphibians is the experimentally produced adrenogenital syndrome in the frog. When estrogen is administered to larvae, the adrenals become hyperplastic. Moderate doses cause feminization of males, but high doses cause masculinization of females. The adrenal hyperplasia is not produced in the absence of the pituitary (Witschi, 1953; Chang and Witschi, 1955b).

In reptiles the administration of estrogens to males causes reduction of testis size and also of epididymis (Gorbman, 1939; Forbes, 1941). In the female stimulation of sexual receptivity (Greenberg and Noble, 1944) and of oviduct growth (Gorbman, 1939) have been reported. But, as stated by Miller (1959) "the specific role of ovarian hormones whatever their nature or source, remains undetermined in the reptiles."

In birds also dramatic effects of estrogens on sex differentiation have repeatedly been reported (Kozelka and Gallagher, 1934; Willier *et al.*, 1935, 1937; Wolff and Ginglinger, 1935; Dantchakoff, 1935, 1936; Pincus and Hopkins, 1958). In females the ovaries and the internal genitalia are generally not affected to any extent. But application of estrogens to young, genetically male embryos leads to the development of an ovotestis on the left side; the right testis may or may not be affected, depending upon the dose given. Generally the degree of sex reversal of genetic males is roughly proportional to the estrogen doses applied (Willier *et al.*, 1935, 1937; Pincus and Hopkins, 1958). The whole question of modifications in sex and secondary sexual characteristics is treated in detail by Domm (1939) and Witschi (1961).

On the ovary of the adult female estrogens exert both a direct and an indirect effect. Small doses may cause direct stimulation of follicular maturation, but large doses may interfere severely with the normal ovarian cycle. Normally the estrogens are believed to cause a release of the luteinizing hormone from the pituitary, resulting in maturation of the follicle, and ovulation.

The effects of estrogen on the uterus are numerous. The normal proliferation of the endometrium preceding ovulation is considered to be a genuine estrogen effect, and has been experimentally demonstrated in humans, monkeys, and rodents. The manifestations of estrogen action are most pronounced in the surface epithelia and in the endometrial glands, but great species variations exist with respect to the histochemical picture of the different structures, indicating that other factors may modify the action of the estrogens. The composition of the uterus as a whole, is profoundly affected as shown by Mueller *et al.* (1958) in the rat. Characteristic are increases in water imbibition, glycogen deposition, and incorporation of amino acids into nucleic acids and proteins.] ⚹ .

Using rat uterine growth as a parameter for estrogen potency, Velardo (1958a) tested a number of naturally occurring estrogens, and found that the activity decreases in the following order: estradiol-17β, estrone, 16α-hydroxyestrone, 16β-hydroxyestrone, estriol, 16-epiestriol.

In birds the oviduct responds markedly to estrogens, even in low doses. Prolific growth of this organ can be brought about by estrogens alone, but additional effects are seen when either androgen or gestogen is given simultaneously (Brant and Nalbandov, 1956).

Myometrial contractility is similarly influenced by estrogens; the effect being generally a stimulatory one. In the rat, uterine contractions are rhythmic during estrus, and uterine contractions are more frequent in cattle during estrus than during other stages of the cycle. Estrogens may act directly, but may also sensitize the myometrium to the action of oxytocin.

In many species secretion of cervical mucus is stimulated by estrogens. Its consistency is lowered by estrogens (Glover, 1960).

[In rodents cornification of the vaginal epithelium is a result of estrogen action. In other species cornification is less pronounced, both during estrus and after estrogen administration.]

It is generally assumed that the combined action of estrogens and gestogens is necessary for the establishment of pregnancy, and for the normal functions of the pregnant uterus. From a comparative point of view it is interesting to note the apparently large species variations which exist in regard to qualitative and quantitative aspects of hormone production during pregnancy. One might assume that the high amounts of estrogens produced during pregnancy in women and in mares by far exceed the quantities necessary for the adequate supply of target organs.

2. EXTRAGENITAL EFFECTS

Among the extragenital effects of estrogenic hormones the influence on mammary development and function is well known. Duct formation and growth are in most species considered to be effected by estrogens alone. This is especially marked in the mouse. In the guinea pig lobule–alveolar growth is also stimulated by estrogens. Other species range between these extremes. According to Reece (1958) the dog, cat, and rabbit show a pattern similar to that of the mouse, and the rhesus monkey, goat, and cow react more like the guinea pig. Also, mammary function is profoundly affected by estrogens. Moderate doses can provoke milk secretion in nonlactating animals. High doses or high production suppress milk formation, as demonstrated in the pregnant cow, in which milk production decreases markedly from about the fifth month, concomitant with a rapid increase in estrogen production. Estrogens also influence the composition of milk. A marked increase in free butyric acid combined with off-flavor of the milk has been observed after administration of estradiol-17β to a lactating cow (Lunaas, 1960).

Numerous effects of estrogens on metabolism are known in mammals and birds. In ruminants implantation or injection of long-acting estrogen preparations are used commercially to improve feed gain and weight increase (Gassner et al., 1958). Most dramatic perhaps are the effects in birds, in which marked changes in blood and tissue composition take place during periods of ovarian activity and following estrogen administration (see Lorenz, 1954). Among the most marked changes are lipemia and the elevation of blood calcium and phosphorus concentrations. Lipemia has been recorded in hens (Lorenz et al., 1938), doves and pigeons (Riddle and Senum, 1939), ducks (Landauer et al., 1941), and turkeys (Davidson et al., 1946). The lipemic response as well as the increased levels in blood minerals (Riddle and Dotti, 1936) are thought to be related to the formation of the eggs. Along with the increase in blood minerals produced experimentally, hyperossification may also occur. This has been demonstrated in pigeons (Pfeiffer and Gardner, 1938) chickens (Zondek, 1937), ducks (Landauer et al., 1941) and sparrows (Edgren, 1955). These responses in birds are contrary to those seen in mammals, in which estrogens tend to suppress the levels of both lipids and calcium in the blood.

In birds which have sex-dimorphic feathers estrogens are responsible for the normal female plumage, influencing both the distribution of pigment and the shape of the feathers (Domm, 1939; Parkes and Emmens, 1944; Witschi, 1961).

Sexual receptivity in many species is induced by estrogens. But the manifestations and duration of this action are subject to species variation. In rodents continuous estrus can be produced by frequent administration of an estrogen. In the cow continued estrogen injections fail to cause estrual behavior for more than a short period, indicating that other factors are also important for development of heat.

V. ANDROGENS

As already mentioned (Section II,A) androstenedione has recently been isolated both from ovarian and placental tissues, and the available evidence suggests that this androgen is a very important precursor in the biosynthesis of estrogens. The role played by progesterone as intermediate in the production of corticosteroids, and its presence in significant amounts in adrenal venous blood, is analogous to the possibility that during periods of high ovarian estrogen production, androstenedione and/or testosterone may be released into the ovarian veins in amounts sufficient to exert physiological effects.

Experimental evidence points to ovarian androgens as physiological substances. Ovarian grafts in male mouse castrates are capable of maintaining full functional activity of the accessory glands (Hill, 1937). In the hen there is a correlation between comb size and ovarian activity; in the nonlaying hen the comb undergoes atrophy, whereas in the laying hen the comb size increases. This phenomenon can be reproduced with androgens, but not with estrogens or gestogens (Parkes, 1950).

VI. RELAXIN

A. Natural Sources

Bioassays show that relaxin is widely distributed among vertebrates, having been detected in humans, horse, cattle, pig, dog, cat, rabbit, guinea pig, rat, mouse, whale, chicken, and shark (Hisaw and Zarrow, 1950; Steinetz et al., 1959). Since it is usually considered to be a hormone of pregnancy, it is interesting that it has now also been detected in the ovary of the nonpregnant sow (Albert et al., 1947), and rat, in the serum of estrous dogs, and in the testis of the rooster (Steinetz et al., 1959). Its main sources in the pregnant animal appear to be the ovary and the placenta. The relative role of these organs for the production of relaxin seems in some way to be related to the degree of necessity of the ovaries for the maintenance of pregnancy. Thus in the mouse, rat, and sow, which require the ovaries throughout most of the gestation period, relaxin is probably mainly produced in the ovaries. In animals like the guinea pig, on the other hand, in which ovariectomy may be performed at midterm without interruption of pregnancy, the placenta is probably the main source, since relaxation of the pelvis occurs also in the absence of the ovaries (Hisaw and Zarrow, 1950).

B. Levels in Tissues and Body Fluids

The bioassay of relaxin is usually carried out by palpation of the pelvic symphysis of estrogen-primed guinea pigs after relaxin administration, 1 guinea pig unit (GPU) being taken as the least amount which causes a palpable relaxation in 9 of a group of 12 castrated animals weighing between 350 and 800 gm (Hisaw and Zarrow, 1950).

Very few data are available for nonpregnant animals. For pregnant sow ovaries values between 675 (Steinetz et al., 1959) and 9600 GPU/gm tissue (Albert et al., 1947) have been reported. Values per gm tissue have been recorded for other species: rabbit, 25–30 (Zarrow, 1949); rat, 98–720; mouse, 114–200; fin whale, 24; blue whale, 536; shark, 4–10 (Steinetz et al., 1959). Concentrations in the placenta vary also considerably. In most species the levels are low; values in the range 0.5 to 4 GPU/gm tissue having been reported for the sow, cat, fin whale, and blue whale. The rabbit placenta on the other hand shows values in the range of 50–75 (Zarrow, 1949) to 137 GPU/gm (Steinetz et al., 1959). In this species high levels are also found in blood serum (of the order of 10 GPU per ml). In the sow, cat, mouse and guinea pig the reported values lie between 0.1 and 2 GPU/ml. For women Zarrow et al. (1955) reported levels of 0.2 GPU/ml serum at 7–10 weeks of pregnancy, increasing to 2 GPU at 38–42 weeks. The hormone disappeared within 24 hours after delivery.

C. Biological Functions

Pelvic changes occur during pregnancy in a wide variety of mammalian species, but the degree of relaxation during pregnancy and labor is subject to great variation. Very pronounced changes take place in the guinea pig and mouse. In the guinea pig relaxation of the pelvis can be brought about experimentally by estrogens, gestogens, a combination of the two, or by relaxin (Zarrow, 1948). The length of treatment required depends upon the combination of hormones given. The estrogen as well as the relaxin effect is direct, but that of progesterone in all probability is indirect. The latter hormone is only active in the presence of a functional uterus. It is therefore assumed that it induces relaxin formation. In the mouse also pelvic relaxation can be induced by either estrogens or relaxin, but progesterone shows an inhibitory effect (Hall, 1949).

In immature rats uterine water uptake is largely stimulated by relaxin. A transient increase in glycogen, nitrogen, and dry weight in the uterus of estrogen-primed, spayed rats has also been observed (Zarrow and Brennan, 1957; Brennan and Zarrow, 1959).

In vitro spontaneous uterine motility is inhibited by relaxin in the guinea pig (Krantz et al., 1950), rat, and mouse (Sawyer et al., 1953; Wiquist, 1959). In human pregnancy relaxin has been reported to inhibit premature uterine contractions (McCarthy et al., 1957).

The relaxin effect on the uterine cervix is important. Experimental evidence for cervical softening has been presented for the cow (Graham and Dracy, 1953, the sow (Zarrow et al., 1956), the woman (Birnberg and Abitbol, 1957), and the rat (Kroc et al., 1958). In the sow the reaction was accompanied by changes in water and mucopolysaccharide content, and in the rat by changes in water and glycogen content.

Extensive investigations by Steinetz and his co-workers indicate that relaxin plays a role in balance with the steroid hormones in the maintenance of normal pregnancy. It is also suggested that it may play a role in the initiation of parturition in the rat and mouse, since changes in the balance of relaxin and progesterone alter the response to oxytocin injections (Steinetz et al., 1959).

The extragenital effects upon the mammary gland must be mentioned. In the guinea pig, mouse, and rat relaxin influences lobule–alveolar growth (Reece, 1958). In both intact and castrated mice relaxin plus estrogen effectively stimulates lobule–alveolar growth. Ten times more (by weight) progesterone than relaxin is required to cause the same effect (Wada and Turner, 1958). The authors suggest that progesterone may affect mammary development by inducing relaxin formation.

VII. CONCLUDING REMARKS

The first appearance of the female gonadal hormones in phylogeny and the stage at which they began to exert physiological functions are questions of major importance in comparative endocrinology.

Progesterone and estradiol-17β, which had previously been shown to occur naturally in a long series of vertebrates ranging from fishes to primates, are also present in the ovaries of some invertebrates like the sea urchin and the mollusk. Relaxin, the occurrence of which has been demonstrated in a variety of mammals, was recently detected also in shark ovaries. These observations indicate a biological role for the female gonadal hormones over a considerably wider range of animal species than previously anticipated. The chemical nature of gonadal hormones in amphibians and reptiles is unknown. However, since female gonadal hormones of mammalian origin are able to cause the expected effects when given to lower vertebrates, it seems reasonable to expect the presence of hormones of similar or identical nature in these forms.

Since, as far as is known, progesterone is a precursor for androgens and estrogens, it is tempting to assume that the enzyme systems for the biosynthesis of this compound were developed earlier in evolution than those needed for the formation of the other two groups of hormones. Although it is known that luteal bodies can be found in representatives of all classes of vertebrates and in some protochordates, an established luteal function is unusual except in mammals. However, progesterone is also produced by follicular elements, and the functional corpus luteum represents a specialized structure in which the ability to transform progesterone to C_{19} and C_{18} steroids may to some extent have been lost.

Little is known about the physiological functions of the female gonadal hormones of lower animals. It has been suggested that the presence of estrogens in fish ova may have a bearing on the maintenance of a large hyperemic uterus after ovulation (Hisaw, 1959). In amphibians gonadal hormones are believed to maintain the secondary sexual characteristics. In reptiles ovariectomy causes regression of the oviducts. This can be prevented by the administration of estrogens or androgens (Miller, 1959), indicating a possible natural role for these hormones.

Sexual behavior is greatly influenced by female gonadal hormones, but generally it seems that their importance in this respect decreases, as other factors assume more importance during ontogeny.

Finally, it seems that the same steps in the biosynthesis of female gonadal hormones occur in all species studied. Although this indicates a great similarity in the distribution of the enzymes responsible for the biosynthetic processes, there are marked quantitative variations. Furthermore, there are marked qualitative species differences in the distribution of the enzymes involved in the catabolism of these hormones. The physiological and phylogenetic implications of these observations require elucidation.

References

Ainsworth, L., and Common, R. H. (1962). *Nature* **195**, 77.

Ainsworth, L., Carter, A. L., and Common, R. H. (1962). *Can. J. Biochem. and Physiol.* **40**, 123–136.

Aitken, E. H., Preedy, J. R. K., Eton, B., and Short, R. V. (1958). *Lancet* ii 1096–1099.

Albert, A., Money, W. L., and Zarrow, M. X. (1947). *Endocrinology* **40**, 370–374.

Allen, E., Danforth, C. H., and Doisy, E. A., eds. (1939). "Sex and Internal Secretions." Williams & Wilkins, Baltimore, Maryland.

Allen, W. M., and Wintersteiner, O. (1934). *Science* **80**, 190–191.

Ashby, K. R. (1957). *J. Embryol. Exptl. Morphol.* **5**, 225–249.

Atherden, L. M. (1959). *Biochem. J.* **71**, 411–415.

Austad, R., and Garm, O. (1959). *Nature* **184**, 999–1000.

Axelrod, L. R., and Werthessen, N. T. (1960). *Arch. Biochem. Biophys.* **86**, 53–55.

Baggett, B., Engel, L. L., Savard, K., and Dorfman, R. J. (1955). *J. Biol. Chem.* **221**, 931–941.

Baggett, B., Engel, L. L., Balderas, L., Lanman, G., Savard, K., and Dorfman, R. J. (1959). *Endocrinology* **64**, 600–608.

Balfour, W. E., Comline, R. S., and Short, R. V. (1957). *Nature* **180**, 1480–1481.

Balfour, W. E., Comline, R. S., and Short, R. V. (1959). *Nature* **183**, 467–468.

Bassett, E. G., Sewell, O. K., and White, E. P. (1955). *New Zealand J. Sci. Technol.* **36**, 437–449.

Beall, D. (1939). *Nature* **144**, 76.

Beall, D. (1940). *Biochem. J.* **34**, 1293–1298.

Beall, D., and Edson, M. (1936). *Biochem. J.* **30**, 577–581.

Beall, D., and Reichstein, T. (1938). *Nature* **142**, 479.

Beck, A. B. (1950). *Australian J. Agr. Research* **1**, 322–337.

Berkowitz, P. (1937). *Proc. Soc. Exptl. Biol. Med.* **36**, 416–418.

Birnberg, C. H., and Abitbol, M. M. (1957). *Obstet. Gynecol. Survey* **10**, 366–370.

Bloch, K. (1957). *Vitamins and Hormones* **15**, 119–150.

Boling, J. G., and Blandau, R. J. (1939). *Endocrinology* **25**, 359–364.

Botticelli, C. R., Hisaw, F. L., Jr., and Wotiz, H. H. (1960). *Proc. Soc. Exptl. Biol. Med.* **103**, 875–877.

Botticelli, C. R., Hisaw, F. L., and Wotiz, H. H. (1961). *Proc. Soc. Exptl. Biol. Med.* **106**, 887–889.

Bragdon, D. E. (1951). *J. Exptl. Zool.* **118**, 419–436.

Bragdon, D. E., Lazo-Wasem, E. A., Zarrow, M. X., and Hisaw, F. L. (1954). *Proc. Soc. Exptl. Biol. Med.* **86**, 477–480.

Brant, J. W. A., and Nalbandov, A. V. (1956). *Poultry Sci.* **35**, 692–700.

Brennan, D. M., and Zarrow, M. X. (1959). *Endocrinology* **64**, 907–913.

Breuer, H. (1960). *Nature* **185**, 613–614.

Breuer, H., and Knuppen, R. (1958). *Nature* **182**, 1512.

Breuer, H., and Knuppen, R. (1960). *Biochim. et Biophys. Acta* **39**, 408–411.

Breuer, H., and Nocke, L. (1959). *Biochim. et Biophys. Acta* **36**, 271–272.

Breuer, H., and Pangels, G. (1960). *Z. physiol. Chem. Hoppe-Seyler's* **322**, 177–183.

Breuer, H., Nocke, L., and Knuppen, R. (1958a). *Z. physiol. Chem. Hoppe-Seyler's* **311**, 275–278.

Breuer, H., Nocke, L., and Knuppen, R. (1958b). *Naturwissenschaften* **45**, 397–398.

Breuer, H., Knuppen, R., and Pangels, G. (1959a). *Acta Endocrinol.* **30**, 247–258.

Breuer, H., Knuppen, R., and Nocke, W. (1959b). *Biochem. J.* **71**, 26P.

Breuer, H., Knuppen, R., and Pangels, G. (1959c). *Z. physiol. Chem. Hoppe-Seylers'* **317**, 248–256.

Breuer, H., Nocke, L., and Knuppen, R. (1959d). *Biochim. et Biophys. Acta* **33**, 254–256.

Breuer, H., Nocke, L., and Knuppen, R. (1959e). *Z. physiol. Chem. Hoppe-Seyler's* **315**, 72–79.

Brown, J. B. (1955). *Lancet* i 320–323.

Brown, J. B. (1956). *Lancet* i 704–707.

Brown, J. B. (1959). *J. Obstet. Gynaecol. Brit. Empire* **66**, 795–803.

Bryans, F. E. (1951). *Endocrinology* **48**, 733-740.

Burrows, H. (1949). "Biologic Actions of Sex Hormones," 2nd ed. Cambridge Univ. Press, London and New York.

Bush, I. E., Klyne, W., and Short, R. V. (1960). *J. Endocrinol.* **20**, i–ii.

Butenandt, A. (1929). *Deut. med. Wochschr.* **55**, 2171–2173.

Butenandt, A., Westphal, U., and Hohlweg, W. (1934). *Z. physiol. Chem. Hoppe-Seyler's* **227**, 84–98.

Chang, C. Y., and Witschi, E. (1955a). *Endocrinology* **56**, 597–605.

Chang, C. Y., and Witschi, E. (1955b). *Proc. Soc. Exptl. Biol. Med.* **89**, 150–152.

Chieffi, G., and Lupo, C. (1961). *Nature* **190**, 169–170.

Clary, M. L., Cameron, A., and Craver, B. N. (1951). *Proc. Soc. Exptl. Biol. Med.* **77**, 778–783.

Clausen, H. T. (1940). *Endocrinology* **27**, 700–704.

Corey, E. L. (1939). *Proc. Soc. Exptl. Biol. Med.* **41**, 397–398.

Dantchakoff, V. (1935). *Compt. rend. acad. sci.* **201**, 161–163.

Dantchakoff, V. (1936). *Bull biol. France et Belg.* **70**, 241–307.

Davidson, J. A., Wolterink, F. L., and Reineke, E. P. (1946). *Poultry Sci.* **25**, 400.

Davis, M. E., and Plotz, E. J. (1957a). *Bull. Margaret Hague Maternity Hosp.* **10**, 53–66.

Davis, M. E., and Plotz, E. J. (1957b). *Recent Progr. in Hormone Research* **13**, 347–388.

Dean, F. D., and Chester Jones, I. (1959). *J. Endocrinol.* **18**, 366–371.

DeJongh, S. E., Kober, S., and Laqueur, E. (1931). *Biochem. Z.* **240**, 247–262.

Dempsey, E. W., Hertz, R., and Young, W. C. (1936). *Am. J. Physiol.* **116**, 201–209.

Deulofeu, V., and Ferrari, J. (1934). *Z. physiol. Chem. Hoppe-Seyler's* **226**, 192–194.

Diczfalusy, E. (1952). *Acta Endocrinol.* **10**, 373–389.

Diczfalusy, E. (1953). *Acta Endocrinol. Suppl.* **12**, pp. 1–174.

Diczfalusy, E., and Halla, M. (1958). *Acta Endocrinol.* **27**, 303–313.

Diczfalusy, E., and Lauritzen, C. (1961). "Ostrogene heim Menschen." Springer, Berlin.

Diczfalusy, E., and Lindquist, P. (1956). *Acta Endocrinol.* **22**, 203–223.

Diczfalusy, E., and Magnusson, A.-M. (1958). *Acta Endocrinol.* **28**, 169–185.

Diczfalusy, E., Tillinger, K.-G., and Westman, A. (1957). *Acta Endocrinol.* **26**, 303–312.

Diczfalusy, E., Menini, E., Tillinger, K.-G., and Westman, A. (1959). *Acta Endocrinol.* **30**, 539–550.

Diczfalusy, E., Franksson, C., and Martinsen, B. (1961). *Acta Endocrinol.* **38**, 59–72.

Dingemanse, E., Laqueur, E., and Mühlbock, O. (1938). *Nature* **141**, 927.

Doisy, E. A., Veler, C. D., and Thayer, S. A. (1929). *Am. J. Physiol.* **90**, 329–330.

Doisy, E. A., Veler, C. D., and Thayer, S. A. (1930). *J. Biol. Chem.* **86**, 499–509.

Domm, L. V. (1939). *In* "Sex and Internal Secretions" (E. Allen, C. H. Danforth, and E. A. Doisy, eds.), pp. 227–327. Williams & Wilkins, Baltimore, Maryland.

Dorfman, R. J. (1955). *In* "The Hormones" (G. Pincus and K. V. Thimann, eds.), Vol. 3, pp. 589–664. Academic Press, New York.

Dutt, R. H., and Casida, L. E. (1948). *Endocrinology* **43**, 208–217.

Edgar, D. G. (1952). *Nature* **170**, 543–544.

Edgar, D. G. (1953). *J. Endocrinol.* **10**, 54–64.

Edgar, D. G., and Ronaldson, J. W. (1958). *J. Endocrinol.* **16**, 378–384.

Edgren, R. A. (1955). *Endocrinology* **56**, 491–493.

El Attar, T., and Turner, C. W. (1958). *Missouri Univ. Research Bull. No.* **641**.

Engel, L. L. (1957). *Cancer* **10**, 711–715.

Engel, L. L., Baggett, B., and Halla, M. (1958). *Biochim. et Biophys. Acta* **30**, 435–436.

Erichsen, S., and Velle, W. (1960). *Acta Endocrinol.* **34**, 27–32.

Fevold, H. R., and Eik-Nes, K. B. (1961). *Federation Proc.* **20**, 197.

Fitzpatrick, R. J. (1957). *In* "The Neurohypophysis" (H. Heller, ed.), pp. 203–220. Academic Press, New York.

Forbes, T. R. (1941). *J. Morphol.* **68**, 31–69.

Forbes, T. R. (1950). *Am. J. Obstet. Gynecol.* **60**, 180–186.

Forbes, T. R. (1951). *Endocrinology* **49**, 218–224.

Forbes, T. R., and Hooker, C. W. (1957). *Endocrinology* **61**, 281–286.

Fox, T. W. (1955). *Poultry Sci.* **34**, 598–602.

Fraenkel, L., Martins, T., and Mello, R. F. (1940). *Endocrinology* **27**, 836–838.

Francis, F. E., and Kinsella, R. A. (1955). *Federation Proc.* **14**, 213.

Frandsen, V. A. (1959). *Acta Endocrinol.* **31**, 603–607.

Frieden, E. H., Stone, N. R., and Layman, N. W. (1960). *J. Biol. Chem.* **235**, 2267–2271.

Gallien, L. (1950). *Arch. anat. microscop. et morphol. exptl.* **39**, 337–360.

Gallien, L. (1959). *In* "Comparative Endocrinology" (A. Gorbman, ed.), pp. 479–487. Wiley, New York.

Gassner, F. X. (1952). *Recent Progr. in Hormone Research* **7**, 165–208.

Gassner, F. X., and Longwell, B. B. (1947). *Federation Proc.* **6**, 109.

Gassner, F. X., Reifenstein, E. C., Jr., Algeo, J. W., and Mattox, W. E. (1958). *Recent Progr. in Hormone Research* **14**, 183–217.

Gaudry, R., and Glen, W. L. (1959). *Ind. chim. belge.* **24**, 435–439. (Cited from *Chem. Abstr.* **54**, 9030h, 1960.)

Gaunt, R., and Hays, H. W. (1938). *Science* **88**, 576–577.

Girard, A., Sandulesco, G., Fridenson, A., Gaundefroy, C., and Rutgers, J. J. (1932a). *Compt. rend. acad. sci.* **194**, 1020–1022.

Girard, A., Sandulesco, G., Fridenson, A., and Rutgers, J. J. (1932b). *Compt. rend. acad. sci.* **195**, 981–983.

Glen, W. L., Barber, R., McConkey, H. M., and Grant, G. A. (1956). *Nature* **177**, 753.

Glover, F. A. (1960). *J. Endocrinol.* **20**, 56–64.

Goldzieher, J. W., and Roberts, I. S. (1952). *J. Clin. Endocrinol. and Metabolism* **12**, 143–150.

Gorbman, A. (1939). *Proc. Soc. Exptl. Biol. Med.* **42**, 811–813.

Gorski, J. (1958). The Identification and Sources of the Progestational Hormones of the Bovine. Ph.D. Thesis, State College of Washington.

Gorski, J., and Erb, R. E. (1959). *Endocrinology* **64**, 707–712.

Gorski, J., Erb, R. E., Dickson, W. M., and Butler, H. C. (1958). *J. Dairy Sci.* **41**, 1380–1386.

Gottfried, H., Hunt, S. V., Simpson, T. H., and Wright, R. S. (1962). *J. Endocrinol.* **24**, 425–430.

Graham, E. F., and Dracy, A. E. (1953). *J. Dairy Sci.* **36**, 772–777.

Gray, C. L., and Bishoff, F. (1955). *Am. J. Physiol.* **180**, 279–281.

Greenberg, B., and Noble, G. K. (1944). *Physiol. Zool.* **17**, 392–439.

Greene, R. R., Wells, J. A., and Ivy, A. C. (1939). *Proc. Soc. Exptl. Biol. Med.* **40**, 83–86.

Hagopian, M., and Levy, L. K. (1958). *Biochim. et Biophys. Acta* **30**, 641.

Hall, K. (1949). *Quart. J. Exptl. Physiol.* **35**, 65–75.

Hansel, W., and Trimberger, G. W. (1952). *J. Dairy Sci.* **35**, 65–70.

Harris, G. W. (1955). "Neural Control of the Pituitary Gland." Arnold, London.

Hartmann, M., and Wettstein, A. (1934). *Helv. Chim. Acta* **17**, 878–882.

Häussler, E. P. (1934). *Helv. Chim. Acta* **17**, 531–535.

Heard, R. D. H., and Hoffman, M. M. (1940). *J. Biol. Chem.* **135**, 801–802.

Heard, R. D. H., Jacobs, R., O'Donnel, V. J., Peron, F. G., Saffran, J. C., Solomon, S. S., Thompson, L. M., Willoughby, H., and Yates, C. H. (1954). *Recent Progr. in Hormone Research* **9**, 383–410.

Heard, R. D. H., Jellinck, P. H., and O'Donnel, V. J. (1955). *Endocrinology* **57**, 200–204.

Heard, R. D. H., Bligh, E. G., Conn, M. C., Jellinck, P. H., O'Donnel, V. J., Rao, B. G., and Webb, J. L. (1956). *Recent Progr. in Hormone Research* **12**, 45–77.

Hildemann, W. H. (1954). *J. Exptl. Zool.* **126**, 1–15.

Hill, R. T. (1937). *Endocrinology* **21**, 495–502.

Hisaw, F. L. (1926). *Proc. Soc. Exptl. Biol. Med.* **23**, 661–663.

Hisaw, F. L. (1959). *In* "Comparative Endocrinology" (A. Gorbman, ed.), pp. 533–552. Wiley, New York.

Hisaw, F. L., and Zarrow, M. X. (1950). *Vitamins and Hormones* **8**, 151–178.

Hurst, R. O., Kuskis, F., and Blendell, J. F. (1957). *Can. J. Biochem. and Physiol.* **35**, 637–640.

Jellinck, P. H. (1959). *Biochem. J.* **71**, 665–670.

Kent, G. C., and Lieberman, M. J. (1949). *Endocrinology* **45**, 29–32.

Ketz, H.-A. (1961). *Biochem. Z.* **334**, 73–78.

King, R. J. B. (1960). Oestrogen Metabolism. Ph.D. Thesis, University of Edinburgh.

Klyne, W., and Wright, A. A. (1956a). *Biochem. J.* **62**, 21P.

Klyne, W., and Wright, A. A. (1956b). *J. Endocrinol.* **14**, xxxiii.

Klyne, W., and Wright, A. A. (1957). *Biochem. J.* **66**, 92–101.

Klyne, W., and Wright, A. A. (1959). *J. Endocrinol.* **18**, 32–45.

Knudsen, O., and Velle, W. (1961). *J. Reproduct. and Fertility.* **2**, 130–138.

Kozelka, A. W., and Gallagher, T. F. (1934). *Proc. Soc. Exptl. Biol. Med.* **31**, 1143–1144.

Krantz, J. C., Jr., Bryant, H. H., and Carr, C. J. (1950). *Surg. Gynecol. Obstet.* **90**, 372–375.

Kristoffersen, J. (1960). *Acta Endocrinol.* **33**, 417–427.

Kristoffersen, J., and Velle, W. (1960). *Nature* **185**, 253–254.

Kristoffersen, J., Lunaas, T., and Velle, W. (1960). *Nature.* **190**, 1009.

Kroc, R. L., Steinetz, B. G., and Beach, V. L. (1958). *Ann. N. Y. Acad. Sci.* **75**, 942–980.

Küst, D. (1934). *Klin. Wochschr.* **13**, 1782–1784.

Landauer, W., Pfeiffer, P. A., Gardner, W. U., and Shaw, J. C. (1941). *Endocrinology* **28**, 458–464.

Layne, D. S., and Marrian, G. F. (1958). *Biochem. J.* **70**, 244–248.

Layne, D. S., Common, R. H., Maw, W. A., and Fraps, R. M. (1957). *Proc. Soc. Exptl. Biol. Med.* **94**, 528–529.

Layne, D. S., Common, R. H., Maw, W. A., and Fraps, R. M. (1958). *Nature* **181**, 351–352.

Lehtinen, A., Nurmikko, V., and Hartiala, K. (1958). *Acta Chem. Scand.* **12**, 1585–1588.

Levin, L. (1945). *J. Biol. Chem.* **158**, 725–726.

Loke, K. H., and Marrian, G. F. (1958). *Biochim. et Biophys. Acta* **27**, 213.

Loke, K. H., Marrian, G. F., Johnson, W. S., Meyer, W. L., and Cameron, D. D. (1958). *Biochim. et Biophys. Acta* **28**, 214.

Lorenz, F. W. (1954). *Vitamins and Hormones* **12**, 235–275.

Lorenz, F. W., Entenman, C., and Chaikoff, I. L. (1938). *J. Biol. Chem.* **122**, 619–633.

Lunaas, T. (1960). *Acta Chem. Scand.* **14**, 773–775.

Lunaas, T. (1962). *J. Reproduct. and Fertility* **4**, 13–20.

Lunaas, T., and Velle, W. (1960). *Acta Physiol. Scand.* **50**, Suppl. 175, 95–97.

Lutwak-Mann, C., and Adams, C. E. (1957). *J. Endocrinol.* **15**, 43–55.

Lythle, T. M., and Lorenz, F. W. (1958). *Nature* **182**, 1681.

McCarthy, J. J., Erving, H. W., and Laufe, L. E. (1957). *Am. J. Obstet. Gynecol.* **74**, 134–138.

MacCorquodale, D. W., Thayer, S. A., and Doisy, E. A. (1936). *J. Biol. Chem.* **115**, 435–448.

MacRae, H. F., and Common, R. H. (1960). *Poultry Sci.* **39**, 707–712.

MacRae, H. F., Zaharia, W., and Common, R. H. (1959). *Poultry Sci.* **38**, 318–321.

Markee, J. E., and Berg, B. (1944). *Stanford Med. Bull.* **2**, 55–60.

Marrian, G. F. (1929). *Biochem. J.* **23**, 1090–1098.

Marrian, G. F. (1949). *Recent Progr. in Hormone Research* **4**, 3–23.

Marrian, G. F., and Bauld, W. S. (1955). *Biochem. J.* **59**, 136–141.

Marrian, G. F., Loke, K. H., Watson, E. J. D., and Panattoni, M. (1957). *Biochem. J.* **66**, 60–65.

Meites, J., Webster, H. D., Young, F. W., Thorp, F., and Hatch, R. N. (1951). *J. Animal Sci.* **10**, 411–416.

Melampy, R. M., Emmerson, M. A., Rakes, J. M., Hanka, L. J., and Eness, P. G. (1957). *J. Animal Sci.* **16**, 967–975.

Meyer, A. S. (1955a). *Biochim. et Biophys. Acta* **17**, 441–442.

Meyer, A. S. (1955b). *Experientia* **11**, 99–102.

Migeon, C. J., Wall, P. E., and Bertrand, J. (1959). *J. Clin. Invest.* **38**, 619–629.

Miller, M. R. (1959). *In* "Comparative Endocrinology" (A. Gorbman, ed.), pp. 499–516. Wiley, New York.

Miller, W. R., Turner, C. W., Fukushima, D. K., and Salamon, I. I. (1956). *J. Biol. Chem.* **220**, 221–225.

Mitchell, J. E., and Hobkirk, R. (1959). *Biochem. Biophys. Research Communs.* **1**, 72–74.

Moore, N. W., and Robinson, T. J. (1957). *J. Endocrinol.* **15**, 360–365.

Mueller, G. C., Herranen, A. M., and Jervell, K. F. (1958). *Recent Progr. in Hormone Research* **14**, 95–139.

Nalbandov, A. V. (1959). *In* "Comparative Endocrinology" (A. Gorbman, ed.), pp. 524–532. Wiley, New York.

Neher, B. H., and Fraps, R. M. (1950). *Endocrinology* **46**, 482–488.

Neher, B. H., and Zarrow, M. X. (1954). *J. Endocrinol.* **11**, 323–330.

Nellor, J. E., and Cole, H. H. (1956). *J. Animal Sci.* **15**, 650–661.

Noall, M. W., Salhanick, H. A., and Zarrow, M. X. (1952). *Federation Proc.* **11**, 265.

Nyman, M. A., Geiger, J., and Goldzieher, J. W. (1959). *J. Biol. Chem.* **234**, 16–18.

Oertel, G. W., West, C. D., and Eik-Nes, K. B. (1959). *J. Clin. Endocrinol. and Metabolism* **19**, 1619–1625.

Panigel, M. (1956). *Ann. sci. nat. Zool. et biol. animale* **18**, 569–668.

Parkes, A. S. (1950). *Recent Progr. in Hormone Research* **5**, 101–114.

Parkes, A. S., and Emmens, C. W. (1944). *Vitamins and Hormones* **2**, 361–408.

Paul, K. G., and Wiquist, N. (1960). *Acta Endocrinol.* **35**, 435–440.

Pearlman, W. H., and Cerceo, E. (1952). *J. Clin. Endocrinol. and Metabolism* **12**, 916 (abstract).

Pearlman, W. H., Rakoff, A. E., Cantarow, A., and Paschkis, K. E. (1947). *J. Biol. Chem.* **170**, 173–179.

Pfeiffer, C. A., and Gardner, W. U. (1938). *Endocrinology* **23**, 485–491.

Pigon, H., Lunaas, T., and Velle, W. (1961). *Acta Endocrinol.* **36**, 131–140.

Pincus, G. (1955). *In* "The Hormones" (G. Pincus and K. V. Thimann, eds.), Vol. 3, pp. 665–684. Academic Press, New York.

Pincus, G., and Hopkins, T. F. (1958). *Endocrinology* **62**, 112–118.

Pope, G. S., and Roy, J. H. B. (1953). *Biochem. J.* **53**, 427–430.

Portius, H. J., and Repke, K. (1960). *Naturwissenschaften* **47**, 43.

Prelog, V., and Führer, J. (1945). *Helv. Chim. Acta* **28**, 583–590.

Prelog, V., and Meister, P. (1949). *Helv. Chim. Acta* **32**, 2435–2439.

Raeside, J. I. (1957). *Proc. Soc. Exptl. Biol. Med.* **95**, 300–302.

Raeside, J. I., and Turner, C. W. (1951). *J. Dairy Sci.* **34**, 496.

Raeside, J. I., and Turner, C. W. (1955). *J. Dairy Sci.* **38**, 1334–1343.

Ralph, C. L., and Fraps, R. M. (1960). *Endocrinology* **66**, 269–272.

Reece, R. P. (1958). *In* "The Endocrinology of Reproduction" (J. T. Velardo, ed.), pp. 213–240. Oxford Univ. Press, London and New York.

Repke, K., and Markwardt, F. (1954). *Arch. exptl. Pathol. Pharmacol. Naunyn-Schmiedeberg's* **223**, 271–279.

Riddle, O., and Dotti, L. B. (1936). *Science* **84**, 557–559.

Riddle, O., and Senum, T. (1939). *Anat. Record* **75**, 58.

Riegel, B., Hartop, W. L., Jr., and Kittinger, G. W. (1950). *Endocrinology* **47**, 311–319.

Ring, J. R. (1944). *Endocrinology* **34**, 269–275.

Robertson, H., and Coulson, W. F. (1958). *Nature* **182**, 1512.

Robinson, T. J., and Moore, N. W. (1956). *J. Endocrinol.* **14**, 97–109.

Rowlands, I. W., and Short, R. V. (1959). *J. Endocrinol.* **19**, 81–86.

Ryan, K. J. (1958). *Federation Proc.* **17**, 138.

Ryan, K. J. (1959). *J. Biol. Chem.* **234**, 2006–2008.

Ryan, K. J., and Engel, L. L. (1953a). *Endocrinology* **52**, 277–286.

Ryan, K. J., and Engel, L. L. (1953b). *Endocrinology* **52**, 287–291.

Salhanick, H., Jones, J. E., and Berliner, D. (1956). *Federation Proc.* **15**, 160.

Samuels, L. T., Helmreich, M. L., Lasater, M. B., and Reich, H. (1951). *Science* **113**, 490–491.

Sandberg, A. A., and Slaunwhite, W. R. (1957). *J. Clin. Invest.* **36,** 1266–1278.

Sandberg, A. A., and Slaunwhite, W. R. (1958). *J. Clin. Endocrinol. and Metabolism* **18,** 253–265.

Savard, A., Thompson, H. G., Gut, M., and Dorfman, R. J. (1960). *Endocrinology* **67,** 276–278.

Sawyer, W. H., Frieden, E. H., and Martin, A. C. (1953). *Am. J. Physiol.* **172,** 547–552.

Schwenk, E., and Hildebrandt, F. (1932). *Naturwissenschaften* **20,** 658–659.

Serchi, G. (1953). *Chimia (Switz.)* **8,** 10. (Cited from *Chem. Abstr.* **47,** 12496c, 1953.)

Shoppee, C. W. (1958). "Chemistry of the Steroids," Butterworths, London.

Short, R. V. (1956). *Nature* **178,** 743–744.

Short, R. V. (1957). *CIBA Foundation Colloq. on Endocrinol.* **11,** 367–375.

Short, R. V. (1958). Ph.D. Thesis, Cambridge. Cited from Rowlands and Short, 1959.

Short, R. V. (1959). *J. Endocrinol.* **19,** 207–210.

Short, R. V. (1960a). *J. Endocrinol.* **20,** 147–156.

Short, R. V. (1960b). *J. Endocrinol.* **20,** xv–xvi.

Short, R. V. (1960c). Personal communication.

Short, R. V. (1962). *J. Endocrinol.* **23,** 401–411.

Short, R. V., and Eckstein, P. (1961). *J. Endocrinol.* **22,** 15–22.

Short, R. V., and Eton, B. (1959). *J. Endocrinol.* **18,** 418–425.

Short, R. V., and Moore, N. W. (1959). *J. Endocrinol.* **19,** 288–293.

Skjerven, O. (1956). *Acta Endocrinol. Suppl.* **26,** pp. 1–101.

Slaunwhite, R. W., and Samuels, L. T. (1956). *J. Biol. Chem.* **220,** 341–352.

Slaunwhite, R. W., Jr., and Sandberg, A. A. (1959). *Proc. Soc. Exptl. Biol. Med.* **101,** 544–546.

Slotta, K. H., Ruschig, H., and Fels, E. (1934). *Chem. Ber.* **67,** 1270.

Smith, G. W., Smith, O. W., Huffman, M. N., Thayer, S. A., MacCorquodale, D. W., and Doisy, E. A. (1939). *J. Biol. Chem.* **130,** 431.

Smith, O. W. (1960). *Endocrinology* **67,** 698–707.

Steinetz, B. G., Beach, V. L., and Kroc, R. L. (1957). *Endocrinology* **61,** 271–280.

Steinetz, B. G., Beach, V. L., and Kroc, R. L. (1959). *In* "Recent Progress in the Endocrinology of Reproduction" (C. W. Lloyd, ed.), pp. 389–427. Academic Press, New York.

Svendsen, R. (1960). *Acta Endocrinol.* **35,** 161–187.

Sweat, M. L., Grosser, B. I., Berliner, D. L., Swim, H. E., Nabors, C. J. Jr., and Dougherty, T. F. (1958). *Biochim. et Biophys. Acta* **28,** 591–596.

Szego, C. M., and Roberts, S. (1956). *J. Biol. Chem.* **221,** 619–628.

Taylor, W. (1956). *Biochem. J.* **62,** 332–335.

Taylor, W., and Scratcherd, T. (1961). *Biochem. J.* **81,** 398–405.

Turner, C. W. (1958). *J. Dairy Sci.* **41,** 630–640.

Turner, C. W., Frank, A. H., Lomas, C. H., and Nibler, C. W. (1930). *Missouri Univ. Agr. Expt. Sta. Research Bull. No.* **150,** pp. 1–43.

Ulberg, L. C., Grummer, R. H., and Casida, L. E. (1951). *J. Animal Sci.* **10,** 665–671.

Veenhuisen, E. L., Erb, R. E., and Gorski, J. (1960). *J. Dairy Sci.* **43,** 270–277.

152 W. VELLE

Velardo, J. T. (1958a). *Ann. N. Y. Acad. Sci.* **75**, 441–460.

Velardo, J. T. (1958b). *In* "The Endocrinology of Reproduction" (J. T. Velardo, ed.), pp. 101–212. Oxford Univ. Press, London and New York.

Velle, W. (1957). *Acta Chem. Scand.* **11**, 1793–1794.

Velle, W. (1958a). Undersøkelser over naturlig forekommende østrogener hos drøvtyggere og gris. Ph.D. Thesis, Norger Veterinaerhøgskole, Oslo.

Velle, W. (1958b). *Acta Endocrinol.* **28**, 186–191.

Velle, W. (1958c). *Acta Endocrinol.* **28**, 192–196.

Velle, W. (1958d). *Acta Endocrinol.* **28**, 255–261.

Velle, W. (1958e). *Acta Endocrinol.* **29**, 109–114.

Velle, W. (1958f). *Acta Endocrinol.* **29**, 381–394.

Velle, W. (1958g). *Acta Endocrinol.* **29**, 395–400.

Velle, W. (1959). *Acta Vet. Scand.* **1**, 19–26.

Velle, W. (1960). Unpublished results.

Velle, W., and Erichsen, S. (1960). *Acta Endocrinol.* **33**, 277–286.

Velle, W., and Pigon, H. (1960). *Acta Endocrinol. Suppl.* **50**, 1117–1118.

Venning, E., and Browne, J. S. L. (1936). *Proc. Soc. Exptl. Biol. Med.* **34**, 792–793.

Venning, E., and Browne, J. S. L. (1937). *Endocrinology* **21**, 711–712.

Villee, C. A., Hagermann, D. D., and Joel, P. B. (1960). *Recent Progr. in Hormone Research* **16**, 49–77.

Wada, H., and Turner, C. W. (1958). *Proc. Soc. Exptl. Biol. Med.* **99**, 194–197.

Westerfeld, W. W., Thayer, S. A., MacCorquodale, D. W., and Doisy, E. A. (1938). *J. Biol. Chem.* **126**, 181–193.

Wiest, W. G (1958). *Federation Proc.* **17**, 335.

Wiest, W. G. (1959). *J. Biol. Chem.* **234**, 3115–3121.

Willier, B. H., Gallagher, T. F., and Koch, F. C. (1935). *Proc. Natl. Acad. Sci. U.S.* **21**, 625–631.

Willier, B. H., Gallagher, T. F., and Koch, F. C. (1937). *Physiol. Zool.* **10**, 101–122.

Wintersteiner, O., and Hirschmann, H. (1937). *J. Biol. Chem.* **119**, cvii.

Wintersteiner, O., Schwenk, E., and Whitman, B. (1935). *Proc. Soc. Exptl. Biol. Med.* **32**, 1087–1088.

Wintersteiner, O., Schwenk, E., Hirschmann, H., and Whitman, B. (1936). *J. Am. Chem. Soc.* **58**, 2652–2653.

Wiquist, N. (1959). *Acta Endocrinol. Suppl.* **46**, 15–32.

Witschi, E. (1953). *J. Clin. Endocrinol. and Metabolism* **13**, 316–329.

Witschi, E. (1961). *In* "Biology and Comparative Physiology of Birds" (A. J. Marshall, ed), Vol. 2, pp. 115–168. Academic Press, New York.

Wolff, M. E., and Ginglinger, A. (1935). *Arch. Anat. histol. et embryol.* **20**, 219–278.

Wotiz, H. H., Botticelli, C., Hisaw, F. L., Jr., and Ringler, I. (1958). *J. Biol. Chem.* **231**, 589–592.

Wotiz, H. H., Botticelli, C. R., Hisaw, F. L., Jr., and Olsen, A. G. (1960). *Proc. Natl. Acad. Sci. U. S.* **46**, 580–583.

Wrenn, T. R., Bitman, J., and Sykes, J. F. (1958). *J. Dairy Sci.* **41**, 1071–1076.

Wright, A. A. (1958). *Vet. Record* **70**, 662–667.

Wright, A. A., and Klyne, W. (1955). *Proc. Intern. Congr. Biochem. 3rd Congr., Brussels, 1955, Abstr.* p. 139.

Yamamoto, T. (1953). *J. Exptl. Zool.* **123**, 571–594.

Young, W. C., ed. (1961). "Sex and Internal Secretions," 3rd Edition, 2 Vols. Williams & Wilkins, Baltimore, Maryland.

Zander, J. (1954). *Nature* **174**, 406–407.

Zander, J. (1955). *Klin. Wochschr.* **33**, 697–701.

Zander, J. (1957). *Klin. Wochschr.* **35**, 1101.

Zander, J. (1959). *In* "Recent Progress in Endocrinology of Reproduction" (C. W. Lloyd, ed.), pp. 255–282. Academic Press, New York.

Zander, J., and von Münstermann, A.-M. (1956). *Klin. Wochschr.* **34**, 944–953.

Zander, J., Forbes, T. R., von Münstermann, A.-M., and Neher, R. (1958). *J. Clin. Endocrinol. and Metabolism* **18**, 337–353.

Zander, J., Brendle, E., von Münstermann, A.-M., Diczfalusy, E., Martinsen, B., and Tillinger, K.-G. (1959). *Acta Obstet. Gynecol. Scand.* **38**, 724–736.

Zarrow, M. X. (1948). *Endocrinology* **42**, 129–140.

Zarrow, M. X. (1949). *Proc. Soc. Exptl. Biol. Med.* **71**, 705–707.

Zarrow, M. X., and Brennan, D. M. (1957). *Proc. Soc. Exptl. Biol. Med.* **95**, 745–747.

Zarrow, M. X., and Neher, G. M. (1955). *Endocrinology* **56**, 1–8.

Zarrow, M. X., Holmström, E. G., and Salhanick, H. A. (1955). *J. Clin. Endocrinol. and Metabolism* **15**, 22–27.

Zarrow, M. X., Neher, G. M., Sikes, D., Brennan, D. M., and Bullard, J. F. (1956). *Am. J. Obstet. Gynecol.* **72**, 260–264.

Zondek, B. (1934). *Nature* **133**, 209–210.

Zondek, B. (1937). *Folia clin. orient* **1**, 1–36.

~ *5* ~

Male Gonadal Hormones

G. J. VAN OORDT

University of Utrecht, Utrecht, The Netherlands

I. INTRODUCTION

From the remotest times, perhaps since prehistoric days, it is known that castrated domestic animals show great differences when compared with normal members of the same species. A bull, castrated as a young animal becomes a tame ox, which can be handled easily, and a castrated cockerel develops only very small head appendages; moreover, its behavior differs largely from that of a normal cock; the quiet capon does not crow and the pugnacity of the normal animal is not present.

Successful transplantations of testes were performed as long ago as in about 1770 by John Hunter, who in addition, in 1792, was the first to describe postcastrate changes in the accessory sex organs of mammals.

In Hunter's time and also during the first half of the nineteenth century it was still generally accepted that the functional relation between the gonads and the so-called secondary sexual characters was exclusively mediated through the nervous system; thus, it was thought that the changes occurring in a castrated animal were caused by the severance of the nerves between the testes and the rest of the body.

Experiments of Berthold (1849), however, were not in favor of this view; this investigator removed the testes of cocks from the normal site but left them in the body cavity between the intestines; moreover, he implanted the male gonads of another cock into the body cavity of a capon. If the concept of the nervous connection had been right, his experimental animals should have shown castration phenomena. This, however, was not so; the animals remained completely normal. At autopsy Berthold found that the testes had not regressed and had attached themselves to the wall of the body cavity, where they had become richly vascularized. Implantation experiments with testes into other parts of the body had the same result.

Although Berthold did not conclude that the testes secrete substances into the blood which influence other parts of the body, he was the first to assume that the influence exercised by the testes on the rest of the body is not mediated through the nervous system but should be ascribed to changes in the blood that circulates through the testes. Later Claude Bernard and his pupil Brown-Séquard expressed similar ideas.

Brown-Séquard's rejuvenation experiments (1889) in particular led to the concept that active substances which regulate certain processes in the body are present in the testes. It took, however, several decades before David et al. (1935) in Laqueur's laboratory succeeded to obtain a pure, active extract from bull testicles. But since Brown-Séquard attempted to prepare testis extracts for the first time, he may be regarded as the founder of modern sex hormone research.

Several important papers relating to the internal secretion of the testis were published during the end of the nineteenth and the beginning of the twentieth centuries.

In 1894 Steinach reported that in castrated male frogs the copulation pads and the strong musculature of the forelegs regress so that amplexus is no longer performed. Moreover, he found in castrated juvenile male rats that such accessory sex glands as the prostate and vesicular glands[1] remain very small and that neither erection nor copulation occur in castrated adults.

---

[1] Usually called seminal vesicles erroneously.

Bouin and Ancel concluded in 1903 that the mammalian testis hormone is formed in the interstitial or Leydig cells. Some years later the castration experiments with fowls of Pézard (1911, 1918) and the masculinizing and feminizing experiments of Steinach (1912, 1913) and of his associate Lipschütz (1919) attracted much attention. When after about 1935 chemically pure sex hormones became available, these investigations stimulated much other work, first mainly concerned with morphological and later with functional aspects.

II. PHYSIOLOGY OF THE ANDROGENS

In vertebrate embryos the Müllerian as well as the Wolffian ducts with their accessory organs are generally present in both sexes. In the male embryo the Wolffian ducts and their derivatives develop further, whereas the Müllerian ducts and their derivatives remain rudimentary. The reverse applies to the female embryo.

In young or adult animals the accessory sex organs react readily to castration and to heterologous gonad transplantations or to administration of heterologous sex hormones. Thus, the sex hormones do not induce new characteristics but (like other hormones) only modify the development of pre-existing physical or mental characters.

It should also be stressed that frequently the results of hypophysectomy resemble those of castration: hypophysectomy is followed by regression of the gonads and when the latter is very pronounced castration effects develop. A good example of this has been given recently by Dodd et al. (1960), who described the results of hypophysectomy in the male lamprey, Lampetra fluviatilis.

Experiments relating to castration, transplantation of gonads and administration of sex hormones, have been done in representatives of nearly all vertebrate classes.

A. Secondary Sexual and Ambisexual Characters

In male vertebrates the testis hormone causes the phenomena related to male copulatory behavior and develops and maintains the so-called secondary sexual characters. The latter can be defined as the characters, morphological, physiological, or mental, by which the male and the female of a certain species differ from each other. The gonads are defined as the primary sexual characters. According to this definition the accessory sexual glands and organs are considered secondary sexual characters.[2]

---

[2] For convenience "sex characters" will be used instead of "secondary sexual characters."

Scientific castration experiments have shown that some sex characters change after castration, and are consequently influenced by the sex hormones (dependent sex characters)[3] but that others are not affected by gonadectomy and they are therefore called independent sex characters.

This may be elucidated by an example derived from investigations on birds.

When a male of one of the common breeds of poultry, for instance a single-combed Brown Leghorn, is castrated, either as a chicken or as a cockerel or cock, the following differences from control animals appear after some time (Pézard, 1911, 1918; Zawadowsky, 1922): the head appendages (comb, wattles, and ear lobes) are small and pale; the carriage of the bird is not erect, and the male sexual instinct is absent. Capons do not crow and fight each other, and they no longer take interest in the normal hens of the pen. The weight of the castrated animal increases, owing to deposition of fat (Horowitz, 1934). Castration, however, does not influence the development of the spurs in chickens; on the contrary, in capons the spurs generally develop even more strongly than in normal birds. Neither is the plumage affected by castration: thus a capon possesses the same beautifully colored long feathers on neck, shoulders, rump, and tail as the normal cock (Fig. 1). Further, the size of the bird is not affected by castration. Of the internal organs the ductus deferens remains thin and straight in a capon, castrated as a chicken (Domm, 1927).

It may therefore be concluded that in cocks of the Leghorn breed the following sex characters are dependent on the testis hormone: the carriage of the cock, the marked development of the head appendages, the male sexual instinct and behavior, and the convoluted deferent ducts. Independent sex characters, i.e., sex characters which are not affected by castration, are the plumage, the size of the bird, and the development of large spurs. With the exception of the size, which is a genetic characteristic in both sexes, a young ovariectomized female chicken develops into a castrate with the same characteristics as a capon of the same breed (cf. Fig. 1). For instance, the plumage of the cock or capon develops also in the ovariectomized hen. It is clear, therefore, that in the female the development of the cocky plumage is inhibited by the ovary. It can thus be said that after castration the male as well as the female chicken are turned into a "neutral" animal. (For further changes which occur in ovariectomized hens with regard to the right gonad, see Section II,E.)

---

[3] In many instances these characters appear also to be dependent, partly or wholly, on other hormones. For instance, the head appendages of Leghorn cocks and hens are also under the influence of estrogen and progesterone (Bolton, 1953) or of the thyroid hormone (Blivaiss, 1947, 1951; Brard, 1953) and the breeding plumage of male weaver finches is mediated (see Section II, E) by the adenohypophysis (Witschi, 1937a).

FIG. 1. Brown Leghorns; (*a*) a castrated male or female bird; (*b*) a normal hen, and (*c*) a normal cock. After Pézard, from Sand (1926).

In some species in which the male and female possess the same external appearance, characters may be present which are dependent on the gonads in both sexes. In addition to the plumages of the hen-feathered poultry breeds (see Section II,E) a good example of such "ambisexual" characters is the yellow bill of the male and female starling (*Sturnus vulgaris*) during the reproductive period [outside this period or after castration the bill becomes dark in both sexes (Witschi and Fugo, 1940)]. The almost black head, and the crimson bill and feet of the male and female European black-headed gull (*Larus ridibundus*) and the North American laughing gull (*L. atricilla*) during the breeding period provide other examples.

Van Oordt and Junge (1933) have demonstrated that in the black-headed gull, castrated in the nonbreeding season, the dark head and the crimson bill and feet do not develop during the next reproductive period and Noble and Wurm (1940) have observed the same phenomenon in the castrated male as well as in the ovariectomized female laughing gull.

B. Action of Androgens in Fishes

The lampreys (Petromyzontidae) possess well-developed sex characters in both sexes, but castration experiments have not as yet been performed.

Knowles has shown (1939) that testosterone[4] and estrogen injected into immature lampreys induce changes associated with sexual maturity. Following injection of testosterone or estrogen the cloacal labia of immature male or female adults became swollen; ammocoetes reacted only slightly.

In elasmobranchs some investigations have shown the existence of sex characters, dependent on the male hormone. Hisaw and Abramowitz (1939), Goddard and Dodd (cf. Dodd, 1955), and Thiebold (1954) have found some growth of the claspers after the administration of testosterone to embryonic and young sharks or skates.

Teleosts, which usually have pronounced sex characteristics, have often been used for castration experiments. Castrated male sticklebacks (*Gasterosteus* sp.) lose their nest-building instinct (Bock, 1928; Craig-Bennett, 1931). As in the Japanese bitterling, *Acheilognathus* (Tozawa, 1929), the beautiful nuptial coloration (caused in *Gasterosteus aculeatus* mainly by pigment dispersal in the erythrophores) does not develop after castration. Moreover, the kidney tubules, which in the male increase markedly in diameter during the reproductive season (Fig. 2) and secrete the mucus with which particles of the nest are attached to each other, return to the nonbreeding condition after total castration and can again be increased in size by administration of testosterone (Craig-Bennett, 1931; Ikeda, 1933; Ogura, 1958). The same phenomenon could be established by Ogura (1958) by injecting testosterone into female *Gasterosteus*. According to Tavolga (1955) the seminal vesicles of *Bathygobius* are also dependent on the male sex hormone.

In many other teleosts seasonal assumption of nuptial coloration as well as permanent sexual differences in pigmentation have been obtained by administration of testosterone (see Pickford and Atz, 1957, p. 37). That the gonads influence the sex characters follows also from the fact that in functional sex reversal many sex characters are also changed.

---

[4] The term testosterone will be used when the chemically pure testis hormone is considered; "androgen" refers to the testis hormone generally.

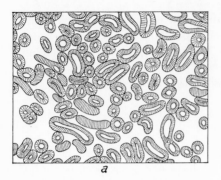 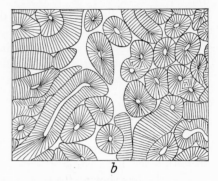

| *a* | *b* |

FIG. 2. Sections through kidneys of a stickleback, *Gasterosteus pungitius*; (a) during the autumn and (b) during the reproductive period. After van Oordt (1924).

In the cyprinodonts, a teleost family in which most males have very distinct sex characters, it has been found that many of these characters [e.g., the gonopodium, a transformed anal fin or the "sword," the elongated tail fin and the pointed pectoral fins of the swordtail, *Xiphophorus helleri* (see Fig. 3), are dependent on the testis hormone (cf. Régnier, 1938; Eversole, 1939; Grobstein, 1942; Turner, 1942; Vivien, 1952)].

If testosterone propionate is administered to female guppies (*Lebistes reticulatus*) male sex characters are formed in the same order of appearance as during the normal development of the male (Hildemann, 1954). In castrated male guppies, in which the gonopodia have been removed, femalelike anal fins are regenerated (Hopper, 1949). Ishii and Egami (1957) have pointed out that under the influence of testosterone the anterior rays of the dorsal fin of juvenile male as well as female filefish (*Monacanthus cirrhifer*) resemble the adult male.

According to Ishii (1960), testosterone pellets implanted in pregnant females of *Ditrema temmincki* cause the death of the embryos and regression of the ovary walls.

During the breeding season the adult male of the minnow (*Hyborhynchus*) is characterized by several tubercles on the head, whereas the female possesses a large anal papilla. By injecting testosterone propionate Ramaswami and Hasler (1955) induced the growth of tubercles in males outside the breeding season as well as in females; in the latter, however, a paradoxical effect was obtained in addition: the anal papilla increased enormously. Ramaswami and Hasler think therefore that in female *Hyborhynchus* factors for tubercle development are inherently present, and that under normal conditions the tubercle growth in the female is suppressed by the ovary. Similarly, in *Amia* the caudal ocellus, present in males only, develops in females after ovariectomy (Zahl and Davis, 1932).

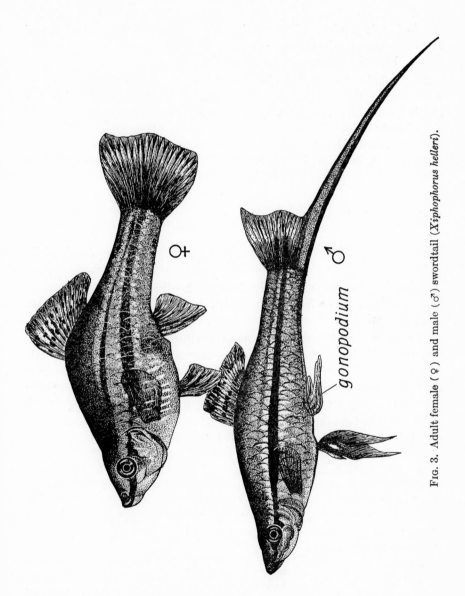

Fig. 3. Adult female (♀) and male (♂) swordtail (*Xiphophorus helleri*).

Papers on the effect of testis transplantation or the administration of androgens to normal or ovariectomized female fishes are numerous. Okada and Yamashita (1944), for instance, succeeded in producing masculinization in female ovariectomized *Oryzias latipes* after testis implantation, and in the female loach (*Misgurnus anguillicaudatus*) male sex characters develop after the same procedure (Egami, 1954).

To conclude, the morphological sex characters of most male teleosts are dependent on the male gonad. In castrated male teleosts, or in normal or ovariectomized females the sex characters proper to the male develop after the administration of androgens (of synthetic or mammalian origin). Frequently reproductive behavior is also regulated by the sex hormones. In some species, however, it seems to be dependent on the central nervous system or on the adenohypophysis (see Section II, G).

C. Action of Androgens in Amphibians

Urodeles as well as anurans have been used as experimental animals in castration, gonad transplantation, and sex hormone experiments.

Steinach (1894) was apparently the first who did castration experiments in amphibians. Later Nussbaum (1909), Aron (1924, 1926, 1927, 1929), and many others continued and extended his investigations.

Castration experiments in the newt, *Triturus cristatus*, showed that, e.g., the following periodical sex characters are dependent on the male sex hormone (Aron, 1924): the nuptial dress, of which the high tailcrest is the main feature, and the pronounced development of the cloacal glands.

In male anurans belonging to the genera *Rana* and *Bufo*, it was found that the marked development of the "thumb-pads" or copulation-callosities and their glands, of the strong muscles of the forelegs, and of the epithelium of the seminal vesicle are caused by the male sex hormone (Aron, 1926). Conversely, testosterone produced precocious thumb-pads in prepuberal male toads (*Bufo arenarum*) (Penhos, 1956). Steinach (1894, 1910) found that in male frogs, castrated some time earlier, the clasping reflex appears in the next breeding season, but is subsequently reduced or even lost. Similarly, Burgos (1950) found that the clasping reflex disappeared gradually in castrated toads.

Since all sexual characters are potentially present in both sexes (see Section II, p. 156), it is understandable that testes, grafted into ovariectomized females, cause the development of male sex characters. Welti (1925, 1928), for example, in ovariectomized female *Bufo bufo* was able to induce thumbpads, sex call, and mating behavior by grafting testes.

D. Action of Androgens in Reptiles

This vertebrate class has been scantily investigated.

Sauria. In lizards the skin coloration, dorsal crests and spines, femoral and pre-anal pores, the epididymis, and the urinary sex segment are distinct male sex characters. Mathey (1929), Padoa (1933) and Neeser (1940) showed in male lizards that after castration the femoral glands and the skin pigmentation become identical (femoral glands) or almost identical (skin pigmentation) with those of the female. Herlant (1933) and Regamey (1935) found that in the male lizard the sex segment of the kidney is dependent on testosterone. Takewaki and Fukuda (1935) observed that testis implantation in castrated male *Takydromus* causes regeneration of the kidneys and that the regressed epididymis becomes again secretory. According to Kehl and Combescot (1955), the female urinary sex segment of *Uromastix* after the injection of androsterone is changed into a segment similar to that of the male; testosterone has also a masculinizing effect on the female ducts of this lizard.

Ophidia. No experiments on the regulation of the sexual characters by the reproductive glands have been performed in snakes.

Crocodilia. Forbes (1938, 1939) pointed out that in young alligators (*Alligator mississipiensis*) the genital tubercles of both sexes hypertrophy after administration of testosterone propionate. In the female the oviducts were paradoxically stimulated, in young male alligators the epididymis and ductus deferens hypertrophied after intra-abdominal implantation of testosterone pellets.

Chelonia. Risley (1941) has reported that testosterone propionate, injected into 2-month-old female *Malaclemmys*, masculinized the sex ducts and copulatory organ; the same applied to young specimens of *Emys leprosa* (Stefan, 1958). Moreover, Evans (1951a, 1951b, 1952) found that in male *Pseudemys scripta* the tail and the claws of the forelegs (and in male *Terrapene carolina* the claws of the rear legs), which play an important role during mating, are dependent on the male sex hormone.

E. Action of Androgens in Birds

The dependence of the plumage on the gonads varies widely in avian species. In the house sparrow (*Passer domesticus*), for instance, plumage of both males and females is independent (Keck, 1934). According to Zawadowsky (1926b) and Hachlow (1927), this is so also in the chaffinch (*Fringilla coelebs*) and in the bullfinch (*Pyrrhula pyrrhula*). Nowikow (1939) even found that in the ptarmigan (*Lagopus mutus*), in which the male has four and the female three different successive types of plumage in the

Fig. 4. Castrated ruff (*Philomachus pugnax*); plumage resembles that of a reeve during the summer. After van Oordt and Junge (1936).

course of a year, the same types of plumage succeed each other after castration. In the male ostrich the long feathers are an independent sex character (Duerden, 1919). In the ruff (*Philomachus pugnax*) the beautiful male breeding plumage, which is only present during the reproductive period, is a dependent character (Figs. 4 and 5). It is also accepted that the female plumage, worn by the reeve during the whole year, is not dependent on the ovaries (van Oordt and Junge, 1936).

Keck (1934) has stated that the bill color of the male sparrow (*Passer domesticus*) is a dependent character: in spring, under the influence of testosterone, black pigment is deposited in the horn-colored bill. In the female red-billed weaverbird (*Quelea quelea*), however, during the breeding season the ovary inhibits the deposition of red pigment in the bill

FIG. 5. Castrated ruff (*Philomachus pugnax*) with a regenerated testis; plumage resembles that of a normal ruff during the reproductive period. After van Oordt and Junge (1936).

which turns bright yellow. In ovariectomized birds and in birds outside the breeding season the bill is red in both sexes (Witschi, 1937a).

Many experiments have also been done in which testis hormones have been injected or testes have been implanted into intact or ovariectomized adult female birds. No unexpected results have been obtained; generally, sex characters dependent on the testis hormone develop in the experimental animals. In intact female birds characters appropriate to both sexes can be obtained.

It follows from the castration experiments reported that the sex hormones have stimulating as well as inhibitory activities. Neither the male nor the female hormone are stored in the body; indications of gonadal insufficiency appear therefore very soon after castration.

It has also been established—first by Pézard (1922)—that there are no intermediate stable states between the castrate and the normal male with fully developed sex characters. Pézard stressed the fact that, as a rule, the development of the sex characters follows an "all-or-none" law, i.e., the sex characters develop as the hormonal threshold is reached, and if so, they develop fully. This threshold differs for different organs. However, in some instances this law does not appear to be valid (see, e.g., Benoit, 1927).

The results of Rowan (1926, 1938) in Canada, who exposed juncos (*Junco hyemalis*) in the autumn to ordinary electric light and obtained male birds in full spring condition in midwinter (i.e., singing birds with large, fertile gonads) suggested to him that the sex hormones play a prominent role in starting the northward migration in spring. Since, however, castrated birds also migrate (Rowan, 1932; Putzig, 1937, 1938; Hann, 1939) the role which the gonads play in migration cannot be as important as Rowan thought. From more recent investigations, especially those of Wolfson who found (1945) that photo-stimulation leading to gonad activation is followed by fat deposition in migratory, but not in nonmigratory birds, it may be assumed that this fat deposition is induced by the sex hormone.

Investigations on a breed of birds in which the sexes strongly differ from each other were described (Section II,A) when the regulation of the sex characters by the gonads was discussed. In the "hen-feathered" breeds, however, the cock and the hen possess the same "henny" plumage. In the Sebright Bantam for example, the hen-feathered cocks are distinguishable from the hens by their size, the strongly developed head appendages, the spurs, the sexual behavior, etc., but not by the feathers, which are "henny," i.e., short in both sexes. When the cocks are castrated, they develop during the next molt a plumage which differs completely from the typical plumage of the breed, but which is present in the cocks of most other breeds of fowls, i.e., "long" neck-, shoulder-, rump-, and tail feathers are grown (Morgan, 1919; Roxas, 1926; Eliot, 1928). Ovariectomized hens of this breed wear the same long feathers as the Sebright Bantam capon. Hence the neutral plumage of the hen-feathered breeds is different from the cock's as well as from the hen's plumage; the development of the "cocky" plumage is inhibited by the testes. In the normal breeds the cock's plumage represents the neutral one.

Finally, the interesting results of work on sex reversal in hens should briefly be mentioned. True functional sex reversal has been obtained in addition to the changes caused in the hen after ablation of the left ovary (see Section II, A). It may occur that the right, rudimentary gonad of such ovariectomized hens regenerates some time after the operation (after several months) (Fig. 6) and is transformed into a hormone-secreting and even sperm-producing testis (Benoit, 1923; Zawadowsky, 1926a; Domm, 1927, 1929a,b). Such birds begin to crow and the small head appendages of the ovariectomized hen develop into large ones, indistinguishable from

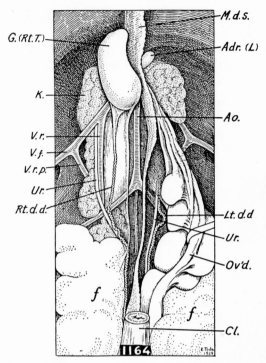

FIG. 6. Internal reproductive organs of an ovariectomized hen. The right gonad has developed into a testis. After Domm (1931).

those of a normal cock. At autopsy convoluted deferent ducts may be found. The hormone secreted by the right gonad is thought to be testosterone or a closely related compound. Hewitt (1947) has claimed that the presence of intact adrenals is essential to the transformation of the right gonad into a testis.

Summing up, we can say that the testis hormone has a very pronounced effect on many avian sex characters. However, the development of at least some sex characters may also be regulated by other hormones (see also footnote 3).

In weaver finches of the genera *Euplectes*, *Vidua*, and *Pyromelana*, the anterior pituitary and gonadal hormones cooperate in regulating the plumage (Witschi, 1937a). According to this author the male birds, which during the period of sexual quiescence wear the same modest plumage as the females, grow their brilliant plumage under the influence of the pituitary; if a female bird is ovariectomized it also acquires this plumage in the breeding season. In the intact female, however, the ovary impedes this development, and in the male the testis hormones have no influence on it;

castrated birds show the same sequence of plumage during the year as normal birds. Witschi has shown that the anterior pituitary is responsible for the appearance of the beautiful nuptial plumage. According to Segal (1957) the active principle is the luteinizing factor (LH).

F. Action of Androgens in Mammals

Although the mammals are exceptionally suitable for the study of the relationship between the gonads and the accessory sex organs, it is beyond the scope of this book to treat the results obtained extensively. Examples only will be given.

1. REGULATION OF HAIR COLOR

According to Zawadowsky who studied castration effects in ruminants (1922, 1929), the hair color of the bull of a certain breed of Ukrainian cattle and of the male of the antelope *Portax pictus* is dependent on the testis (Fig. 7). After castration of young bulls or male *Portax* antelopes the castrates acquire the same hair color as the female; thus the hair color of the latter is an independent sex character.

2. ANTLERS OF DEER

Already Fowler (1894), quoting Russell (1755), pointed out that in young castrated deer the antlers do not develop, and that if the deer is castrated when it carries antlers, they are not cast off. It has also been known for a long time that in old male roe deer (*Capreolus capreolus*), in which the male sex hormone is apparently no longer secreted, the velvet of the antlers is not shed and that the antlers persist after the midwinter period of reproduction. Since the velvet continues to grow steadily, it assumes the form of a wig ("wig-antlers").

In the white-tailed deer (*Odocoileus virginianus*) in which the growth of the visible antler starts in April, and in which the velvet is shed in September, Wislocki *et al.* (1947) and Waldo and Wislocki (1951), in castration experiments, have found that the male sex hormone is responsible for the shedding of the velvet, turning living skin into dead skin. When the testes regress, the casting off of the antlers follows. The maximal regression of the testes and of the male accessory glands occurs at the time when the antlers begin to grow. When the animal is castrated after the velvet has been shed, the calcified antlers are cast off; in the next year they are renewed and then retained. The hypothesis of Waldo and Wislocki (1951) that antler growth is mediated by the adenohypophysis and that the

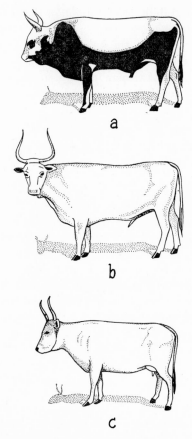

FIG. 7. A normal bull (*a*), an ox (*b*), and a normal cow (*c*) of the same Ukrainian breed. After Zawadowsky (1922).

hormones of the adenohypophysis and of the testes supplement each other in the regulation of the periodicity of antler growth was proved by Hall *et al.* (1960) who succeeded in hypophysectomizing a young male white-tailed deer, and observed that the antlers did not grow at all. From these results and from those of Waldo and Wislocki, Hall *et al.* concluded that antler growth in late winter is initiated by the adenohypophysis, probably in response to the lengthening days (for the influence of light on testicular functions see Section II,E). Later (in July), when the secretion of testicular androgen, influenced by the pituitary, follows, antler growth is almost complete. It is thought that the "antler-growth" adenohypophyseal hormone is inhibited by androgen secretion and that as a result the velvet dries out and is cast off in August or September. The testicular androgens appear to maintain the stability of the union of the dead antler tissue with the live frontal bone. When the days are short, the stimulation of the testes by the pituitary declines, the union between antlers and bone is no longer supported and the antlers are shed (December). During the winter the adenohypophyseal and testicular function and antler growth are all at low ebb, but in late winter the cycle is resumed.

 3. ACCESSORY SEX ORGANS

After John Hunter's classic work (1792) more than a century passed before Steinach (1894, 1910) made similar investigations on a larger scale.

He found that in castrated male rats and guinea pigs the accessory sex organs (vesicular glands, coagulatory glands, the prostate, Cowper's glands, the penis, preputial glands, and scrotal sacs) showed not only a marked decrease in size but also in function. After implantation of testes into castrated animals the organs recovered. He showed also that after transplantation of gonads of the other sex into castrated or spayed animals the accessory organs developed under the influence of the hormone secreted by the transplanted gland. One of the most conspicuous examples of this has been described by Steinach's co-worker Lipschütz (1918a) and by Sand (1926) who noted that after a testis had been transplanted into a spayed guinea pig or rat, the clitoris developed into a large penislike structure (Fig. 8).

The submandibular salivary glands[5] of the mouse are also dependent on the male sex hormone. Lacassagne (1940a) found that these glands are larger in the male than in the female, and that after extirpation of the testes the serous tubules of the submandibular gland regress in size. The glands assume female characteristics but revert to the male type after an injection of testosterone. The salivary glands in the female mouse remain almost unchanged after ovariectomy (Lacassagne, 1940b). The enzyme content of the saliva secreted by the submandibulary glands is also dependent on the male sex hormone (Raynaud and Rebeyrotte, 1949); the enzymatic activity is greater in males than in females. It decreases in males after castration, and increases in females after the injection of testosterone.

Since thyroidectomy produces this atrophy of the serous tubules of the submandibulary gland and atrophy is more pronounced after hypophysectomy than after castration (Lacassagne and Chamorro, 1940), it is thought (Leblond and Grad, 1948; Grad and Leblond, 1949) that the thyroid gland is also necessary for the maintenance of the serous tubules.

---

[5] Often erroneously called "submaxillary salivary glands."

FIG. 8. External genital organs of (a) an ovariectomized female rat, (b) a masculinized female rat with markedly hypertrophied clitoris, and (c) a normal male rat. After Sand (1926).

When testosterone is administered to hypophysectomized mice the amylase content of the atrophic gland increases. It is assumed therefore that testosterone affects the amylase content directly (Mühlbock *et al.*, 1953).

4. SPERMATOGENESIS

The results of investigations on the influence of testosterone on mammalian spermatogenesis have often been contradictory, but it is usually accepted that testosterone has a stimulating effect on this process. It has been stated by Walsh *et al.* (1934) and confirmed by Nelson (1940) and Wells (1942) that in hypophysectomized rats the degeneration of the

seminal epithelium can be prevented and spermatogenesis can be maintained by normal doses of injected testosterone. According to Gaarenstroom and de Jongh (1946, p. 11), this depends on a lengthening of the
duration of life of the sperm cells (maintenance effect). Moreover, testosterone supports the growth of the seminiferous tubules under the influence
of the pituitary follicle stimulating hormone (FSH). Gaarenstroom and de
Jongh believe, therefore, that for normal spermatogenesis in mammals two
factors are necessary: FSH and a certain amount of testosterone within the
testis.

On the other hand, testosterone, injected in large quantities into normal
mammals, seems to depress the gonadotropic action of the anterior pituitary and this is followed by a decrease of the testosterone concentration in
the testis and a regression of spermatogenesis. If, however, testosterone is
withdrawn, the gonadotropic hormone is secreted in increased quantities
and spermatogenesis may even be enhanced (rebound-phenomenon; Heller
et al., 1950).

In addition it must be mentioned that Riisfeldt (1949) found in rats that
the amount of hyaluronidase in the testes increases under the influence of
androgens.

In amphibians Blair (1946), Penhos (1953, 1956), and Iwasawa (1957)
have shown that after administration of testosterone spermatogenesis is
slightly stimulated or that the testicular weight increases. However, these
authors did not state whether the whole spermatogenetic process or only
part of it is affected by testosterone. Cei et al. (1955) and P. G. W. J. van
Oordt and Basu (1960) investigating Leptodactylus chaquensis and Rana
temporaria obtained the following almost identical results. In Leptodactylus
large doses of testosterone caused degeneration of the secondary spermatogonia and primary spermatocytes, and the mitotic capacity of the
primary spermatogonia was impeded; in Rana temporaria the implantation
of testosterone pellets was followed by impaired formation and development of secondary spermatogonia but the mitotic capacity of the primary
spermatogonia was not affected. The primary and secondary spermatocytes
and the spermatids were slightly stimulated. Testosterone was also found
to impair the formation and development of the secondary spermatogonia
in Rana esculenta (P. G. W. J. van Oordt and Schouten, 1961). Since in
almost all amphibians the period of the most intense spermatogenetic
activity does not correspond with the secretory activity of the interstitial
cells, P. G. W. J. van Oordt concluded in his survey (1960) that normally
the male sex hormone does not stimulate the development of spermatocytes
and spermatids and that in amphibians with a discontinuous spermato-

genetic cycle the male sex hormone might be one of the factors preventing the onset of spermatogenesis during the resting and spermiation periods.

It is generally accepted that the normal influence of testosterone upon spermatogenesis is mainly an indirect one, i.e., that the hormone acts by way of the gonadotropic activity of the pituitary gland (see Section II, H).

5. MAMMALIAN SEMEN

Testosterone not only influences the vesicular glands, the prostate, and other accessory organs of the male mammal, but also the secretory function in the accessory glands, viz., the formation of fructose and citric acid. In castrated mammals these accessory glands are very small and both secretions are absent. If, however, androgens are administered the glands regenerate and fructose and citric acid reappear in the semen (Mann and Parsons, 1947; Mann, 1954, 1956; see also Section VI,B).

6. THERMOREGULATION OF THE SCROTUM

Andrews (1940) has described an interesting action of testosterone on the scrotum. In castrated mammals the capacity of the scrotum to relax and to contract in response to changes in environmental temperature is lost; thus, in the normal male the thermoregulatory function of the scrotum is controlled by the testes.

7. ACTION OF ANDROGENS IN THE FEMALE

The ovaries of many vertebrates are known to secrete androgens also (see Section III). Suitable animals (e.g., castrated and juvenile females, or females in the quiescent season, when the reproductive organs are small) will therefore react to injections of testosterone. For instance, testosterone appears to have a slight effect on the endometrium and on the opening of the vagina in prepubertal female rats and mice.

A direct influence of testosterone on mammalian ovaries has also been described. According to Gaarenstroom and de Jongh (1946, p. 87), the antra in the follicles of the rat ovary are formed under the influence of testosterone, which is presumably secreted by the interstitial cells of the ovary. These workers assume also that ovarian testosterone causes one or more blood vessels (which have grown out from the theca interna into the cumulus oophorus of the follicle) to burst at the distal ends; consequently the pressure in the follicle increases and ovulation follows. There is also some evidence, summarized by Folley and Malpress (1948), that testosterone causes mammary growth, especially when given with an adequate dose of estrogen.

The testicular hormone has also distinct actions on other endocrine glands:

8. ADENOHYPOPHYSIS

Although androgens are less effective than estrogens in inhibiting the gonadotropic function of the anterior pituitary, the effects of castration upon this gland are very distinct. This follows from the following observations: (a) After castration, the anterior pituitary gains in weight and secretes a larger quantity of gonadotropic hormones; this can be proved by implantation or by injection of an extract of such a gland into young female mice or by parabiosis. If in the latter case a castrated male or an ovariectomized female rat is united with a hypophysectomized female rat, the anterior hypophysis of the castrated or ovariectomized animal secretes such a large quantity of gonadotropic hormone that the gonads and, as a result of this, also the accessory organs of the hypophysectomized female, increase markedly in size (Fig. 9). (b) Distinct cytological effects of castration are detectable in the adenohypophysis: the so-called "castration cells" appear, i.e., strongly secreting chromophil cells, to which the formation of gonadotropic hormone is attributed. (c) The hypersecretion of the anterior lobe in a castrated male can be prevented by injection of testosterone or implantation of testes.

9. ADRENAL CORTEX

Not only the hypophyseal secretion of the gonadotropins but also that of adrenocorticotropin and of thyrotropin appears also to be controlled by the gonads. In particular, the influence of the sex hormones on the adrenocorticotropin secretion should be stressed. Corticotropin secretion is stimulated by small quantities of estrogens but inhibited by androgens. Corticotropin is, therefore, secreted in larger quantities by the female than by the male. After castration of a male mammal, the adrenal cortex increases slightly in weight, but decreases in weight in an ovariectomized female. In most mammals the cortex in the female is much more developed than in the male especially in the deeper layers (Parkes, 1945; Chester Jones, 1948). The sexual differences in the adrenal cortex must thus be considered as a true sex character.

In the embryonic adrenals of many mammals, and especially in the adrenals of newborn mice a "X-zone" is interposed between the cortical zonula reticularis and the medulla (Howard-Miller, 1927; Deanesly, 1928). This zone is particularly well developed in the young female mouse and adds much to the sexual differences in size between the adrenal cortices of young female and male animals. In young male mice the X-zone regresses

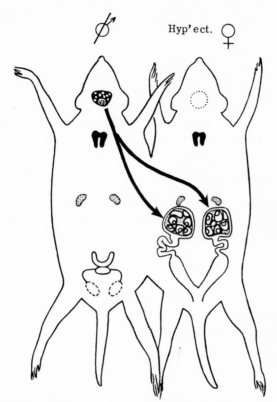

FIG. 9. Parabiosis of a male castrated and female hypophysectomized rat. The gonads and reproductive ducts of the hypophysectomized female have markedly increased in size. Slightly modified after Witschi from Houssay *et al.* (1955).

and is transformed into a connective tissue capsule. In female mice the X-zone persists until the first pregnancy. It also persists in young castrated male mice or it redevelops. After testosterone administration to normal young male mice the X-zone disappears precociously but in castrated young male mice injected with estrogen it is still present. It is probable, therefore, that the X-zone of young mice disappears due to the influence of the male sex hormone (Deanesly and Parkes, 1937). Sakiz (1958) found that the X-zone persists throughout life in ovariectomized mice, and that it reappears after castration of 34-day-old males.

The function of the X-zone is unknown. Grollman (1936) claimed that it produces androgens but this has been denied by Chester Jones (1955). Since, however, ACTH can stimulate the regression of the X-zone in both normal and ovariectomized virgin female mice, Deanesly (1958) has recently suggested that the mouse adrenal cortex itself produces androgens.

10. Metabolism

Information about the influence of androgens on the metabolism in the lower vertebrates is very limited. In fishes, Raffy and Fontaine (1930) noted an increase in oxygen consumption when male guppies (*Lebistes*) mature sexually, and in male goldfish when injected with extracts of carp pituitaries (Hasler and Meyer, 1942). Since this does not happen in castrated goldfish, this action must be mediated by the testes. An increase in oxygen consumption in young salmon after injection of methyltestosterone has also been reported (Hoar *et al.*, 1952).

In the immature fowl, increased nitrogen retention has been found after androgen administration (Jackson and Brown, 1958). In doves and fowl the male has a higher basic metabolic rate than the female. In castrated fowl and mammals the basal metabolic rate is subnormal. Whether this is mediated by the thyroid gland is not certain.

As long ago as in 1936 and 1937 Kochakian (Kochakian and Murlin, 1936; Kochakian, 1937, 1950) found that androgens cause nitrogen retention in the castrated dog. Since then, many investigations on the anabolic effect of androgen on proteins in mammals have been published. Body weight is increased and muscle growth stimulated.

Testosterone causes hypertrophy of the temporal muscles of prepubertally castrated male guinea pigs and of normal and spayed female guinea pigs (Papanicolaou and Falk, 1938). In the rat, however, only the perineal musculature reacts to testosterone. The respiration of the epithelium, but not that of the musculature of the vesicular glands, is also conditioned by the male sex hormone (Levey and Szego, 1955). The fact that androgens promote protein anabolism in the muscles serves as a basis for the Hershberger test (Hershberger *et al.*, 1953; see also Shemano *et al.*, 1951) in the rat. The weight of the levator ani in androgen-treated castrated rats is used as the index for the anabolic, and the weight of the glandula vesicularis as the index for the androgenic activity.

The anabolic action of testosterone in mammals is so strong that testosterone has been regarded as a growth hormone. Its action differs, however, from that of the somatotropic hormone.

11. Other Regulatory Effects of the Male Sex Hormone

The thymus increases after castration and regresses under the influence of androgens (and estrogens) (Plagge, 1953; Houssay *et al.*, 1955, p. 636). Gonadal hormones appear also to have a delaying action on body growth. This is very obvious in the human male, for after prepuberal castration the male develops long limbs because the epiphyseal fissures close later than normally. The muscles are weak. In high dosages testosterone propionate produces inhibition of hair growth in normal, castrated, and hypophysectomized rats (Houssay et al., 1960). Androgens have also a "renotropic" influence.

Finally it seems that androgens (like estrogens) enhance mitoses in certain organs as, for instance, in the epidermis of mouse ears (Bullough and van Oordt, 1950).[6] The increase in size of the sebaceous glands of mice after testosterone administration (de Graaf, 1942) may also be attributed to this mitogenic influence (Ebling, 1948, 1957).

G. Psychic Effects of Androgens

Sexual behavior is affected by the sex hormones. In fishes, there are distinct alterations of sexual behavior after ablation of the gonads. In castrated male sticklebacks (Gasterosteus aculeatus) nest-building activities are absent (Baggerman, 1957). Tavolga observed (1955) on the other hand that, after castration, males of the gobiid fish Bathygobius soporator show the same courtship behavior as intact males, and Aronson (1959) reported that in males of the cichlid fish Aquidens latifrons all elements of the mating pattern were still present up to $1\frac{1}{2}$ months after castration, whereas certain nest-building activities had noticeably declined. That in some fishes behavioral phenomena are not controlled by the testes has also been found by Noble and Kumpf (1936, 1941) in Hemichromis and in Betta and by Aronson (1951) in Tilapia.

It seems possible therefore that in some species the reproductive behavior is mainly regulated by the central nervous system or perhaps directly by the adenohypophysis. It has been claimed that the migratory behavior of some fishes is caused by the gonadal hormones. Since, however, sterile Colisa labiosa × lalia hybrids showed this behavior very markedly (Forselius, 1957), this assumption cannot be true (see Section II,E, which described the same phenomenon in castrated migratory birds).

In castrated male frogs, the clasping reflex is absent if castration is performed well before the breeding period (Steinach, 1910). Immature toads, on the other hand, treated with androgens will develop mating responses (Blair, 1946).

In reptiles, castrated male Anolis carolinensis show full sexual activity after the injection of testosterone (Noble and Greenberg, 1941).

As a rule, the sexual activities of castrated birds are reduced, notably when they are operated upon as young birds. Carpenter (1933), however,

---

[6] Carter (1953), however, holds the opposite opinion with respect to the influence of estrogen.

found that some of his completely castrated pigeons copulated after the operation, but later mating activities gradually declined.

Hamilton (1938) induced precocious aggressiveness and crowing in 10-day-old male Leghorn chicks by injecting testosterone propionate, and Noble and Zitrin (1942) evoked the complete sexual behavioral pattern of the adult cock in male chicks: crowing started on the fourth, and mating on the fifteenth day of age. In female canaries Leonard (1939), Shoemaker (1939), and Frederiks (1941) induced singing by the administration of testosterone.

The regulation of the behavioral pattern of the laughing gull (*Larus atricilla*) is particularly interesting. As mentioned before, the morphologically ambisexual characters of this species are regulated by testosterone in both sexes; this also applies to calls and postures, common to male and female, as well as to those of the male during the breeding period. Purely female behavior, however, is caused by estrogen (Noble and Wurm, 1940).

In conclusion some findings may be mentioned related to a phenomenon called "peck-order" by Allee (1942). It is well known (Schjelderup-Ebbe, 1922) that in a group of hens, confined together, some individuals dominate others by pecking but are not pecked in return. Thus a kind of social hierarchy exists in such a group, and if the position of one individual has been established it is usually permanent. It is thought that this behavior is based on recognition. A similar hierarchy is found in many animals, which live in groups (see Collias, 1944).

The hierarchy in a group of hens can be changed (Allee et al., 1947, 1955) by the injection of testosterone; if hens of lower rank are repeatedly injected with male sex hormone they improve their rank in the brood, and may even rise to the highest rank, dominating all others. It is, therefore, assumed that the rank in a brood of hens derives from the quantity of testosterone secreted by the ovaries of each bird. A similar rise in hierarchy was induced with testosterone by Noble and Borne (1940) in teleosts, i.e., in swordtails (*Xiphophorus helleri*), by Evans (1946) in a group of male reptiles (*Sceloporus*), and by Shoemaker (1939) in female canaries.

Although castrated male mammals may continue for long periods to show copulatory behavior to a diminished degree, it is generally accepted that androgens have an important but not an exclusive influence on sexual behavior and mating reactions; usually injections of testosterone restore normal behavior very soon. On the other hand, precocious sexual behavior can be easily induced by treatment with testosterone propionate in young male rats, but not in guinea pigs (Gerall, 1958). Beach (1947) has pointed out that in primates the sexual behavior in both males and females, castrated prepuberally, is much more pronounced than in castrated lower mammals.

It is thought that the stimulating effect of testosterone in the immature rat is mainly due to an increased tactile sensitivity of the glans penis, in which the cornified, genital papillae disappear in castrates. However, their number increases markedly under the influence of androgens (Beach and Levinson, 1950).

In female mammals estrus is chiefly regulated by estrogen; it has, however, been found that injection of large quantities of androgen can cause an estruslike behavior in prepuberally castrated female rats (Beach, 1942) or mating behavior in normal female rats (Koster, 1943). Male rats treated with testosterone may also show female mating behavior (Beach, 1941).

In his book "Hormones and Behavior" (1948) Beach has suggested that the sex hormones operate by sensitizing preorganized mechanisms within the central nervous system. Very important in this respect are the character and intensity of external stimuli offered by the presence of a receptive female; untreated male rats display the male copulatory behavior in the presence of estrous females.

H. Antagonism and Synergism of Androgens and Estrogens

Generally speaking the antagonism between the effects of the male and female hormones on the sex organs is an indirect one. This conclusion (Moore and Price, 1930, 1932) is based on the fact that androgens as well as estrogens inhibit the gonadotropic action of the adenohypophysis, or, according to recent investigations, impede the secretion by the hypothalamus of the gonadotropic hormone releaser. When, therefore, high doses of testosterone are injected into a normal female mammal, the gonadotropic activity of the anterior pituitary decreases and ovarial function is reduced followed by a regression of the female sex characters. Conversely, a regression of the male sex characters occurs after the injection of estrogen into normal male animals. Estrogens are more efficacious than androgens in this respect.

A direct effect of testosterone, when injected into an ovary of a guinea pig, has also been postulated (Marescaux and Deminatty, 1955). In hypophysectomized rats, Payne et al. (1956) found an inhibitory action of testosterone on the ovarial gain of weight induced by stilbestrol.

Moreover, there appears to be a direct antagonism between the effects of male and female hormones on the accessory sex organs. For instance, testosterone diminishes the local effect of estrogen on the cornification of the vaginal epithelium (Mellman et al., 1956), and the effect of androsterone on the capon's comb can be impeded by injecting estrogens simultaneously (Mühlbock, 1938; Hoskins and Koch, 1939). This effect on the capon's comb is held to be a direct one (Mühlbock, 1940). Bruzzone and Lipschütz (1953) found that the growth of the clitoris, produced by administering androgen to castrated female guinea pigs, can be considerably retarded by a simultaneous injection of small quantities of estradiol benzoate.

After pregnant mare serum had been given to juvenile female sparrows Pfeiffer and Kirschbaum (1941) found that their ovaries secreted an androgen so that their bill became jet black. When, however, estrogen was injected simultaneously, the bill remained yellow.

A summation of the effects of androgens and estrogens given in certain concentrations has been observed in some instances. For example, the normal structure of some accessory sex organs appears to be the result of the action of both androgen and estrogen (see Section III). Korenchevsky and Dennison (1936) demonstrated that testosterone is capable of enlarging the uterus and of increasing the gain of weight produced by estrogen. The same applied also to young spayed rats when both hormones were administered in high doses. Leathem and Wolf showed (1955) that in the immature rat a combination of testosterone propionate and estradiol benzoate produces larger vesicular glands than did either steroid alone. Again, androgens which normally inhibit the effect of estrogens (Dorfman and Shipley, 1956) can, when administered to young spayed rats in high doses, increase the uterine growth produced by large quantities of estrogens (Edgren et al., 1960).

III. THE ACTION OF TESTICULAR ESTROGEN AND OVARIAN TESTOSTERONE

It is well known that the testis produces not only the male hormone but also an estrogenic hormone, and that the ovary secretes not only estrogens but also androgens (see Ponse, 1955). The testicular estrogen has, in addition to testosterone, an important action on the development of certain male accessory organs.[7]

In the early 1930's de Jongh (Heringa and de Jongh, 1934) stressed this "paradoxical" influence of estrogen on such accessory male glands as the vesicular glands (or "seminal vesicles") and the prostate of some mammals (mouse, rat, guinea pig). When, on the other hand, castrated rats with rudimentary accessory glands were injected with testosterone, only the epithelium of the glands reacted. To induce the development of the fibromuscular parts of the vesicular glands and of the coagulatory part of the prostate, estrogen had to be injected as well.

---

[7] For a detailed survey of the influence of estrogens on the male accessory genital system, see Thorborg (1948).

Thus it became more and more probable that both testosterone and estrogen are necessary for the normal development of the accessory glands mentioned, and that their normal structure is the result of a synergistic action of both hormones (see also Section II, H, and Paesi *et al.*, 1953).

The fact that both male and female sex hormones are present in the urine of the male and female of many mammalian species provides a further indication that male and female sex hormones are formed in both sexes. Beall (1940) extracted estrogens from horse testes, and Zondek as long ago as in 1934 pointed out that large quantities of estrogen are present in the urine of the stallion, but none in the urine of geldings. If compounds with sex hormone activity persist in the urine of castrated animals, they are assumed to derive from the adrenal cortex.

The production of androgens by the ovaries has been demonstrated as follows: Pfeiffer and Kirschbaum (1941) showed that the yellow bills of sexually inactive female sparrows become jet black—like those of the male during the reproductive period—after pregnant mare serum has been administered. The much enlarged ovaries secreted an androgen comparable to that of the testis in the reproduction period.

It has already been pointed out in Section II,A, that the so-called ambisexual characters are dependent on the gonads. This is due to the influence of the male sex hormone, for in castrated male and female black-headed or laughing gulls (*Larus ridibundus* or *L. atricilla*) these characters do not appear. They develop in castrated male or female gulls after the administration of testosterone, but not of estrogen (Noble and Wurm, 1940). Thus we see that in the female gull the ovary secretes not only estrogen but also testosterone. The same holds for the starling, in which the yellow bill of both sexes represents an ambisexual character during the breeding season, caused by testosterone secreted by the testes or the ovary (Witschi and Fugo, 1940).

Since the comb of the hen of most poultry breeds is larger and more vascular than that of the capon, and becomes very turgid at the time of laying, it is thought that the left ovary, in addition to estrogen secretes a combgrowth-promoting substance, probably related to or perhaps identical with testosterone.

The gonads of cock-feathered and hen-feathered poultry breeds offer another interesting problem. In the first place, the question had to be answered whether there is a hormonal difference between the testes of a cock-feathered and of a hen-feathered breed. This has been answered in the negative (Roxas, 1926; Greenwood, 1928). For, when testes of a Leghorn (a cock-feathered breed) are exchanged for the testes of a hen-feathered breed (e.g., of a Campine or Sebright) the plumage of the experimental birds does not change.

Danforth and Foster (1929) and Danforth (1930) concluded from these experiments that the feather follicles of these breeds reacted differently to the female sex hormone, and Danforth formulated the hypothesis that the feather follicles of the hen-feathered cock are so sensitive to the estrogen secreted by the testis, that they react only to estrogen, or react better to estrogen than to the testosterone which is secreted by the testis. By means of skin transplantations in chicks of "normal" and "henny" feathered breeds Danforth and Foster (1929) produced convincing evidence for this hypothesis. In summary, their results were as follows: (a) Skin of a Leghorn hen (a "normal" breed) grafted on a Leghorn cock: development of cocky feathers in the transplant. (b) Skin of a Campine hen (a "henny" breed) grafted on a Leghorn cock: development of henny feathers. (c) Campine cock skin grafted on a Leghorn cock: development of henny feathers. (d) Leghorn cock skin grafted on a Campine cock: development of cocky feathers.

From these results and from the fact that no changes occur following cross-transplantations of Leghorn and Campine hen skin, it can be deduced that the testes secrete estrogen in addition to testosterone. According to Parkes and Emmens (1944), however, it is probable that the capacity of the testis to feminize the plumage in such a breed as the Sebright Bantam is due to the fact that the plumage reacts to testosterone in the same way as to estrogens.

The secretion of androgens by the ovaries of mammals has also been convincingly demonstrated. When, for instance, extracts of mammalian ovaries or ovarian transplants from mammals are brought into contact with sensitive receptors, the capon's comb (Parkes, 1937) or the vesicular gland of castrated adult rats (Katsh, 1950), the changes in the receptors indicate that androgens have been secreted by these ovaries.

This is particularly obvious when the ovaries have been stimulated by gonadotropins. Pfeiffer and Hooker (1942), for instance, transplanted ovaries to the ears of castrated male mice and later administered pregnant mare serum with the result that the vesicular glands were manifestly stimulated. Johnson (1958) connected a castrated male rat parabiotically with another castrated male in which an ovary was implanted. Because of the large quantity of gonadotropic hormone formed in the anterior hypophysis of the castrated male, the ovary of the other rat produced such large amounts of androgen that the ventral prostate of the male increased at least fivefold. When a female rat was parabiotically connected to a castrated female, the gonadotropin also stimulated the development of the residual prostatic tissue in the female by way of the enlarged ovaries (Fig. 10).

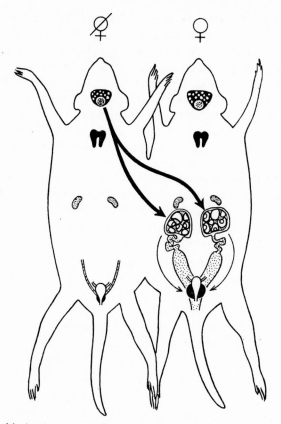

FIG. 10. Parabiosis of an ovariectomized female rat and a normal female rat. In the latter the ovaries have markedly increased in size; under the influence of the male hormone produced in these ovaries the female prostatic tissue has strongly developed. Slightly modified after Johnson (1958).

In conclusion it may be said that testosterone is neither a specific male nor estrogen a specific female hormone. Both sex hormones—though in different quantities—are necessary for the development of most, if not all, sex characters.

IV. SOURCE OF SEX HORMONES IN THE MALE

It is by now generally accepted that the mammalian testis produces only one male hormone, i.e., testosterone. The existence of a second testis hormone, "inhibin," was formerly postulated (Martins and Rocha, 1931; McCullagh, 1932); this hormone was supposed to inhibit the production of gonadotropins by the anterior pituitary. This is no longer accepted since the inhibiting action of the testis on the anterior hypophysis can be ascribed to testosterone or to estrogen, which as already mentioned is also secreted by the testes of mammals and birds (see also Ponse, 1955). Testicular estrogen has also an important influence on certain sexual characters (see Section III). Hence the entire physiological role of the testis derives from the secretion of testosterone and estrogens.

A. The Source of Testicular Androgen

The first biologists interested in the source of the male sex hormone were Bouin and Ancel, who claimed in 1903 that it is formed in the Leydig or interstitial cells, present in the interstitial tissue between the tubules. They concluded this from observations on cryptorchid pigs, in which the generative part of the testes was almost totally degenerated, whereas intact interstitial cells were present in normal quantities indicating that the sex characters were not affected. The same observations were made on animals with tied ductus deferentes.

This concept was later adopted by many other workers (e.g. Steinach, 1913; Lipschütz, 1918b). Steinach and Lipschütz even went so far as to call the sum of the interstitial cells the "puberty gland." Other workers however believed that the male sex hormone is produced in the generative part of the testis, i.e., in the testis tubules. The most prominent supporter of this theory was Stieve (1921).

In addition to the investigations on cryptorchid testes, a number of other results have been obtained which also demonstrate that the male sex hormone is secreted by the interstitial cells. For example, after irradiation with X-rays in doses which cause atrophy of the seminal epithelium without injury to the interstitial tissue, androgen continues to be secreted (Follenius, 1953). On having damaged the interstitial cells of the testes of rats by feeding a diet deficient in vitamin B complex, Moore and Samuels (1931) found that the seminal epithelium remained normal, but that the accessory sex glands like the prostate and the vesicular glands underwent atrophy.

It is now generally accepted that in the homeothermic amniotes the male sex hormone is secreted in the interstitial cells. This assumption rests on the following evidence: First, the appearance of secretory phenomena in interstitial cells is histologically demonstrable. Second, after the injection of interstitial cell-stimulating pituitary hormone into young mammals and birds or into birds during the nonreproductive period, the nonfunctional interstitial cells change into cells with a distinctly secretory appearance (Fig. 11). Third, these alterations are correlated with certain changes

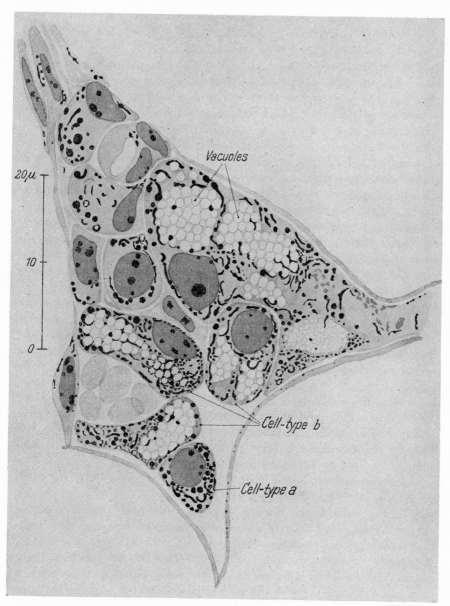

FIG. 11. Different types of interstitial cells of a male juvenile mouse, after having been treated with chorion gonadotropin. After Sluiter (1945).

in and developments of sex characters such as those occurring during the
reproductive period (Sluiter, 1945; Sluiter and van Oordt, 1947, 1949;
Taber, 1949; Marshall, 1949); and last, during this period the level of
17-ketosteroids in the urine rises (Nelson, 1956).

Although the presence of true Leydig cells in mammals and birds is well
established, it is still a matter of dispute in which part of the testis the
male hormone is secreted in fishes, amphibians, and reptiles.

Courrier in 1922 described interstitial cells in the testes of the three-
spined stickleback, *Gasterosteus aculeatus*, and correlated their presence
with the development of sex characters (nuptial coloration, development
of secretory kidney tubules). Van Oordt (1924) found that in the ten-
spined stickleback maximal numbers of interstitial cells are present after
the spermatogenetic period, whereas in the testes of *Xiphophorus helleri*
interstitial cells are lacking when the sex characters ("sword," gonopod,
and transformed pectoral fins) are developing (van Oordt, 1925; Régnier,
1938). According to Craig-Bennett (1931), however, the maximal development of interstitial cells in *Gasterosteus aculeatus* coincides with full male
nuptial coloration, and Follenius (1953) noted in guppies (*Lebistes reticulatus*) irradiated with X-rays that the tubules of the testis became sterile,
though the interstitial tissue was not affected and the development of the
sex characters proceeded normally.

A well-developed interstitial cell cycle has also been described in some
amphibian species, and a correlation with changes in sex characters has
been established. Although definite proof that the male sex hormone is
formed in the interstitial cells of the amphibian testis is still lacking, there
is some evidence for assuming this; the histochemical investigations of
Ashbel *et al.* (1951) and of Burgos (1955) in *Rana pipiens*, of Niwelinski
(1954) in *Xenopus laevis*, and of de Kort *et al.* (see P. G. W. J. van Oordt,
1960) in *Rana esculenta* indicate that the interstitial testis cells of these
amphibians produce ketosteroids. Moreover, Burgos and Ladman (1957)
have found that low doses of purified luteinizing hormone (LH) stimulate
the interstitial cells in *Rana pipiens*.

According to Kehl and Combescot (1955) the interstitial cells of the
saurians change seasonally in size, number, and structure, and alterations
in accessory sexual characters are associated with changes in the interstitial cells; therefore, a correlation between these two facts seems entirely
possible. In the lizard *Xantusia vigilis*, however, neither quantitative nor
qualitative changes occur in the interstitial cells of the testis at the time
the sex characters develop (M. R. Miller, 1948).

The available data on the histology and cytology of the interstitial cells
and their correlation to the development or maintenance of sex characters
in poikilothermic vertebrates are so scarce that detailed investigations
with up-to-date methods seem highly desirable.

B. The Source of Testicular Estrogen and of Ovarian Androgen

It has already been mentioned that the testes of mammals and birds secrete estrogen. It is not known, however, where this estrogen is formed. Some workers assume that its source is the Sertoli cells, since it has been observed that in animals with Sertoli cell tumors the quantity of secreted estrogen increases enormously. Others, like Maddock (Maddock and Nelson, 1952; Maddock et al., 1952), claim that estrogen is formed in the Leydig cells.

It has also been postulated that the androgen, found in the ovaries of birds and mammals, has its source in the ovarial interstitial cells (Taber, 1951; Marshall and Coombs, 1957), but definite information is lacking (see Parkes, 1950, 1955).

Many workers have claimed that the mammalian adrenal cortex produces corticosteroids with a masculinizing effect. For instance, Katsh et al. (1948) found that adrenal cortical tissue, transplanted to the vesicular gland in adult adrenalectomized and castrated rats, almost prevented the regression of this gland, which usually occurs after castration. The investigations of Deanesly (1958) make it likely that the X-zone of the mouse adrenal cortex produces androgens (see Section II,F,9).

It is, however, still doubtful whether the adrenal cortex secretes androgens under normal conditions. According to Chester Jones (1955), "there is evidence that the adrenal of young rats can at best secrete minute amounts of androgens transiently." But under clinical conditions (in the adrenogenital syndrome) there is "an unequivocal and copious adrenal secretion of sex hormones." On the other hand, Dorfman (1955) claims that four adrenal steroids produced by the adrenals may be designated as proandrogens, since they are in part metabolically converted to androgenic steroids.

It is also accepted that small amounts of androgen are formed by the placenta. For instance, Stark and Voss (1957) found an androgen in human placenta that activated the capon's comb.

To sum up, one can say that androgens are produced by the testis, ovary, adrenal cortex, and perhaps by the placenta. Testosterone is a product of the testis and perhaps also of the ovary but probably not of the adrenal cortex.

V. FACTORS REGULATING TESTICULAR FUNCTIONS

Testicular functions are regulated by interoceptive or internal and by exteroceptive or environmental factors.

One of the most important interoceptive factors is the gonadotropic influence of the adenohypophysis, a question fully treated in Chapter 13.

Another interoceptive factor which is particularly significant for the spermatogenesis of most mammals is the temperature-regulating function of the scrotum.

While the majority of the mammals possess scrotal sacs, some animals, viz., rhinoceroses, seals, elephants, and whales, are testicond, i.e., the testes remain in the abdominal cavity throughout life. Some Insectivores and Chiroptera have no typical scrotal sacs, but during the breeding season the thin abdominal wall is distended by the testes and thus forms a pseudo-scrotal sac. In most mammalian species there is, however, a true "descensus testiculorum." In many mammals the testes descend only during the reproductive period. In man and in domesticated mammals, the testes occasionally do not descend through the inguinal canal to the scrotal sac, but are retained in the abdominal cavity. Such cryptorchid testes are sterile, because sperm is not formed.

It was found, notably by Moore and his co-workers (Moore, 1926; Moore and Chase, 1923; Moore and Oslund, 1924; Moore and Quick, 1924) that testes of rats, guinea pigs, and rabbits when replaced through the wide inguinal canals into the abdominal cavity, became sterile after some weeks (experimental cryptorchism). In further experiments it was proved that this sterility is due to the fact that the temperature in the abdominal cavity is about 3°C higher than in the scrotal sac.

It follows from these findings that in mammals with a descensus testi-culorum normal sperm function is only possible at temperatures which are some degrees lower than that in the abdominal cavity. The interstitial cells are not affected by the high temperature; Bouin and Ancel (1903) have shown that cryptorchic mammals still possess their sex characters. This observation led these authors to assume that the male sex hormone is produced by the interstitial cells (cf. Section IV,A).

In many vertebrates which inhabit the temperate zones and also in animals exposed to the dry and rainy periods of the tropics, a very pro-nounced seasonal testicular (and ovarial) periodicity is present and ga-metogenesis is strictly a seasonal event. This periodicity is often influenced by exteroceptive factors, the most important of which are temperature and light.

In some fishes a rise in the environmental temperature appears to play a very important role in stimulating the testes and, indirectly, the male sex characters (*Gasterosteus*: Courrier, 1922; Craig-Bennett, 1931; *Apeltes*: Merriman and Schedl, 1941; *Fundulus*: Matthews, 1939; *Gambusia*: Medlen, 1951; *Rhodeus*: Verhoeven and van Oordt, 1955). In other fishes the influence of light is much more important than that of temperature.

In amphibians light does not seem to play a very important role (P. G. W. J. van Oordt, 1960). High temperatures, however, can strongly stimu-late spermatogenesis (P. G. W. J. van Oordt, 1956; van Oordt *et al.*, 1959).

In frog and toad tadpoles with undifferentiated gonads, Witschi (1914, 1929) found that the temperature is an effective factor in modifying the balance between the gonadal cortex and the medulla. High temperatures (25–30°C) favor the development of the medulla into a testis; low temperatures (10°C) inhibit the development of the medulla and favor that of the cortex. Thus male tadpoles dominate at high temperatures and female tadpoles at low ones.

The most extensive and valuable studies of the influence of light on testicular functions have been made in birds. Rowan (1926, 1929, 1932, 1938), working in Canada, discovered that light, but not temperature, affects the reproductive activities of certain species of birds in a very conspicuous manner. Because in spring the enlargement of the gonads of birds coincides with the increase in daylight, Rowan submitted juncos (*Junco hyemalis*, a North American species of bunting), in late autumn and in midwinter when their testes are minute, to increasing amounts of light by means of artificial illumination after sunset. Thus the length of day was increased and Rowan could induce a breeding condition in the male birds[8] during the winter months. At the end of December the male juncos were singing all the time, despite the very low temperatures (−20° to −45°C) at which they were kept. Post-mortem investigations revealed that their testes were much enlarged, spermatogenesis being maximal. Since these birds showed male reproductive behavior and characters, it was concluded that the interstitial cells were also stimulated.

Among seasonally breeding mammals Bissonnette (1932) found that the testes of ferrets, which were artificially illuminated outside the breeding season, matured precociously, and that female ferrets came into heat earlier under these circumstances. Species, such as the ground squirrels (*Citellus*), which hibernate underground and emerge in spring in full breeding condition failed to respond to light treatments in the laboratory (Wells, 1935).

It was concluded from these investigations that in temperate zones light, though not the only factor, plays a very important role in stimulating the gonads of male birds in spring.

In some instances it was found that it was not the longer duration of daylight in spring but the decrease in autumn which caused the gonads to develop. This applies to goats (Bissonnette, 1941) and sheep (Yeates, 1949) and also to deer since their rutting season occurs in autumn. The same phenomenon has been established in the brook trout (*Salvelinus fontinalis*), a species of fish which spawns in autumn (Hoover and Hubbard, 1937).

---

[8] The factors by which female songbirds can be brought to a breeding condition are more complex; light is one of these factors.

By which pathway does the stimulus of light influence the testes of birds? Bissonnette (1936), Ringoen and Kirschbaum (1937), and others experimented with birds which were completely draped in light-proof material, or which were made to wear silk caps with or without eyeholes over their heads. Benoit and his co-workers (Benoit, 1936; Benoit and Ott, 1944) exposed young ducks to high intensities of light after their optic nerves had been severed, or whose eyes had been blinded or completely removed, or which had been hypophysectomized. These experiments led to the conclusion that in normal birds light stimulates the anterior lobe of the pituitary by way of the eye and the central nervous system (the hypothalamus), and that the anterior lobe is activated to secrete gonadotropic hormones. These in turn act on the testis so that spermatogenesis starts and sperm cells are formed.

It is interesting that after the reproductive period has passed the testes do not react to light for a considerable time. This refractory period was first recognized in the starling by Bissonnette and Wadlund (1932), later emphasized by Riley (1936, 1937) and studied in detail by many other investigators, notably A. H. Miller (1948), Wolfson (1952, 1959), and Laws (1961).

This refractory period is very useful to birds, first because after the breeding season there is still enough light to maintain the enlargement of the gonads, and, second, because the migratory bird may during its southward flight reach low latitudes or even pass the equator (i.e., regions where the exposure to light increases). This would normally produce stimulation of the gonad but is prevented because the bird is temporarily refractory to light.

It is probable that the adenohypophysis and (or) the hypothalamus are insensitive to light during the refractory period. Thus, the testes do not react because they are not stimulated by injected gonadotropins (A. H. Miller, 1948).

In addition to the exteroceptive factors mentioned several other influences are known which affect reproductive processes. However, only darkness and confinement may be considered to influence reproduction or periodical reproductive phenomena unfavorably.

VI. BIOCHEMISTRY OF ANDROGENS

A. Isolation, Metabolism, and Biosynthesis

Although it is known that testicular extracts (see Section I) were prepared by Brown-Séquard (1889), and that McGee in 1927 obtained a preparation from bull testes which induced growth of capon's combs, it is now generally accepted that pure testicular hormone (testosterone) was first isolated in 1935 by David *et al.* in Laqueur's laboratory. Shortly afterward testosterone (Fig. 12,*e*) was synthesized by Butenandt and Hanisch (1935) and by Ruzicka (1935).

In mammals the group of androgens consists of several chemical substances, the most potent of which is testosterone. These compounds are synthesized in at least two endocrine glands (testis and ovary), and perhaps also in the adrenal cortex and in the placenta, as well as in peripheral tissues of which the liver is the most important.

The first studies on the metabolism of androgens were reported by Callow (1939) and by Dorfman *et al.* (1939), who found that testosterone was converted to the urinary 17-ketosteroids, androsterone (Fig. 12,*g*) and etiocholanolone (Fig. 12,*h*). The introduction of new techniques (microchromatography, spectrophotography, and isotopic labeling) greatly increased our knowledge of the biosynthesis and metabolism of the androgens. Popják (1958) has elucidated the biosynthetic pathway from acetate to the steroid molecule of cholesterol (Fig. 12,*a*) which is thought to be the basic material of all steroid hormones.

At present two major pathways for the biosynthesis of androgens have been established. The first concerns the testis and ovary, and perhaps to a limited extent the adrenals and probably also the placenta. This pathway is as follows: acetate → cholesterol (Fig. 12,*a*) → progesterone (Fig. 12,*c*) → androstenedione (Fig. 12,*d*) → testosterone (Fig. 12,*e*). The second biosynthetic pathway applies exclusively to the adrenals and probably involves: acetate → cholesterol → dehydroepiandrosterone (Fig. 12,*b*) → androstenedione (Fig. 12,*d*) → 11β-hydroxyandrostenedione (Fig. 12,*f*). In the liver, androgens may be formed from circulating corticosteroids by enzymatic removal of two carbon atoms.

The catabolic products of testosterone and other androgens are formed by oxidative and reductive changes in the molecule, as well as by hydroxylation; they appear in the urine as 17-ketosteroids. The *in vivo* conversion of testosterone to estrogenic steroid hormones has been established.

Steinach and Kun reported in 1937 that after testosterone administration to normal and castrated male rats, increased amounts of estrogens are excreted in the urine. That testosterone can be converted into estrogen in the organism was proved by Heard *et al.* (1955), who showed that in a pregnant mare testosterone labeled with C^{14} was converted to labeled estrogen.

It is thought that androgens (and estrogens) are inactivated by the liver. This certainly occurs *in vitro* in liver homogenates. Moreover, Burrill and Greene (1940) and Biskind (1940) have found that, after implantation of a testis into the spleen, castration phenomena cannot be prevented, which, of course, is the case, when the testis is implanted subcutaneously.

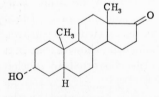

(a) Cholesterol　　　　$R_1 : -OH$
　　　　　　　　　　　　　$R_2 : -C_8H_{17}$
(b) Dehydroepiandrosterone　$R_1 : -OH$
　　　　　　　　　　　　　$R_2 : =O$

(c) Progesterone　　　　$R_1 : -H$
　　　　　　　　　　　　　$R_2 : -CO·CH_3$
(d) Androstenedione　　　$R_1 : -H$
　　　　　　　　　　　　　$R_2 : =O$
(e) Testosterone　　　　$R_1 : -H$
　　　　　　　　　　　　　$R_2 : -OH$
(f) 11β-Hydroxy-　　　$R_1 : -OH$
　　　androstenedione　　$R_2 : =O$

(g) Androsterone

(h) Etiocholanolone

FIG. 12. Formulas of various steroid hormones. For further particulars, see text.

According to Freud *et al.* (1937) a substance can be extracted from testes and urine, which has no action by itself but which increases the action of testosterone and related compounds on the vesicular glands (but not on the capon's comb!). This unidentified substance (the X-substance) is thought to be a higher organic acid.

It has already been mentioned that many representatives of lower vertebrate classes react to androgens of mammalian origin or synthetic androgens. Therefore, it is sometimes assumed (but not proved) that testosterone is also the male hormone of these lower vertebrates.

From the investigation of Hazleton and Goodrich (1937), who, after the injection of extracts of salmon testes into capons, obtained comb growth, or of Potter and Hoar (1954), who stimulated comb growth in chicks with similar extracts, it has also been concluded that these extracts may have contained testosterone. However, biochemical investigations concerning the identity of the sex hormones in nonmammalian vertebrates are insufficient; more work on this problem is needed.

B. Methods of Biological Assay

Biological assay methods for androgens are numerous. The most important ones are:

1. Ejaculation test (Moore *et al.*, 1930). In the guinea pig as well as in the rat, a copulation plug is formed after emission of the semen in the vagina of the female. This occurs because the male ejaculate hardens rapidly, due to the action of a prostatic enzyme on the secretory product of the seminal vesicle. By passing an alternating electrical current through the head of a male guinea pig (or rat) an ejaculation can also be obtained, but this is not possible in castrated animals, in which the seminal vesicles and prostate are atrophied. The function of these glands can be restored by the injection of testosterone (or other androgens) and the weight of the ejaculate may then serve as an index of the potency of the injected androgen.

2. Fructose test. Mann and Parsons (1947) found in many mammalian species, including man, that fructose (and citric acid) are absent in the accessory gland secretion after castration but reappear after the injection of androgens. The quantity of fructose in the semen may be used for assaying androgenic compounds.

3. Spermatozoon motility test (Moore, 1928). This assay method is based on the observation that androgenic substances can prolong the life of spermatozoa in the epididymis of castrated guinea pigs, and that spermatozoa in an isolated epididymis retain their viability longer under their influence.

rther tests are based on the regression of the vesicular glands
(˳˳˳˳ and Voss, 1930), the prostate, Cowper's glands, and the epithelium
of the ductus deferens after castration and on their restitution after androgen treatment, or on the increase in weight of these organs after injection
of the hormone into immature male rats.

5. Capon comb growth test (Pézard, 1911; de Fremery et al., 1930).
The capon's comb which responds to injected androgens or to direct
inunction of the male hormone with an increase in size can also be used as
an assay method.

VII. FUNCTION OF THE FETAL TESTIS

A. Medullarin and Cortecin

There is some evidence that true sex hormones are formed in the fetal
testis. However, it has also been shown that in earlier developmental stages
in addition to genetic factors, humoral factors play an essential role in
the sexual differentiation of the gonads.

According to Witschi (1942) these humoral factors are represented by
medullarin and cortecin in the gonads of young larval amphibians and
presumably also occur in the "indifferent" gonads of other vertebrates,
e.g., in mammals (MacIntyre, 1956). These substances are formed in the
medulla and cortex of the gonadal primordia. Medullarin is supposed to
inhibit the development of the cortex so that the medulla develops into a
testis. Cortecin inhibits the development of the medulla, allowing the
cortex to develop into an ovary. Neither medullarin nor cortecin have
been obtained in a pure state; it is uncertain whether they are identical
with the embryonic hormones, the existence of which has been demonstrated by many workers as, e.g., by Jost, Wolff, and others (see Section
VII, C). According to Fugo (1940) medullarin and cortecin are also formed
in the gonadal primordia after hypophysectomy.

B. The Freemartin

One of the best indications for the existence of an embryonic testis
hormone is the occurrence of the freemartin which, according to the investigations of Lillie (1916, 1917) and of Keller and Tandler (1916), is the
female of heterosexual cattle twins, in which the fetal membranes became
united at an early developmental stage and in which vascular anastomoses
were established. Under these conditions, the female twin is diverted
toward masculinization.

The modification can go so far that a stage is reached in which the intersexual female possesses gonads with sterile testicular tubules (Fig. 13), rudiments of a scrotum, and well-developed Wolffian ducts in addition to reduced Müllerian ducts. The external genital organs, however, remain always of the female type.

The fact that the female is masculinized only if the vessels of the fetal membranes fuse reciprocally serves as an indication that the freemartin develops under the influence of a hormone. In the testes of the male twin (which remains normal) interstitial cells occur earlier than in the gonads of the female twin (Bascom, 1923), indicating again that the male fetal sex hormone, originating earlier than the female fetal sex hormone, masculinizes the female.

An objection against this concept of the origin of the freemartin (Lillie, 1917) is the fact that in mammals true freemartins have never been produced experimentally. Nor is it known why in marmosets (Wislocki, 1939) the heterosexual twins are completely normal, notwithstanding the fact that their fetal blood vessels anastomose reciprocally. It should also be noted that with the exception of cows, freemartins are extremely rare in mammalian species.

In birds a spontaneous case has been described by Lutz and Lutz-Ostertag (1958) in a double-yoked hen's egg, the development of which could be followed to the eighteenth day of incubation. In the female embryo, which was connected by vascular anastomoses with the male, the posterior region of the Müllerian ducts was reduced; in the male the left testis contained some cortical nodules.

Wolff and Haffen (1952) succeeded in producing parabioses between primordial male and female duck gonads, cultured in vitro. Feminization of the male gonad by the secretions of the female gonad was observed, i.e., the male gonad developed a very distinct cortex (Fig. 14).

Experimental freemartin-like conditions[9] have also been obtained in mammals, birds, and amphibians: In mammals by administration of the heterologous sex hormones directly to embryos or in the circulation of the pregnant mother (Dantchakoff, 1937; Greene et al., 1939; Raynaud, 1939), in birds by injecting the embryo directly (Willier et al., 1935; Wolff and Ginglinger, 1935; Dantchakoff, 1938) or by implantation of embryonic gonads (Wolff, 1946), and in amphibians by the use of parabiotic larvae (Burns, 1925, 1930, 1931; Witschi, 1927, 1936, 1937b; Witschi and McCurdy, 1929, and others). In amphibians the female is usually masculinized, but feminization of the male may also occur.

[9] See the reviews of Witschi (1950) and Jost (1960). For the action of sex hormones in amphibians, see Gallien (1955).

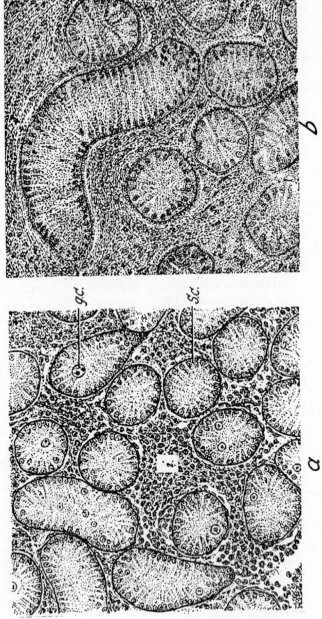

Fig. 13. (a) Section through the normal testis of a young bull (g.c., germ cells; S.c., Sertoli cells; i., interstitial cells).
(b) Section through a freemartin gonad, showing sterile sex cords and interstitial tissue. After Willier (1921).

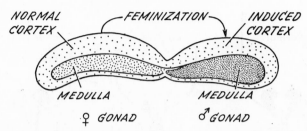

FIG. 14. Parabiosis between a potential male and female gonad cultivated *in vitro;* feminization of the male gonad. After Wolff and Haffen (1952).

C. The Fetal Testis Hormone

To prove the existence of fetal sex hormones, castration experiments have to be carried out. The investigations of Moore (1941, 1943), however, who used the embryo-like pouch-young of the American opossum (*Didelphys virginiana*) as experimental animals, did not appear to be in favor of their existence. Though Moore succeeded in castrating the young opossums, changes in sex differentiation could not be detected. He, therefore, concluded that in opossums sex differentiation takes place in accordance with their genetic constitution and that embryonic sex hormones do not play a part.

These investigations favored the concept that during embryonic life the gonads of mammals do not secrete sex hormones, and that those sex characters which are macroscopically visible at birth do not develop under their influence.

More recent investigations, particularly those of Jost (1947, 1948, 1953, 1955, 1960) who succeeded in castrating rabbit embryos *in utero*, seem, however, to suggest that in placental mammals the development of certain sex characters takes place under the influence of the fetal gonad. When male rabbit embryos were castrated on or after the twenty-second day after conception (the duration of pregnancy is 32 days) development proceeded normally. When this operation was done before the twenty-second day, and preferably on the nineteenth, the existence of a male embryonic sex hormone was strongly indicated in that the male embryonic sex characters did not develop, and the embryo became femalelike.

It follows that the embryonic testis produces a hormone which favors the differentiation of the Wolffian system and inhibits the development of the Müllerian system in male embryos. It is, therefore, possible that Moore castrated his young opossums too late.

When Jost ovariectomized female embryos *in utero*, they developed normally; hence in the absence of the male embryonic sex hormone the female embryonic sex characters come into appearance.

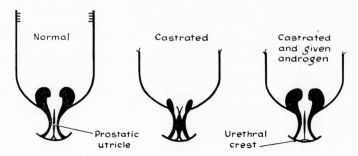

Fig. 15. Accessory sex organs of a normal and a castrated fetal rat and of a castrated fetal rat treated with androgens. After Wells *et al.* (1954).

Some of these results were confirmed by Raynaud and Frilley (1947) in mouse embryos after destruction of the gonadal regions by X-rays. Wells and Fralick (1951) and Wells *et al.* (1954), who castrated fetal rats *in utero*, showed that the development of some accessory reproductive organs of the male rat is influenced by the testis before birth (Fig. 15). Wolff and Wolff (1949; see also Wolff, 1959) castrated male and female duck embryos with X-rays. The Müllerian ducts persisted in both male and female castrated duck embryos. The bulla of the syrinx, as well as the genital tubercle (which are large in normal male and small in normal female ducks) were large in the embryos of both sexes. Thus in the female embryo the development of the syrinx and of the genital tubercle is impeded by the female embryonic hormone. In male embryos on the other hand, the development of the syrinx can be prevented by injected estrogen (Lewis and Domm, 1948). The results of Price and Pannabecker (1956, 1959), who cultured the reproductive tract of male rats with fetal testes or ovaries, also favor the concept of the existence of embryonic sex hormones.

The chemical structure of these hormones is unknown; they may differ from the steroid hormones produced by the adult gonads.

References

Allee, W. C. (1942). *Biol. Symposia* **8**, 139–162.

Allee, W. C., Allee, M. N., Ritchey, F., and Castles, E. W. (1947). *Ecology* **28**, 310–315.

Allee, W. C., Foreman, D., Banks, E. M., and Holabird, C. H. (1955). *Physiol. Zoöl.* **28**, 89–115.

Andrews, F. N. (1940). *Proc. Soc. Exptl. Biol. Med.* **45**, 867–869.

Aron, M. (1924). *Arch. biol. (Liége)* **34**, 1–166.

Aron, M. (1926). *Arch. biol. (Liége)* **36**, 3–97.

Aron, M. (1927). *Verhandl. 1 Intern. Kongr. Sexualforsch.* **1**, 1–17.

Aron, M. (1929). *Bull. histol. appl. physiol. et pathol. et tech. microscop.* **6**, 189–204.

Aronson, L. R. (1951). *Am. Museum Novitates No.* **1484**, 1–26.

Aronson, L. R. (1959). *In* "Comparative Endocrinology" (A. Gorbman, ed.), Chapter 5, pp. 98–120. Wiley, New York.

Ashbel, R., Cohen, R. B., and Seligman, A. M. (1951). *Endocrinology* **49**, 265–281.

Baggerman, B. (1957). *Arch. néerl. zool.* **12**, 105–318.

Bascom, K. F. (1923). *Am. J. Anat.* **31**, 223–252.

Beach, F. A. (1941). *Endocrinology* **29**, 409–412.

Beach, F. A. (1942). *Endocrinology* **31**, 673–678.

Beach, F. A. (1947). *Physiol. Revs.* **27**, 240–307.

Beach, F. A. (1948). "Hormones and Behavior." Hoeber, New York.

Beach, F. A., and Levinson, G. (1950). *J. Exptl. Zool.* **114**, 159–171.

Beall, D. (1940). *Biochem. J.* **34**, 1293.

Benoit, J. (1923). *Compt. rend. acad. sci.* **177**, 1074–1076.

Benoit, J. (1927). *Compt. rend. soc. biol.* **97**, 275–278.

Benoit, J. (1936). *Bull. biol. France et Belg.* **70**, 487–533.

Benoit, J., and Ott, L. (1944). *Yale J. Biol. and Med.* **17**, 27–46.

Berthold, A. A. (1849). *Arch. Anat. u. Physiol. Anat. Abt.* **16**, 42–46.

Biskind, G. R. (1940). *Proc. Soc. Exptl. Biol. Med.* **43**, 259–261.

Bissonnette, T. H. (1932). *Proc. Roy. Soc.* **B110**, 322–336.

Bissonnette, T. H. (1936). *J. Comp. Psychol.* **22**, 93–103.

Bissonnette, T. H. (1941). *Physiol. Zoöl.* **14**, 379–383.

Bissonnette, T. H., and Wadlund, A. P. R. (1932). *J. Exptl. Biol.* **9**, 339–350.

Blair, A. P. (1946). *J. Exptl. Zool.* **103**, 365–400.

Blivaiss, B. B. (1947). *J. Exptl. Zool.* **104**, 267–310.

Blivaiss, B. B. (1951). *Am. J. Anat.* **89**, 381–404.

Bock, F. (1928). *Z. wiss. Zoöl.* **130**, 455–468.

Bolton, W. (1953). *J. Endocrinol.* **9**, 440–445.

Bouin, P., and Ancel, P. (1903). *Arch. zool. exptl. et gén.* (4) **1**, 437–523.

Brard, E. (1953). *Compt. rend. soc. biol.* **147**, 570–575.

Brown-Séquard, M. (1889). *Compt. rend. soc. biol. Séance*, June 1, 1889.

Bruzzone, S., and Lipschütz, A. (1953). *Acta Endocrinol.* **13**, 28–34.

Bullough, W. S., and van Oordt, G. J. (1950). *Acta Endocrinol.* **4**, 291–305.

Burgos, M. H. (1950). *Rev. soc. arg. biol.* **26**, 359–371.

Burgos, M. H. (1955). *J. Morphol.* **96**, 283–300.

Burgos, M. H., and Ladman, A. J. (1957). *Endocrinology* **61**, 20–34.

Burns, R. K. (1925). *J. Exptl. Zool.* **42**, 31–90.

Burns, R. K. (1930). *J. Exptl. Zool.* **55**, 123–170.

Burns, R. K. (1931). *J. Exptl. Zool.* **60**, 339–388.

Burrill, M. W., and Greene, R. R. (1940). *Endocrinology* **26**, 645–650.

Butenandt, A., and Hanisch, G. (1935). *Z. physiol. Chem.* **237**, 89–97.

Callow, N. H. (1939). *Biochem. J.* **33**, 559–564.

Carpenter, C. R. (1933). *J. Comp. Psychol.* **16**, 25–57.

Carter, S. B. (1953). *J. Endocrinol.* **9**, 19–29.

Cei, J. M., Andreozzi, M. L., and Acosta, D. I. (1955). *Arch. farm. y bioquim. Tucumán* **7**, 119–153.

Chester Jones, I. (1948). *Quart. J. Microscop. Sci.* **89**, 53–74.

Chester Jones, I. (1955). *Brit. Med. Bull.* **11**, 156–160.

Collias, N. E. (1944). *Physiol. Zoöl.* **17**, 83–123.

Courrier, R. (1922). *Arch. anat. histol. et embryol.* **2**, 115–144.

Craig-Bennett, A. (1931). *Phil. Trans. Roy. Soc. London Ser.* **B219**, 197–279.

Danforth, C. H. (1930). *Biol. generalis* **6**, 99–108.

Danforth, C. H., and Foster, F. (1929). *J. Exptl. Zool.* **52**, 443–470.

Dantchakoff, V. (1937). *Ergeb. Biol.* **40**, 101–163.

Dantchakoff, V. (1938). *Biol. Centr.* **58**, 302–328.

David, K., Dingemanse, E., Freud, J., and Laqueur, E. (1935). *Z. physiol. Chem.* **233**, 281–282.

Deanesly, R. (1928). *Proc. Roy. Soc.* **B103**, 503.

Deanesly, R. (1958). *J. Endocrinol.* **17**, ii.

Deanesly, R., and Parkes, A. S. (1937). *Quart. J. Exptl. Physiol.* **26**, 393–402.

de Fremery, P., Freud, J., and Laqueur, E. (1930). *Arch. ges. Physiol. Pflüger's* **225**, 740–741.

de Graaf, H. J. (1942). *Acta Brevia Neerl. Physiol. Pharmacol. Microbiol.* **12**, 67–68.

Dodd, J. M. (1955). *Mem. Soc. Endocrinol. No.* 4, 166–187.

Dodd, J. M., Evennett, P. J., and Goddard, C. K. (1960). *Symposia Zool. Soc. London* **1**, 77–103.

Domm, L. V. (1927). *J. Exptl. Zool.* **48**, 31–173.

Domm, L. V. (1929a). *Wilhelm Roux' Arch. Entwicklungsmech. Organ.* **119**, 171–187.

Domm, L. V. (1929b). *Biol. Bull.* **56**, 459–496.

Domm, L. V. (1931). *Anat. Record* **49**, 211–249.

Dorfman, R. I. (1955). *In* "The Hormones" (G. Pincus and K. Thimann, eds.), Vol. 3, pp. 589–664. Academic Press, New York.

Dorfman, R. I., and Shipley, R. A. (1956). "Androgens." Wiley, New York.

Dorfman, R. I., Cook, J. W., and Hamilton, J. B. (1939). *J. Biol. Chem.* **130**, 285–295

Duerden, J. E. (1919). *J. Genet.* **8**, 155–198.

Ebling, F. J. (1948). *J. Endocrinol.* **5**, 299–302.

Ebling, F. J. (1957). *J. Endocrinol.* **15**, 297–306.

Edgren, R. A., Calhoun, D. W., and Harris, T. W. (1960). *Acta Endocrinol.* **34**, 213–224.

Egami, N. (1954). *J. Fac. Sci. Univ. Tokyo* **7**, 113–119.

Eliot, T. S. (1928). *Physiol. Zoöl.* **1**, 286–324.

Evans, L. T. (1946). *Anat. Record* **94**, Suppl., 405–406.

Evans, L. T. (1951a). *Science* **114**, 277–279.

Evans, L. T. (1951b). *Anat. Record* **109**, Suppl., 370.

Evans, L. T. (1952). *Anat. Record* **112**, 251–258.

Eversole, E. (1939). *Endocrinology* **25**, 318–330.

Follenius, E. (1953). *Bull. biol. France et Belg.* **87,** 68–91.

Folley, S. J., and Malpress, F. H. (1948). *In* "The Hormones" (G. Pincus and K. Thimann, eds.), Vol. 1, pp. 695–805. Academic Press, New York.

Forbes, T. R. (1938). *Anat. Record* **72,** 87–96.

Forbes, T. R. (1939). *Anat. Record* **75,** 51–58.

Forselius, S. (1957). *Zool. bidrag Uppsala* **32,** 97–598.

Fowler, G. H. (1894). *Proc. Zool. Soc. (London)* 485–494.

Frederiks, H. H. J. (1941). *Acta Brevia Neerl. Physiol. Pharmacol. Microbiol.* **11,** 74–75.

Freud, J., Dingemanse, E., and Polak, J. J. (1937). *Arch. intern. pharmacodynamie* **57,** 369–402.

Fugo, N. W. (1940). *J. Exptl. Zool.* **85,** 271–298.

Gaarenstroom, J. H., and de Jongh, S. E. (1946). "A Contribution to the Knowledge of the Influences of Gonadotropic and Sex Hormones on the Gonads of Rats." Elsevier, New York.

Gallien, L. (1955). *Mem. Soc. Endocrinol. No.* **4,** 188–204.

Gerall, A. A. (1958). *Endocrinology* **63,** 280–284.

Grad, B., and Leblond, C. P. (1949). *Endocrinology* **45,** 250–266.

Greene, R. R., Burrill, M. W., and Ivy, A. C. (1939). *Am. J. Anat.* **65,** 415–470.

Greenwood, A. W. (1928). *Proc. Roy. Soc.* **B103,** 73–81.

Grobstein, C. (1942). *J. Exptl. Zool.* **89,** 305–328.

Grollman, A. (1936). "The Adrenals." Williams & Wilkins, Baltimore, Maryland.

Hachlow, V. A. (1927). *Wilhelm Roux' Arch. Entwicklungsmech. Organ.* **110,** 279–300.

Hall, Th. C., Ganoy, W. F., Taft, E. B., and Aub, J. C. (1960). *Proc. 1st Intern. Congr. Endocrinol., Copenhagen, 1960,* 525–526.

Hamilton, J. B. (1938). *Endocrinology* **23,** 53–57.

Hann, H. W. (1939). *Bird Banding* **10,** 122–124.

Hasler, A. D., and Meyer, R. K. (1942). *J. Exptl. Zool.* **91,** 391–404.

Hazleton, L. W., and Goodrich, F. J. (1937). *J. Am. Pharm. Assoc. Sci. Ed.* **26,** 420–421.

Heard, R. D. H., Jellinck, P. H., and O'Donnell, V. J. (1955). *Endocrinology* **57,** 200–204.

Heller, C. G., Nelson, W. O., Hill, I. C., Henderson, E., Maddock, W. O., and Jungck, E. C. (1950). *J. Clin. Endocrinol.* **10,** 816.

Heringa, G. C., and de Jongh, S. E. (1934). *Z. Zellforsch. u. mikroskop. Anat.* **21,** 629–634.

Herlant, M. (1933). *Arch. biol. (Liége)* **44,** 347–468.

Hershberger, L. G., Shipley, E. G., and Meyer, R. K. (1953). *Proc. Soc. Exptl. Biol. Med.* **83,** 175–180.

Hewitt, W. F., Jr. (1947). *Anat. Record* **98,** 159–180.

Hildemann, W. H. (1954). *J. Exptl. Zool.* **126,** 1–16.

Hisaw, F. L., and Abramowitz, A. A. (1939). *Rept. Woods Hole Oceanogr. Inst. for 1928* **22.**

Hoar, W. S., McKinnon, D., and Redlich, A. (1952). *Can. J. Zool.* **30,** 273–286.

Hoover, E. E., and Hubbard, H. F. (1937). *Copeia* 206–210.

Hopper, A. F. (1949). *J. Exptl. Zool.* **110,** 299–320.

Horowitz, R. (1934). *Biol. Generalis* **10**, 569–592.

Hoskins, W. H., and Koch, F. C. (1939). *Endocrinology* **25**, 266–274.

Houssay, B. A. *et al.* (1955). "Human Physiology," 2nd ed. McGraw-Hill, New York.

Houssay, A. B., Nallar, R., and Saurer, E. I. (1960). *Acta Physiol. Latinoam.* **9**, 35–49.

Howard-Miller, E. (1927). *Am. J. Anat.* **40**, 251–293.

Hunter, J. (1792). "Observations on the Glands Situated Between the Rectum and Bladder, Called Vesiculae Seminales," 2nd ed. Nicol, London.

Ikeda, K. (1933). *Japan. J. Zoöl.* **5**, 135–157.

Ishii, S. (1960). *Annotationes Zool. Japon.* **33**, 172–177.

Ishii, S., and Egami, N. (1957). *Annotationes Zool. Japon.* **30**, 77–82.

Iwasawa, H. (1957). *Zool. Mag. (Tokyo)* **66**, 416.

Jackson, N., and Brown, W. O. (1958). *Poultry Sci.* **37**, 886–889.

Johnson, D. C. (1958). *Endocrinology* **62**, 340–347.

Jost, A. (1947). *Arch. anat. microscop. et morphol. exptl.* **36**, 151–200; 242–270; 271–315.

Jost, A. (1948). *Biol. Revs. Cambridge Phil. Soc.* **23**, 201–236.

Jost, A. (1953). *Recent Progr. in Hormone Research* **8**, 379–418.

Jost, A. (1955). *Mem. Soc. Endocrinol. No.* **4**, 237–248.

Jost, A. (1960). *In* "Fermente, Hormone, Vitamine" (R. Ammon and W. Dirscherl, eds.), Vol. II, 382–389. Thieme, Stuttgart.

Katsh, S. (1950). *Endocrinology* **47**, 370–383.

Katsh, S., Gordon, A. S., and Charipper, H. A. (1948). *Anat. Record* **101**, 47–57.

Keck, W. N. (1934). *J. Exptl. Zoöl.* **67**, 315–341.

Kehl, R., and Combescot, C. (1955). *Mem. Soc. Endocrinol. No.* **4**, 57–74.

Keller, K., and Tandler, J. (1916). *Wien. tierärztl. Monatsschr.* **3**, 513–526.

Knowles, F. G. W. (1939). *J. Exptl. Biol.* **16**, 535–547.

Kochakian, C. D. (1937). *Endocrinology* **21**, 750–755.

Kochakian, C. D. (1950). *Symposium on Steroid Hormones, 1950*, pp. 113–149.

Kochakian, C. D., and Murlin, J. R. (1936). *Am. J. Physiol.* **117**, 642–661.

Korenchevsky, D., and Dennison, M. (1936). *J. Pathol. Bacteriol.* **43**, 345–356.

Koster, K. (1943). *Endocrinology* **33**, 337–348.

Lacassagne, A. (1940a). *Compt. rend. soc. biol.* **133**, 180–181.

Lacassagne, A. (1940b). *Compt. rend. soc. biol.* **133**, 227–229.

Lacassagne, A., and Chamorro, A. (1940). *Compt. rend. soc. biol.* **134**, 223–224.

Laws, D. F. (1961). *Z. Zellforsch. Abt.* **A54**, 276–306.

Leathem, J. H., and Wolf, R. C. (1955). *Mem. Soc. Endocrinol. No.* **4**, 220–236.

Leblond, C. P., and Grad, B. (1948). *Anat. Record* **100**, Suppl., 716.

Leonard, S. L. (1939). *Proc. Soc. Exptl. Biol. Med.* **41**, 229–230.

Levey, H. A., and Szego, C. M. (1955). *Am. J. Physiol.* **183**, 371–376.

Lewis, L. B., and Domm, L. V. (1948). *Physiol. Zoöl.* **21**, 65–69.

Lillie, F. R. (1916). *Science* **43**, 611–613.

Lillie, F. R. (1917). *J. Exptl. Zool.* **23**, 371–452.

Lipschütz, A. (1918a). *Wilhelm Roux' Arch. Entwicklungsmech. Organ.* **44**, 196–206.

Lipschütz, A. (1918b). *Wilhelm Roux' Arch. Entwicklungsmech. Organ.* **44**, 207–212.

Lipschütz, A. (1919). "Die Pubertätsdrüse und ihre Wirkungen." Bircher, Bern.

Loewe, S., and Voss, H. E. (1930). *Klin. Wochenschr.* 481–487.

Lutz, H., and Lutz-Ostertag, Y. (1958). *Arch. anat. microscop. et morphol. exptl.* **47**, 205–210.

McCullagh, D. R. (1932). *Science* **76**, 19.

McGee, L. C. (1927). *Proc. Inst. Med. (Chicago)* **6**, 242.

MacIntyre, M. N. (1956). *Anat. Record* **124**, 27–45.

Maddock, W. O., and Nelson, W. O. (1952). *J. Clin. Endocrinol. and Metabolism* **12**, 985–1014.

Maddock, W. O., Epstein, M., and Nelson, W. O. (1952). *Ann. N. Y. Acad. Sci.* **55**, 657–673.

Mann, T. (1954). "The Biochemistry of Semen." Methuen, London.

Mann, T. (1956). *Recent Progr. in Hormone Research* **12**, 353–376.

Mann, T., and Parsons, U. (1947). *Nature* **160**, 294.

Marescaux, J., and Deminatti, M. (1955). *Compt. rend. soc. biol.* **149**, 404–407.

Marshall, A. J. (1949). *Quart. J. Microscop. Sci.* **90**, 265–280.

Marshall, A. J., and Coombs, C. J. F. (1957). *Proc. Zool. Soc. (London)* **128**, 545–589.

Martins, T., and Rocha, A. (1931). *Endocrinology* **15**, 421–434.

Mathey, R. (1929). *Z. Zellforsch. u. mikroskop. Anat.* **8**, 671–690.

Matthews, S. A. (1939). *Biol. Bull.* **77**, 92–95.

Medlen, A. B. (1951). *Copeia* 188–192.

Mellman, W. J., Cordray, A. C., and Dohan, F. C. (1956). *Acta Endocrinol.* **21**, 57–64.

Merriman, D., and Schedl, H. P. (1941). *J. Exptl. Zool.* **88**, 413–450.

Miller, A. H. (1948). *J. Exptl. Zool.* **109**, 1–11.

Miller, M. R. (1948). *Univ. Calif. Berkeley Publs. Zool.* **47**, 197–224.

Moore, C. R. (1926). *Biol. Bull.* **51**, 112–128.

Moore, C. R. (1928). *J. Exptl. Zool.* **50**, 455–494.

Moore, C. R. (1941). *Physiol. Zoöl.* **14**, 1–45.

Moore, C. R. (1943). *J. Exptl. Zool.* **94**, 415–461.

Moore, C. R., and Chase, H. D. (1923). *Anat. Record* **26**, 344–345.

Moore, C. R., and Oslund, R. M. (1924). *Am. J. Physiol.* **67**, 595–607.

Moore, C. R., and Price, D. (1930). *Proc. Soc. Exptl. Biol. Med.* **28**, 38–40.

Moore, C. R., and Price, D. (1932). *Am. J. Anat.* **50**, 13–71.

Moore, C. R., and Quick, W. J. (1924). *Am. J. Physiol.* **68**, 70–79.

Moore, C. R., and Samuels, L. T. (1931). *Am. J. Physiol.* **96**, 278–288.

Moore, C. R., Price, D., and Gallagher, T. F. (1930). *Am. J. Anat.* **45**, 71–107.

Morgan, T. H. (1919). *Carnegie Inst. Wash. Publ.* **285**.

Mühlbock, O. (1938). *Acta Brevia Neerl. Physiol. Pharmacol. Microbiol.* **8**, 50–54.

Mühlbock, O. (1940). *Acta Brevia Neerl. Physiol. Pharmacol. Microbiol.* **10**, 10–13.

Mühlbock, O., Looyen, S. G., and Hardjanto (1953). *Ned. Tijdschr. Geneesk.* **97**, 2760–2761.

Neeser, V. (1940). *Rev. suisse zool.* **47**, 153–159.

Nelson, W. O. (1940). *Am. J. Physiol.* **129**, 430.

Nelson, W. O. (1956). *3rd Congr. Panam. Endocrinol. Santiago de Chile, 1954.* **1**, 293–296.

Niwelinski, J. (1954). *Folia Biol. (Warsaw)* **2**, 87–98.

Noble, G. K., and Borne, R. (1940). *Anat. Record* **78**, Suppl., 147.

Noble, G. K., and Greenberg, B. (1941). *Proc. Soc. Exptl. Biol. Med.* **47**, 32–37.

Noble, G. K., and Kumpf, K. F. (1936). *Anat. Record* **67**, Suppl., 113.

Noble, G. K., and Kumpf, K. F. (1941). *Anat. Record* **70**, Suppl., 97.

Noble, G. K., and Wurm, M. (1940). *Anat. Record* **78**, Suppl., 50–51.

Noble, G. K., and Zitrin, A. (1942). *Endocrinology* **30**, 327–334.

Nowikow, B. G. (1939). *Compt. rend. acad. sci. U.R.S.S.* **25**, 554–556.

Nussbaum, M. (1909). *Arch. ges. Physiol. Pflüger's* **126**, 519–577.

Ogura, C. (1958). *J. Fac. Sci. Hokkaido Univ., Ser. VI* **14**, 45–50.

Okada, Y. K., and Yamashita, H. (1944). *J. Fac. Sci. Univ. Tokyo Sect. IV*, **6**, 383–437.

Padoa, E. (1933). *Arch. ital. anat. embriol.* **31**, 205–252.

Paesi, F. J. A., van Soest, E. M., and de Jongh, S. E. (1953). *Acta Physiol. Latinoam.* **3**, 153–157.

Papanicolaou, G. N., and Falk, E. A. (1938). *Science* **87**, 238–239.

Parkes, A. S. (1937). *Nature* **139**, 965.

Parkes, A. S. (1945). *Physiol. Revs.* **25**, 203–254.

Parkes, A. S. (1950). *Recent Progr. in Hormone Research* **5**, 101–114.

Parkes, A. S. (1955). *Brit. Med. Bull.* **11**, 105–110.

Parkes, A. S., and Emmens, C. W. (1944). *Vitamins and Hormones* **2**, 361–408.

Payne, R. W., Hellbaum, A. A., and Owens, J. N., Jr. (1956). *Endocrinology* **59**, 306–316.

Penhos, J. C. (1953). *Rev. soc. arg. biol.* **29**, 200–203.

Penhos, J. C. (1956). *Acta Physiol. Latinoam.* **6**, 95–99.

Pézard, A. (1911). *Compt. rend. acad. sci.* **153**, 1027–1029.

Pézard, A. (1918). *Bull. biol. France et Belg.* **52**, 1–176.

Pézard, A. (1922). *J. physiol. pathol. gén.* **20**, 200.

Pfeiffer, C. A., and Hooker, C. W. (1942). *Anat. Record* **83**, 543–571.

Pfeiffer, C. A., and Kirschbaum, A. (1941). *Yale J. Biol. and Med.* **13**, 315–322.

Pickford, G. E., and Atz, J. W. (1957). "The Physiology of the Pituitary Gland of Fishes." New York Zool. Soc., New York.

Plagge, J. C. (1953). *Anat. Record* **116**, 237–246.

Ponse, K. (1955). *3e Réunion endocrinol. langue franc.* pp. 89–138.

Popják, G. (1958). *Ann. Rev. Biochem.* **27**, 533–560.

Potter, G. D., and Hoar, W. S. (1954). *J. Fisheries Research Board Can.* **11**, 63–68.

Price, D., and Pannabecker, R. (1956). *Ciba Foundation Colloq. on Aging* **2**, 3–13.

Price, D., and Pannabecker, R. (1959). *Arch. anat. micr. et morphol. exptl.* 48bis, 223–244.

Putzig, P. (1937). *Vogelzug* **8**, 116–130.

Putzig, P. (1938). *Vogelzug* **9**, 189–200.

Raffy, A., and Fontaine, M. (1930). *Compt. rend. soc. biol.* **104**, 287–288.

Ramaswami, L. S., and Hasler, A. D. (1955). *Physiol. Zoöl.* **28**, 62–68.

Raynaud, A. (1939). *Bull. biol. France et Belg.* **72**, 297–354.

Raynaud, A., and Frilley, M. (1947). *Ann. endocrinol. (Paris)* **8**, 400–419.

Raynaud, J., and Rebeyrotte, P. (1949). *Compt. rend. acad. sci.* **229**, 84–86.

Regamey, J. (1935). *Rev. suisse zool.* **42**, 87–168.

Régnier, M. (1938). *Bull. biol. France et Belg.* **72**, 385–493.

Riisfeldt, O. (1949). *Endocrinology* **45**, 622–623.

Riley, G. M. (1936). *Proc. Soc. Exptl. Biol. Med.* **34**, 331–332.

Riley, G. M. (1937). *Anat. Record* **67**, 327–351.

Ringoen, A. R., and Kirschbaum, A. (1937). *Proc. Soc. Exptl. Biol. Med.* **36**, 111–113.

Risley, P. L. (1941). *J. Exptl. Zool.* **87**, 477–515.

Rowan, W. (1926). *Proc. Boston Soc. Nat. Hist.* **38**, 147–189.

Rowan, W. (1929). *Proc. Boston Nat. Hist. Soc.* **39**, 151–208.

Rowan, W. (1932). *Proc. Natl. Acad. Sci. U.S.* **18**, 639–654.

Rowan, W. (1938). *Biol. Revs. Cambridge Phil. Soc.* **13**, 374–402.

Roxas, H. A. (1926). *J. Exptl. Zool.* **46**, 63–119.

Russell, R. (1755). "The Oeconomy of Nature in Acute and Chronical Diseases of the Glands." London.

Ruzicka, L. (1935). *J. Am. Chem. Soc.* **57**, 2011–2012.

Sakiz, E. (1958). *Compt. rend. acad. sci.* **246**, 1461–1463.

Sand, K. (1926). *In* "Handbuch der normalen und pathologischen Physiologie" (A. Bethe *et al.*, eds.), Vol. 14, Part I, pp. 215–240 and 251–292. Springer, Berlin.

Schjelderup-Ebbe, T. (1922). *Z. Psychol.* **88**, 225–252.

Segal, S. J. (1957). *Science* **126**, 1242–1243.

Shemano, I., Gordan, G. S., and Eisenberg, E. (1951). *Proc. Soc. Exptl. Biol. Med.* **78**, 612–613.

Shoemaker, H. H. (1939). *Proc. Soc. Exptl. Biol. Med.* **41**, 299–302.

Sluiter, J. W. (1945). *Z. Zellforsch., Abt.* **A33**, 311–335.

Sluiter, J. W., and van Oordt, G. J. (1947). *Quart. J. Microscop. Sci.* **88**, 135–150.

Sluiter, J. W., and van Oordt, G. J. (1949). *Quart. J. Microscop. Sci.* **90**, 1–11.

Stark, G., and Voss, H. E. (1957). *Ärztl. Forsch.* **11**, I/310–I/313.

Stefan, Y. (1958). *Ann. endocrinol. (Paris)* **19**, 481–506.

Steinach, E. (1894). *Arch. ges. Physiol. Pflüger's* **56**, 304–338.

Steinach, E. (1910). *Zentr. Physiol.* **24**, 551–566.

Steinach, E. (1912). *Arch. ges. Physiol. Pflüger's* **144**, 71–108.

Steinach, E. (1913). *Zentr. Physiol.* **27**, 717–723.

Steinach, E., and Kun, H. (1937). *Lancet* **ii**, 845.

Stieve, H. (1921). *Ergeb. Anat. u. Entwicklungsgeschichte* **23**, 1–249.

Taber, E. (1949). *Am. J. Anat.* **85**, 231–261.

Taber, E. (1951). *Endocrinology* **48**, 6–16.

Takewaki, K., and Fukuda, S. (1935). *J. Fac. Sci. Univ. Tokyo Sect. IV*, **4**, 63–76.

Tavolga, W. N. (1955). *Physiol. Zoöl.* **28**, 218–232.

Thiebold, J. J. (1954). *Bull. biol. France et Belg.* **88**, 130–145.

Thorborg, J. V. (1948). *Acta Endocrinol.* **1**, Suppl., 2.

Tozawa, T. (1929). *Folia Anat. Japon.* **7**, 407–417.

Turner, C. L. (1942). *Biol. Bull.* **83**, 389–400.

van Oordt, G. J. (1924). *Wilhelm Roux' Arch. Entwicklungsmech. Organ.* **102**, 379–405.

van Oordt, G. J. (1925). *Brit. J. Exptl. Biol.* **3**, 43–59.

van Oordt, G. J., and Junge, G. C. A. (1933). *Wilhelm Roux' Arch. Entwicklungsmech. Organ.* **128**, 166–180.

van Oordt, G. J., and Junge, G. C. A. (1936). *Wilhelm Roux' Arch. Entwicklungsmech. Organ.* **134**, 112–121.

van Oordt, G. J., van Oordt, P. G. W. J., and van Dongen, W. J. (1959). *In* "Comparative Endocrinology" (A. Gorbman, ed.), Chapter 29, pp. 488–498. Wiley, New York.

van Oordt, P. G. W. J. (1956). "Regulation of the Spermatogenetic Cycle in the Common Frog *(Rana temporaria).*" Ph.D. Thesis, Utrecht.

van Oordt, P. G. W. J. (1960). *Symposia Zool. Soc. (London)* **2**, 29–52.

van Oordt, P. G. W. J., and Basu, S. L. (1960). *Acta Endocrinol.* **33**, 103–110.

van Oordt, P. G. W. J., and Schouten, S. C. M. (1961). *J. Reproduction Fertility* **2**, 61–67.

Verhoeven, B., and van Oordt, G. J. (1955). *Koninkl. Ned. Akad. Wetenschap. Proc.* **C58**, 628–634.

Vivien, J. H. (1952). *Compt. rend. acad. sci.* **234**, 2394–2395.

Waldo, C. M., and Wislocki, G. B. (1951). *Am. J. Anat.* **88**, 351–396.

Walsh, E. L., Cuyler, W. K., and McCullagh, D. R. (1934). *Am. J. Physiol.* **107**, 508–512.

Wells, L. J. (1935). *Anat. Record* **62**, 409–444.

Wells, L. J. (1942). *Anat. Record* **82**, 565–585.

Wells, L. J., and Fralick, R. L. (1951). *Am. J. Anat.* **89**, 63–107.

Wells, L. J., Cavanaugh, M. W., and Maxwell, E. L. (1954). *Anat. Record* **118**, 109–134.

Welti, E. (1925). *Compt. rend. soc. phys. hist. nat. Genève* **42**, 133–135.

Welti, E. (1928). *Rev. suisse zool.* **35**, 75–200.

Willier, B. H. (1921). *J. Exptl. Zool.* **33**, 63–127.

Willier, B. H., Gallagher, T. F., and Koch, F. C. (1935). *Proc. Natl. Acad. Sci. U.S.* **21**, 625–631.

Wislocki, G. B. (1939). *Am. J. Anat.* **64**, 445–483.

Wislocki, G. B., Aub, J. C., and Waldo, C. M. (1947). *Endocrinology* **40**, 202–224.

Witschi, E. (1914). *Arch. mikroskop. anat. u. Entwicklungsmech.* **85**, 9–113.

Witschi, E. (1927). *Biol. Bull.* **52**, 136–147.

Witschi, E. (1929). *J. Exptl. Zool.* **52**, 267–291.

Witschi, E. (1936). *Anat. Record* **66**, 483–503.

Witschi, E. (1937a). *Cold Spring Harbor Symposia Quant. Biol.* **5**, 180–190.

Witschi, E. (1937b). *J. Exptl. Zool.* **75**, 313–373.

Witschi, E. (1942). *Cold Spring Harbor Symposia Quant. Biol.* **10**, 145–151.

Witschi, E. (1950). *Arch. anat. microscop. et morph. exptl.* **39**, 215–246.

Witschi, E., and Fugo, N. W. (1940). *Proc. Soc. Exptl. Biol. Med.* **45**, 10–14.

Witschi, E., and McCurdy, H. M. (1929). *Proc. Soc. Exptl. Biol. Med.* **26,** 655–657.

Wolff, Et. (1946). *Arch. anat. microscop. et morph. exptl.* **36,** 69–90.

Wolff, Et. (1959). *In* "Comparative Endocrinology" (A. Gorbman, ed.), Chapter 35, pp. 568–581. Wiley, New York.

Wolff, Et., and Ginglinger, A. (1935). *Arch. anat. histol. et embryol.* **20,** 223–278.

Wolff, Et., and Haffen, K. (1952). *Arch. anat. microscop. et morph. exptl.* **41,** 184–207.

Wolff, Et., and Wolff, Em. (1949). *Compt. rend. soc. biol.* **143,** 529–531.

Wolfson, A. (1945). *Condor* **47,** 95–127.

Wolfson, A. (1952). *J. Exptl. Zool.* **121,** 311–326.

Wolfson, A. (1959). *In* "Comparative Endocrinology" (A. Gorbman, ed.), Chapter 3, pp. 38–70. Wiley, New York.

Yeates, N. T. M. (1949). *J. Agr. Sci.* **39,** 1–42.

Zahl, P. A., and Davis, D. D. (1932). *J. Exptl. Zool.* **63,** 291–307.

Zawadowsky, M. (1922). "Das Geschlecht und die Entwicklung der Geschlechts-merkmale." Moskow.

Zawadowsky, M. (1926a). *Trans. Lab. Exptl. Biol. Zoo-Park Moskow* **2,** 164–179.

Zawadowsky, M. (1926b). *Wilhelm Roux' Arch. Entwicklungsmech. Organ.* **108,** 563–571.

Zawadowsky, M. M. (1929). *Endokrinologie* **5,** 363–416.

Zondek, B. (1934). *Nature* **133,** 209.

~6~

Adrenocortical Hormones

J. G. PHILLIPS* AND D. BELLAMY

Department of Zoology, University of Sheffield, England

I. ANATOMY AND HISTOLOGY

The adrenal cortex in Mammalia and its homologue in the lower vertebrates display wide variation in gross appearance and anatomical location. It is, however, characterized by a remarkable uniformity in its cellular components (Chester Jones, 1957). More precisely, adrenocortical tissue is built from single cords of cells which are variously arranged so as to impart diverse structural appearances to the whole gland. The extremes of phylogenetic diversity is demonstrated by the zoned cortex of the eutherian mammals and the indeterminate arrangement of adrenocortical tissue of fishes (Chester Jones and Phillips, 1960). Intermediate in this respect is the condition found in birds, reptiles, and amphibians where cords of cells, though anastomosing in various planes, are arranged in a more orderly fashion, being aligned generally in one direction. One of the most noticeable trends found in the adrenal glands of vertebrates is the variable degree of intermingling of chromaffin and adrenocortical tissue. In the Elasmobranchii the two types of tissue are separate, and the chromaffin cells are metamerically arranged. In the Teleostei there is occasional association of cortical and chromaffin tissue; this intermingling becomes more pronounced in the Amphibia, Reptilia, and Aves. This change from

---

* Present address: Department of Zoology, University of Hong Kong, Hong Kong.

scattered islets of chromaffin tissue to aggregations of cells into larger masses reaches its final expression in the mammals in which the chromaffin tissue appears as a single mass of cells. This mass is situated at one pole of the gland in the Prototheria (Wright et al., 1957) and occupies a central position in the Metatheria and Eutheria. The significance of these trends is not known. From earlier work on the mammal a functional division between the various zones of the adrenal cortex was predicted (Swann, 1940; Greep and Chester Jones, 1950; Greep, 1961); it has now received more direct experimental proof (reviewed by Ayres, 1960). It is concluded that the outer zone (zona glomerulosa) is mainly responsible for the secretion of aldosterone and the inner zones predominantly, but not exclusively, secrete hormones whose major role is in the regulation of carbohydrate metabolism. It is therefore of great interest to the comparative endocrinologist to determine whether the apparently undifferentiated adrenocortical tissue of lower vertebrates can nevertheless be similarly divided into more than one type of functional cell or whether all the cells in the apparently homogeneous tissue of these animals secrete both types of hormones. The question is also raised as to whether the cellular differentiation which is characteristic of the mammalian adrenal is a later arrival in vertebrate evolution. Certainly, subeutherian vertebrates produce both aldosterone and corticosterone and/or cortisol (Chester Jones and Phillips, 1960; Chester Jones et al., 1959) and it would seem, therefore, that the enzymes responsible for their production, i.e., the 11β-hydroxylating, 17α-hydroxylating, and the 18-oxidase systems are shared by all the cells. However, it may be that just as in the mammals, in which histological techniques indicated a functional division of adrenocortical cells (Deane and Greep, 1946; Greep and Deane, 1947), a similar division will be shown in lower vertebrates, for removal of the pituitary in lower vertebrates is followed by atrophic changes in the adrenocortical tissue which do not uniformly affect the whole tissue. Some cells retain their normal histological appearance and these may be the true homologues of the zona glomerulosa of the mammals (Chester Jones, 1957; Pickford and Atz, 1957).

II. THE ADRENAL HORMONES

A. Steroids in Adrenal Tissue

Pathological destruction or experimental removal of the adrenal glands leads to death. This fact has been known for over 100 years from the classical work of Thomas Addison (1855) and Brown-Sequard (1856).

Later, Osler (1896) found that adrenocortical insufficiency could be successfully treated with a crude glycerine extract of hog adrenal tissue. The
inability of adrenaline, the secretion of the adrenal medulla, to substitute
for the life-maintaining properties of whole adrenal extracts (Wheeler and
Vincent, 1927; Zwemer, 1927), and the subsequent preparation of a biologically active extract of cortical tissue by Rogoff (1932) and Hartman and
Brownell (1930), among others, confirmed that the cortical tissue was the
essential component of the adrenal gland.

Earlier analyses of extracts of the adrenal cortex revealed the presence
of several steroid substances. The first to be isolated, characterized and
shown to possess adrenocortical activity was 11β,21-dihydroxy-4-pregnene-
3,20-dione (corticosterone) by de Fremery et al. (1937). By 1943, thirty
different related steroids had been isolated but only six of them were shown
to be biologically active. Major advances in the field of steroid analysis
were made by four groups of workers led by Reichstein (Basel), Kendall
(Mayo Clinic), Cartland and Kuizenga (Upjohn), and Wintersteiner
(Squibb). All the active and a large number of the inactive compounds are
C_{21} steroids. Practically all have highly oxidized side chains, many with
an oxygen atom at C-11; all the active compounds have a Δ^4-3-ketone
group in ring A of the molecule and a 20,21-ketol or 17,20,21-dihydroxy-
acetone group (Klyne, 1957). All the active compounds are derivatives of
corticosterone (Table I).

After removal of the known substances from adrenal extracts there
still remained a fraction which was highly effective in prolonging the life
of adrenalectomized rats. The development of a reliable assay procedure
established that the residual fraction contained an unidentified steroid
which in its action on sodium metabolism was many times more potent
than deoxycorticosterone (Grollman, 1939; Hartman and Spoor, 1940).
With the advances in separation of steroids by paper chromatography it
was demonstrated that the unknown compound occupied the same position as cortisone in some solvent systems but possessed a far greater
mineralocorticoid activity than could be explained by the chemically determined amounts of cortisone in that area. Since the known steroids
which affected mineral metabolism could not be contaminants in this
area of the chromatogram, it was concluded than an unknown steroid,
highly potent in electrolyte metabolism was also present. Simpson et al.
(1952) showed that a similar substance could be demonstrated by chromatography of extracts of adrenal vein blood of both the rhesus monkey
and dog. They found that in the solvent system benzene–aqueous methanol,
this substance could be separated from cortisone and they tentatively
named it "electrocortin." Isolation and characterization of this substance
was finally achieved through the collaborative effort of three teams of

TABLE I

PRINCIPAL ADRENOCORTICAL HORMONES[a]

Empirical formula	Trivial name	Systematic name	Main alphabetical designation
$C_{21}H_{28}O_5$	Cortisone	$17\alpha,21$-Dihydroxy-4-pregnene-3,11,20-trione	Kendall's compound E
$C_{21}H_{30}O_4$	Corticosterone	$11\beta,21$-Dihydroxy-4-pregnene-3,20-dione	Kendall's compound B
$C_{21}H_{30}O_5$	Cortisol or hydrocortisone	$11\beta,17\alpha,21$-Trihydroxy-4-pregnene-3,20-dione	Kendall's compound F
$C_{21}H_{28}O_4$	11-Dehydrocorticosterone	21-Hydroxy-4-pregnene-3,11,20-trione	Kendall's compound A
$C_{21}H_{30}O_4$	7-Hydroxy-11-deoxy-corticosterone	$17\alpha,21$-Dihydroxy-4-pregnene-3,20-dione	Reichstein's compound S
$C_{21}H_{30}O_3$	Deoxycorticosterone or DOC	21-Hydroxy-4-pregnene-3,20-dione	
$C_{21}H_{28}O_5$	Aldosterone	$11\beta,21$-Dihydroxy-3,20-dioxo-4-pregnene-18-al	

[a] Klyne (1957).

workers from the Middlesex Hospital, the CIBA Laboratories, Basel and
the University of Basel (Simpson *et al.*, 1954). The new substance, the
18-aldehyde of corticosterone, was renamed aldosterone. In solution the
aldehyde form exists in equilibrium with the cyclohemiacetal form, the
latter predominating.

That aldosterone may not be the last physiologically active substance
isolated from adrenocortical extracts is suggested by the work of Neher
et al. (1958) who have recently isolated 3β, 16α-dihydroxy-5α-pregnan-20-
one from hog adrenals and claim it to be active in promoting sodium
excretion in the rat. Further, dehydroepiandrosterone, long thought to be
an adrenal hormone, has been isolated from adrenal tissue (Bloch *et al.*,
1956); testosterone has also been found in adrenal extracts (Anliker *et
al.*, 1956).

For obvious reasons, analysis of large volumes of adrenal tissue for
adrenocorticosteroid content has mostly been carried out on adrenal
glands of cattle (Shoppee, 1958). Information on comparable volumes of
tissue from other species is lacking but Péron (1960) has recently reported
large scale studies on both incubated and homogenized adrenals from the
rat. At present little work has been carried out on extracts obtained from
lower vertebrates. Grollman *et al.* (1934) demonstrated that the symptoms
of adrenocortical insufficiency in the adrenalectomized cat could be ameli-
orated by the injection of a crude extract of elasmobranch interrenal (adrenocortical) tissue. From this it was concluded that substances with
biological activity similar to those found in mammalian adrenocortical
tissue are present in the presumed homologue of the adrenal cortex in the
Elasmobranchii. Santa (1940) compared an extract of selachian interrenal
tissue and deoxycorticosterone acetate using as the basis of the test their
ability to contract the melanophores of the carp. More recently, Fontaine
and Leloup-Hatey (1959) provided direct evidence for the presence of
adrenocorticosteroids in the teleostean homologue of the mammalian
adrenal cortex. They found that the interrenal tissue of the salmon contains significant amounts of corticosteroids, cortisol being present in larger
amounts than corticosterone. In addition, these authors found that the
corpuscles of Stannius contain corticosteroids and tentatively suggested
that this tissue is homologous with the zona glomerulosa of the mammalian
adrenal cortex. This observation has not, however, received confirmation;
Ford (1959) and Bondy (unpublished results) failed in their attempts to
extract corticosteroids from the corpuscles of Stannius of other species.
Further, Phillips and Mulrow (1959b) were unable to demonstrate that
the corpuscles of Stannius synthesized the familiar adrenocorticosteroids
from precursor progesterone. The same investigators (Phillips and Mulrow, 1959a), however, showed that the interrenal tissue of *Fundulus*

heteroclitus possessed enzyme systems which enabled this tissue to convert progesterone into both aldosterone and cortisol, an observation which argues in favor of the fish interrenal tissue being the true homologue of the mammalian adrenal cortex (Chester Jones and Phillips, 1960). Newcomer (1959) demonstrated the presence of both free and conjugated Δ^4-3-ketosteroids in the avian adrenal gland and found a decrease in free steroids after long term adrenocorticotropin (ACTH) treatment, whereas hexestrol increased the free steroid content of the adrenal glands, resembling in this respect the results obtained in the rat (McKerns, 1957). In the chick the adrenal inhibitor o,p'-dichlorodiphenyldichloroethane caused a decrease in both the free and conjugated steroids of blood but decreased free and total (free plus conjugated) steroids in the adrenal gland and produced an increase in adrenal gland size (Newcomer, 1959). It is interesting that microsomal fractions of adrenal glands from white Leghorn cockerels possess enzyme systems which effect both conjugation of adrenal steroids with glucuronide and the hydrolysis of glucuronide-bound adrenocorticosteroids (Newcomer and Heninger, 1960).

B. Secretion of Adrenal Hormones

1. Biosynthesis of Adrenocorticosteroids

Many steroids can be extracted from adrenal tissue and the question arises as to which are intermediary substances and which are the biologically active final products, particularly in view of the possibility that abnormal substances may arise during the chemical manipulations involved in extraction. The isolation of biologically active steroids from adrenal venous effluent partly clarified the situation but since most studies have been conducted on acutely stressed animals the results must be considered as being representative of the normal physiology only with extreme caution. This cautionary note applies more specifically to studies in which the glands have been either transfused with blood through the arterial supply (Hilton, 1960), transfused through the adrenal vein, with the gland capsule lacerated to release the blood (Macchi and Hechter, 1954) or sliced and homogenized. Nevertheless, such studies have provided sufficient information to conclude that the biosynthesis of adrenocorticosteroids probably involves the intermediate synthesis of cholesterol from acetate (Srere *et al.*, 1948), although synthesis of corticosteroids by pathways which do not involve cholesterol as an obligatory intermediate remains a distinct possibility (see review by Grant, 1960). Cholesterol may be degraded *in vivo* to pregnenolone by scission of the side chain and then oxidized in ring A to progesterone. A series of hydroxylations at C-11 and C-21 and in some cases at C-17 results in the synthesis of the familiar adrenal hormones from this intermediary substance. The pathway of aldosterone biosynthesis is not clear at present but Mulrow and Cohn (1959) were able to demonstrate the conversion of corticosterone-C^{14} to aldosterone-C^{14} by human adrenal slices and Kahnt et al. (1955) demonstrated incorporation of radioactive deoxycorticosterone (DOC-21-C^{14}) into aldosterone using beef adrenal homogenates (Ross 1959, p. 42). The literature on the biosynthesis of adrenocortical hormones in mammals is voluminous and excellent reviews are available (Hechter and Pincus, 1954; Hayano et al., 1956; Dorfman, 1959; Grant, 1960, 1962). Information now available for biogenesis of adrenocortical hormones in lower vertebrates suggests that the biosynthetic pathways in mammalian adrenocortical tissue are common to all vertebrates. The interrenal tissue of Fundulus heteroclitus has the capacity to convert tritiated progesterone to tritiated aldosterone and cortisol (Phillips and Mulrow, 1959a); the latter hormone has been found in the plasma of this species (Chester Jones et al., 1959). With similar techniques the head kidney of the silver eel can also be shown to convert tritiated progesterone to cortisol but the identification of aldosterone in this species has not been firmly established (Janssens and Phillips, unpublished experiments). Four species of teleosts were studied by Nandi and Bern (1960) who found that the interrenal tissue of Anoplopoma fimbria, Mugil cephalus, and Tilapia mossambica produced detectable amounts of adrenocorticosteroids of the cortisol-cortisone type, but in one species, Bodianus bilunulatus, despite the use of adequate volumes of interrenal tissue, adrenocorticosteroids could not be detected. ACTH, added to the incubation medium containing trout head kidneys, increased but did not qualitatively change the secretory products of the adrenal tissue (Nandi and Bern, 1960; Nandi, unpublished experiments). Macchi (1955, 1956) found that the adrenal tissue of the American bullfrog (Rana catesbeiana) produced adrenocorticosteroids in vitro as shown by the presence of blue tetrazolium-reducing substances in the medium after incubation. After the addition of ACTH there was a twofold increase in tetrazolium-reducing substances. More recently, Carstensen et al. (1959, 1961) in the same species, showed that aldosterone and corticosterone were the only Δ^4-3-ketosteroids produced in significant amounts by the adrenals of this anuran when studied in vitro. The ratio of aldosterone to corticosterone produced in the presence of purified ACTH was approximately 4:1 and thus this species is the first in which aldosterone has been demonstrated to be the principal adrenocorticosteroid, at least in vitro. Aldosterone production was also stimulated by the addition of bullfrog pituitaries to the incubation medium; this suggests that there is a substance with a biological activity similar to that of purified mammalian ACTH in the pituitary gland of the bullfrog—thus supplying direct evidence for the existence of a pituitary–adrenal relationship in amphibians. The remarkable capacity of the adrenals of bullfrogs to synthesize aldosterone has been employed by Ulick and Solomon (1960) as a method for the synthesis of aldosterone-C^{14} from progesterone-4-C^{14}. A yield of 4% may be obtained which they state to be indicative of a biosynthetic capacity similar to that reported by Stachenko and Giroud (1959) for capsule strippings of bovine adrenals. Biosynthetic studies on avian adrenals have been carried out by de Roos (1960a, b). He found that corticosterone is the predominant secretion produced *in vitro* by the domestic fowl (*Gallus domesticus*), domestic pigeon (*Columba livia*), and the western gull (*Larus occidentalis*); aldosterone occurred in small but detectable amounts, and cortisol and 11-dehydrocorticosterone appeared in trace quantities. More recently, Phillips and Chester Jones (unpublished experiments) have demonstrated that, under *in vitro* conditions similar to those used by deRoos (1960a, b), adrenocortical tissue from the domestic duck converted tritiated progesterone to tritiated aldosterone, corticosterone, and, to a lesser extent, to cortisol. Thus it would seem that the biosynthetic pathways in adrenocortical tissue of lower vertebrates are similar to those found in mammals. This phylogenetic relationship is supported by the general similarity of the adrenocorticosteroids found in the blood of representatives of the various vertebrate classes (Phillips and Chester Jones, 1957; Chester Jones et al., 1959; Phillips, 1959; Idler et al., 1959b; Chester Jones and Phillips, 1960). Further, the pattern of secretion, with the notable exception of the bullfrog (Carstensen et al., 1961), is remarkably uniform throughout the Vertebrata.

On using adrenal homogenates obtained from toads (*Bufo marinus*), Crabbé (1961) confirmed the earlier findings for amphibians (see above) by demonstrating the production of both aldosterone and corticosterone from progesterone-4-C^{14} which was added as a precursor. Similar studies on adrenal slices from two species of reptiles—the lizard (*Lacerta viridis*) and the snake (*Natrix natrix*)—have recently been carried out) Phillips et al., 1962b). They were able to demonstrate the production from progesterone of both aldosterone and corticosterone, the latter predominating. Whereas mammalian ACTH had little or no effect, the adrenocortical inhibitor, amphenone, effectively inhibited the synthesis of both components of the secretion. It would seem, therefore, that reptiles resemble both amphibians and birds in producing aldosterone and corticosterone as the major adrenocortical secretions. The earlier work of deRoos (1960a, b) has now been reported more fully (deRoos, 1961) with additional information on the white Peking duck (*Anas platyrhynchus*).

2. RELEASE OF HORMONES

Vogt (1943) was the first to provide evidence that the biological activity of blood obtained from the adrenal vein was higher than that of the peripheral circulation. There are now numerous methods for the separation and analysis of adrenocortical secretions (*Mem. Soc. Endocrinol. No. 8*; Bush, 1960). Such methods when combined with bioassay estimations provide ample evidence for the quantitative assessment of hormones in body fluids and of their biological potency.

The significance of adrenocorticosteroid levels measured in adrenal venous effluent must, however, be considered in the light of two major complicating factors. First, the majority of studies have been made on animals undergoing severe stress from surgery and anesthesia and consequently do not reflect the activity of the adrenal gland in the normal resting state. To overcome this objection some workers have used trained animals with surgically isolated adrenals so that adrenal venous samples can be taken with a minimum of distress to the donor (Denton et al., 1959; McDonald and Reich, 1959). Secondly, the presence of a particular steroid in adrenal venous effluent does not constitute proof that it arises in adrenal tissue (see Hechter and Pincus, 1954), and in order to determine the amounts of steroids contributed to the blood by the adrenal gland it is necessary to measure concentration differences for each steroid across the gland by estimating their concentration in adrenal arterial and venous blood (Farrell and Richards, 1953). However, with these reservations in mind it can be claimed with a considerable degree of certainty that of the many steroids present in the adrenal tissue only a few are released into the circulation. The major constituents of the adrenocortical secretion are cortisol and/or corticosterone and aldosterone, with other corticosteroids occurring in trace amounts, and androgens of which 11β-hydroxyandrostenedione is the most prominent (Nelson et al., 1950; Bush, 1951, 1953; Simpson et al., 1952; Farrell and Lamus, 1953; Romanoff et al., 1953; Hechter and Pincus, 1954; Chester Jones, 1957; Dorfman, 1959; reviews by Bush, 1960; Nelson, 1960; Short, 1960). Moreover, the amounts of these principal hormones released by the adrenal glands account qualitatively and quantitatively for the physiological activity of the adrenal secretion.

The earlier prediction from indirect studies on various members of the lower vertebrate classes (Chester Jones, 1956, 1957; Pickford and Atz, 1957) that a pituitary-adrenal axis operates in all vertebrate animals and that the adrenal hormones are similar in nature from fish to mammal has now received considerable experimental confirmation (Fontaine and Hatey, 1954; Rinfret and Hane, 1955; Chester Jones et al., 1959, 1962a;

Hane and Robertson, 1959; Phillips, 1959; Urist and Deutsch, 1960; Chester Jones and Phillips, 1960; Nagra *et al.*, 1960; Brown, 1961). All species thus far studied have been found to possess, either in blood directly leaving the adrenal glands or in peripheral blood, corticosteroids of the cortisol-corticosterone cortisone type, and in some species aldosterone had also been detected (Phillips and Chester Jones, 1957; Chester Jones *et al.*, 1959; Phillips *et al.*, 1959; Ronald and Idler, unpublished data) (see Table II). The failure to find aldosterone in all the investigations most probably reflects the low concentration of this hormone in biological fluids and emphasizes the necessity for analyzing large volumes of plasma to reveal its presence (Phillips *et al.*, 1959; Ronald and Idler, unpublished data; Idler *et al.*, 1959b). From a pooled volume of salmon plasma Phillips *et al.* (1959) isolated appreciable amounts of cortisol, corticosterone and cortisone, and trace amounts of aldosterone together with three unknown Δ^4-3-ketones. The concentration of aldosterone was similar to that found in human peripheral blood (Table II; Simpson and Tait, 1955; Wettstein, 1954). Investigation of the same species of salmon by Ronald and Idler (unpublished data) has confirmed the presence of aldosterone in salmon peripheral blood though the concentrations were found to be higher (male, 1.84 μg/100 ml; female, 1.58 μg/100 ml). More recently, Idler (personal communication) working on the same fractions could not firmly characterize the substance as aldosterone by further chemical modification of the molecule and concludes that the major portion of the original fraction was, in fact, a contaminant. These observations may account for the large differences reported for this species by Ronald and Idler and by Phillips *et al.* (1959). Crabbé (1961) observed in the toad that the level of plasma corticosterone exceeded that of aldosterone, which is in contrast to the results obtained from the adrenal homogenate incubations (Section II, B, 1), and he attributed this discrepancy to a possible shorter biological half-life for aldosterone—an observation which has been found for man (Ayres *et al.*, 1958). Nevertheless, the concentration of aldosterone in toad plasma exceeds by a factor of 10 that found for man (Ayres *et al.*, 1957). Idler *et al.* (1959a) found 17α-hydroxyprogesterone, and Idler *et al.* (1960) report its 20β-dihydro-epimer in salmon blood; both findings constitute the first reports of the occurrence of these steroids in blood.

To those interested in the evolutionary aspects of adrenal form and function, the Agnatha occupy a unique position. Any discussion of physiological changes which have occurred during the evolution of the vertebrate body must consider the role adrenocorticosteroids play within this group; most particularly those concerned in the sphere of electrolyte and water

TABLE II

ADRENOCORTICOSTEROIDS IN REPRESENTATIVE SPECIES OF DIFFERENT CLASSES OF CHORDATES

Animal	Sex	Type of corticosteroid	Concentration (μg/100 ml peripheral plasma unless otherwise stated)	Remarks	References
CEPHALOCHORDATA					
Amphioxus lanceolatus	—	No adrenocorticosteroids found in 142 gm whole Amphioxus		—	1
VERTEBRATA. AGNATHA, CYCLOSTOMATA					
Petromyzontia					
Petromyzon marinus (Lamprey)	♂	Cortisol	47	Normal fresh water landlocked lamprey of Lake Superior	1
	♂	Corticosterone	4	Normal fresh water landlocked lamprey of Lake Superior	1
	♀	Cortisol	28	Normal fresh water landlocked lamprey of Lake Superior	1
	♀	Corticosterone	5	Normal fresh water landlocked lamprey of Lake Superior	1
Myxinoidea					
Polistotrema stouti (Pacific hagfish)	♂ + ♀	Cortisol	10	Normal, in sea water	1
	♂ + ♀	Corticosterone	14	Normal, in sea water	1
Myxine glutinosa (Atlantic hagfish)	♂ + ♀	Cortisol	10.6	Normal, in sea water	2
	♂ + ♀	Corticosterone	27.2	Normal, in sea water	2

VERTEBRATA. GNATHOSTOMATA
ELASMOBRANCHII

Charcharinus milbertei (Brown shark)	♀	Cortisol	2.6	Normal, in sea water	3
	♀	Corticosterone	5.9	Normal, in sea water	3
Charcharinus leucas (Bull shark)	♂	Cortisol	0.9	Normal, in sea water	3
	♂	Corticosterone	1.8	Normal, in sea water	3
	♀	Cortisol	2.9	Normal, in sea water	3
	♀	Corticosterone	1.7	Normal, in sea water	3
Charcharinus obscurus (Dusky shark)	♀	Cortisol	3.3	Normal, in sea water	3
	♀	Corticosterone	2.7	Normal, in sea water	3
Charcharinus maculipinnis (Black-tipped shark)	♂	Cortisol	2.9	Normal, in sea water	3
	♂	Corticosterone	0.8	Normal, in sea water	3
Galeocerdo cuvieri (Tiger shark)	♀	Cortisol	1.6	Normal, in sea water	3
	♀	Corticosterone	5.2	Normal, in sea water	3
Dasyatus americana (Sting ray)	♀	Cortisol	4.3	Normal, in sea water	3
	♀	Corticosterone	4.0	Normal, in sea water	3
Myliobatus freminvillii (Eagle ray)	♂	Cortisol	6.8	Normal, in sea water	4
	♂	Corticosterone	20.4	Normal, in sea water	4
Raja eglanteria (Ray)	♀	Cortisol	5.3	Normal, in sea water	3
Raja clavata (Ray)	♂ + ♀	Corticosterone	8.0	Normal, in sea water	5
Scyliorhinus canicula (Dogfish)	♂ + ♀	Cortisol	2.5[a]	Normal, in sea water	5

ACTINOPTERYGII

Gadus morhua (Cod)	♂ + ♀	Cortisol	1.0[a]	Normal, in sea water	5
Pseudopleuronectes americanus	♂ + ♀	Cortisol	16.0	Normal, in sea water	4
Menticirrhus americanus (Southern king fish)	♂ + ♀	Cortisol	21.5	Normal, in sea water	4
Pogonias cromis (Channel bass)	♂	Cortisol	2.0	Normal, in sea water	4
Catostomus comersoni (Shortnosed sucker)	♂	Cortisol	44.0	Normal, in fresh water	3
	♂	Corticosterone	7.7	Normal, in fresh water	3
	♀	Cortisol	20.0	Normal, in fresh water	3
	♀	Corticosterone	18.5	Normal, in fresh water	3

TABLE II—Continued

Animal	Sex	Type of corticosteroid	Concentration (μg/100 ml peripheral plasma unless otherwise stated)	Remarks	References
ACTINOPTERYGII					
Catostomus catostomus (Longnosed sucker)	♂	Cortisol	29.8	Normal, in fresh water	3
	♂	Corticosterone	11.4	Normal, in fresh water	3
Cyprinus carpio (Carp)	♀	Cortisol	18.0	Normal, in fresh water	3
	♀	Corticosterone	3.8	Normal, in fresh water	3
	♂	Cortisol	24.4	Normal, in fresh water	6
	♀	Cortisol	43.8	Normal, in fresh water	6
	♂	Cortisol	24.8	Normal, in fresh water	4
	♀	Cortisol	31.3	Normal, in fresh water	4
		17-Hydroxycorticosteroids	1.83 ± 0.47	Unstressed	7
				Slightly stressed	7
		17-Hydroxycorticosteroids	5.05 ± 1.25	a. Carried few meters	
		17-Hydroxycorticosteroids	8.95 ± 3.31	b. Carried 50 meters	
				Stressed by forced swimming	7
		17-Hydroxycorticosteroids	27.5 ± 3.31	a. For 30 min.	
		17-Hydroxycorticosteroids	28.1 ± 9.15	b. For 60 min.	
		17-Hydroxycorticosteroids	23.5 ± 5.58	c. For 120 min.	
Fundulus heteroclitus (Killifish)	♂	Cortisol	15.2		4
	♀	Cortisol	8.2		4
Onchorhynchus nerka (Sockeye salmon)	♀	Cortisol	17.0	Anadromous migration	8
	♀	Cortisone	37.0	a. 300 miles (approx.) from sea	

Salmo salar (Atlantic salmon) ... *Onchorhynchus tschawytscha* (Pacific salmon)

♂	Cortisol	5.2	b. 640 miles from sea, spawning and spent	9
♂	Cortisone	6.1		
♂	Corticosterone	7.3		
♂	Aldosterone	0.12		
♂ + ♀	Cortisol	26.0	Anadromous migration	10
♂ + ♀	Cortisone	41.0	Anadromous migration	10
♂	Cortisol	11.0	Anadromous migration	10
♂	Cortisone	22.0	Anadromous migration	10
	17-Hydroxycorticosteroids	19.6	Parr stage (venous blood)	11
	17-Hydroxycorticosteroids	12.7	Parr stage (arterial blood)	11
	17-Hydroxycorticosteroids	85.5	Smolt stage (venous blood)	11
	17-Hydroxycorticosteroids	99.4	Smolt stage (arterial blood)	11
♂	17-Hydroxycorticosteroids	50.2	Anadromous migration (venous blood)	11
♂	17-Hydroxycorticosteroids	31.4	Anadromous migration (arterial blood)	11
♀	17-Hydroxycorticosteroids	45.3	Anadromous migration (venous blood)	11
♀	17-Hydroxycorticosteroids	34.7	Anadromous migration (arterial blood)	11
♂	17-Hydroxycorticosteroids	31.7	Spawning (venous blood)	11
♂	17-Hydroxycorticosteroids	21.2	Spawning (arterial blood)	11
♀	17-Hydroxycorticosteroids	30.6	Spawning (venous blood)	11
♀	17-Hydroxycorticosteroids	25.7	Spawning (arterial blood)	11
♂ + ♀	17-Hydroxycorticosteroids[b]	11.8	Sea-run adult	12
♂	17-Hydroxycorticosteroids[b]		Adult anadromous migration	12
		41.4 ± 12	a. 125 miles from sea	
		49.0 ± 21	b. 285 miles from sea	
♀	17-Hydroxycorticosteroids[b]	53.4 ± 13	285 miles from sea	12

221

TABLE II—Continued

Animal	Sex	Type of corticosteroid	Concentration of (μg/100 ml peripheral plasma unless otherwise stated)	Remarks	References
ACTINOPTERYGII					
Onchorhynchus tschawytcha (Pacific salmon)	♂	17-Hydroxycorticosteroids[b]	29.0 ± 11	Anadromous migration (325 miles from sea) — Caught in 1957	12
	♂	17-Hydroxycorticosteroids[b]	32.4 ± 13	Spawning and spent — 1958	12
	♀	17-Hydroxycorticosteroids[b]	88.5 ± 35	Spawning and spent — 1957	12
	♀	17-Hydroxycorticosteroids[b]	77.4 ± 28	Spawning and spent — 1958	12
Salmo gairdnerii (Rainbow trout)	♂ + ♀	17-Hydroxycorticosteroids[b]	2.7	Nonmigratory (immature)	12
	♂	17-Hydroxycorticosteroids[b]	10.0	Sp. var. (mature)	12
	♂	17-Hydroxycorticosteroids[b]	21.6 ± 5	Anadromous migration (118 miles from sea)	12
	♀	17-Hydroxycorticosteroids[b]	34.1 ± 15	Anadromous migration (118 miles from sea)	12
CHOANICHTHYES					
Protopterus annectens	♂ + ♀	Cortisol	15.0	—	5
AMPHIBIA					
Xenopus laevis (South African toad)	♂ + ♀	Cortisol	7.0[a]	Mixture of adrenal and renal blood	5
Amphiuma	♂	Cortisol	1.5		4
	♀	Cortisol	1.3		4
	♂	Corticosterone	4.1		4
	♀	Corticosterone	2.1		4

222

Species	Sex	Steroid	Concentration	Source	Ref.
REPTILIA					
Natrix natrix var. (Grass snake)	♀	Cortisol	8.5	Adrenal venous blood after ACTH administration	5
	♀	Corticosterone	156	Adrenal venous blood after ACTH administration	5
AVES					
Gallus domesticus (capon)	♂	Cortisol	3.0	Adrenal venous blood (normal)	5
	♂	Corticosterone	312.0	Adrenal venous blood	5
	♂	Cortisol	3.5	Adrenal venous blood (ACTH)	5
	♂	Corticosterone	65.5	Adrenal venous blood	5
	♂	Aldosterone	1.0	Adrenal venous blood	5
	♂	Corticosterone	7.3 ± 0.3	Adrenal venous blood	13
Gallus domesticus (Wisco white)	♂	Corticosterone	44.3 ± 5.5	Adrenal venous blood (normal)	13
	♂	Corticosterone	143.7 ± 50.7	Adrenal venous blood (ACTH)	12
Phasianus colchicus (Ring necked pheasant)	♂	Corticosterone	8.6 ± 0.8	(Normal)	12
	♂	Corticosterone	34.8 ± 4.7	Adrenal venous plasma (normal)	13
	♂	Corticosterone	7.8 ± 0.7	(castrate)	13
	♂	Corticosterone	33.1 ± 7.2	Adrenal venous plasma (castrate)	13
Catheturus sp. (Broad-breasted bronze turkey)	♂	Corticosterone	7.8 ± 0.4	Adrenal venous plasma	13
	♂	Corticosterone	42.4 ± 5.3	Adrenal venous plasma	13
MAMMALIA					
Laboratory rat	♂	Corticosterone	167 ± 16.6	Adrenal venous effluent	14
	♀	Corticosterone	210 ± 31.4	a. proestrous	14
	♀	Corticosterone	126 ± 7.8	b. estrous	14
	♀	Corticosterone	72 ± 6.1	c. metestrous	14
	♀	Corticosterone	68 ± 8.1	d. diestrous	14
Dog		Corticosterone	217	Adrenal venous plasma	18
		Cortisol	330	Adrenal venous plasma	18
		Aldosterone	3.5	Adrenal venous plasma	18

TABLE II—Continued

Animal	Sex	Type of corticosteroid	Concentration (μg, 100 ml peripheral plasma unless otherwise states)	Remarks	References
MAMMALIA		Corticosterone	121	Cell fraction of adrenal venous blood (μg/100 ml)	18
		Cortisol	285	Cell fraction of adrenal venous blood (μg/100 ml)	18
		Aldosterone	5.7	Cell fraction of adrenal venous blood (μg/100 ml)	18
Man	♂	Corticosterone	12.2 ± 0.3		15
	♂	Cortisol	11.4 ± 3.7		16
	♀	Cortisol	8.8 ± 2.9		16
	♀♂	Corticosterone	1.8 ± 3.1		16
	♀	Corticosterone	0.8 ± 1.6		16
	♀	Aldosterone	0.03		17

References

1. Chester Jones and Phillips (1960)
2. Phillips et al. (1962a)
3. Phillips (1959)
4. Chester Jones et al. (1959)
5. Phillips and Chester Jones (1957)
6. Bondy et al. (1957)
7. Leloup-Hatey (1958)
8. Idler et al. (1959a)
9. Phillips et al. (1959)
10. Idler et al. (1959b)
11. Fontaine and Hatey (1954)
12. Hane and Robertson (1959)
13. Nagra et al. (1960)
14. Dean et al. (1959)
15. Guillemin et al. (1958)
16. Bondy and Upton (1957)
17. Ayres et al. (1957)
18. Holzbauer and Vogt (1961)

a μg/100 ml whole blood.
b Predominantly cortisol.

metabolism, for within the family Myxinoidea are members which are exceptional in that the major inorganic ions in plasma are in apparent equilibrium with those of the surrounding sea water (Chester Jones and Phillips, 1960; Morris, 1960; Bellamy and Chester Jones, 1961). Recent investigations (Phillips *et al.*, 1962a) on *Myxine glutinosa* confirms the earlier work on *Polistotrema stouti* in which cortisol and corticosterone were found in peripheral blood (Phillips, 1959). However, the analysis of 8500 ml of plasma obtained from *Myxine* failed to reveal the presence of detectable amounts of aldosterone. These results therefore raise the possibility that this hormone arose concomitantly with the need for renal sodium retention by fresh water vertebrates. A full discussion of the implications of these findings can be found elsewhere (Chester Jones and Phillips, 1960; Chester Jones *et al.*, 1962a).

3. TRANSPORT AND FATE OF ADRENOCORTICAL HORMONES

A proportion of the adrenocorticosteroids present in blood is loosely bound to plasma proteins. The corticosteroid-binding protein is an α-globulin. When the steroid levels rise beyond the physiological range the steroids begin to bind with albumin. Evidence points to a role for globulin as a buffer mechanism to adjust against rapid changes in circulating levels of corticosteroids. Sudden increases in corticosteroid output would result in increased binding, and this pool can then act as a reservoir for a time when corticosteroid production wanes (Mills, 1961). Corticosteroids are metabolized by reactions which probably involve the reduction of the steroid nucleus and its substituents, with or without subsequent scission of the sidechain (see review by Cameron, 1957). The metabolic products of the corticosteroids are excreted in the urine mainly as the glucuronide or sulfate conjugates. The reader is referred to recent reviews on this topic (Dorfman and Ungar, 1953; Bush, 1957; Klyne, 1957; Antoniades, 1960; Daughaday, 1960; Mills, 1961, 1962). Only one report of similar studies on a lower vertebrate is available; on free and conjugated Δ^4-3-ketosteroids in the adrenals and blood of chickens (Newcomer, 1959).

C. Control of Adrenocortical Secretion

1. CORTISOL AND CORTICOSTERONE

The dependence of the adrenal cortex upon a normal and functioning pituitary gland received experimental proof from the pioneering study of Smith (1930). Since that time the occurrence of an adrenocortical-hypophyseal axis in all vertebrates has been established and it would seem that any variations which occur between one group and another are generally variations in degree rather than kind (Swann, 1940; Chester Jones, 1957; Pickford and Atz, 1957; Pickford, 1959a, b; Dixon, 1960). It must be recognized however, that the interrelationship of the pituitary and adrenal cortex is part of a complex endocrine system which is finely integrated in the normal animal, and interference with any one part of this system may be reflected by changes in the functional capacity of the other components of the system. These changes are not always easy to analyze and assess. Thus the capacity of the adrenal cortex is influenced by the functional state of other endocrine glands as well as by the pituitary gland (Chester Jones, 1957; Dean et al., 1959; Sandberg, 1960).

Profound changes both in the histological appearance and in the se-cretory capacity of the adrenal gland follow hypophysectomy. The atrophic changes which ensue are confined for the most part to the inner zones of the adrenal gland which stand in sharp contrast to the apparently normal appearance of the zona glomerulosa. These changes are preceded by a rapid drop in the secretion of the glucocorticoid component; however, a steady but low rate of secretion persists (Sweat and Farrell, 1954). This rate of secretion is unchanged by factors which in the normal animal would elicit an increase in the corticosteroid output and approximates to the lowest rates of secretion found in the unstressed animal (Pickford and Vogt, 1951; Egdahl and Richards, 1956). The pituitary factor responsible for the changes in histology and secretion is ACTH and stimulation by ACTH of the adrenal in the hypophysectomized animal restores, and if present in sufficient quantities, greatly surpasses the normal secretory rates. Doubt exists as to whether ACTH is a single compound or a complex of more than one substance (Stack-Dunne, 1953; Nowell and Chester Jones, 1958). It is probable that the native ACTH is a protein but the small-est active components isolated from the pituitary are large polypeptides con-sisting of amino acids in known sequence (Bell, 1954; Li et al., 1955). In-jection of these polypeptides restores the functional capacity of the adrenal cortex in the hypophysectomized animal. The inhibition of corticotropin release is probably controlled by a feed-back mechanism in which the adrenocortical hormone level in blood acts on the pituitary to regulate the release of ACTH. Although many steroids are known to inhibit the release of ACTH it is probably that cortisol, because of its high activity in this respect, is responsible at least in the human (Sayers and Sayers, 1947, 1948; Dorfman, 1955). However, this conclusion may be an over-simplification of the mechanism concerned (Sydnor and Sayers, 1954). In those animals (rabbit and rat) which secrete predominantly corti-costerone it is presumably this steroid which effectively limits the release of ACTH. The direct stimulation of the release of ACTH is probably mediated by substances carried to it by the blood (i.e., it is humoral), the nerve supply to the adenohypophysis being scant. More than one factor may be involved since autotransplants of the adenohypophysis to sites away from the hypothalamus release ACTH in response to some but not all stressing stimuli (Fortier 1952). Thus transplants respond to adrenaline and histamine, i.e., to systemic stresses but not to emotional or neurotropic stresses which act via the hypothalamus. However, there seems to be inadequate evidence for a rigorous separation into these two categories, for Hume (1952), McCann (1953), and Briggs and Munson (1954) have described stimuli which can be considered systemic, exerting their effect through the mediation of the central nervous system. Harris (1948, 1955) postulates the presence of a chemical transmitter synthesized by the hypothalamus and released into the hypothalamo–hypophyseal portal system to stimulate the release of ACTH. This factor, now called the "corticotropin-releasing factor" (CRF), remains as yet unidentified. The available evidence for the mechanism of its action is reviewed by Vogt (1960), and possible mechanisms for the regulation of ACTH secretion by the central nervous system have been described by Mason (1958). A valuable review on the mechanism of adrenocortical control has recently appeared (Saffran, 1962).

2. ALDOSTERONE

Aldosterone, the major adrenocorticosteroid concerned in electrolyte metabolism, is relatively free from adenohypophyseal control. This was forecast before the isolation of aldosterone. For although adrenalectomized animals require additional salt for survival (Chester Jones, 1957), the hypophysectomized animal preserves in large measure the ability to regulate electrolyte and water metabolism. Further, indirect studies using changes in adrenal histology led Deane and Greep (1946), Deane and McKibbin (1946), Deane and Shaw (1947) and Greep and Deane (1947) to postulate that the zona glomerulosa is principally concerned in the synthesis of a salt-regulating hormone. This postulate has received ample confirmation in recent years (Ayres, 1960). It seems, therefore, that in the hypophysectomized animal a healthy zona glomerulosa produces almost normal amounts of aldosterone and remains relatively unaffected by the absence of ACTH. On the other hand the inner zones which are ACTH dependent undergo profound changes after hypophysectomy and there ensues a marked decline in the output of the cortisol-corticosterone type of hormone. These changes together account for the differences between the sequelae of adrenalectomy and hypophysectomy.

Aldosterone secretion thus persists in the rat after hypophysectomy, with a disproportional decrease in the two components of the adrenocortical secretion; corticosterone secretion decreases to a much larger extent than aldosterone secretion (Singer and Stack-Dunne, 1955). Moreover, inhibition of ACTH release has little effect on aldosterone production (Farrell et al., 1956) and this is also true in most cases for animals treated with ACTH (Farrell et al., 1955). Nevertheless, ACTH appears to be one factor among the many which affect the output of aldosterone (Singer and Stack-Dunne, 1955; Muller et al., 1956; Rauschkolb et al., 1956; Davis et al., 1957; Giroud et al., 1958; McDonald and Reich, 1959; Lucis et al., 1961). Thus, the role of ACTH is far from clear. Further, the two components δ_1- and β-corticotropin qualitatively and quantitatively differ in their effect on steroidogenesis. δ_1-Corticotropin stimulates the production of both cortisol and aldosterone whereas β-corticotropin stimulates aldosterone secretion but is much less potent in this respect than δ_1-corticotropin (Farrell et al., 1958). It seems therefore that ACTH can affect aldosterone secretion but it is not the principal regulating factor. Assuming that ACTH acts at an early stage in the biosynthetic sequence between cholesterol and pregnenolone and that subsequent transformations in the biosynthetic pathways leading to the final secretory product are free from ACTH control, it is difficult to understand fully the mechanisms of ACTH action with regard to aldosterone. For if corticosterone is the immediate precursor of aldosterone (Mulrow and Cohn, 1959) then a comparable increase in aldosterone could be expected along with an increase in glucocorticoids after ACTH administration, since an increase in availability of the precursor would lead to enhanced aldosterone production via the 18-oxidase system. However, the limiting factor in response to ACTH may be a saturation of the enzyme systems involved in aldosterone biosynthesis and may result in a shift to biosynthetic pathways leading to a greater formation of the glucocorticoid component (Lucis et al., 1961). The presence of a specific aldosterone stimulator controlling the 18-oxidase system within the zona glomerulosa may account for these differences, and Farrell and his associates (see Farrell 1958; 1960) marshal evidence to support the existence of such a substance which they have named adrenoglomerulotropin. This lipid factor obtained from pineal extracts has been found to stimulate aldosterone secretion selectively and a second factor, also of pineal origin, inhibits both aldosterone and cortisol secretion. They suggest that the control of aldosterone secretion may involve an excitatory-inhibitory system in which the pituitary corticotropin adrenoglomerulotropin and "anticorticotropin" interact to determine the secretory rate of aldosterone from the adrenal (Farrell, 1960). However, the work of Coghlan et al. (1960) on pinealectomized sheep does not indicate that this gland plays a role in the adrenal response to change in Na^+ balance.

Other pituitary hormones may also play a role in the control of aldosterone secretion. Growth hormone elevates urinary aldosterone levels in man (Beck et al., 1957) and the presence of a specific substance from posterior pituitary extracts which causes enhancement of aldosterone production in vitro has been reported by Giroud et al. (1958).

Many workers have reported changes in aldosterone secretion as a result of alteration in the electrolyte content of the diet. A consistent concomitant of sodium deprivation is increased aldosterone secretion (Ayres et al., 1958; Rosnagle and Farrell, 1956). Conversely, sodium-loading decreases aldosterone production (Luetscher and Curtis, 1955). The response to sodium restriction is inhibited or reduced by the simultaneous denial of potassium (Laragh and Stoerk, 1957; Johnson et al., 1957), and potassium-loading under similar circumstances results in increased levels (Bartter, 1956; Laragh and Stoerk, 1957; Johnson et al., 1957). When considering these changes in aldosterone output, direct studies on the hormone concentration in the adrenal venous effluent of the rat confirm that potassium depletion decreases aldosterone output (Singer and Stack-Dunne, 1955). In the sheep, reduction of Na^+ and increase of K^+ concentration causes increased aldosterone secretion (Coghlan et al., 1960). Moreover, McDonald and Reich (1959) have shown that adrenal secretion in the normal, resting, undisturbed sheep comprises cortisol with small amounts of corticosterone, and that aldosterone occurs in significant amounts only after sodium depletion. Moderate sodium depletion results in no change in the glucocorticoid component of the adrenal secretion but severe depletion, although unable to elevate the aldosterone level further, causes a significant increase in cortisol and corticosterone secretion rates. It seems, therefore, that with maximum aldosterone production intensification of the stress which elicits aldosterone secretion is met by an enhancement of the secretion of the glucocorticoids and that this component of the adrenal secretion may have importance in electrolyte regulation in severe sodium deprivation (see also Coghlan et al., 1960).

The effect of changes in intravascular fluid volume on the secretion of aldosterone has received considerable attention from Bartter and his associates (Bartter et al., 1958; Bartter and Gann, 1960). When the intravascular volume was expanded aldosterone secretion decreased and the converse situation obtained when the intravascular volume was contracted. They concluded that alterations in aldosterone levels caused by changes in body sodium and consequently in extracellular fluid volume ultimately depends upon a function of intravascular volume. It is probable, however, that intravascular volume changes are only one factor contributing to the determination of aldosterone production. Stretching of the right, but not the left, atrium in dogs depresses aldosterone secretion to one-half of that found in control animals (McCally et al., 1958) and they suggest the presence of receptors in this area as part of a reflex system for aldosterone control.

Many other factors alter aldosterone output. The reader is referred to recent reviews by Farrell (1958), August et al. (1958), Luetscher and Lieberman (1958), Denton et al. (1959), Ross (1959), Vogt (1960) and Wright (1962). Of particular interest, however, are the recent reports of a possible involvement of the renin-angiotensin mechanism within the kidney in controlling aldosterone secretion after hemorrhage in the hypophysectomized dog (Ganong and Mulrow, 1961; Davis et al., 1961).

The evidence for the existence of ACTH in lower vertebrates is scanty and has been obtained mainly by indirect studies involving hypophysectomy and injection of mammalian ACTH preparations. It is probable, however, that pituitaries of lower vertebrates contain a substance with properties similar to mammalian ACTH which increases adrenocorticosteroid output (Pickford and Atz, 1957; Chester Jones, 1957; Pickford, 1959a, b; Chester Jones and Phillips, 1960). Direct evidence for the stimulatory activity of ACTH in fish (Nandi and Bern, 1960), in frogs (Macchi, 1955, 1956; Carstensen et al., 1959, 1961), and in birds (de Roos, 1960a, b; Newcomer, 1959; Nagra et al., 1960)—and work by Brown (1961)—support this conclusion. Two attempts have been made to isolate fish ACTH. Ito et al. (1952) used pituitaries of Katsuwonus vagans and, using the methods of Li et al. (1951) for fractionation, found ascorbic acid-depleting activity in the acid-heat treated "prolactin" fraction. Rinfret and Hane (1955) found in lyophilized and fractionated pituitaries of the Pacific salmon (Oncorhynchus keta) a component which was capable of depleting the stores of adrenal ascorbic acid in the rat. They conclude that their preparation qualitatively resembles ACTH of mammalian origin.

III. FUNCTIONS OF THE ADRENOCORTICAL HORMONES

A. Effect of Corticosteroids on Ion Movement

The success of animals in achieving independence from their external environment is often a function of regulatory processes which maintain the water and electrolyte content of the body within well-defined limits. Hormones, though not initiating these processes, are essential regulatory substances and their effect on target organs which are ultimately responsible for the regulation of the internal environment is the subject of the present discussion.

The control of electrolyte and water metabolism is influenced for the most part by the secretions of the adrenal cortex and the posterior lobe of the pituitary. It has been observed earlier (Section II, B, 2) that the adrenal steroids of widely different animals have a similar chemical structure. Further, these steroids are released into the circulation in approximately equal amounts in fish, amphibians, reptiles, birds, and mammals. The hormones emanating from the posterior lobe of the pituitary exhibit only minor differences in structure (Sawyer *et al.*, 1960). Examination of the function of these two types of hormones in a wide variety of animals indicates that they regulate the same processes by which water and electrolytes move across cell membranes. Thus, the adrenocorticosteroids produce similar effects in the kidney tubule, gills, skin, gut, bladder, and a variety of glands. The common feature of all the target organs is that they are composed of epithelial cells with the capacity for allowing transcellular salt and water movement.

1. KIDNEY

Most studies on the role of adrenocorticosteroids on the metabolism of inorganic ions have been carried out in conjunction with work on renal function. This approach stems from the now classical experiments which showed that adrenalectomy removed a factor favoring sodium retention by the body.

One of the main characteristics of the adrenalectomized animal is that large quantities of sodium are excreted in the urine. The sodium depletion may be prevented by the administration of corticosteroids. When steroid hormones are given to the normal animal there is a reduction in the excretion of sodium and an increase in the potassium content of the urine. This effect is obtained with relatively small doses (Ingle *et al.*, 1946); larger amounts of steroid may stimulate sodium excretion (Thorn *et al.*, 1941). In rats, doses between 1 and 10 μg decrease sodium excretion, doses of between 10 and 500 μg produce natriuresis because of a greatly increased filtration rate, but larger doses (above 1 mg) cause a reduction in sodium loss due to a fall in renal blood flow (Streeten *et al.*, 1955). Although all steroids secreted by the adrenal gland stimulate sodium retention in small doses, aldosterone is the most potent in this respect.

Corticosteroids appear to influence the process by which sodium and potassium are handled by the renal tubular system, indicating an effect on ion transport. At the present time the main transport mechanisms which are thought to modify the sodium and potassium content of the glomerular filtrate are active transport of sodium and potassium into the tubular cells, with chloride following passively, and exchange of tubular sodium for intracellular potassium or hydrogen ions. Since the corticosteroids produce reciprocal changes in the sodium and potassium content of urine it is likely that the hormones stimulate the processes by which tubular sodium is exchanged for intracellular potassium and hydrogen ion. For example, it was found that prolonged treatment with deoxycorticosterone (DOC) decreases Na^+ excretion and increases the tubular secretion of both H^+ and K^+ (Kuhlman et al., 1939; Perera, 1948). However, most corticosteroids produce greater sodium retention than potassium and hydrogen ion excretion which makes it likely that the hormones also stimulate the active uptake of sodium from the tubule by a mechanism which is not associated with ion exchange reactions. In this connection it has been found that steroids may differ in their site of action on the renal tubule. Thus cortisol appears to stimulate mainly the Na^+–K^+ reaction whereas aldosterone has a general stimulatory effect on all mechanisms for sodium uptake (Mills et al., 1961).

Most of the experimental evidence for the action of adrenocortical hormones on urinary electrolyte excretion has been obtained following the injection of steroids into mammalian species. When similar experiments are carried out with lower vertebrates the results are often equivocal. For example, recent work (Chester Jones et al., 1962b) suggests that exogenous aldosterone does not affect renal sodium excretion in the freshwater eel. In contrast, aldosterone has an effect on the electrolyte excretion of toads which is the opposite of that found in mammals (Crabbé, 1961). However, it is clear from the results of adrenalectomy that the adrenal gland exerts a similar control of sodium reabsorption in mammals, birds, and amphibia (for references, see Chester Jones, 1957). As yet there is no definite evidence that the adrenal cortex is involved in the excretion of electrolytes by reptiles although reptilian tissue is known to synthesize both corticosterone and aldosterone (Phillips et al., 1962b).

2. Muscle and Other Tissue Cells

The present consensus is that the intracellular sodium and potassium content of a wide variety of tissues, particularly muscle, is maintained by a process which depends on the constant active extrusion of sodium from the cell. Potassium is thought to diffuse across the cell membrane until electrochemical equilibrium is reached. It is of interest therefore to know whether the sodium extrusion mechanism which maintains a favorable environment for metabolic reactions, is influenced by hormones in all body cells.

Adrenalectomy and corticosteroid administration indicate that the cortical hormones are necessary for maintaining the normal levels of sodium and potassium in muscle. Lack of adrenal steroids result in a loss of cellular sodium and a gain in potassium. Superficially this situation resembles that in the kidney tubule; in muscle the active efflux of sodium appears to be inhibited by corticosteroids whereas in the tubule the active influx into the tubular cells is stimulated. However, further examination shows that the ion content of muscle in the adrenalectomized animal is the result of a new equilibrium and mainly dependent upon the renal effect of hormone deprivation (Conway and Hingerty, 1946). The only result which appears to be independent of changes in renal function is a rise in the total indiffusible intracellular negative charges. This has the effect of increasing the amount of potassium present at electrochemical equilibrium, and accounts for the movement of about 40% of the potassium which enters the muscle after adrenalectomy (Conway and Hingerty, 1946). These results are in agreement with the effects of DOC on the ion content of normal rat tissue. However, some of the results of aldosterone administration, particularly on brain electrolytes, have no simple explanation in terms of a limited renal effect (Woodbury and Withrow, 1962).

Therefore there is as yet no evidence that adrenal hormones influence active sodium transport across the cell membrane of mammalian muscle. This is equally true of red blood cells in which mineralocorticoids added *in vitro* have no effect on the potassium–sodium exchange mechanism which is thought to be responsible for the maintenance of ion gradients across the cell membrane (Glynn, 1957; Kumar and Sheth, 1961). All experiments on the distribution of sodium and potassium across cell membranes indicate that the low level of intracellular sodium is maintained by processes linked with the production of metabolic energy (Ussing et al., 1960). There is also a good deal of indirect evidence that ATP is the prime energy source for sodium transport and most of the experiments on the effect of steroids on ionic regulation have been interpreted in relation to an effect on the energy-requiring mechanism. However, it has recently been pointed out that the flow of sodium out of the cell against a diffusion gradient may be dependent upon the net flux of other substances, e.g., metabolic water, across the cell membrane (Nims and Thurber, 1961). Thus, although experiments suggest the likelihood that adrenocortical hormones may affect sodium distribution by altering the rate of aerobic energy production (an inhibitory effect; see Section III, B, 4), it is also necessary to take into account the possibility of changes in the permeability of the cell membrane to a variety of solutes. It may be significant, in this respect, that vasopressin (known to affect passive water movement) brings about an increase in both the water and sodium content of muscle (Friedman and Sréter, 1961). At the moment the few direct effects of adrenocortical hormones on cells which are not specialized for ionic regulation defy interpretation because they are often contradictory (Conway, 1956; Wilson, 1957; Hechter and Lester, 1960; Chester Jones et al., 1962b). If one attempts to generalize, it appears that some of the apparent confusion is relation to the molecular differences between various steroids which are often used indiscriminately (Cier, 1961).

3. GILLS

One of the functions of the gills of fresh water teleosts is to take up sodium from the external environment to balance that lost by renal excretion. The influx of sodium through the gills appears to be an active process in that sodium moves against a chemical potential gradient and is dependent upon oxidative metabolism (Krogh, 1939; Bellamy, 1961). The regulatory mechanism by which sodium transport in the gill is adjusted to meet a gain or loss of body sodium is not known. In normal circumstances the fresh water fish is unlikely to meet with factors which produce drastic changes in its internal environment and the mechanism controlling the gills may be solely a chemical feed-back. In this connection it has been shown that the rate of sodium uptake by the goldfish is reduced after adaptat:on to solutions of increasing sodium concentration (from about 0.04 mM to 0.14 M, Favre, 1960). Presumably this effect is related to the decreased osmotic gradient, causing a fall in urine production and consequently a decreased renal loss of sodium.

It has recently been emphasized that the permeability of the gill membrane measured *in vivo* may be greatly influenced by handling during the experiment (Maetz, 1962). In the case of goldfish, this complication may be avoided by using fish which have been adapted to the laboratory environment for several days and by carrying out the necessary manipulations by remote control. Under these conditions it was observed that adrenocortical hormones did not alter sodium movement through the gills, whereas peptides of the posterior pituitary gland produced an immediate stimulation of sodium influx (Maetz, 1962).

One would not expect hormonal control mechanisms to have a long-term importance in stenohaline fish; a more suitable experimental animal might be one of the euryhaline forms. Recent work on membrane potentials suggests that two mechanisms for ion transport occur together in euryhaline species. In one mechanism sodium movement is active while chloride follows passively; in the other—operating in the reverse direction—chloride moves actively and sodium passively (Potts, 1962; House, 1962). Only one of these mechanisms is dominant in a given environment, which is either hypertonic or hypotonic to the body fluids. In euryhaline teleosts like the eel, salmon, and trout, it is possible that the migration from fresh water to sea water calls into play a separate mechanism for active ion efflux in the gills and causes the inactivation of the corresponding mechanism for ion uptake (see also Pellamy, 1961). Although posterior pituitary hormones appear to be important in this adaptation (Maetz, 1962), the change may also involve alterations in the levels of circulating adrenocortical hormones. Indeed, recent experiments on the eel, under conditions where it is not subject to stress on handling (Bellamy and Chester Jones, 1961b), showed that aldosterone injections decreased the time taken for the sea-water eel to adapt to a fresh-water environment (as measured by the decrease in the rate of sodium loss through the gills; Bellamy unpublished). Conversely, the administration of aldosterone to a fresh-water animal reduced the net sodium uptake through the gills (Chester Jones *et al.* 1962b). Possibly these effects, which took several hours to develop, have a common basis not directly related to the active ion transport system but to the passive sodium loss through the gills. The passive permeability to sodium is known to be high for eels in a sea-water environment and low in fresh water (Bellamy, 1961). Thus by decreasing the "leakiness" of the gill epithelium to sodium, active sodium uptake, which in isolated gills balances passive sodium loss (Bellamy, 1961), would be reduced. This interpretation is in agreement with the effect of DOC on the uptake of sodium by the fresh-water trout (Holmes, 1959), and of aldosterone on other transport systems (see below). In apparent contradiction to this idea, it has been found that NaCl injected into fresh-water trout was excreted through the gills in increased amounts after the administration of DOC and cortisol (Chester Jones *et al.*, 1959; Holmes, 1959). At the same time the steroid injections produced an increase in the gradient for sodium efflux across the gill membranes (Holmes, 1959) so that the change in sodium loss could not be dissociated from the effects of steroids on sodium distribution in the fluid compartments of the body. At the end of the experiments, the Na^+ concentration in the gills of the steroid-injected animals was twice that of the control group, whereas the terminal rate of Na^{24} loss was the same or slightly lower than in the untreated animals. These results may be interpreted to mean that the hormones brought about reduction in the passive permeability of the gill membrane to sodium. Thus, it appears, that corticosteroids decrease the rate of sodium loss by diffusion across the gills and may act in conjunction with posterior pituitary peptides [which facilitate the access of ions to the transport system (Leaf, 1960; Frazier *et al.*, 1962)], to increase the net sodium uptake by the gills of euryhaline teleosts in fresh water.

The actual mechanism of sodium uptake is not known, but it may well involve the sodium–potassium exchange reaction found in frog skin (Koefoed-Johnsen and Ussing, 1958). This system is unlikely to be present in the outer gill membranes of marine eels because the active extrusion process is not affected by the removal of potassium from the external environment (Bellamy and Sharratt, unpublished), and in this respect the observations favor the presence of a chloride pumping system suggested for the brackish water blenny (*Blennius phalis*) in a hypertonic environment (House, 1962).

4. Amphibian Skin

Amphibian skin has been found to take up sodium from solutions in contact with the external surface, apparently to compensate for the loss of urinary sodium. The mechanism is primarily one of sodium transport against an electrochemical gradient and requires the expenditure of metabolic energy (for references see Ussing et al., 1960). Chloride ions move passively in response to the electrostatic attraction of sodium ions.

Although some experiments have failed to detect any changes in sodium movement through skin after adenohypophysectomy (Jørgensen, 1947), others have shown definite effects which may be attributed to the action of corticosteroids. Thus, adrenalectomized frogs show an increased loss of sodium by diffusion through the skin (Fowler and Chester Jones, 1955). Experiments with isolated skins from frogs pretreated with ACTH indicated that adrenal hormones maintain the skin in a state of low permeability to sodium loss (Myers et al., 1956). More detailed work showed that ACTH inhibited the net rate of sodium uptake by frog skin but the method used did not differentiate between alterations in uptake and loss (Huf and Wills, 1953). This work on frogs has recently been confirmed and extended to show that removal of the anterior pituitary results in an increased sodium efflux and a decreased active uptake (Myers et al., 1961). These changes were opposed by mammalian ACTH and aldosterone. It was also shown that ACTH acted through the interrenal tissue, that is, although corticosteroids increased sodium transport in interrenalectomized frogs, ACTH had no effect (Williams and Angerer, 1959; see also Bishop et al., 1961).

Changes in sodium movement across frog skin are usually produced by the injection of hormones into the intact animal, but the administration of steroid hormones in this way is not essential to obtain an effect. Apparently, sodium transport may be stimulated by the addition of hydrocortisone to the medium bathing isolated frog skin (McAfee and Locke, 1961). As with the intact animal, there is a considerable time lag before a change occurs.

The bladder of the toad is capable of transporting sodium from urine to the blood, and when removed from the animal it is found that the transport system has similar properties to those of isolated frog skin (Leaf, 1960). Using isolated bladder preparations it has recently been observed that aldosterone administration to the intact animal increased net sodium transport (Crabbé, 1961). A similar increase was also elicited by mild sodium depletion and this treatment was associated with an increased level of plasma aldosterone. It thus appears that aldosterone has the same affect on toad bladder in aiding sodium conservation as it has on frog skin.

From the experiments on amphibian membranes there are apparently two effects of adrenocortical steroids on sodium movement, namely, decreased passive permeability to sodium and an increase in active sodium transport. In most of the experiments, active sodium transport has been calculated from the short circuit current across isolated membranes and refers to a net ion movement. It is well established that sodium movement usually occurs in both directions across biological membranes. Thus, it is possible that some of the above results on net sodium transport (active) were produced by an alteration in the back diffusion of sodium and not by an activation of the sodium pumping mechanism. The postulate that corticosteroids may stimulate sodium transport in this way by preventing the passive leakage of sodium would provide an explanation for some of the anomalous effects of aldosterone on eel gills (see Section III, A, 3) and the avian nasal gland (see Section III, A, 5).

5. THE NASAL GLAND

The nasal gland of certain aquatic birds is known to be capable of secreting a fluid, mainly an NaCl solution, which is hypertonic to the plasma. Because the concentrating power of the gland is greater than that of the kidney it is thought to have a survival value in sea birds where there is a possibility of ingesting fluids with an NaCl content higher than that of the body fluids.

A recent review (Schmidt-Nielsen, 1960) gives the historical background to the developments in this field. The first report of an effect of hormones on salt excretion by the nasal gland is that of Fänge et al. (1958). In herring gulls (Larus argentatus) to which a load of hypertonic NaCl solution had been administered they found that injections of adrenaline caused only a transient excretion of sodium chloride, and attributed the block to a vasomotor effect. More recent investigations (Holmes et al., 1961a; Phillips et al., 1961; Holmes et al., unpublished) showed that in the normal duck, given a hypertonic NaCl load directly into the intestine, both the amount and rate of nasal gland secretion, principally an NaCl solution, was significantly increased by the administration of either cortisol, aldosterone, cortexone, or mammalian ACTH. Other experiments in which ducks were given a less hypertonic load of NaCl together with the steroid hormones previously used by Holmes et al. revealed that DOC and cortisol stimulated the nasal secretion whereas aldosterone had no effect (Phillips and Bellamy, 1962). In the latter preparations, in sharp contrast to those of Holmes et al. (1961a), no urine was voided. This difference indicates that the enhancement of the nasal secretion found by Holmes et al. (1961a) after aldosterone treatment was the result of increased sodium retention by the kidneys.

The nasal secretion of NaCl after a saline load was abolished by adrenalectomy. Further, the response was diminished though not obliterated in the subtotally adrenalectomized duck and could be completely reestablished by the injection of cortisol. It was concluded from these studies that the probable sequence of endocrine events after a hypertonic saline load was initiated by the sharp rise in the blood osmolarity which occasioned a release of antidiuretic hormone (ADH); this hormone acting either directly or through the mediation of ACTH resulted, in turn, in enhanced secretion of corticosteroids. It was further concluded that a glucocorticoid acting in combination with ADH determined the typical biphasic response to a saline load. There was an initial renal excretion of the load of short duration which was followed by secretion by the nasal gland. The latter process is thought to be brought about by the direct action of a cortisol-like hormone on the gland. Further evidence has recently been obtained which supports the validity of the presumed role of the glucocorticoid hormone. Holmes *et al.* (1961b) in long term experiments on gulls showed that the adrenal glands of birds with only sea water to drink were larger than those from a control group which drank fresh water and they argued that it would be difficult to imagine that this increased size of the adrenal gland was in response to the need for a specific increase in mineralocorticoid-producing tissue.

More recently, in a histological study of adrenal glands obtained from ducks maintained for long periods on sea water compared with those obtained from fresh-water-fed ducks, Phillips and Benson (unpublished observations) have found that the hypertroph which occurs in the adrenal glands of the sea-water-fed animals is produced by an increase in the cortical portion alone.

The biosynthesis of adrenocortical hormones in the white Peking duck (the species used by Holmes *et al.*, 1961b, and Phillips *et al.* 1961) have recently been investigated by deRoos (1961). Under *in vitro* conditions the major corticosteroids produced were aldosterone and corticosterone. These two components occurred in roughly equal quantities. The addition of ACTH to the medium markedly stimulated the production of corticosterone but the synthesis of aldosterone remained unaltered. Similar studies on the same species (Phillips, unpublished observations) have confirmed these findings and extended them to an investigation of the relative biosynthetic capacities of adrenal tissue obtained from fresh-water and salt-water-fed ducks. Under identical *in vitro* conditions, adrenals obtained from salt-water-fed ducks (2.5% NaCl for 8 days) show a marked enhancement of corticosterone production and, concomitantly, a block in the production of aldosterone when compared with adrenal tissue obtained from fresh-water-fed ducks. These observations lend support to the thesis advanced by Phillips *et al.* (1961) that the pattern of hormonal response which forms part of the controlling mechanism of the nasal gland secretion is an enhancement of the glucocorticoid component of the adrenocortical secretion, presumably corticosterone. Direct confirmation of this hormonal shift following salt loading in the duck, by measurements of corticosterone and aldosterone in peripheral blood, has still to be made. In this connection, it is significant that corticosterone has been found more effective than either cortisol or DOC in stimulating the nasal gland to secrete (Phillips and Bellamy, 1962).

The normal concentrations of sodium and potassium in the nasal gland secretion of the duck are about four times higher than those of serum. The administration of corticosteroids reduced the sodium concentration of the secretion by about 8%; in some cases the potassium concentration was also decreased (Holmes *et al.*, 1961a). The formation of the nasal secretion is likely to involve the active transport of sodium, and perhaps also potassium, into the collecting ducts. Since the details of the mechanism by which sodium is transported across the gland are still in doubt (Hokin and Hokin, 1960), it is not profitable to speculate on a possible role of the adrenocorticosteroids.

6. Summary

The most commonly observed action of corticosteroids on ionic regulation is the stimulation of the energy-requiring movement of ions against a concentration gradient. There are several possibilities with regard to the mode of action of the steroids on the transport system. It could be stimulated directly by an increased access of sodium to the system itself [an effect analogous to that of pituitary hormones on toad bladder (Leaf, 1960)], or by a catalytic action of steroids on some limiting reaction in the process. There is also the possibility of an indirect effect such as the stimulation of the synthesis of a molecule which is part of the structure of the transport unit or which modifies the boundary membrane to prevent sodium leakage down a diffusion gradient (cf. Ogston and Sherman, 1961).

One of the main difficulties in the interpretation of the results of adrenocorticoid administration is that the nature of the transport mechanism itself is as yet poorly understood. In the kidney tubule, nasal gland, and possibly fish gills the system is mainly one which transports sodium, and results in either an absorption or secretion of NaCl. In other cells a sodium–potassium exchange reaction appears to be involved. Active chloride transport is also a distinct possibility in some tissues. It is perhaps unlikely that each one of these different systems would respond to adrenocortical steroids in the same way.

B. Metabolic Effects of Corticosteroids

A general view of the metabolic effects of the hormones produced by the adrenal cortex suggests that they increase the ability of the body to form glycogen at the expense of the synthesis of proteins and fats. This appears clear from the initial results of hormone deprivation or administration. However, the action of the cortical hormones on the whole animal cannot be limited to carbohydrate metabolism and the stimulation of glycogen synthesis is related to the action of steroids on several metabolic pathways.

1. CARBOHYDRATE METABOLISM

From many experiments with the adrenalectomized rat it is known that the adrenal hormones stimulate glycogen synthesis. Thus, the low levels of liver glycogen and blood glucose after adrenalectomy return to normal after the administration of corticosteroids (for references see Chester Jones, 1957). In apparent contradiction to the results obtained with whole animals, however, similar experiments with isolated preparations of muscle and liver indicate that glycogen synthesis is inhibited by corticosteroids (Seckel, 1940; Teng et al., 1952). These opposing results can be reconciled if it is remembered that the *in vivo* conditions are different from those in tissue preparations because *in vivo* there is the possibility of a mobilization of large protein and fat reserves. Another difference is that in the adrenalectomized animal, in which it is possible for liver glycogen to be formed from dietary glucose (Cori and Cori, 1927), the intracellular glucose concentration appears to be one of the factors limiting glycogen synthesis. It seems, therefore, that the low glycogen level in the fasted, adrenalectomized animal is a secondary effect dependent upon a diminished level of intracellular glucose; that is, the initiation of any process which leads to the formation of glucose could bring about glycogen formation.

To summarize, the experiments with the whole animal show that adrenal steroids stimulate gluconeogenesis, and the work on isolated tissues suggests that corticosteroids also introduce a limiting factor into the reaction sequence:

$$\text{Glucose} \rightleftharpoons \text{glucose-6-P} \rightleftharpoons \text{glucose-1-P} \rightleftharpoons \text{glycogen}$$

The latter effect is not sufficient to prevent glycogen formation if a source of glucose is readily available. Thus, the net glycogen synthesis which follows the administration of corticosteroids to the adrenalectomized animal appears to be due to a balance between two opposing effects, an increase in the formation of glucose precursors and a decrease in the capacity of the animal to maintain a high level of glucose phosphates.

Evidence in support of the latter concept comes from some of the first *in vitro* experiments which showed that hexokinase in crude extracts of muscle from alloxan-diabetic rats was inhibited by adrenal cortical preparations (Cori, 1946). Other work with purer enzymes confirms this (Bacilia and Barron, 1954) thus showing that cortical hormones inhibit the phosphorylation of glucose.

It has since been established that cortisone increases the liver glucose-6-phosphatase activity in normal rats. This effect appears to depend on the dietary state of the animal and may be linked to enzyme formation (for references see Ashmore and Weber, 1959). A similar mechanism possibly accounts for the stimulation by cortisol of glucose-6-phosphatase and fructose 1,6-diphosphatase in adrenalectomized rats (Kvam and Parks, 1960; see also Blecher and White, 1959, 1960). The impairment of phosphorylation induced by corticosteroids is thought to be responsible for the decreased glucose transport across the cell membrane (insulin dependent) which follows hypophysectomy and adrenalectomy (Morgan *et al.*, 1961; Flink, 1961).

In the whole animal the action of corticosteroids on the above enzymes in the absence of a source of glucose other than glycogen would be to maintain a high, steady level of intracellular glucose as a balance between the stimulation of glycogenolysis, the inhibition of glycolysis (therefore an inhibition of glucose oxidation, Cori and Cori, 1926, 1927), and the excretion of glucose. This situation is never seen experimentally because another, more important, effect of corticosteroids is a stimulation of the formation of glucose precursors from protein (Section III, B, 2). Under these circumstances, although glycosuria is observed (Ingle, 1949), there is a large flow of carbon from protein degradation which overcomes the resistance to glycogen formation (also induced by corticosteroids).

The absence of corticosteroids in the fasting, adrenalectomized animal would be expected to give rise to a low level of intracellular glucose (and glycogen) by removing the "brake" on glucose oxidation and at the same time depressing gluconeogenesis. This is in agreement with experiments which show that adrenalectomy brings about a fall in the levels of muscle glucose-6-phosphate and fructose-6-phosphate (Conway, 1956) and markedly reduces the incorporation of bicarbonate into glycogen (Ashmore *et al.*, 1961.)

The removal of cortical hormones has no effect on the incorporation of bicarbonate into the blood glucose (Ashmore *et al.*, 1961). This result, when taken together with the inhibitory effect of adrenalectomy on hexose phosphatases, indicates that in the normal animal phosphatase activity is not a limiting factor in glucose formation. Conversely the injection of cortisone into normal animals increased the conversion of pyruvate into both glycose and glycogen. In keeping with an elevated glucose-6-phosphatase activity it was possible to demonstrate that pyruvate was preferentially converted to glucose (Landau *et al.*, 1962).

2. PROTEIN METABOLISM

A characteristic result of adrenalectomy is a reduction in the level of urinary nonprotein nitrogen, mainly urea. This trend can be reversed by cortical hormones (for references see Ingle, 1950; Engel, 1951). The effect of adrenalectomy is related to a true fall in urea synthesis and is not the result of an alteration in the excretory mechanisms as, for example, appears to be the case with the rise in allantoin excretion (Choitz and Gaebler, 1960). The phenomenon is not limited to the whole animal because cortisol stimulates the formation of urea by the isolated perfused liver from adrenalectomized animals (Miller, 1960).

These results indicate that adrenal hormones increase the breakdown of amino acids, probably at the expense of tissue proteins. Indeed, in the perfused liver urea appears to be formed from amino acids derived from tissue and plasma proteins (Miller, 1960).

Since tissue proteins are in equilibrium with their component amino acids, the effects of adrenocortical hormones on protein metabolism could be due either to an increased activity of enzymes concerned with protein and amino acid breakdown or to an inhibition of protein synthesis. In this respect there have been few studies on the interaction of steroids with the systems involved in protein synthesis but recent work suggests that changes in the amino acid activating enzymes are not involved in the response to corticosteroids (Korner, 1960a; Smith *et al.*, 1961).

Very little work has been carried out on the effects of cortical hormones on purified enzymes but it is established that the activity of arginase, proteases, cathepsins, transaminases, amino acid oxidases, and deaminases is altered by corticosteroids resulting in an acceleration of both protein hydrolysis and amino acid breakdown (Lieberman and Teich, 1953; Villano and D'Onofrio, 1955; Rose *et al.*, 1959; Rosen *et al.*, 1959; Crabbé and Nichols, 1960; Talanti and Hopsu, 1961; McLean, 1961).

In recent years attention has been paid to the influence of hormones on the rate of incorporation of radioactive amino acids into protein—a process which is thought to be related to protein synthesis. Adrenalectomy was found to increase the rate of incorporation of radioactive amino acids and amino acid precursors into the proteins of isolated diaphragm whereas corticosteroid administration had the reverse effect (Manchester *et al.*, 1959; Wool and Weinshelbaum, 1959, 1960). These changes could be due to alterations in the rate of protein degradation. However, Korner (1960a) working with the microsomal fraction isolated from the liver of adrenalectomized animals found that the stimulation of amino acid incorporation was only transient and was followed by a decreased rate of incorporation which eventually fell below that of microsomes from normal animals. Thus in long term experiments it appears that adrenalectomy inhibits protein synthesis in isolated tissue preparations whereas corticosteroids have a stimulatory effect (Korner, 1960a). This seems also to be the situation in similar experiments with whole animals (Lee and Williams, 1952). Korner (1960a) explains the apparent paradox by assuming that the enzyme systems which incorporate amino acids into protein are unstable in the absence of free amino acids. Since the immediate effect of adrenalectomy appears to be the inhibition of glucose formation this is taken to mean that the flow of carbon from amino acids to glucose is prevented and amino acids from peripheral tissues accumulate in the liver. Thus the components of the protein synthesizing system, perhaps the molecules of ribonucleic acid (RNA), are stabilized and the activity of the system is actually increased. Later, the lack of corticosteroids inhibits protein breakdown, and the resultant drop in the intracellular concentration of amino acids in the liver is thought to render the protein synthesizing system unstable. In this connection it has been observed that the decrease in protein synthesis after adrenalectomy is correlated with a decreased turnover of microsomal RNA (Reid, 1961). As yet there is a lack of convincing experimental evidence for the above hypothesis. For instance, there is no indication that the effect of adrenalectomy on the enzymes concerned with amino acid degradation precedes the effect on proteases. The hypothesis must also be reviewed in the light of recent work on mice, which shows that adrenalectomy brings about a slight fall in the free amino acids of liver (Kaplan and Shimizu, 1962) and other experiments in which cortisol administration increased the liver weight of normal rats (Goodlad and Munro, 1959) and stimulated the synthesis of serum albumin (Clark, 1953; see also Korner, 1960b). In the latter experiments there was no evidence that a transient inhibition of protein synthesis *in vivo* was an important result of corticosteroid secretion. In any case the concensus seems to be that the steroid-induced changes in the capacity of isolated tissue to synthesize protein, as measured by the amino acid exchange reaction, are secondary effects which cannot be separated from changes in the rate of protein breakdown or the inhibition of energy production from glycolysis or oxidative reactions (Blecher and White, 1960; Section III, B, 4.)

The protein catabolism induced by corticosteroids is of interest in relationship to the metabolic characteristics of mammalian hibernation. Indeed, there is much evidence which suggests that several of the biochemical changes which accompany cold acclimatization, notably, increased amino acid oxidation, transamidination, and urea excretion, are mediated through enhanced adrenocortical secretion (see review by Smith and Hoijer, 1962). It may be that a similar hormonal response is involved in estivation [e.g. Dipnoi (Smith, 1930)] and the adaptation of certain aquatic vertebrates to an environment which is hypertonic to the body fluids [Elasmobranchii (Smith, 1936); Amphibia (Balinsky et al., 1961; Gordon et al., 1961)]. These adaptations are characterized by dehydration and tissue urea retention, changes which are concordant with increased corticosteroid secretion in mammals and birds. Therefore, a study of possible alterations in adrenocortical secretion following environmental changes in lower vertebrates would be of great interest. From work on the normal animal it appears that DOC produces a transient increase in the rate of incorporation of amino acids into the protein of kidney homogenates (a property shared with some androgenic steroids) whereas cortisol has a definite inhibitory effect (Frieden et al., 1961). This type of result, taken together with the stimulatory effects of corticosteroids on amino acid uptake by liver (Kaplan and Shimizu, 1961) underlines the necessity for a complete re-evaluation of the effects of corticosteroids on protein metabolism.

3. Fat Metabolism

Adrenalectomy produces a rise in the rate of incorporation of deuterium into body fat indicating that one of the effects of cortical hormones is to introduce a limiting reaction into the pathway of fat synthesis (Welt and Wilhelmi, 1950). The results which were obtained with whole animals were later confirmed with liver slices taken from normal rats treated with ACTH and incubated in the presence of deuterium (Brady et al., 1951). In these experiments there was no detectable increase in the total amount of fat so that the increased incorporation of deuterium may represent a general increased fat turnover resulting from a stimulation of energy production (Section III, B, 4).

It is more likely that adrenocortical hormones stimulate fat synthesis. For example, in Cushing's syndrome an increased deposition of fat at certain sites may be correlated with a high adrenal steroid secretion. Also many observations have shown that corticosteroids favor fat storage (for references see Ingle, 1950). The interrelations of carbohydrate, protein, and fat metabolism center about pyruvate, a common precursor (Fig. 1).

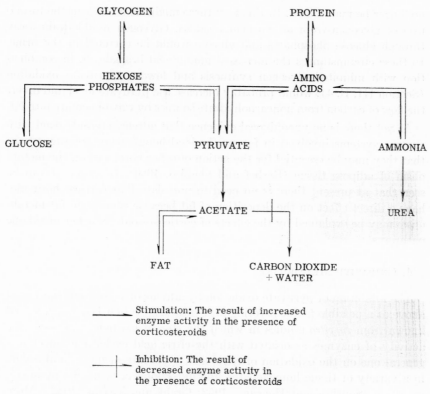

FIG. 1. Interrelations of carbohydrate, protein, and fat metabolism.

Indeed, the level of pyruvate normally may well limit the rate of fat synthesis and any process leading to the formation of pyruvate, for example, glycolysis, amino acid breakdown, or decreased pyruvate oxidation would favor the formation of fat. In this connection, recent work (Fajans, 1961) showed that prednisone decreased the utilization of administered pyruvate and appeared to divert pyruvate carbon away from the citric acid cycle (see also Landau et al., 1962).

One of the initial trends in steroid diabetes, that is the deposition of glycogen, is reversed after a prolonged administration of steroid hormones. In long term experiments the emphasis is placed upon the formation of fat, and the liver becomes devoid of glycogen (Ingle, 1950). Since one of the effects of cortical hormones is to increase the rate of hydrolysis of hexose phosphates (probably involving synthesis of phosphatases), it is possible that under prolonged stimulation by steroids the level of hexose phosphates is lowered to such a degree that a net glycogen synthesis can no longer be maintained. In this way there might be a block in the formation of glycogen from amino acid residues. Glycogen would drain away through glucose phosphates and glucose would be excreted in the urine. In these circumstances the increased amino acid breakdown, in combination with inhibited glycogen synthesis and lowered pyruvate oxidation (Section III, B, 4), would probably increase the pyruvate level and divert the flow of carbon from noncarbohydrate sources by way of acetate into fat.

As yet there is no unequivocal evidence that adrenal steroids react with enzyme systems involved in fat synthesis although there are suggestions that they may be essential for the action of other hormones on the metabolism of adipose tissue (Reshef and Shapiro, 1960). However, it can be seen that at present there is no need to postulate that cortical hormones have a direct effect on the deposition of fat because changes in fat metabolism may be explained by the effects of corticosteroids on other metabolic pathways.

4. OXIDATIVE METABOLISM

The inhibition of pyruvate oxidation by adrenocorticosteroids, indicated above as a possible factor favoring fat synthesis (Section III, B, 3), is well known from *in vitro* studies in which the steroid hormones influence the activity of enzymes associated with the citric acid cycle. The effect is a general one on the oxidation of citric acid cycle intermediates and occurs in a variety of tissue homogenates, the mitochondria being the main site of action (Sourkes and Heneage, 1952; Grant and Taylor, 1952). More detailed investigations show that adrenal steroids inhibit mainly the activity of mitochondrial enzymes which require reduced diphosphopyridine nucleotide (DPNH) as a cofactor (Guidry et al., 1952; Cochran and Du Bois, 1954). Recent work has shown that the inhibition of mitochondrial oxidation can be prevented if a cofactor supplement is added to the incubation medium (Gallagher, 1960), and the experiments suggest that corticosteroids produce a change in the properties of mitochondria which allows the loss of endogenous pyridine nucleotides by diffusion during the measurement of respiration. However, the action of corticosteroids on oxidative reactions cannot be confined to an effect on the permeability of the mitochondrial membrane because Yielding and Tomkins (1959) have obtained evidence that a variety of steroids inhibit a highly purified preparation of DPNH oxidase derived from mammalian mitochondria and microbial sources. They suggest that steroids react directly in catalytic amounts with a lipid component of the systems.

In the above experiments, corticosterone and DOC were more effective than cortisone in inhibiting DPNH oxidation. The results of other experiments with intact mitochondria showed that cortisone inhibited cytochrome oxidase activity and uncoupled the phosphorylation of adenosinediphosphate (ADP) from respiration (Kerppola and Pitkänen, 1960). The latter effect was greatest when isocitrate and α-oxoglutarate were used as substrates and it was suggested that substrate level phosphorylations were involved (Kerppola, 1960). Possibly the various cortical hormones have different sites of action in the mitochondria. It is not known how important the changes in oxidative metabolism are in the whole animal. The effect on respiration is not specific to cortical steroids because a variety of androgens and estrogens, sometimes at a lower concentration, give the same general result (Lieberman and Teich, 1953; Blecher and White, 1959; Yielding and Tomkins, 1959; Endahl and Kochakian, 1961).

5. EFFECTS OF CORTICAL HORMONES IN LOWER VERTEBRATES

Adrenocorticosteroids have been demonstrated in the blood of members of all classes of the Vertebrata (Chester Jones *et al.*, 1959; Phillips and Chester Jones, 1957). Among the lower vertebrates, fishes have been studied in greatest detail from the point of view of adrenocortical function. In the skate, for example, adrenalectomy results in a decrease in liver glycogen and a fall in the level of circulating blood sugar (Hartman *et al.*, 1944). The converse effect on blood sugar was obtained by the injection of cortical hormones into the toadfish (Nace, 1955, 1956). Further, the hypophysectomized eel (in the absence of ACTH) has low levels of liver glycogen with impaired gluconeogenesis (see review, Pickford and Atz, 1957). Although circumstantial, other evidence from fish subjected to stress (i.e., during normal migration or forced swimming) suggests a basic similarity in adrenal function between fish and mammals. For instance, during the migration of salmon there is an apparent increase in the size and activity of the adrenal tissue, an elevated level of 17-hydroxycorticosteroids, and an increase in liver glycogen (Fontaine and Hatey, 1954; Leloup-Hatey, 1958; Chester Jones and Phillips, 1960).

In amphibians the liver and muscle glycogen is lowered after adrenalectomy and these trends can be reversed by injection of pituitary hormones (Houssay *et al.*, 1925, 1935). A direct influence of corticosteroids on glucose metabolism in amphibians was demonstrated by Maes (1937) who found that after adrenalectomy there was both hypoglycemia and a fall in liver glycogen, and by Hunter and Johnson (1960) who showed that cortisol increased liver glycogen in normal frogs. Thus is appears that in mammals, fishes, and amphibians cortical steroids have the same effects on carbohydrate metabolism. It cannot be stated with certainty that the steroid hormones have the same action on the metabolic processes in reptiles and birds but the available evidence suggests that such a conclusion is valid (e.g., Phillips *et al.*, unpublished observations; Bell, 1961; Holmes *et al.*, 1961; Greenman and Zarrow, 1961; Coulson and Hernandez, 1962).

6. SUMMARY

A summary of the interactions of the various metabolic pathways is shown in Fig. 1. It is not possible with certainty to explain all the effects of cortical hormones by assuming that they have only one site of action. However, it seems that many effects of steroids on enzyme activity cannot be demonstrated when the hormones are added to isolated tissues. This may be because one common effect is to stimulate enzyme formation, a process which may take several hours. In agreement with this assumption are the observations which show that *in vivo* effects of corticosteroids invariably involve an increase in enzyme activity. Lieberman and Teich (1953) list some enzymes which have an increased activity after the administration of corticosteroids: arginase, D-amino acid oxidase, proline oxidase, peptidase, catalase, and glucuronidase. The activity of several of these enzymes was reduced by adrenalectomy. Glucose-6-phosphatase, phosphohexose isomerase, lactic dehydrogenase, and fructose-1,6-diphosphatase may be added to the list (Kvam and Parks, 1960, Weber *et al.*, 1961).

The effect of cortisol on the hexose phosphatase activity of adrenalectomized rats can be inhibited by the administration of ethionine, a biologically inert analog of methionine. This inhibition is prevented by giving methionine at the same time. Thus it may well be that a common action of corticosteroids is to stimulate the synthesis of specific enzymes by a process affecting the incorporation of one or more amino acids which are essential for enzyme activity. Such a mechanism, however, would not account for the immediate effects which may be obtained when corticosteroids are added to tissue slices or cell-free preparations (e.g., the stimulation of hexokinase and inhibition of oxygen uptake).

It has been suggested that some of the effects of adrenocortical hormones are the indirect result of the adaptation of enzyme synthesis to changes in the level of substrate (Freedland and Harper, 1958). The evidence for this idea rests mainly on experiments which show that some of the effects of corticosteroids may be duplicated by dietary changes. Thus an increase in the proportion of dietary protein produces an increased transaminase and phosphatase activity (Rosen *et al.*, 1959; Freedland and Harper, 1958).

Finally, it is not generally appreciated that some of the experimental results attributed to the direct action of glucocorticoids on intermediary metabolism may be produced by the effects of these steroids on mineral metabolism. For example, glycolysis in resting muscle is stimulated by an increase in the level of potassium in the solution bathing the tissue (e.g., Kaye and Mommaerts, 1960) and this reaction may be compared with the effect of adrenalectomy in elevating the intracellular potassium concentration and decreasing the level of glycogen. Also it is well known that the activity of a variety of enzymes is markedly dependent upon the concentration of sodium and potassium (for references see Ussing et al., 1960). Thus, from work on isolated enzyme systems and intact tissue it is likely that deviation from the optimum concentration of 20 mM sodium and 150 mM potassium in the cells may well bring about changes in glycolysis and oxidative reactions.

References

Addison, T. (1855). "On the Constitutional and Local Effects of Disease of the Supra Renal Capsules." Highley, London.

Anliker, R., Rohr, O., and Marti, M. (1956). Helv. Chim. Acta 39, 1100–1106.

Antoniades, H. N. (1960). In "Hormones in Human Plasma" (H. N. Antoniades, ed.), pp. 456–477. Churchill, London.

Ashmore, J., and Weber, G. (1959). Vitamins and Hormones 17, 91–132.

Ashmore, J., Stricker, F., Love, W. C., and Kilsheimer, G. (1961). Endocrinology 68, 599–606.

August, J. T., Nelson, D. H., and Thorn, G. W. (1958). New Engl. J. Med. 259, 917–923, 967–971.

Ayres, P. J. (1960). Biochem. Soc. Symposia (Cambridge, Engl.) No. 18, 50–58.

Ayres, P. J., Garrod, O., Tait, S. A. S., Tait, J. F., Walker, G., and Pearlman, W. H. (1957). CIBA Foundation Colloquia on Endocrinol. 11, 309–326.

Ayres, P. J., Barlow, J., Garrod, O., Kellie, A. E., Tait, S. A. S., Tait, J. F., and Walker, G. (1958). Intern. Symposium Aldosterone, Geneva, 1957, pp. 73–95

Bacilia, M., and Barron, E. S. G. (1954). Endocrinology 54, 591–603.

Balinsky, J. B., Cragg, M. M., Baldwin, E. (1961). Comp. Biochem. Physiol. 3, 236–244.

Bartter, F. C. (1956). Metabolism 5, 369–383.

Bartter, F. C., and Gann, D. S. (1960). Circulation 21, Suppl. 1016–1023.

Bartter, F. C., Biglieri, E. G., Pronove, P., and Delea, C. S. (1958). Intern. Symposium Aldosterone, Geneva, 1957, pp. 100–110.

Beck, J. C., McGarry, E. E., Dyrenfurth, I., and Venning, E. H. (1957). Science 125, 884–885.

Bell, D. J. (1961). Nature 190, 913.

Bell, P. H. (1954). J. Am. Chem. Soc. 76, 5565–5567.

Bellamy, D. (1961). Comp. Biochem. Physiol. 3, 125–135.

Bellamy, D., and Chester Jones, I. (1961a). *Comp. Biochem. Physiol.* **3**, 175–183.

Bellamy, D., and Chester Jones, I. (1961b). *Comp. Biochem. Physiol.* **3**, 223–226.

Bishop, W. R., Mumbach, M. W., and Scheer, B. T. (1961). *Am. J. Physiol.* **200**, 451–453.

Blecher, M., and White, A. (1959). *Recent Progr. in Hormone Research* **15**, 391–425.

Blecher, M., and White, A. (1960). *J. Biol. Chem.* **235**, 282–291.

Bloch, E., Dorfman, R. I., and Pincus, G. (1956). *Arch. Biochem. Biophys.* **61**, 245–247.

Bondy, P. K., and Upton, G. V. (1957). *Proc. Soc. Exptl. Biol. Med.* **94**, 585–589.

Bondy, P. K., Upton, G. V., and Pickford, G. E. (1957). *Nature* **179**, 1354.

Brady, R. O., Lukens, F. D. W., and Gurin, S. (1951). *J. Biol. Chem.* **193**, 459–464.

Briggs, F. N., and Munson, P. L. (1954). *J. Clin. Endocrinol. and Metabolism* **14**, 811–812.

Brown, K. I. (1961). *Proc. Soc. Exptl. Biol. Med.* **107**, 538–542.

Brown-Sequard, C. E. (1856). *Compt. rend. soc. biol.* **43**, 422–425.

Bush, I. E. (1951). *J. Physiol. (London)* **115**, 12P.

Bush, I. E. (1953). *J. Endocrinol.* **9**, 95–100.

Bush, I. E. (1957). *CIBA Foundation Colloquia on Endocrinol.* **11**, 263–285.

Bush, I. E. (1960). *Biochem. Soc. Symposia (Cambridge, Engl.) No.* **18**, 1–23.

Cameron, C. B. (1957). *Brit. Med. Bull.* **13**, 119–125.

Carstensen, H., Burgers, A. C. J., and Li, C. H. (1959). *J. Am. Chem. Soc.* **81**, 4109–4110.

Carstensen, H., Burgers, A. C. J., and Li, C. H. (1961). *Gen. and Comp. Endocrinol.* **1**, 37–50.

Chester Jones, I. (1956). *Mem. Soc. Endocrinol. No.* **5**, 102–124.

Chester Jones, I. (1957). "The Adrenal Cortex," Cambridge Univ. Press, London and New York.

Chester Jones, I., and Phillips, J. G. (1960). *Symposia Zool. Soc. London No.* **1**, 17–32.

Chester Jones, I., Phillips, J. G., and Holmes, W. N. (1959). "Comparative Endocrinology" (A. Gorbman, ed.), pp. 582–612. Wiley, New York.

Chester Jones, I., Phillips, J. G., and Bellamy, D. (1962a). *Brit. Med. Bull.* **18**(2), 110–113.

Chester Jones, I., Phillips, J. G., and Bellamy, D. (1962b). 3rd International Symposium on Comparative Endocrinology, Oiso, Japan, *Gen. and Comp. Endocrinol.* Suppl. **1**, 36–46.

Choitz, H. C., and Gaebler, O. H. (1960). *Proc. Soc. Exptl. Biol. Med.* **104**, 475–477.

Cier, J. F. (1961). *J. Physiol. (Paris)* **53**, 3–74.

Clark, I. (1953). *J. Biol. Chem.* **200**, 69–76.

Cochran, K. W., and Du Bois, K. P. (1954). *Endocrinology* **55**, 10–20.

Coghlan, J. P., Denton, D. A., Goding, J. R., and Wright, R. D. (1960). *Postgrad. Med.* **36**, 76–102.

Conway, E. J. (1956). *Mem. Soc. Endocrinol. No.* **5**, 3–24.

Conway, E. J., and Hingerty, D. (1946). *Biochem. J.* **40**, 561–568.

Cori, C. F. (1946). *Harvey Lectures Ser.* **41**, 253–261.

Cori, C. F., and Cori, G. T. (1926). *J. Biol. Chem.* **70**, 557–576.

Cori, C. F., and Cori, G. T. (1927). *J. Biol. Chem.* **74**, 473–494.

Coulson, R. A., and Hernandez, T. (1962). *Am. J. Physiol.* **202,** 83–87.

Crabbé, J. (1961). *Endocrinology* **69,** 673–682.

Crabbé, J., and Nichols, G. (1960). *Am. J. Physiol.* **199,** 871–875.

Daughaday, W. H. (1960). *In* "Hormones in Human Plasma" (H. N. Antoniades, ed.), pp. 495–512. Churchill, London.

Davis, J. O., Bahn, R. C., Goodkind, M. J., and Ball, W. C. (1957). *Am. J. Physiol.* **191,** 329–338.

Davis, J. O., Carpenter, C. C. J., Ayres, C. R., Holman, J. E., and Bahn, R. C. (1961). *J. Clin. Invest.* **40,** 684–696.

Dean, F. D., Cole, P. M., and Chester Jones, I. (1959). *J. Endocrinol.* **18,** iii–iv.

Deane, H. W., and Greep, R. O. (1946). *Am. J. Anat.* **79,** 117–137.

Deane, H. W., and McKibbin, J. M. (1946). *Endocrinology* **38,** 385–400.

Deane, H. W., and Shaw, J. W. (1947). *J. Nutrition* **34,** 1–20.

de Fremery, P., Laqueur, E., Reichstein, T., Spanhoff, R. R., and Uyldert, I. E. (1937). *Nature* **139,** 26.

Denton, D. A., Goding, J. R., and Wright, R. D. (1959). *Brit. Med. J.* **II,** 447–456, 522–530.

deRoos, R. (1960a). *Endocrinology* **67,** 719–721.

deRoos, R. (1960b). *Anat. Record* **138,** 343.

deRoos, R. (1961). *Gen. Comp. Endocrinol.* **1,** 494–512.

Dixon, H. B. F. (1960). *In* "Proceedings of the Sheffield Corticotropin Conference" (H. F. West, ed.), p. 9–13. Ferring-Ab, Malmö.

Dorfman, R. I. (1955). *CIBA Foundation Colloqia on Endocrinol.* **8,** 112–140.

Dorfman, R. I. (1959). *In* "Comparative Endocrinology" (A. Gorbman, ed.), pp. 613–623. Wiley, New York.

Dorfman, R. I., and Ungar, F. (1953). "Metabolism of Steroid Hormones." Burgess Publ., Minneapolis, Minnesota.

Egdahl, R. H., and Richards, J. B. (1956). *Am. J. Physiol.* **185,** 235–238.

Endahl, B. R., and Kochakian, C. D. (1961). *Biochim. Biophys. Acta* **54,** 15–25.

Engel, F. L. (1951). *Recent Progr. in Hormone Research* **6,** 277–313.

Fajans, S. S. (1961). *Metabolism* **10,** 951–965.

Fänge, R., Schmidt-Nielsen, K., and Robinson, M. (1958). *Am. J. Physiol.* **195,** 321–326.

Farrell, G. L (1958). *Physiol. Revs.* **38,** 709–728

Farrell, G. L. (1960). *Circulation* **21,** Suppl., 1009–1015.

Farrell, G. L., and Lamus, B. (1953). *Proc. Soc. Exptl. Biol. Med.* **84,** 89–93.

Farrell, G. L., and Richards, J. B. (1953). *Proc. Soc. Exptl. Biol. Med.* **83,** 628–631.

Farrell, G. L., Rauschkolb, E. W., and Royce, P. C. (1955). *Am. J. Physiol.* **182,** 269–272.

Farrell, G. L., Banks, R. C., and Koletsky, S. (1956). *Endocrinology* **58,** 104–108.

Farrell, G. L., Fleming, R. B., Rauschkolb, E. W., Yatsu, F. M., McCally, M., and Anderson, C. H. (1958). *Endocrinology* **62,** 506–512.

Favre, L. C. (1960). Thesis presented to Faculté des Sciences, Paris, for Diplome d'Etudes Superieures de Sciences Naturelles.

Flink, E. B. (1961). *Ann. Rev. Physiol.* **23,** 229–262.

Fontaine, M., and Hatey, J. (1954). *Compt. rend. acad. sci.* **239**, 319–321.

Fontaine, M., and Leloup-Hatey, J. (1959). *J. physiol. Paris* **51**, 468–469.

Ford, P. (1959). *In* "Comparative Endocrinology" (A. Gorbman, ed.), pp. 728–734. Wiley, New York.

Fortier, C. (1952). *CIBA Foundation Colloquia on Endocrinol.* **4**, 124–138.

Fowler, M. A., and Chester Jones, I. (1955). *J. Endocrinol.* **13**, vi–vii.

Frazier, H. S., Dempsey, E. F., and Leaf, A. (1962). *J. Gen. Physiol.* **45**, 529–543.

Freedland, R. A., and Harper, A. E. (1958). *J. Biol. Chem.* **233**, 1–4.

Frieden, E. H., Cohen, E. H., and Harper, A. A. (1961). *Endocrinology* **68**, 862–866.

Friedman, S. M., and Sréter, F. A. (1961). *Endocrinology* **69**, 386–388.

Gallagher, C. H. (1960). *Biochem. J.* **74**, 38–43.

Ganong, W. F., and Mulrow, P. J. (1961). *Nature* **190**, 1115–1116.

Giroud, C. J. P., Stachenko, J., and Piletta, P. (1958). *Intern. Symposium Aldosterone, Geneva, 1957*, pp. 56–72.

Glynn, I. M. (1957). *J. Physiol. (London)* **136**, 148–173.

Goodlad, G. A. J., and Munro, H. N. (1959). *Biochem. J.* **73**, 343–348.

Gordon, M. S., Schmidt-Nielsen, K., and Kelly, H. M. (1961). *J. Exptl. Biol.* **38**, 659–678.

Grant, J. K. (1960). *Biochem. Soc. Symposia (Cambridge, Engl.) No.* **18**, 24–39.

Grant, J. K. (1962). *Brit. Med. Bull.* **18**(2), 99–105.

Grant, J. K., and Taylor, W. (1952). *Biochem. J.* **52**, xxiv.

Greenman, D. L., and Zarrow, M. X. (1961). *Proc. Soc. Exptl. Biol. Med.* **106**, 459–462.

Greep, R. O. (1961). *In* "The Adrenal Cortex" (H. D. Moon, ed.), pp. 23–45. Hoeber, New York.

Greep, R. O., and Chester Jones, I. (1950). *In* "Symposium on Steroid Hormones" (E. S. Gordon, ed.), pp. 330–360. University of Wisconsin Press, Madison, Wisconsin.

Greep, R. O., and Deane, H. W., (1947). *Endocrinology* **40**, 417–425.

Grollman, A. (1939). *J. Pharmacol. Exptl. Therap.* **67**, 257–264.

Grollman, A., Firor, W. M., and Grollman, E. (1934). *Am. J. Physiol.* **108**, 237–240.

Guidry, M. A., Segaloff, A., and Altshul, A. M. (1952). *Endocrinology* **50**, 29–36.

Guillemin, R., Clayton, G. W., Smith, J. D., and Lipscomp, H. S. (1958). *Endocrinology* **63**, 349–358.

Hane, S., and Robertson, O. H. (1959). *Proc. Natl. Acad. Sci. U. S.* **46**, 886–893.

Harris, G. W. (1948). *Physiol. Revs.* **28**, 139–179.

Harris, G. W. (1955). "Neural Control of the Pituitary Gland," Monographs of the Physiological Society, No. 3. Arnold, London.

Hartman, F. A., and Brownell, K. A. (1930). *Proc. Soc. Exptl. Biol. Med.* **27**, 88–89.

Hartman, F. A., and Spoor, H. J. (1940). *Endocrinology* **26**, 871–876.

Hartman, F. A., Lewis, L. A., Brownell, K. A., Angerer, C. A., and Sheldon, F. F. (1944). *Physiol. Zoöl.* **17**, 228–231.

Hayano, M., Saba, N., Dorfman, R. I., and Hechter, O. (1956). *Recent Progr. in Hormone Research* **12**, 79–123.

Hechter, O., and Lester, G. (1960). *Recent Progr. Hormone Research* **16**, 139–186.

Hechter, O., and Pincus, G. (1954). *Physiol. Revs.* **34**, 459–496.

Hilton, J. G. (1960). *Circulation* **21**, Suppl., 1038–1047.

Holmes, W. N. (1959). *Acta Endocrinol.* **31**, 587–602.

Holmes, W. N., Butler, D. G., and Phillips, J. G. (1961a). *J. Endocrinol.* **23**, 53–61.

Holmes, W. N., Phillips, J. G., and Butler, D. G. (1961b). *Endocrinology.* **69**, 483–495.

Holzbauer, M., and Vogt, M. (1961). *J. Physiol. (London)* **157**, 137–156.

Hokin, L. E., and Hokin, M. R. (1960). *J. Gen. Physiol.* **44**, 61–85.

House, C. R. (1962). Proc. British Biophys. Soc., Edinburgh, Scotland.

Houssay, B. A., Mazzocco, P., and Rietti, C. T. (1925). *Compt. rend. soc,biol.* **93**, 967–968.

Houssay, B. A., Benedetto, E. di., and Mazzocco, P. (1933). *Compt. rend. soc. biol.* **113**, 465–467.

Huf, E. G., and Wills, J. (1953). *J. Gen. Physiol.* **36**, 473–487.

Hume, D. M. (1952). *CIBA Foundation Colloquia on Endocrinol.* **4**, 87–99.

Hunter, N. W., and Johnson, C. E. (1960). *J. Cellular Comp. Physiol.* **55**, 275–280.

Idler, D. R., Ronald, A. P., and Schmidt, P. J. (1959a). *Can. J. Biochem. and Physiol.* **37**, 1227–1238.

Idler, D. R., Ronald, A. P., and Schmidt, P. J. (1959b). *J. Am. Chem. Soc.* **81**, 1260–1261.

Idler, D. R., Fagerlund, U. H. M., and Schmidt, P. J. (1960). *Biochem. Biophys. Research Communs.* **2**, 133–137.

Ingle, D. J. (1949). *Ann. N. Y. Acad. Sci.* **50**, 576–595.

Ingle, D. J. (1950). *In* "Symposium on Steroid Hormones" (E. S. Gordon, ed.), pp. 150–194. University of Wisconsin Press, Madison, Wisconsin.

Ingle, D. J., Li, C. H., and Evans, H. M. (1946). *Endocrinology* **39**, 32–42.

Ito, Y., Takabatake, E., and Ui, H. (1952). *J. Pharm. Soc. Japan* **72**, 1029–1033.

Johnson, B. B., Lieberman, A. H., and Mulrow, P. J. (1957). *J. Clin. Invest.* **36**, 757–766.

Jørgensen, C. B. (1947). *Nature* **160**, 872.

Kahnt, F. W., Neher, R., and Wettstein, A. (1955). *Experientia* **11**, 446–447.

Kaplan, S. A., and Shimizu, C. S. N. (1961). *Am. J. Physiol.* **200**, 1035–1038.

Kaplan, S. A., and Shimizu, C. S. N. (1962). *Am. J. Physiol.* **202**, 695–698.

Kaye, L., and Mommaerts, W. F. H. M. (1960). *J. Gen. Physiol.* **44**, 405–413.

Kerppola, W. (1960). *Endocrinology* **67**, 252–263.

Kerppola, W., and Pitkänen, E. (1960). *Endocrinology* **67**, 162–165.

Klyne, W. (1957). "The Chemistry of the Steroids." Methuen, London.

Koefoed-Johnsen, V., and Ussing, H. H. (1958). *Acta Physiol. Scand.* **42**, 298–308.

Korner, A. (1960a). *J. Endocrinol.* **20**, 256–265.

Korner, A. (1906b)). *In* "Metabolic Effects of Adrenal Hormones" (E. W. Wolstenholme, and M. O'Connor, eds.), pp. 38–50. CIBA Foundation Study Group **6**. Churchill, London.

Krogh, A. (1939). "Osmotic Regulation in Aquatic Animals." Cambridge Univ. Press, London and New York.

Kuhlman, D., Rogan, C., Ferrebee, J. W., Atchley, D. W., and Loeb, R. F. (1939). *Science* **90**, 406–408.

Kumar, M. A., and Sheth, U. K. (1961). *J. Endocrinol.* **21**, 453–458.

Kvam, D. C., and Parks, R. E. (1960). *Am. J. Physiol.* **198**, 21–24.

Landau, B. R., Mahler, R., Ashmore, J., Elwyn, D., Hastings, A. B., and Zottu, S. (1962). *Endocrinology* **70**, 47–53.

Laragh, J. H., and Stoerk, H. C. (1957). *J. Clin. Invest.* **36**, 383–392.

Leaf, A. (1960). *J. Gen. Physiol.* **43**, 1st Suppl. 175–189.

Lee, N. D., and Williams, R. H. (1952). *Endocrinology* **51**, 451–456.

Leloup-Hatey, J. (1958). *Compt. rend. acad. sci.* **246**, 1088–1091.

Li, C. H., Liddle, G. W., Reinhardt, W. O., and Bennett, L. L. (1951). *Proc. Soc. Exptl. Biol. Med.* **78**, 665–668.

Li, C. H., Geschwind, I. I., Cole, R. D., Raacke, I. D., Harris, J. I., and Dixon, J. S. (1955). *Nature* **176**, 687–689.

Lieberman, S., and Teich, S. (1953). *Pharmacol. Revs.* **5**, 285–380.

Lucis, O. J., Dyrenfurth, I., and Venning, E. H. (1961). *Can. J. Biochem. and Physiol.* **39**, 901–913.

Luetscher, J. A., and Curtis, R. H. (1955). *Ann. Internal Med.* **43**, 658–666.

Luetscher, J. A., and Lieberman, A. H. (1958). *A.M.A. Arch. Internal Med.* **102**, 314–330.

McCally, M., Anderson, C. H., and Farrell, G. L. (1958). *In* Programme of the 40th meeting of the Endocrine Society, p. 119.

McAfee, R. D., and Locke, W. (1961). *Am. J. Physiol.* **200**, 797–800.

McCann, S. M. (1953). *Am. J. Physiol.* **175**, 13–20.

Macchi, I. A. (1955). *Biol. Bull.* **109**, 373–374.

Macchi, I. A. (1956). *J. Clin. Endocrinol. and Metabolism* **10**, 942.

Macchi, I. A., and Hechter, O. (1954). *Endocrinology* **55**, 387–402.

McDonald, I. R., and Reich, M. (1959). *J. Physiol. (London)* **147**, 33–50.

McKerns, K. W. (1957). *Endocrinology* **60**, 130–135.

McLean, P. (1961). *Nature* **191**, 1302–1303.

Maes, J. (1937). *Arch. intern. Physiol.* **45**, 135–139.

Maetz, J. (1962). *Symposium Zool. Soc. (London).* In press.

Manchester, K. L., Randle, P. J., and Young, F. G. (1959). *J. Endocrinol.* **18**, 395–408.

Mason, J. W. (1958). *In* "Reticular Formation of the Brain," Henry Ford Hospital Symposium, pp. 645–662. Little, Brown, Boston, Massachusetts.

Miller, L. L. (1960). *Nature* **185**, 248.

Mills, I. H. (1961). *Mem. Soc. Endocrinol. No.* **11**, 81–89.

Mills, I. H. (1962). *Brit. Med. Bull.* **18**(2), 127–133.

Mills, J. N., Thomas, S., and Williamson, K. S. (1961). *J. Physiol. (London)* **156**, 415–423.

Morgan, H. E., Regen, D. M., Henderson, M. J., Sawyer, T. K., and Park, C. R. (1961). *J. Biol. Chem.* **236**, 2162–2168.

Morris, R. (1960). *Symposia Zool. Soc. London No.* **1**, 1–16.

Muller, A. F., Riondel, A. M., and Manning, E. L. (1956). *Lancet* **ii**, 1021–1024.

Mulrow, P. J., and Cohn, G. L. (1959). *Proc. Soc. Exptl. Biol. Med.* **101**, 731–734.

Myers, R. M., Fleming, W. R., and Scheer, B. T. (1956). *Endocrinology* **58**, 674–676.

Myers, R. W., Bishop, W. R., and Scheer, B. T. (1961). *Am. J. Physiol.* **200**, 444–450.

Nace, P. F. (1955). *Biol. Bull.* **109**, 366.

Nace, P. F. (1956). *Anat. Record* **124**, 340.

Nagra, C. L., Baum, G. J., and Meyer, R. K. (1960). *Proc. Soc. Exptl. Biol. Med.* **105**, 68–70.

Nandi, J., and Bern, H. A. (1960). *Endocrinology* **66**, 295–303.

Neher, R., Desaulles, P., Vischer, E., Wieland, P., and Wettstein, A. (1958). *Helv. Chim. Acta* **41**, 1667–1692.

Nelson, D. H. (1960). *In* "Hormones in Human Plasma" (H. N. Antoniades, ed.), pp. 335–350. Churchill, London.

Nelson, D. H., Reich, H., and Samuels, L. T. (1950). *Science* **111**, 578–579.

Newcomer, W. S. (1959). *Am. J. Physiol.* **196**, 276–278.

Newcomer, W. S., and Heninger, R. W. (1960). *Proc. Soc. Exptl. Biol. Med.* **105**, 32–35.

Nims, L. F., and Thurber, R. E. (1961). *Am. J. Physiol.* **201**, 995–998.

Nowell, W. N., and Chester Jones, I. (1958). *In* "Pathophysiologia Diencephalica" (S. B. Curri and L. Martini, eds.), pp. 248–260. Springer, Berlin.

Ogston, A. G., and Sherman, T. F. (1961). *J. Physiol. (London)* **156**, 67–74.

Osler, W. (1896). *Bull. Johns Hopkins Hosp.* **7**, 208–219.

Perera, G. A. (1948). *Proc. Soc. Exptl. Biol. Med.* **68**, 48–50.

Peron, F. G. (1960). *Endocrinology* **66**, 458–469.

Phillips, J. G. (1959). *J. Endocrinol.* **18**, xxxvii–xxxix.

Phillips, J. G., and Bellamy, D. (1962). *J. Endocrinol.* **24**, vi–vii.

Phillips, J. G., and Chester Jones, I. (1957). *J. Endocrinol.* **18**, iii.

Phillips, J. G., and Mulrow, P. J. (1959a). *Proc. Soc. Exptl. Biol. Med.* **101**, 262–264.

Phillips, J. G., and Mulrow, P. J. (1959b). *Nature* **184**, 558.

Phillips, J. G., Holmes, W. N., and Bondy, P. K. (1959). *Endocrinology* **65**, 811–818.

Phillips, J. G., Holmes, W. N., and Butler, D. G. (1961). *Endocrinology* **69**, 958–969.

Phillips, J. G., Chester Jones, I., and Bellamy, D. (1962b). *J. Endocrinol.* **25**, 233–237.

Phillips, J. G., Chester Jones, I., Bellamy, D., Greep, R. O., Day, L. R., and Holmes, W. N. (1962a). *Endocrinology*, **71**, 329–331.

Pickford, G. E. (1959a). *Yale J. Biol. and Med.* **31**, 341–361.

Pickford, G. E. (1959b). *In* "Comparative Endocrinology" (A. Gorbman, ed.), pp. 404–420. Wiley, New York.

Pickford, G. E., and Atz, J. W. (1957). "The Physiology of the Pituitary Gland of Fishes." New York Zoological Society, New York.

Pickford, M., and Vogt, M. (1951). *J. Physiol. (London)* **112**, 133–141.

Potts, W. T. W. (1962). *Inst. Biol. J.* **9**, 11.

Rauschkolb, E. W., Farrell, G. L., and Koletsky, S. (1956). *Am. J. Physiol.* **184**, 55–58.

Reid, E. (1961). *Mem. Soc. Endocrinol. No.* **11**, 149–163.

Reshef, L., and Shapiro, B. (1960). *Metabolism* **9**, 551–555.

Rinfret, A. P., and Hane, S. (1955). *Proc. Soc. Exptl. Biol. Med.* **90**, 508–510.

Rogoff, J. M. (1932). *J. Am. Med. Assoc.* **79**, 1309–1315.

Romanoff, E. B., Hudson, P., and Pincus, G. (1953). *J. Clin. Endocrinol. and Metabolism* **13**, 1546–1548.

Rose, H. G., Robertson, M. G., and Schwartz, T. B. (1959). *Am. J. Physiol.* **197**, 1063–1069.

Rosen, F., Roberts, N. R., Budnick, L. E., and Nichol, C. A. (1959). *Endocrinology* **65**, 256–264.

Rosnagle, R. S., and Farrell, G. L. (1956). *Am. J. Physiol.* **187**, 7–10.

Ross, E. J. (1959). "Aldosterone in Clinical and Experimental Medicine." Blackwell, Oxford.

Saffran, M. (1962). *Brit. Med. Bull.* **18**(2), 122–126.

Sandberg, A. A. (1960). *In* "Hormones in Human Plasma" (H. N. Antoniades, ed.), pp. 363–398. Churchill, London.

Santa, N. (1940). *Compt. rend. soc. biol.* **133**, 417–419.

Sawyer, W. H., Munsick, R. A., and Van Dyke, H. B. (1960). *Circulation* **21**, Suppl., 1027–1037.

Sayers, G., and Sayers, M. A. (1947). *Endocrinology* **40**, 265–273.

Sayers, G., and Sayers, M. A. (1948). *Recent Progr. in Hormone Research* **2**, 81–115.

Schmidt-Nielsen, K. (1960). *Circulation* **21**, Suppl., 955–967.

Seckel, H. P. G. (1940). *Endocrinology* **26**, 97–103.

Sexton, A. W. (1955). *Dissertation Abstr.* **15**, 2270.

Shoppee, C. W. (1958). "Chemistry of the Steroids." Butterworths, London.

Short, R. V. (1960). *Biochem. Soc. Symposia (Cambridge, Engl.) No.* **18**, 59–84.

Simpson, S. A., and Tait, J. F. (1955). *CIBA Foundation Colloquia on Endocrinol.* **8**, 204–227.

Simpson, S. A., Tait, J. F. and Bush, I. E. (1952). *Lancet* **263** (No. II), 226–227.

Simpson, S. A., Tait, J. F., Wettstein, A., Neher, R., von Euw, J., Schindler, O., and Reichstein, T. (1954). *Helv. Chim. Acta* **37**, 1163–1200.

Singer, B., and Stack-Dunne, M. (1955). *J. Endocrinol.* **12**, 130–145.

Smith, A. L., Koeppe, O. J., and Franz, J. M. (1961). *Endocrinology* **69**, 872–874.

Smith, H. W. (1930). *J. Biol. Chem.* **88**, 97–130.

Smith, H. W. (1936). *Biol. Revs. Cambridge Phil. Soc.* **11**, 49–82.

Smith, P. E. (1930). *Am. J. Anat.* **45**, 205.

Smith, R. E., and Hoijer, D. J. (1962). *Physiol. Revs.* **42**, 60–142.

Sourkes, T. L., and Heneage, P. (1952). *Endocrinology* **50**, 73–82.

Srere, P. A., Chaikoff, I. L., and Dauben, W. G. (1948). *J. Biol. Chem.* **176**, 829–833.

Stachenko, J., and Giroud, C. J. P. (1959). *Endocrinology* **64**, 730–742.

Stack-Dunne, M. P. (1953). *CIBA Foundation Colloquia on Endocrinol.* **5**, 133.

Streeten, D. H. P., Pont, M. E., and Conn, J. W. (1955). *J. Lab. Clin. Med.* **46**, 729–732.

Swann, H. G. (1940). *Physiol. Revs.* **20**, 493–521.

Sweat, M. L., and Farrell, G. L. (1954). *Proc. Soc. Exptl. Biol., Med.* **87**, 615–618.

Sydnor, K. L., and Sayers, G. (1954). *Endocrinology* **55**, 621–636.

Talanti, S., and Hopsu, V. K. (1961). *Endocrinology* **68**, 184–185.

Teng, C. T., Sinex, F. M., Deane, H. W., and Hastings, A. B. (1952). *J. Cellular Comp. Physiol.* **39**, 73–88.

Thorn, G. W., Engel, L. L., and Lewis, R. A. (1941). *Science* **94**, 348–349.

Ulick, S., and Solomon, S. (1960). *J. Am. Chem. Soc.* **82**, 249.

Urist, M. R., and Deutsch, N. M. (1960). *Proc. Soc. Exptl. Biol. Med.* **104**, 35–39.

Ussing, H. H., Kruhoffer, P., Thaysen, J. H., and Thorn, N. A. (1960). "The Alkali Metals in Biology, Hefter's Handbuch der experimentellen Pharmakologie, Erganzungsband 13. Springer, Berlin.

Villano, F., and D'Onofrio, F. (1955). *Boll. soc. ital. biol. sper.* **31**, 1407–1410.

Vogt, M. (1943). *J. Physiol. (London)* **102**, 341–356.

Vogt, M. (1960). *Biochem. Soc. Symposia (Cambridge, Engl.) No.* **18**, 85–95.

Weber, G., Banerjee, G., and Bronstein, S. B. (1961). *J. Biol. Chem.* **236**, 3106–3111.

Welt, I. D., and Wilhelmi, A. E. (1950). *Yale J. Biol. and Med.* **23**, 99–104.

Wettstein, A. (1954). *Experientia* **10**, 397–416.

Wheeler, T. D., and Vincent, S. (1927). *Trans. Roy. Soc. Can. V*, **11**, 125–129.

Williams, M. W., and Angerer, C. A. (1959). *Proc. Soc. Exptl. Biol. Med.* **102**, 112–114.

Wilson, D. L. (1957). *Am. J. Physiol.* **190**, 104–108.

Woodbury, D. M., and Withrow, C. D. (1962). *Proc. Intern Congress Hormonal Steroids, Milan,* in press.

Wool, I. G., and Weinshelbaum, E. I. (1959). *Am. J. Physiol.* **197**, 1089–1092.

Wool, I. G., and Weinshelbaum, E. I. (1960). *Am. J. Physiol.* **198**, 1111–1114.

Wright, A., Chester Jones, I., and Phillips, J. G. (1957). *J. Endocrinol.* **15**, 100–107.

Wright, R. D. (1962). *Brit. Med. Bull.* **18**(2), 159–163.

Yielding, K. L., and Tomkins, G. M. (1959). *Proc. Natl. Acad. Sci. U. S.* **45**, 1730–1739.

Zwemer, R. L. (1927). *Am. J. Physiol.* **79**, 658–665.

~ 7 ~

Chromaffin Cell Hormones

U. S. von EULER

Fysiologiska Institutionen, Karolinska Institutet, Stockholm, Sweden

I. INTRODUCTION

In the study of the occurrence of the specific cells containing catecholamines, the brownish staining with bichromate solutions has been used extensively as an indicator for the presence of these cells. With the aid of this technique, supplemented by a number of other stains, numerous attempts have been made to detect and localize catecholamine-containing cells in the organism.

After Henle's (1865) original observations on adrenal medullary cells Stilling (1898) found a similar coloration with potassium bichromate of groups of cells in peripheral sympathetic ganglia in various animals and called them chromaffin cells. He also named the bodies consisting of cells staining in a similar way paraganglia. Poll (1906) called the cells phaeochrome, a term which has been mostly used in connection with tumors. Other terms (pléochrome, fuscogenic) have also been suggested but have not found general acceptance.

The nature of the chromaffin reaction became better known when it was found that adrenaline, isolated by Abel and Geiling (1899) and Takamine (1901), on oxydation, gave darkly stained products. As shown by Verne (1922) not only adrenaline but many other aromatic reducing substances react to chrome salts in this way. Gérard et al. (1930) provided evidence that the coloring was caused by oxidation of adrenaline which was then oxidized further to melanin-like darkly stained substances. They also showed that other oxidizing agents could cause a similar reaction; e.g., iodates which were colorless in themselves. From these findings it became obvious that the term "chromaffin" is hardly appropriate, and also that the reaction is not specific for adrenaline.

Catecholamine-containing cells also give a number of other reactions such as (1) a green color with a weak solution of ferric chloride (Vulpian reaction), (2) a blue stain with ferric–ferricyanide (Schmorl's reaction), (3) blackening with osmium tetroxide (Mulon's reaction), and (4) reduction of silver salts and gold chloride. These reactions have been critically examined in papers by Lison (1953), Bachmann (1954), Pearse (1960), Coupland and Heath (1961a), and by Bloom et al. (1961). The use of silver staining has been of great value for studies of the chromaffin system in embryos and fetuses (Boyd, 1960). This author also points out the important difference between the argentaffin reaction (dark staining with silver salts) and the argyrophilic or argentophilic reaction obtained with silver salts after adding a reducing agent.

However, critical studies particularly in later years have thrown doubt on the specificity of several methods used histologically for the demonstration of such cells, and have prompted the development of new, more specific staining methods. Among recent methods which seem to be sufficiently specific the recently developed modifications of Palmgren's stain (Johnels and Palmgren, 1960; Bloom et al., 1961) may be mentioned. For this reason earlier reports about the presence of chromaffin tissue have to be regarded with some reserve. This is particularly the case when the chromaffin tissue is located at atypical sites.

A corroborative method to demonstrate catecholamine-producing cells is to make extracts of the tissue consisting of or containing such cells and subject them to biological or chemical assay. The methods available at present are very sensitive and detect catecholamines in tissues in which the identification of chromaffin cells presents great difficulties (cf. Lever *et al.*, 1959). In tissues containing, for instance, 0.1 μg of a catecholamine/gm (which often can be readily detected by biological or chemical methods), the frequency of chromaffin cells will presumably be only 1/100,000 of that in the suprarenal medulla which contains 10 mg catecholamines/gm. Chromaffin cells in such tissues would thus easily escape detection.

The term "chromaffin cells" is clearly not ideal and should perhaps be replaced by a more precisely defined one. In view of the recent findings of Coupland and Heath (1961a), even the more general term "catecholamine-containing cells" is somewhat ambiguous since it might well include certain mast cells capable of storing not only dopamine, but perhaps also adrenaline and noradrenaline. A histochemical distinction between dopamine and other catecholamines appears difficult to achieve, and yet the differentiation between these cells is of great functional significance. In the case of the suprarenal glands the hazards in differentiation are seemingly not too great but for other regions it may be difficult to distinguish between adrenaline-containing "true" chromaffin cells and mast cells which may have taken up adrenaline. Coupland and Heath (1961b) apparently use the term chromaffin cells in the sense of pressor amine-containing chromaffin cells, as distinguished from mast cells and enterochromaffin cells.

II. CATECHOLAMINE-PRODUCING CELL SYSTEMS

A. Adrenaline and Noradrenaline-Producing Cells

Chromaffin cell hormones, *in sensu strictiori*, should comprise all hormone-like agents present in cells which exhibit chromaffin reactions. As discussed in Section I, such cells might be of a manifold nature and include, among others, cells containing 5-hydroxytryptamine. In this chapter only the catecholamine-producing chromaffin cells will be considered. This group comprises at present three different catecholamines: adrenaline, noradrenaline, and dopamine or 3-hydroxytyramine. The structural characteristics of the cells producing the first two amines seem to be different from the special type which produces dopamine (Section II,B). The post-synaptic catechol-producing neurons will not be considered in this group but will be treated separately in Volume II, Chapter 19. The term chromaffin cells will be used here to indicate adrenaline and noradrenaline-producing cells, and the cells containing dopamine will be called dopamine cells, following the suggestion of Falck *et al.* (1959).

The sympathetic chains are generally believed to derive from the neural crest of the ectoderm (Boyd, 1960). Some of the fibers reach the neighborhood of the primordium of the adrenal cortex accompanied by cells (chromaffinoblasts) which differentiate into chromaffin cells. This may explain why chromaffin cells are found in a variety of organs supplied with sympathetic nerves. A systematic study of chromaffin cell distribution has not been made so far, partly for lack of adequate methods. It is to be expected that with improved techniques this gap in our knowledge will be filled. Chromaffin cells have also been found in sympathetic ganglia and presumably occur all along sympathetic nerves. Some indirect evidence for this will be given in Volume II, Chapter 19.

The chromaffin cells of the suprarenals are connected with the autonomic centers by presynaptic fibers, in a way analogous to the presynaptic sympathetic nerves. It is still largely a matter of conjecture how the synaptic connection develops; it appears that the chromaffin cells, having developed in the periphery, orientate themselves to make contact with the ending of presynaptic neurons by some kind of trophotaxis. It is not even known whether all chromaffin cells in the tissues or organs outside the suprarenals are innervated. This applies, for instance, to the chromaffin cell groups present in the prostate and vesicular glands (Euler, 1934). Some recent observations may possibly contribute to the solution of this problem. Armin and Grant (1959) noted a release of catecholamines (presumably adrenaline) in adrenalectomized animals which had been rendered hypoglycemic by insulin. Similarly Euler *et al.* (1961) noted an increased output of adrenaline in urine of adrenalectomized patients during insulin hypoglycemia. These results seem to indicate that the peripheral chromaffin cell system is also connected with the autonomic centers and can be activated in a similar way to the adrenal medulla.

The adult chromaffin cell of the adrenal medulla differs from the forms observed during fetal life. Thus Boyd (1960) has described argyrophil cells of branched appearance in the adrenal medulla of the human fetus and other chromaffin cell groups during prenatal life, e.g., in the superior para-aortic paraganglion. The heart of the cyclostome *Myxine glutinosa* contains large amounts of catecholamines, although this organ, according to several studies from this laboratory [recently confirmed by Augustinsson *et al.* (1956)], wholly lacks an extrinsic nerve supply. A recent study has shown (Bloom *et al.*, 1961) that the cyclostome heart contains an abundance of chromaffin cells (Fig. 1), particularly in those parts in which the catecholamine content is high. The cells also show fiber-like extensions which appear to form a network. It seems that this hitherto unknown chromaffin

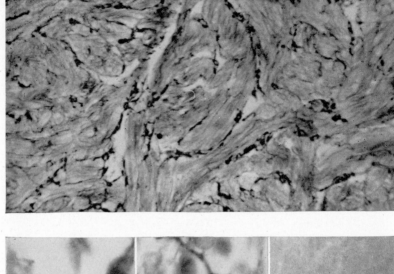

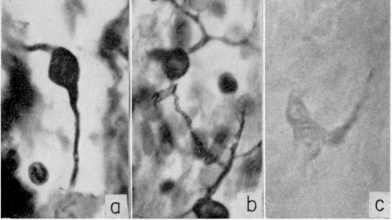

FIG. 1. Upper figure: Light photomicrograph of *Petromyzon* atrium showing the widely dispersed system of darkly staining catecholamine cells stained by the modified Palmgren method. Magnification: ×150. Lower figure: Light photomicrograph of specific cells from portal vein heart of *Myxine*; *a* and *b* stained by the modified Palmgren method, *c* after treatment with bichromate-chromate. Note bipolar appearance of cells in *a* and branched system of cytoplasmic protrusions in *b*. Magnification: ×800. From Bloom *et al.* (1961).

cell system might represent a primitive kind of sympathetic system which presumably functions independently of nervous connections. Further investigations will have to show whether similar systems occur in other phyla or during ontogenesis. The functions of the system described in *Myxine* are largely unknown, but it is well known that in mammals the denervated suprarenal medulla can produce catecholamines and, for instance, can be made to release them by drugs. Chromaffin cell tumors are certainly not innervated, and, apparently, nervous control is not a prerequisite for the production and release of their products.

B. Dopamine-Containing Cells

Dopamine as a naturally occurring product in mammalian tissues was first discovered by Goodall (1951). In 1956 Schümann reported the presence of relatively large amounts of dopamine in bovine splenic nerves. Since these nerves are also rich in noradrenaline (Euler, 1949) the dopamine was considered to represent a precursor store of functional significance for the biosynthesis of the neurotransmitter. Shortly afterwards, Euler and Lishajko (1957) found large amounts of dopamine in bovine lung tissue and bronchi. In view of the small amounts of noradrenaline present in the lungs it was considered unlikely that dopamine should function merely as precursor for noradrenaline, and the possibility of there being special stores for dopamine was considered. In the following year Falck et al. (1959) discovered a type of chromaffin cell in ungulates which was typically present in regions which on extraction yielded dopamine in large quantities (Fig. 2).

Dopamine cells were found in particularly large numbers in the visceral pleura of the bovine lung, in the liver capsule, and in the duodenal mucosa or submucosa (Bertler et al., 1959). The same authors showed also that bovine splenic nerves contained chromaffin cells of this type; this would account for their relatively high dopamine content. As to the nature of

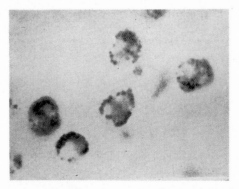

FIG. 2. Group of dopamine cells in cow pleura. Fixation with bichromate-chromate-formalin. Staining by nuclear fast red method. Magnification: ×1450. From Falck et al. (1959).

these cells Bertler *et al.* (1959) discuss the possibility that dopamine may be stored in mast cells which are known to occur abundantly in the pleura and the liver capsule of the cow.

Coupland and Heath (1961b) have confirmed the presence of numerous chromaffin cells of the type described by Falck *et al.* (1959) and by Bertler *et al.* (1959) in the sites reported by these authors. Coupland and Heath (1961b) emphasize the possibility that mast cells are capable of storing dopamine, just as they are able to store histamine by ionic linkage to the strongly acidic heparin. The patchy reaction of the granules observed in some mast cells was tentatively interpreted as being due to varying amounts of the amine taken up by the granules.

Since the dye (nuclear fast red) used for the demonstration of these granular chromaffin cells provides, according to Coupland and Heath, an almost specific stain for acid mucopolysaccharides, the suggested relationship to mast cells received strong support.

Although dopamine has also been demonstrated in brain (Montagu, 1957; and others) and in particularly high amounts in the caudate nucleus (Bertler and Rosengren, 1959a), no evidence has been obtained so far for the presence of specific dopamine cells in this region. The increase in brain dopamine after injection of dopa (Bertler and Rosengren, 1959b) as well as the discharge after reserpine administration (Bertler, 1961) argues strongly in favor of the assumption that the dopamine is present in special cells. Storage particles capable of dopamine uptake have been found in the brain (Weil-Malherbe, 1960).

III. ASSAY METHODS

Both chemical and biological determination methods have been extensively used for the quantitative estimation of chromaffin cell hormones. Although the chemical methods are now more frequently used they are still effectively supplemented by bioassays.

A. Chemical Methods

1. COLORIMETRIC DETERMINATION

All catechol compounds form colored derivatives upon oxidation with suitable agents. The red chromes of adrenaline, noradrenaline, and dopamine can be used for colorimetric determination. In the method of Euler and Hamberg (1949a) the catecholamines are oxidized by iodine to the corresponding iodochrome. A differential estimation of adrenaline and noradrenaline in a mixture can be achieved by performing the oxidation at two different pH values. At pH 4 only adrenaline and about 10% of the noradrenaline is transformed to chromes by iodine treatment for $1\frac{1}{2}$ min but oxidation at pH 6 for 3 min will transform both adrenaline and noradrenaline to the colored products. By using a simple formula the amounts of adrenaline and noradrenaline present in the sample can be computed. The readings can be made in any good photometer at 529 mμ. At this wave length the same photometer readings are obtained for the slightly differently colored products of adrenaline when oxidized at pH 4 and pH 6 respectively. The colorimetric technique is useful when relatively large amounts of the catecholamines are available, such as in adrenal extracts. The amounts necessary for reliable readings should not be less than about 25 μg catecholamines.

2. Fluorimetric Determinations

a. The trihydroxyindole (THI) method. This technique is based on the observations of Ehrlén (1948) and of Lund (1949) that the strongly fluorescent compounds derived from catecholamines on addition of strong alkali (Loew, 1918) can be stabilized with ascorbic acid and used for quantitative estimations. By the technique of Euler and Lishajko (1961a) the catecholamines in the extracts, after adsorption on alumina, are oxidized with potassium ferricyanide at pH 6.2–6.3, eluted with acetic acid and transformed to the corresponding lutines with a mixture of strong alkali and ascorbic acid. By the addition of a small quantity of ethylenediamine to the alkali–ascorbic acid mixture the blanks are maintained at a low value and the stability of the reagent mixture is increased. Adrenolutine and noradrenolutine can be differentially determined in the mixture by measuring fluorescence with two suitable filter sets according to the method reported by Cohen and Goldenberg (1957) and by Price and Price (1957). From the fluorescence of standards the amounts of adrenaline and noradrenaline can be computed by a simple formula. The technique entails losses of about 20–25% of the catecholamines originally present. Using internal standards these losses can be compensated for in the final values. Any reasonably sensitive and stable fluorimeter, such as the Coleman 12 C apparatus, can be used for the purpose. A catecholamine concentration of 0.02 μg per ml eluate can be measured with this method.

In the technique described by Bertler et al. (1958) extracts of the catecholamine-containing material are made with perchloric acid. After removal of the bulk of perchloric acid as potassium perchlorate the extract is passed through a column of Dowex 50 in Na$^+$ form. By elution with 1 N HCl and then by 2 N HCl it is possible to separate a mixture of adrenaline and noradrenaline in the first eluate from dopamine in the second eluate. Bertler *et al.* (1958) used the Aminco spectrophotofluorimeter for assay and measured the fluorescence intensity at activating wavelengths of 410 and 455 mμ and with readings at 540 mμ. The amounts present can then be computed.

After separation from adrenaline and noradrenaline by an ion exchange technique (Carlsson, 1959) dopamine can also be assayed. Iodine is used for oxidation, and after transformation to the dihydroxyindole the pH is adjusted to 5.3 which increases the intensity of fluorescence.

In the method of Kuntzman *et al.* (1961) as adapted for brain, the catecholamines are taken up in butanol, transferred to 0.01 N HCl, oxidized with iodine, and read at the activating wavelength of 400 mμ and at the fluorescent wavelength of 510 mμ after transformation to the lutines. The values are calculated for noradrenaline but will include small amounts of adrenaline which are present in brain extracts.

b. *The ethylenediamine (EDA) method.* This is based on the formation of strongly fluorescent condensation products of catecholamines and ethylene-diamine (Natelson *et al.*, 1949). The reaction has been adapted for quantitative assay of catecholamines by Weil-Malherbe and Bone (1954). After condensation of the catecholamines with ethylenediamine in the previously purified extract, the fluorescent compounds are transferred into isobutanol and read in a fluorimeter. By using the principle of reading at different wavelengths, adrenaline and noradrenaline can be differentially estimated. The method is more sensitive than the THI method but less specific.

B. Biological Methods

After separation by chromatography or by ion-exchange resins, adrenaline and noradrenaline can be assayed by any suitable bioassay preparation. The blood pressure of the rat (Vogt, 1952) or the cat, after adequate sensitization, is particularly suitable for the assay of noradrenaline. With this technique amounts as low as 5 ng (rat) and 20 ng (cat) can usually be detected and assayed.

In mixtures of adrenaline and noradrenaline, the two amines can be measured differentially by using bioassay preparations with sufficiently different activity ratios. Suitable pairs are cat's or rat's blood pressure on the one hand and the chicken rectal caecum or the rat uterus on the other. The latter preparations have a much higher sensitivity for adrenaline than for noradrenaline (Euler, 1956).

When the extracts are purified on alumina, the amines are eluted with 0.25 N sulfuric acid for bioassay.

IV. DISTRIBUTION OF CHROMAFFIN CELL HORMONES

A. Mammals

Research to obtain more knowledge about the distribution of cate-cholamine-producing cells has proceeded along two lines. A large number of studies have been performed on a variety of animals using varying chromaffin cell reactions as a criterion for the existence of such cells. For extensive reviews on this subject the reader is referred to anatomical and histological treatises (e.g. Hartman and Brownell, 1949; Bachmann, 1954). Apparently chromaffin cells occur not only in mammals but also regularly in poikilothermic vertebrates. Cells of this type have also been found in some invertebrates, such as insects and annelids.

The second line of studies has used biological or chemical assay tech-niques for the demonstration of catecholamines. With the development of suitable methods important information on the distribution of cate-cholamines has been obtained, particularly during recent years. Since postsynaptic sympathetic neurons may contain and produce catechol-amines, it is not always possible to ascertain whether the demonstration of catecholamines in a tissue is due to such neurons or to chromaffin cells. One way to distinguish between these possibilities is to study the effect of denervation. If the catecholamines in the organ disappear after de-generation of the postsynaptic nerves, it proves that the catecholamines were contained in the neurons themselves; if the catecholamines persist or increase in amount, they must have been present in chromaffin cells or some other independent store. In mammals it can be regarded as estab-lished that the occurrence of adrenaline in organ extracts indicates the presence of chromaffin cells whereas noradrenaline suggests adrenergic nerve fibers. This may not apply to nonmammals. A rich supply of post-synaptic autonomic nerve fibers to an organ containing noradrenaline, as does the mammalian spleen, suggests catecholamine-producing fibers. A high adrenaline content in conjunction with a smaller nerve supply makes it probable that the organ contains chromaffin cells.

1. ADRENAL MEDULLA

The Vulpian (1856) reaction with ferric salts was probably the first indication of the presence of a special chemical compound in the adrenal medulla. After the demonstration of the strong biological actions of adrenal extracts by Oliver and Schäfer (1895), Abel (1902) and Takamine (1901) isolated an active amine (catechol-N-methylethanolamine) usually referred to as adrenaline. Other names are epinephrine and adrenin. In 1904 ad-renaline and its homologue, noradrenaline, were synthesized by Stolz.

In the adult mammal the adrenal medulla represents the bulk of chromaffin cells. For a long time adrenaline was believed to be the only specific
product elaborated by the adrenal chromaffin cells. Some observations
suggested, however, that related substances differing in some respects
from adrenaline might also occur in these cells. Thus, Schkawera and
Kusnetzow (1923) observed that the properties of the active substance
did not entirely agree with those of adrenaline, and Schild (1933) noted
large enough differences in the biological action of adrenal extracts and
adrenaline to suggest that some other substance was involved. It was not
until 1947, however, that Holtz *et al.*, obtained evidence for the presence
of considerable amounts of noradrenaline in adrenal extracts from the
cat. In the previous year this compound had been recognized as the transmitter substance of adrenergic nerves (Euler, 1946). In the following years
a large number of studies were devoted to the analysis of the catecholamine
content and distribution in adrenal glands of various species. As a result
of these studies it could be shown that the relative amounts of adrenaline
and noradrenaline varied widely in different species. Thus in some animals
the adrenals contained practically only adrenaline and in others noradrenaline was the dominating catecholamine (Table I).

Fairly large variations in the noradrenaline percentage may, however,
occur in the same species. In the cat, for instance, the noradrenaline may
vary from about 20 to 80% of the total adrenal catecholamines. Of interest
is the finding of Butterworth and Mann (1957) that the proportion of
noradrenaline as well as the total amounts of catecholamines are practically the same in each gland of the same animal. This is of great value
from the point of view of obtaining a control when one gland is exposed
to various experimental influences. However, the high percentage of noradrenaline in the whale (Rastgeldi, 1951) and the low figures in the rabbit
(Hökfelt and McLean, 1950) are constant features.

Catecholamine values for adrenal glands are often given as mg/gm of
whole gland. These figures have only a limited significance since the relative weight of the medulla and the cortex vary widely in different species.
Thus the proportion of cortex to medulla in the pig is 3:1 but is about 60:1
in the rabbit. In some instances where estimations have been made on
medullary tissue, the values have been remarkably high. Thus bovine
medullary tissue gave figures of 10–14 mg/gm (Euler and Hamberg,
1949b; Ozaki, 1954); the figures in the whale were similar. In a number
of mammalian species Shepherd and West (1953) and West (1953) found
total catecholamine amounts of 3.25–8 mg/gm in the medullary tissue.

As to the relative distribution of the two amines it can be seen (Table I)
that, in general, the rodents have a low percentage of noradrenaline, and
the lion and the cat have a relatively high percentage. This led Goodall

TABLE I

CATECHOLAMINES IN THE ADRENAL GLANDS OF ADULT MAMMALS

Animal	Noradrenaline %	Total amount of catecholamines (mg/gm whole gland)	Reference
Whale	83; 68	4.0; 2.1	1, 10
Lion	55	0.53	2
Pig	49	2.2	3
Wildebeest	42	1.4	2
Cat	41	1.0	3
Gazelle	39	0.92	2
Hedgehog	39	0.48	9
Goat	37	2.2	7
Sheep	33; 33	0.75; 1.6	3, 2
Cow	29; 28	1.8; 4.2	3, 6
Dog	27	1.5	3
Mouse	25	1.0	3
Squirrel	24	0.84	5
Fox	23	1.4	5
Horse	20	0.84	3
Monkey (Macacus)	19	0.33	5
Man	17; 16	0.60; 0.58	3, 4
Zebra	17	1.9	2
Hare	12	0.35	3
Rat	9	1.2	3
Hamster	8	0.4	3
Guinea pig	2; 11	0.15; 0.63	3, 8
Rabbit	2	0.48	3

1. Burn et al. (1951).
2. Goodall (1951).
3. West (1955).
4. Euler et al. (1954).
5. Euler, unpublished.
6. Euler and Hamberg (1949b).
7. Ozaki (1955).
8. Euler and Hökfelt (1953).
9. Uuspää and Suomalainen (1954).
10. Rastgeldi (1951).

(1951) to postulate that aggressive animals tend to have higher noradrenaline values, whereas adrenaline predominates in their prey.

The occurrence of two hormones with distinctly different actions in the adrenal medulla and the demonstration of differential secretion (Euler and Luft, 1952, Folkow and Euler, 1954) (Fig. 3) raised the question of

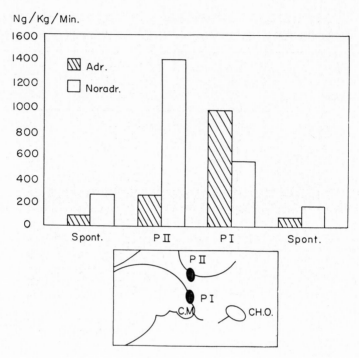

Fig. 3. Adrenaline and noradrenaline secretion from the left adrenal gland in a cat before and during hypothalamic stimulation at two different points as indicated. C.M., mammilary body. CH.O., Optic chiasma. From Folkow and Euler (1954).

differentiated cells, each type producing its specific hormone. The first evidence that this might be the case was obtained by Bänder (1951). Further histochemical studies (for references see Eränkö, 1960) corroborated this finding. Figure 4 from Hillarp and Hökfelt's (1953) paper clearly demonstrates the differential staining of noradrenaline-containing cells (dark) and adrenaline-containing cells (light). Kracht and Klein (1957) could differentiate morphologically different cell types in the medulla of different animals by means of staining with iron hematoxylin according to Weigert. However, the factors governing the differentiation of these cells is not known. A differential behavior of the two kinds of cells has also been observed in regard to the action of reserpine which has a selective depleting action on the noradrenaline-containing cells in the rat (Eränkö and Hopsu, 1958; Camanni et al., 1958).

In the fetus the proportions of adrenaline and noradrenaline differ markedly from those observed in the adult (Fig. 5). West et al. (1953) showed that the adrenal glands during the prenatal period contain prac-

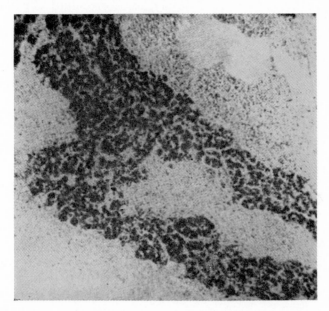

FIG. 4. Cross section of cat adrenal medulla treated with potassium iodate in phosphate buffer at pH 5.4. Noradrenaline cells are darkly stained. Magnification: ×100. From Hillarp and Hökfelt (1953).

tically only noradrenaline; the proportion of adrenaline increases steadily during postnatal life, and reaches a plateau at the age of about 2 years in the human.

The biological significance of the close proximity of the chromaffin cells in the adrenal gland to the cortical tissue has so far not received a convincing explanation. It is noteworthy, however, that this arrangement is not found in all phyla. At any rate it is obvious from the analysis of chromaffin cell tissue which occurs separated from cortical tissue, that the latter is not required for methylation.

Some catecholamine activity (up to 10% of the total) is regularly found in the adrenal cortex of many animals. The proportion of adrenaline and noradrenaline in these cells seems to be the same as in the medulla (Shepherd and West, 1953). Eränkö (1955) has described noradrenaline-containing cell islets in the adrenal cortex of the hamster, which had a richer nerve supply than the central adrenaline-containing medullary tissue.

The presence of dopamine in the normal adrenal gland of the sheep was discovered by Goodall (1951) and has since been shown also in the ox (Shepherd and West, 1953).

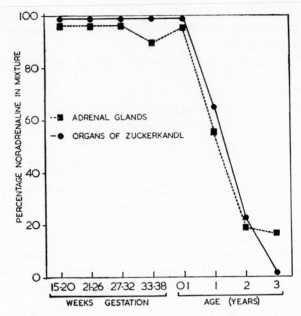

Fig. 5. Relative noradrenaline content of the adrenal gland and organ of Zucker-kandl of fetuses and babies at different ages. From West *et al.* (1953).

2. Accessory Chromaffin Tissue

Chromaffin cell tissue usually situated retroperitoneally along the abdominal aorta, the so-called paraganglia, has been recognized for a long time. The most well-developed of these bodies is the organ of Zuckerkandl which exists during fetal life but later gradually disappears. Its catecholamine content in man has been studied by West *et al.* (1953) who found that it contains only noradrenaline, the peak amount (about 30 µg) being reached at the time of birth. This amount is higher than that of the adrenals at the same time. After birth the catecholamine content falls and by the age of 2–3 years it is negligible. An interesting change in the proportion of catecholamines was noted in the organ of Zuckerkandl after birth; the percentage of adrenaline steadily increased and a parallel change occurred in the adrenals (Fig. 5).

In the adult mammal, chromaffin cells, either single or as aggregates, are found in many sites in the periphery. It has been argued that the presence of adrenaline in organ extracts is an indication of chromaffin cells which may be too scanty to be readily discovered by histological techniques (Euler, 1956). The relatively large amounts of an adrenaline-like substance found in the prostate and vesicular glands of some animals (Collip, 1929) suggested a search for the presence of chromaffin cells in these organs. They were found in several of these organs (Euler, 1934). Adrenaline usually predominated but in the vesicular gland of the bull, noradrenaline (7 μg/gm) constituted nearly all of the amines (Euler and Lishajko, unpublished data). Recently Sjöstrand (1962) has found similar high amounts of noradrenaline in the vas deferens of the guinea pig, associated with a rich nerve supply. Catecholamines have also been found in extracts of the ovary (Euler and Hammarström, 1937).

It has been frequently reported that in some species, the carotid and aortic bodies contain chromaffin cells but opinions differ as to the catecholamine content. Recently, however, Muscholl et al. (1960) have succeeded in showing remarkably high amounts of noradrenaline (1–5 μg/gm)—but no adrenaline—in the carotid bodies of the calf. According to Lever et al. (1959) the glomus cells of the rabbit and the cat contain osmiophilic granules which disappear after treatment with reserpine; the chromaffin reaction is very faint. In cats and rabbits a high proportion of adrenaline has been found in sympathetic prevertebral ganglia which also contain chromaffin cells (Muscholl and Vogt, 1958).

Usually the adrenaline content of organ extracts is small, constituting about 2–10% of the total catecholamine content (cf. Euler, 1956). After section and degeneration of postsynaptic adrenergic nerves the noradrenaline almost entirely disappears but a large part of the adrenaline remains, presumably in chromaffin cells (Euler and Purkhold, 1951; Strömblad, 1960). The finding of Paasonen and Krayer (1959) that reserpine causes depletion of noradrenaline in the rat heart whereas the adrenaline content is unchanged speaks also for a different location of the two amines in mammalian tissue. The statement of Schmiterlöw (1948) that renal vessels of the horse contain adrenaline in larger proportions than other vessels may be due to the presence in this region of more chromaffin cells.

The moderate quantities of dopamine found in most organs probably occur in the dopamine cells.

3. CHROMAFFIN CELL TUMORS

Chromaffin cell tumors produce the same kind of hormones as the adrenal medulla. Holton (1949) observed that such tumors may contain a large proportion of noradrenaline. Assay of tumor tissue extracts from a large number of cases has subsequently shown that adrenaline and noradrenaline may occur in any proportion; tumors consisting only of adrenaline-containing cells are rare (Sack and Koll, 1959). The hormones of chromaffin cell tumors are stored in granules which, however, contain less ATP than adrenal medullary granules (Schümann, 1960). Although the chromaffin cell tumors receive no nerves they may secrete large quantities of catecholamines—up to 100 mg/day. The mechanism of release is not known. It has been suggested (Schümann, 1960) that the amines cannot be stored in the normal way because of lack of ATP in the storage granules.

Tumor-like masses of chromaffin cells have been observed in rat adrenals after prolonged treatment with large doses of nicotine (Eränkö et al., 1959).

B. Birds

The chromaffin cell system in birds appears to be similar to that of mammals in most respects. However, certain differences in the structure of the adrenal medulla can be observed. As shown in Fig. 6, the chromaffin tissue in the avian adrenals does not form a central mass but is intimately mingled with the interrenal tissue which corresponds to the cortical tissue. In some species, e.g. in the stork, they are fused into one organ. In birds the adrenals generally closely adhere to the gonads.

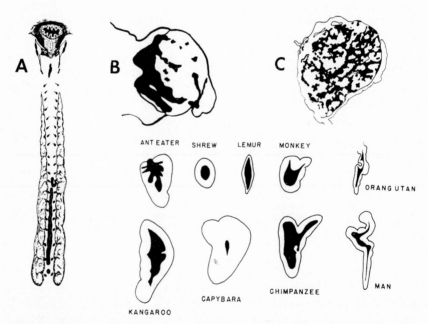

FIG. 6. Adrenal homologues and adrenals in (A) *Mustelis canis* (smooth dogfish) (B) *Anolis carolinensis* (American chameleon), (C) *Accipiter cooperi* (Cooper's hawk), and in various mammals. Chromaffin tissue in black. From Hartman and Brownell (1949).

The catecholamine content has been estimated in some avian species. Because of the low ratio of cortical to medullary tissue (about 1) the catecholamine content is relatively high. Thus it was found to be 10 mg/gm in the domestic fowl and 3 mg/gm in the pigeon (West, 1955). An interesting difference between mammals and birds was noted with respect to the ontogenetic changeover to adrenaline, in that the amounts of catecholamines per gm of gland as well as the proportion of the two amines was almost the same in the newborn and the adult chick. Eränkö (1957) has found scattered "noradrenaline cells" in the hen's medulla.

C. Poikilothermic Vertebrates

In amphibians and especially reptiles interrenal and chromaffin tissues are usually associated. The chromaffin tissue in some reptiles lies mostly on the dorsal side of the interrenal tissue, e.g., in the American chameleon (*Anolis carolinensis*). Wright and Chester Jones (1955) in *Lacerta viridis* found a peripheral layer of noradrenaline cells in the adrenals, extending as tongues and islets into the mass of adrenaline cells. Do Valle and Porto (1945) found 0.5–2.5 mg/gm of adrenaline in the adrenal gland of the snake *Bothrops*. In the turtle, the values were 2.5 mg/gm and 60% noradrenaline (West, 1955).

The catecholamine content has also been determined in the adrenals of frogs and toads. In *Bufo arenarum* Hensel, Houssay *et al.* (1950) found 3.7 mg/gm with 45% noradrenaline, and similar figures were obtained in the frog (3.1 mg/gm with 55% noradrenaline).

The occurrence of extra-adrenal chromaffin tissue in amphibians and reptiles has not been extensively studied, but there is some evidence that many organs in the frog contain cells of this kind. Thus the frog heart contains appreciable amounts of adrenaline, as shown by Loewi in 1936. More recent analyses have given occasional values as high as 17 μg adrenaline per gm cardiac ventricle in *Rana temporaria* (Euler and Lishajko, unpublished data), suggesting extraneuronal storage. In the frog other organs, like the spleen and the liver, contain appreciable quantities of adrenaline but no noradrenaline (cf. Chapter 19, Volume II).

Bertler and Rosengren (1959a) have reported that dopamine contributes very little to the catecholamine content of the brain in amphibians (*Rana temporaria* and *Bufo vulgaris*) which contain chiefly adrenaline.

Chromaffin tissue has been described in large number of teleost species and shows considerable variation, occurring either separated from interrenal tissue (*Salmo* and *Esox*) or embedded in it (*Cottus*) (Jones, 1957; Baecker, 1928; van Overbeeke, 1960; Nandi, 1961). Nandi (1961) has described the location of chromaffin cells between the interrenal and the connective tissue in the wall of postcardinal veins in Scaridae and Labridae. Extracts of some organs yield relatively large amounts of adrenaline and noradrenaline in various proportions (cf. Chapter 19 in Volume II, Table III). Particularly high values have been found in the head kidney of *Gadus callarias* (Euler and Fänge, 1961).

Along the vertebral column of elasmobranchs there are small, paired bodies comprised almost purely of chromaffin cells. Extraction of such bodies from *Squalus acanthias* yielded 9.6 mg/gm catecholamines of which 71% was noradrenaline (Euler, 1953). This result is in agreement with that of Shepherd *et al.* (1953). In *Torpedo marmorata* which is one of the few selachians which possesses a true adrenal gland, the percentage of noradrenaline was similar (Olivereau, 1959) although the total amount of catecholamines per gm of gland was lower (0.75–0.95 mg/gm), as might be expected.

In general it was observed that the percentage of noradrenaline in extracts of organs from the dogfish was higher than that of a teleost (*Gadus callarias*) (Euler and Fänge, 1961).

Holmes (1950) has studied the adrenal homologues in the lungfish *Protopterus* and has confirmed the statement of Giacomini (1906) that chromaffin tissue is located in the walls of the intercostal branches of the dorsal aorta.

The cyclostomes are considered to represent the most primitive vertebrates in which adrenal homologues have been demonstrated. Chromaffin tissue is widely spread in thin strips and scattered cells. Extracts of such tissue give biological effects indicating the presence of catecholamines (Gaskell, 1912).

Noradrenaline and adrenaline have been found in organs of *Myxine glutinosa* (with particularly large amounts in the heart) and in *Petromyzon*. (Chapter 19, Volume II, Table III). Of special interest is the finding that the portal vein heart and the atrium of *Myxine* contain mainly noradrenaline whereas the ventricle is rich in adrenaline. Noradrenaline has also been found in *Branchiostoma lanceolatus* (Euler, 1961).

D. Invertebrates

According to Gaskell (1919) the earliest phylogenetic form of the sympathetic and chromaffin systems are in annelids. His finding of an adrenaline-like substance in *Lumbricus terrestris* has been confirmed recently. Thus Östlund (1954) found 0.13 μg/gm adrenaline and 0.4 μg/gm noradrenaline in the "ganglionic chain" of this annelid. In the supraesophageal ganglion 0.03 μg/gm adrenaline and 0.17 μg/gm noradrenaline were found (Euler,

TABLE II

ADRENALINE AND NORADRENALINE CONTENT OF INSECTS[a,b,c]

Species	Growth stage	Noradrenaline (μg/gm)	Adrenaline (μg/gm)	Adrenaline as percentage of adrenaline and noradrenaline	Dopamine μg/gm (approximate)
Forficula sp.	Imago	1.2	0.010	1	<1
Vanessa urticae	Larva	0.19	<0.010	—	10–15
Tenebrio molitor	Imago	1.1	0.15	12	2–4
Tenebrio molitor	Larva	1.3	0.021	2	10–15
Tenebrio molitor	Larva	2.2	0.061	3	10–15
Musca domestica	Imago	1.9	0.30	14	10–15
Musca domestica	Larva	0.10	<0.010	—	4–8
Apis mellifera	Imago	0.75	0.050	6	5–10
Apis mellifera	Mature pupa	0.22	0.026	11	2–4
Apis mellifera	Immature pupa	0.045	0.049	52	?
Apis mellifera	Larva	0.30	<0.010	—	2–4
Apis mellifera	Imago	0.33	0.010	3	5–10
Apis mellifera	Immature pupa	0.10	0.013	12	?
Apis mellifera	Larva	0.76	0.075	9	5–10

[a] Whole body extracted with trichloroacetic acid.
[b] Biological assay on cat blood pressure and fowl rectal caecum.
[c] From Östlund (1954).

unpublished). Neurosecretory cells of chromaffin-like type have been
described in this organ by Scharrer and Brown (1961).

Chromaffin tissue has been reported to occur in the hypobranchial gland
of the gastropod *Purpura lapillus* (Roaf and Nierenstein, 1907), and Roaf
claimed that an extract from the tissue adjacent to the rectal gland of the
same species had pressor action (1911). These results have been criticized
by Lison (1932), however, who regards the cells described by Roaf as
pseudochromaffin and not adrenaline-producing.

Using a fluorimetric technique Euler (1961) was not able to demonstrate
catecholamines in whole animal extracts of the mollusc *Mytilus edulis*.
Noradrenaline was found in the posterior salivary glands of *Octopus vulgaris* (Euler, 1953) but it is unknown whether chromaffin cells occur in
these glands. Chromaffin cells have been found in some polychaetes (e.g.
Aphrodite aculaeta).

The situation with regard to chromaffin cells in insects is not clear. In
an extensive study Östlund (1954) has shown that a large variety of
insects contain noradrenaline and adrenaline, as well as dopamine, in
appreciable quantities. These amines were found in imagos, larvae, and
pupae. Table II gives some of the data obtained by Östlund. True chromaffin cells do not seem to have been demonstrated in insects, however,
and it is not known in which structures the catecholamines are located.

The finding of catecholamines in insects has been confirmed by Euler
(1961) who found 0.33 µg/gm noradrenaline in whole larvae of *Pieris
brassicae*, but no adrenaline.

It has been reported that extracts of *Paramecia* contain an adrenaline-
like substance (Bayer and Wense, 1936). This claim awaits confirmation.

V. METABOLISM OF CHROMAFFIN CELL HORMONES

A. Formation, Storage

The pathway for the synthesis of adrenaline and noradrenaline originally
suggested by Blaschko (1939) and by Holtz (1939) is now generally recognized and has been verified by isotope techniques. The biosynthetic reaction chain involves oxidation of tyrosine to 3,4-dihydroxyphenylalanine
(dopa), decarboxylation of dopa to dopamine, β-hydroxylation of dopamine
to noradrenaline, and *N*-methylation to adrenaline with the aid of adenosyl-
S-methionine and ATP. All of these steps take place in the cytoplasm of
the chromaffin cell except the β-hydroxylation of dopamine to noradrenaline which occurs in the storage granules after the uptake of the
dopamine (cf. Chapter 19 in Volume II, and Hagen, 1959).

Replenishment occurs at a rapid rate following release after nerve stimulation (Holland and Schümann, 1956). After depletion of the gland with reserpine, replenishment is slower (Callingham and Mann, 1958). Resynthesis can be shown to occur at a rapid rate in spite of depletion after insulin hypoglycemia (Bygdeman et al., 1960).

The catecholamines are stored in special granular structures in the chromaffin cell. Such granules have been observed after staining of adrenal medullary chromaffin cells with osmium (Cramer, 1919). Their nature was elucidated by Blaschko and Welch (1953) and by Hillarp et al. (1953). The storage granules have a diameter of 0.1–0.6 μ. They contain ATP in large amounts (Hillarp et al., 1955) which usually correspond to the amines with respect to available negative and positive charges. Factors causing a release of catecholamines will also cause a corresponding amount of ATP to disappear from the cell (Carlsson and Hillarp, 1956; Schümann, 1956). Storage granules have been isolated and prepared from adrenal medullary preparations of a variety of animals. In gradient centrifugation experiments it has been possible to separate fractions consisting chiefly of noradrenaline-containing granules (Eade, 1956; Schümann, 1957). About 90% of the total catecholamine content of the cow's adrenal medulla has been found in the granules and about 10% appears to be free (Hillarp, 1960).

The isolated granules from chromaffin medullary cells of various species appear to have similar properties. However, it has been reported that the nucleotides occurring in granules from fowl adrenals have relatively higher proportions of AMP and ADP (in addition to ATP) than have bovine granules (Hillarp and Thieme, 1959). The granules are stable for several hours at 5°C but lose their contents rapidly at higher temperatures (Hillarp and Nilson, 1954). On addition of acids and detergents they release the amines as do the storage granules in adrenergic nerves.

Isolated granules are able to take up catecholamines. This uptake is not confined to adrenaline and noradrenaline but also applies to dopamine (Bertler et al., 1961). It is activated by ATP and Mg^{++} and inhibited by reserpine (Carlsson et al., 1962; Kirshner, 1962).

Storage granules have also been prepared from other tissue such as chromaffin tumor cells. They appear to contain less ATP in relation to catecholamines than do adrenal chromaffin cell granules (Schümann, 1960).

In the study of Bloom et al. (1961) chromaffin cell granules were prepared from cyclostome hearts. Of the total catecholamine content about 50–70% were found in the granules, and the rest appeared in free form in the suspension medium. Figure 7 shows an electron microphotograph of a chromaffin cell from the cardiac ventricle of *Myxine glutinosa*.

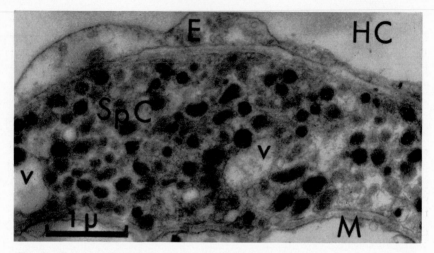

Fig. 7. Electron micrograph of a specific granular cell in the atrium of *Petromyzon*. This cell is separated from a heart cavity (HC) by a thin cytoplasmic rim of an endothelial cell (E). The specific cell borders directly on a heart muscle cell (M). The typical granules are conspicuous, vacuoles (v) are also observed. Magnification: ×22,000. From Bloom *et al.* (1961).

B. Release

The mechanism of release of the hormones from the chromaffin cells is not known in detail. Since it seems that the granules do not leave the chromaffin cell it may be postulated that the granule-bound catecholamines are in equilibrium with free amines in the cytoplasm which, upon nerve stimulation, presumably diffuse out through the cell membrane (Hillarp, 1960). The disturbed equilibrium may cause release of amines from the granules into the cytoplasm, followed by resynthesis in the granules.

Some drugs cause a release of catecholamines from chromaffin cells, either by direct action on the cell membrane (nicotine and nicotine-like substances, acetylcholine, histamine) or by acting on the granules as is assumed for tyramine, phenylethylamine, and some other amines (Fleckenstein and Stöckle, 1955; Burn and Rand, 1958). Reserpine in low concentrations inhibits the spontaneous release of catecholamines from isolated adrenal medullary granules of the rabbit or cat (Euler and Lishajko, 1961b).

The extensive studies on adrenaline secretion of the dog under various conditions have been reviewed by Sataké (1954) and by Malméjac (1959). An increased release of adrenaline in man is usually observed in conditions of stress (Pekkarinen *et al.*, 1961).

Differential release of adrenaline and noradrenaline from the medulla has been demonstrated in the human (Euler and Luft, 1952; Sundin, 1958), the cat (Dunér, 1954), the rabbit (Bygdeman *et al.*, 1960), and the rat (Leduc, 1961) indicating that the specific cells receive secretory nerves connected with special centers.

The maximal secretion rate observed in the cat is about 10 μg catecholamines/min from one adrenal corresponding to about 50 μg per gm adrenal tissue/min, or about one-fourth of the total content, assuming an adrenal weight of 0.2 gm.

The normal adrenaline concentration in human plasma is of the order of 0.1 ng/ml in arterial plasma and somewhat less in peripheral venous plasma. The contribution of noradrenaline from the adrenal glands to the normal plasma content appears to be negligible. Dopamine has not been demonstrated in blood plasma but is excreted in the urine (Holtz *et al.*, 1947; Euler *et al.*, 1951).

C. Inactivation

The chromaffin cell hormones are rapidly inactivated in the mammalian organism, (1) by conjugation with sulfuric or glucuronic acid (Richter, 1940), (2) by oxidative deamination through monoamine oxidase (Blaschko *et al.*, 1937), and (3) by *O*-methylation through the enzyme catechol-*O*-methyl transferase (Armstrong *et al.*, 1957; Axelrod, 1959). The latter enzyme seems to account for the inactivation of a large proportion of circulating catecholamines.

Dopamine is a better substrate for monoamine oxidase than adrenaline and noradrenaline and in the tissues this enzyme appears to be of great importance (Goldstein *et al.*, 1959). This is partly borne out by the relatively large amounts of dihydroxyphenylacetic acid normally excreted in urine (Chr. Euler *et al.*, 1955).

The inactivation rate of adrenaline and noradrenaline has been measured in rabbits and in dogs. The half-life of adrenaline after infusion or injection is 20–40 sec.

VI. PHYSIOLOGICAL AND PHARMACOLOGICAL ACTIONS

A. Mammals and Birds

The chromaffin cell hormones are not essential for life, and removal or inactivation of the adrenal medulla is not accompanied by any striking alterations in the physiology of the organism. This is partly due to the sympathetic (adrenergic) nerve system which controls a large part of the autonomic functions through its neurosecretory product, noradrenaline. It also appears probable that part of the functions of the adrenal medulla can be taken over by chromaffin cell groups in various sites in the body. In certain poikilothermic vertebrates and in invertebrates which lack a true adrenal gland such cells may represent the entire source of chromaffin cell hormones.

The effects of adrenaline in homeothermic animals have been characterized as increasing the efficiency of an organism in fight and flight, and the hormone itself has been termed an "emergency hormone" (Cannon). In the cardiovascular system it increases frequency and strength of the heart beat, and cardiac output, and causes a shift of blood from the skin and the gastrointestinal tract to the skeletal muscles. Other effects of adrenaline are piloerection, dilation of the bronchi and pupils, and relaxation of the gut.

Adrenaline acts as a general stimulant of metabolism; it increases the basal O_2 consumption (Ellis, 1956), mobilizes sugar from the liver and striated muscle, and raises the blood level of free fatty acids (Dole, 1956). Kayser (1939) has concluded that the arousal of hibernating animals is accompanied by a discharge of adrenaline from the adrenals.

Sutherland and Rall (1960) have observed that adrenaline and noradrenaline have equal potencies in stimulating the formation of a cyclic adenylate, $3',5'$-adenosinemonophosphate, which in its turn increases the concentration of phosphorylase in several organs, e.g., the heart, thereby increasing the force of contraction (Haugaard et al., 1959).

In the guinea pig, adrenaline causes a relaxation of the smooth muscle of the taenia coli, which is associated with hyperpolarization of the membrane and inhibition of spike activity (Bülbring, 1957). Adrenaline contraction of the muscularis mucosae of the dog esophagus, on the other hand, is accompanied by depolarization and initiation of spike activity (Burnstock, 1960).

In the nervous system adrenaline in higher doses causes blocking of synaptic transmission in sympathetic ganglia (Bülbring and Burn, 1942; Lundberg, 1952). The stimulating effect in the reticular system described by Bonvallet et al. (1954) may have great physiological significance in modifying the behavioral pattern in situations like fight or flight. Bradley and Mollica (1958) observed stimulation as well as inhibition in single neurons in the reticular system after adrenaline, and Skoglund (1961) found increased excitability of spinal interneurons in the cat with injections of noradrenaline.

It is well known that an injection of adrenaline in the human causes a feeling of uneasiness and apprehension which may reinforce feelings of fright, an effect which is presumably biologically important in inducing flight.

Noradrenaline seems to act chiefly on the cardiovascular system in such a way as to reinforce the effects of adrenergic nerve stimulation; i.e., in maintaining blood pressure homeostasis by stimulation of the heart and general vasoconstriction.

Metabolic actions are also exerted by noradrenaline; e.g., increase of metabolism (non-shivering heat) in cold-exposed rats (Hsieh and Carlson, 1957), increased metabolic rate in newborn kittens (Moore and Underwood, 1960), activation of phosphorylase in the liver and in the heart by stimulation of the formation of a cyclic nucleotide (Sutherland and Rall, 1958), and increase of free fatty acids in the plasma (Havel and Goldfien, 1959).

The action of noradrenaline on the peripheral nervous system is similar to that of adrenaline but weaker (Lundberg, 1952). The psychic effects of noradrenaline are insignificant.

In birds the actions of adrenaline and noradrenaline seem to be similar to those in mammals (Sturkie, 1954). The rectal caecum of the hen is relaxed by adrenaline in low concentrations (10^{-9} gm/ml). Noradrenaline is 10–100 times less active.

B. Poikilothermic Vertebrates

A large number of data on the action of catecholamines on various organs in lower animals is available in the reviews by Hanström (1939), Bacq (1946), Frédéricq (1947), Prosser et al. (1950), and Burn (1950).

In amphibia and reptiles the chromaffin cell hormones stimulate the heart and contract most vessels. In the isolated rectum of the toad *Bufo arenarum* Hensel, the interesting observation was made (Rapela, 1952) that adrenaline caused relaxation, but noradrenaline in small concentrations produces stimulation.

A number of studies have been made on the action of chromaffin cell hormones in fish. In teleosts and elasmobranchs adrenaline and noradrenaline stimulate the heart. In cyclostomes, on the other hand, this effect is very weak or absent (Fänge and Östlund, 1954), although it can be made to appear after pretreatment of an isolated heart with reserpine (Bloom et al., 1961).

The gut reacts differently in different kinds of fish; thus the effect of adrenaline or noradrenaline on an isolated piece of intestine from teleosts is inhibition whereas stimulation is seen in elasmobranchs (Dreyer, 1949; Euler and Östlund, 1957). The intestine of the cyclostome *Myxine glutinosa* reacts only weakly to the catecholamines, but relaxation is seen when adrenaline is added during contraction caused by acetylcholine (Fänge, 1948). The secretory mucosa of the swim bladder muscle of *Ctenolabrus rupestris* is contracted by adrenaline and noradrenaline but the resorbent mucosa is relaxed by the same drugs (Fänge, 1953).

Adrenaline (Spaeth and Barbour, 1917) and noradrenaline (Fänge, Euler and Östlund, unpublished data) have a very marked concentrating effect on the melanophores of some teleosts. This effect, like other effects of the catecholamines, can be blocked by phentolamine, phenoxybenzamine or yohimbine. On the other hand the dispersing effect of catecholamines on the melanophores of *Xenopus laevis* is not antagonized by dibenamine-like compounds, but is inhibited by dichloroisopropylnoradrenaline (Graham, 1961).

The relatively large quantities of catecholamines in the brain of elasmobranchs suggest a study of the central effects of these hormones in this vertebrate class.

C. Invertebrates

As stated in Section IV, catecholamines have been found in considerable amounts in annelids and in insects (Gaskell, 1912, 1919; Östlund, 1954) although their function so far is unknown. Chromaffin cells have been demonstrated in annelids, but it is not known with certainty whether they occur in insects. According to Cameron (1953) the corpus cardiacum of the cockroach *Periplaneta americana* contains a catechol-like substance which stimulates the heart of the same species.

The actions of catecholamines on isolated organs, especially heart and intestine, have been studied in a variety of invertebrates. Stimulating effects on the heart have been reported in annelids, molluscs, crustaceans, arthropods and tunicates (for references see Bacq, 1946; Frédéricq, 1947). On the other hand Gautrelet and Halpern (1935) found no stimulating effects of adrenaline on the heart of *Helix pomatia*, and Euler *et al.* (1952) observed no action of noradrenaline or adrenaline on the heart of *Aplysia*.

A stimulating action of adrenaline on the heart has been observed in *Corethra* larvae and in *Daphnia pulex* (Florey, 1951). Slight changes in heart frequency were observed in *Daphnia* with adrenaline and noradrenaline (Flückiger, 1953). The chromatophores of *Crangon vulgaris* expand after adrenaline and noradrenaline (Florey, 1951). Adrenaline as well as noradrenaline in low concentrations stimulate the isolated rectum of the river crayfish *Cambarus clarcii* Girard (Florey, 1954). Of particular interest are the recent findings of Gerschenfeld and Tauc (1961) that noradrenaline in concentrations of 10^{-b}, in contrast to acetylcholine, hyperpolarizes and inhibits the D-neurons of *Aplysia* ganglion cells, and activates the H-cells. Adrenaline has a similar action but is about 5 times less active than noradrenaline.

In view of these effects of adrenaline and noradrenaline it appears of great interest to ascertain the presence and the location of these hormones in invertebrates.

ACKNOWLEDGMENT

Part of the investigations mentioned in this review have been supported by the Office of Aerospace Research, U.S.A.F. through its European Office under contract AF 61(052)–309.

References

Abel, J. J. (1902). *Bull. Johns Hopkins Hosp.* **13**, 29–36.

Abel, J. J., and Geiling, E. M. K. (1899). *Z. f. physiol. Chem.* **28**, 318.

Armin, J., and Grant, R. T. (1959). *J. Physiol. (London)* **149**, 228–249.

Armstrong, M. D., McMillan, A., and Shaw, K. N. (1957). *Biochim. et Biophys. Acta* **25**, 422–423.

Augustinsson, K.-B., Fänge, R., Johnels, A., and Östlund, E. (1956). *J. Physiol. (London)* **131**, 257–276.

Axelrod, J. (1959). *Physiol. Revs.* **39**, 751–776.

Bachmann, R. (1954). *In* "Handbuch der mikroskopischen Anatomie des Menschen" (W. Bargmann, ed.), Vol. VI, Part 5. Springer, Berlin.

Bacq, Z. M. (1946). *Biol. Revs. Cambridge Phil. Soc.* **22**, 73.

Baecker, R. (1928). *Z. mikroskop.-anat. Forsch.* **15**, 204.

Bänder, A. (1951). *Anat. Anz. Suppl.* **97**, 172–176.

Bayer, G., and Wense, T. (1936). *Arch. ges. Physiol. Pflüger's* **237**, 651–654.

Bertler, Å. (1961). *Acta Physiol. Scand.* **51**, 75–83.

Bertler, Å., and Rosengren, E. (1959a). *Experientia* **15**, 10–11.

Bertler, Å., and Rosengren, E. (1959b). *Experientia* **15**, 382.

Bertler, Å., Carlsson, A., and Rosengren, E. (1958). *Acta Physiol. Scand.* **44**, 273–292.

Bertler, Å., Falck, B., Hillarp, N.-Å., Rosengren, E., and Torp, A. (1959). *Acta Physiol. Scand.* **47**, 251–258.

Bertler, Å., Hall, G., Hillarp, N.-Å., and Rosengren, E. (1961). *Acta Physiol. Scand.* **52**, 167–170.

Blaschko, H. (1939). *J. Physiol. (London)* **96**, 50P–51P.

Blaschko, H., and Welch, A. D. (1953). *Arch. exptl. Pathol. Pharmakol. Naunyn-Schmiedeberg's* **219**, 17–22.

Blaschko, H., Richter, D., and Schlossmann, H. (1937). *Biochem. J.* **31**, 2187–2196.

Bloom, G., Östlund, E., Euler, U. S. von., Lishajko, F., Ritzén, M., and Adams-Ray, J. (1961). *Acta Physiol. Scand.* **53**, Suppl. 185.

Bonvallet, M., Dell, P., and Hiebel, G. (1954). *Electroencephalog. and Clin. Neurophysiol.* **6**, 119–144.

Boyd, J. D. (1960). *Ciba Foundation Symposium on Adrenergic Mechanisms* pp. 63–82.

Bradley, P. B., and Mollica, A. (1958). *Arch. ital. biol.* **96**, 168.

Bülbring, E. (1957). *J. Physiol. (London)* **135**, 412–425.

Bülbring, E., and Burn, J. H. (1942). *J. Physiol.* (*London*) **101**, 289–303.

Burn, J. H. (1950). *Physiol. Revs.* **30**, 177–193.

Burn, J. H., and Rand, M. J. (1958). *J. Physiol.* (*London*) **144**, 314–336.

Burn, J. H., Langemann, H., and Parker, R. H. O. (1951). *J. Physiol.* (*London*) **113**, 123–128.

Burnstock, G. (1960). *Nature* **186**, 727–728.

Butterworth, K. R., and Mann, M. (1957). *J. Physiol.* (*London*) **136**, 294–299.

Bygdeman, S., Euler, U. S. von, and Hökfelt, B. (1960). *Acta Physiol. Scand.* **49**, 21–28.

Callingham, B. A., and Mann, M. (1958). *Nature* **181**, 423–424.

Camanni, F., Losana, O., and Molinatti, G. M. (1958). *Experientia* **14**, 199–201.

Cameron, M. L. (1953). *Nature* **172**, 349–350.

Carlsson, A. (1959). *Pharmacol. Revs.* **11**, 300–304.

Carlsson, A., and Hillarp, N.-Å. (1956). *Acta Physiol. Scand.* **37**, 235–239.

Carlsson, A., Hillarp, N.-Å., and Waldeck, B. (1962). *Med. Exptl.* **6**, 47–53.

Cohen, G., and Goldenberg, M. (1957). *J. Neurochem.* **2**, 71–80.

Collip, J. B. (1929). *Trans. Roy. Soc. Can. Sect. V* [3] **23**, 165–168.

Coupland, R. E., and Heath, I. D. (1961a). *J. Endocrinol.* **22**, 59–69.

Coupland, R. E., and Heath, I. D. (1961b). *J. Endocrinol.* **22**, 71–76.

Cramer, W. (1919). *Sci. Rept. Imp. Cancer Research Fund* **6**, 1–23.

Dole, V. P. (1956). *J. Clin. Invest.* **35**, 150.

Do Valle, J. R., and Porto, A. (1945). *Mem. inst. Butantan* (*São Paulo*) **18**, 247–250.

Dreyer, N. B. (1949). *Arch. intern. pharmacodynamie* **78**, 63–66.

Dunér, H. (1954). *Acta Physiol. Scand.* **32**, 63–68.

Eade, N. R. (1956). *J. Physiol.* (*London*) **132**, 53P–54P.

Ehrlén, I. (1948). *Farm. Rev.* **47**, 242–250.

Ellis, S. (1956). *Pharmacol. Revs.* **8**, 485–562.

Eränkö, O. (1955). *Acta Endocrinol.* **18**, 174–179.

Eränkö, O. (1957). *Nature* **179**, 417–418.

Eränkö, O. (1960). *Ciba Foundation Symposium on Adrenergic Mechanisms* pp. 103–108.

Eränkö, O., and Hopsu, V. (1958). *Endocrinology* **62**, 15–23.

Eränkö, O., Hopsu, V., and Räisänen, L. (1959). *Endocrinology* **65**, 293–297.

Euler, Chr. von, Euler, U. S. von, and Floding, I. (1955). *Acta Physiol. Scand.* **33**, Suppl. 118, 32–38.

Euler, U. S. von. (1934). *J. Physiol.* (*London*) **81**, 102–112.

Euler, U. S. von. (1946). *Acta Physiol. Scand.* **12**, 73–97.

Euler, U. S. von. (1949). *Acta Physiol. Scand.* **19**, 207–214.

Euler, U. S. von. (1953). *Acta Physiol. Scand.* **28**, 297–305.

Euler, U. S. von. (1956). "Noradrenaline." C. C Thomas, Springfield, Illinois.

Euler, U. S. von. (1961). *Nature* **190**, 170–171.

Euler, U. S. von, and Fänge, R. (1961). *Gen. Comp. Endocrinol.* **1**, 191–194.

Euler, U. S. von, and Hamberg, U. (1949a). *Acta Physiol. Scand.* **19**, 74–84.

Euler, U. S. von, and Hamberg, U. (1949b). *Nature* **163**, 642–643.

Euler, U. S. von, and Hammarström, S. (1937). *Skand. Arch. Physiol.* **77**, 163–178.

Euler, U. S. von, and Hökfelt, B. (1953). *Brit. J. Pharmacol.* **8**, 66–68.

Euler, U. S. von, and Lishajko, F. (1957). *Acta Physiol. et Pharmacol. Neerl.* **6**, 295–303.

Euler, U. S. von, and Lishajko, F. (1961a). *Acta Physiol. Scand.* **51**, 348–355.

Euler, U. S. von, and Lishajko, F. (1961b). *Acta Physiol. Scand.* **52**, 137–145.

Euler, U. S. von, and Luft, R. (1952). *Metabolism Clin. and Exptl.* **1**, 528–532.

Euler, U. S. von, and Östlund, E. (1957). *Acta Physiol. Scand.* **38**, 364–372.

Euler, U. S. von, and Purkhold, A. (1951). *Acta Physiol. Scand.* **24**, 212–217.

Euler, U. S. von, Hamberg, U., and Hellner, S. (1951). *Biochem. J.* **49**, 655–658.

Euler, U. S. von, Chaves, N., and Teodosio, N. (1952). *Acta Physiol. Latinoam.* **2**, 101–106.

Euler, U. S. von, Franksson, C., and Hellström, J. (1954). *Acta Physiol. Scand.* **31**, 6–8.

Euler, U. S. von, Ikkos, D., and Luft, R. (1961). *Acta Endocrinol.* **38**, 441–448.

Falck, B., Hillarp, N.-Å., and Torp, A. (1959). *J. Histochem. and Cytochem.* **7**, 323–328.

Fänge, R. (1948). *Arkiv. Zool.* **40A** nr. 11, 1–9.

Fänge, R. (1953). *Acta Physiol. Scand.* **30**, Suppl. 110.

Fänge, R., and Östlund, E. (1954). *Acta Zool. (Stockholm)* **35**, 289–305.

Fänge, R., Östlund, E., and Euler, U. S. von. To be published.

Fleckenstein, A., and Stöckle, D. (1955). *Arch. exptl. Pathol. Pharmakol. Naunyn-Schmiedeberg's* **224**, 401–415.

Florey, E. (1951). *Verhandl. deut. Zool. Ges. Wilhelmshaven* pp. 199–206.

Florey, E. (1954). *Z. vergleich. Physiol.* **36**, 1–8.

Flückiger, E. (1953). *Acta Physiol. Scand.* **27**, 206–216.

Folkow, B., and Euler, U. S. von. (1954). *Circulation Research* **2**, 191–195.

Frédéricq, H. (1947). *Biol. Revs. Cambridge Phil. Soc.* **22**, 297–314.

Gaskell, J. F. (1912). *J. Physiol. (London)* **44**, 59–67.

Gaskell, J. F. (1919). *J. Gen. Physiol.* **2**, 73–85.

Gautrelet, J., and Halpern, N. (1935). *Compt. rend. soc. biol.* **118**, 412–414.

Gérard, P., Cordier, R., and Lison, L. (1930). *Bull. histol. appl. physiol. et pathol. et tech. microscop.* **7**, 133.

Gerschenfeld, H., and Tauc, L. (1961). *Nature* **189**, 924–925.

Giacomini, E. (1906). *Atti accad. nazl. Lincei Rend., Classe sci. fis. mat. e. nat.* **15**, 394.

Goldstein, M., Friedhoff, A. J., Simmons, C., and Prochoroff, N. N. (1959). *Experientia* **15**, 254–256.

Goodall, McC. (1951). *Acta Physiol. Scand.* **24**, Suppl. 85.

Graham, J. D. P. (1961). *J. Physiol. (London)* **158**, 5P–6P.

Hagen, P. (1959). *Pharmacol. Revs.* **11**, 361.

Hanström, B. (1939). "Hormones in Invertebrates." Oxford Univ. Press (Clarendon), London and New York.

Hartman, F. A., and Brownell, K. A. (1949). "The Adrenal Gland." Lea & Febiger, Philadelphia, Pennsylvania.

Haugaard, N., Hess, M. E., Kukovetz, W. R., and Shanfeld, J. (1959). *Pharmacologist* **1**, 62.

Havel, R. J., and Goldfien, A. (1959). *J. Lipid Research* **1**, 102–108.

Henle, J. (1865). *Z. rationelle Med.* **24**, 143.

Hillarp, N.-Å. (1960). Proc. First Intern. Congr. Endocrinol., Copenhagen.

Hillarp, N.-Å., and Hökfelt, B. (1953). *Acta Physiol. Scand.* **30**, 55–68.

Hillarp, N.-Å., and Nilson, B. (1954). *Acta Physiol. Scand.* **31**, Suppl. 113, 79–107.

Hillarp, N.-Å., and Thieme, G. (1959). *Acta Physiol. Scand.* **45**, 328–338.

Hillarp, N.-Å., Lagerstedt, S., and Nilson, B. (1953). *Acta Physiol. Scand.* **29**, 251–263.

Hillarp, N.-Å., Högberg, B., and Nilson, B. (1955). *Nature* **176**, 1032–1033.

Hökfelt, B., and McLean, J. (1950). *Acta Physiol. Scand.* **21**, 258–270.

Holland, W. C., and Schümann, H. J. (1956). *Brit. J. Pharmacol.* **11**, 449–453.

Holmes, W. (1950). *Proc. Roy. Soc.* **B137**, 549–562.

Holton, P. (1949). *J. Physiol.* (*London*) **108**, 525–529.

Holtz, P. (1939). *Naturwissenschaften* **27**, 724.

Holtz, P., Credner, K., and Kroneberg, G. (1947). *Arch. exptl. Pathol. Pharmakol. Naunyn-Schmiedeberg's* **204**, 228–243.

Houssay, B. A., Gerschman, R., and Rapela, C. E. (1950). *Rev. soc. arg. biol.* **24**, 29–38.

Hsieh, A. C. L., and Carlson, L. D. (1957). *Am. J. Physiol.* **190**, 243–246.

Johnels, A. G., and Palmgren, A. (1960). *Acta Zool.* (*Stockholm*) **41**, 313.

Jones, I. C. (1957). *In* "The Adrenal Cortex," pp. 131–141. Cambridge Univ. Press, London and New York.

Kayser, Ch. (1939). *Ann. physiol. physicochim. biol.* **15**, 1087–1219.

Kayser, Ch. (1961). "The Physiology of Natural Hibernation." Pergamon Press, New York.

Kirshner, N. (1962). *J. Biol. Chem.* **237**, 2311–2317.

Kracht, J., and Klein, U. (1957). *Verhandl. deut. Ges. Pathol. Bad Nauheim* pp. 171–176.

Kuntzman, R., Shore, P. A., Bogdanski, D., and Brodie, B. B. (1961). *J. Neurochem.* **6**, 226–232.

Leduc, J. (1961). *Acta Physiol. Scand.* **53**, Suppl. 183.

Lever, J. D., Lewis, P. R., and Boyd, J. D. (1959). *J. Anat.* **93**, 478.

Lison, L. (1932). *Arch. soc. sci. med. biol. Montpellier et Languedoc* **13**, 542.

Lison, L. (1953). "Histochimie et Cytochimie Animales." Gautier-Villars, Paris.

Loew, O. (1918). *Biochem. Z.* **85**, 295–306.

Loewi, O. (1936). *Arch. ges. Physiol. Pflüger's* **237**, 504–514.

Lund, A. (1949). *Acta Pharmacol. et Toxicol.* **5**, 121–128.

Lundberg, A. (1952). *Acta Physiol. Scand.* **26**, 252–263.

Malméjac, J. (1959). *Intern. Congr. Physiol. Sci., 21st Buenos Aires, 1959, Symposia Spec. Lectures.*

Montagu, K. A. (1957). *Nature* **180**, 244–245.

Moore, R. E., and Underwood, M. C. (1960). *J. Physiol.* (*London*) **152**, 52P.

Muscholl, E., and Vogt, M. (1958). *J. Physiol.* (*London*) **141**, 132–155.

Muscholl, E., Rahn, K.-H., and Watzka, M. (1960). *Naturwissenschaften* **14**, 325.

Nandi, J. (1961). *Science* **134**, 389–390.

Natelson, S., Lugovoy, J. K., and Pincus, J. B. (1949). *Arch. Biochem.* **23**, 157–158.

Oliver, G., and Schäfer, E. A. (1895). *J. Physiol. (London)* **18**, 230–276.

Olivereau, M. (1959). *Ann. endocrinol. (Paris)* **20**, 645–653.

Östlund, E. (1954). *Acta Physiol. Scand.* **31**, Suppl. 112.

Ozaki, T. (1954). *Tohoku J. Exptl. Med.* **61**, 83–92.

Ozaki, T. (1955). *Tohoku J. Exptl. Med.* **61**, 345–352.

Paasonen, M. K., and Krayer, O. (1959). *Experientia* **15**, 75.

Pearse, A. G. E. (1960). "Histochemistry," 2nd ed. Churchill, London.

Pekkarinen, A., Castrén, O., Tisalo, G., Koivusalo, M., Laihinen, A., Simola, P. E., and Thomasson, B. (1961). *In* "Biochemistry, Pharmacology and Physiology," pp. 117–137. Pergamon Press, New York.

Poll, H. (1906). *In* "Handbuch d. verg. u. exp. Entwicklungslehre der Wirbeltiere" (O. Hertwig, ed.), Vol. 3. Jena: Fischer.

Price, H. L., and Price, M. L. (1957). *J. Lab. Clin. Med.* **50**, 769–777.

Prosser, C. L., Bishop, D. W., Brown, F. A., Jahn, T. L., and Wulf, V. J. (1950). "Comparative Animal Physiology," Saunders, Philadelphia, Pennsylvania.

Rapela, C. E. (1952). *Rev. soc. arg. biol.* **27**, 260–262.

Rastgeldi, S. (1951). *Acta Physiol. Scand.* **23**, 44–46.

Richter, D. (1940). *J. Physiol. (London)* **98**, 361–374.

Roaf, H. E. (1911). *Quart. J. Exptl. Physiol.* **4**, 89–92.

Roaf, H. E., and Nierenstein, M. J. (1907). *J. Physiol. (London)* **36**, v–viii.

Sack, H., and Koll, J. F. (1959). *Deut. med. Wochschr.* **84**, 733–741.

Sataké, Y. (1954). *Tohoku J. Exptl. Med.* **60**, Suppl. II.

Scharrer, E., and Brown, S. (1961). *F. Fellforsch. u. mikroskop. Anat.* **54**, 530–540.

Schild, H. (1933). *J. Physiol. (London)* **79**, 455–469.

Schkawera, G. L., and Kusnetzow, A. I. (1923). *Z. ges. exptl. Med.* **38**, 37–66.

Schmiterlöw, C. G. (1948). *Acta Physiol. Scand.* **16**, Suppl. 56.

Schümann, H. J. (1956). *Arch. exptl. Pathol. Pharmakol. Naunyn-Schmiedeberg's* **227**, 566–573.

Schümann, H. J. (1957). *J. Physiol. (London)* **137**, 318–326.

Schümann, H. J. (1960). *Klin. Wochschr.* **38**, 11–13.

Shepherd, D. M., and West, G. B. (1953). *J. Physiol. (London)* **120**, 15–19.

Shepherd, D. M., West, G. B., and Erspamer, V. (1953). *Nature* **172**, 509.

Sjöstrand, N. (1962). *Acta Physiol. Scand.* **56**, 376.

Skoglund, C. R. (1961). *Acta Physiol. Scand.* **51**, 142–149.

Spaeth, R. A., and Barbour, H. G. (1917). *J. Pharmacol. Exptl. Therap.* **9**, 431–440.

Stilling, H. (1898). *Arch. mikroskop. Anat. u. Entwicklungsmech.* **52**, 176–195.

Stolz, F. (1904). *Ber. deut. chem. Ges.* **37**, 4149–4154.

Strömblad, B. C. R. (1960). *Experientia* **16**, 417–418.

Sturkie, P. D. (1954). "Avian Physiology," p. 53. Cornell Univ. Press (Comstock), Ithaca, New York.

Sundin, T. (1958). *Acta Med. Scand.* **161**, Suppl. 336.

Sutherland, E. W., and Rall, T. W. (1958). *J. Biol. Chem.* **232**, 1077.

Sutherland, E. W., and Rall, T. W. (1960). *Ciba Foundation Symposium on Adrenergic Mechanisms* pp. 295–304.

290   U. S. VON EULER

Takamine, J. (1901). *Am. J. Physiol.* **73**, 523.

Uuspää, V. J., and Suomalainen, P. (1954). Ann. Acad. Scientiarum Fennicae, Serie A. IV. 1–11.

van Overbeeke, A. P. (1960). "Histological Studies on the Interrenal and the Phaochromic Tissue in Teleostei," Van Munster, Amsterdam.

Verne, J. (1922). *Bull. soc. chim. biol.* **5**, 227.

Vogt, M. (1952). *Brit. J. Pharmacol.* **7**, 325–330.

Vulpian, A. (1856). *Compt. rend. acad. sci.* **43**, 663–665.

Weil-Malherbe, H. (1960). *Ciba Foundation Symposium on Adrenergic Mechanisms* 544–548.

Weil-Malherbe, H., and Bone, A. D. (1954). *Biochem. J.* **58**, 132–141.

West, G. B. (1953). *J. Pharm. (Lond.)* **7**, 460–464.

West, G. B. (1955). *Quart. Rev. Biol.* **30**, 116–137.

West, G. B., Shepherd, D. M., Hunter, R. B., and Macgregor, A. R. (1953). *Clin. Sci.* **12**, 317–325.

Wright, A., and Chester Jones, I. (1955). *Nature* **155**, 1001–1002.

Thyroid Hormones

A. GORBMAN

Barnard College, Columbia University, New York, New York

I. GENERAL INTRODUCTION

The subject of this chapter can be divided into three major topics: thyroid functional morphology, thyroid hormone biosynthesis and its control, and action of the thyroid hormones. As in many active fields of biology, the accumulation of information concerning these three aspects of thyroid comparative physiology has been rapid, broad, and complex, ranging from such apparent extremes as natural history to the biochemistry of cellular organelles. Accordingly, it is today no longer possible, within the assigned limits of length of this chapter, to be encyclopedic. This discussion is admittedly selective and oriented. The orientation will be revealed in the next few paragraphs where an attempt is made to summarize the details to be presented in the body of the chapter.

The basic histological unit of the thyroid gland in all adult vertebrates is the thyroid follicle. This is a spheroid structure whose wall is made up of a single layer of lining cells and whose center is filled with a viscous fluid, the colloid. There is no important difference in the thyroid follicles of the entire vertebrate group. Thus, the comparative anatomy of the thyroid gland is merely a review of the various shapes into which the follicles are grouped. For the physiologist it is important to know that recent evidence shows that most of the actual synthesis of thyroid hormones is in the colloid (Nadler, 1960; Nadler et al., 1960), hence it is extracellular. Furthermore, the hormone is retained in the colloid in the molecule of a large protein, thyroglobulin; the thyroid is the only endocrine organ which stores its product in an extracellular site. Such a mode of hormone formation and storage imposes a further characteristic upon the thyroid secretory cycle. To release the hormone from its protein bondage an enzymatic hydrolysis system also is secreted into the colloid. Regulation of the concentration of this protease, it may be appreciated, is one of the controls over the rate of diffusion (secretion) of hormone from the follicle.

The thyroid hormone is the only one whose specific molecular features include possession of a specific chemical element, in this case iodine. It is now well known that iodine incubated with various proteins will add to the tyrosine residues in those proteins forming mono- and diiodotyrosine (Ludwig and v. Mutzenbecher, 1939; Reineke, 1949). Further, the iodotyrosines will couple to form thyroxine and triiodothyronine even in the absence of enzymes. Iodoproteins in many invertebrate groups have been known almost from the time that iodine first was discovered by Courtois in 1811. This general distribution of iodoproteins (hence iodotyrosines and, in some instances, thyroid hormone itself) in animals and plants may reflect the ease of formation of such compounds in nature, particularly in the iodine-rich marine environment. Thus, the thyroid hormone in the evolutionary scheme preceded the thyroid gland of vertebrates. Viewed in the light of this information, synthesis of thyroxine by the thyroid gland does not seem to be a highly unusual or even specific property. The special contribution of the gland appears to be the concentration of iodine by secreting it into the follicle for efficient and rapid iodoprotein (thyroglobulin) formation. Control and regulation of rates of hormone formation, storage, and release is at least in part a function of the neuroendocrine hypothalamo-hypophyseal system.

Although the secretory unit (follicle) and the hormones formed (thyroxine and triiodothyronine) are the same for all vertebrates, greater differences exist among species in the uses to which these items are put. The best known function of thyroxine, its stimulation of respiratory metabolism in warm-blooded animals, is difficult to demonstrate consistently in cold-blooded species. The best known action of thyroxine in Amphibia is its climactic acceleration of later development (metamorphosis). In other immature and embryonic vertebrates thyroxine does not have the same striking effect, although it has a generalized maturational action upon the integumentary, skeletal, and nervous systems. In all vertebrate groups one of the most basic actions of thyroxine is the stimulation of various aspects of nervous function.

The actions of thyroxine, both metabolic and morphological, are so numerous that they cannot be further summarized or categorized in paragraph form. The wide spectrum of actions of thyroid hormone suggests that it must affect cellular metabolism at some fundamental point that can contribute energy in many directions. Study of this question has not progressed very far, but it does show that certain phosphorylation mechanisms may be regulated by thyroid hormones.

Metabolism of iodine is the most characteristic thyroid function. However, the transport and accumulation of iodine and its incorporation into organic forms are by no means unique functions of the thyroid. The thyroid follicular epithelium is only one of a number of tissues with the ability to transport iodide and other halides. This group of tissues includes the salivary glands, chloride cells of the gill (fishes), gastric mucosa, intestinal mucosa, kidney tubule, and mammary gland. In addition, the notochord of the lamprey accumulates iodide energetically (Leloup, 1952a) by a mechanism which has not been characterized. Cellular transport of halides by certain marine algae is well known, and cytoplasmic accumulation of radioactive labeled iodide has been demonstrated (Kelley and Bailey, 1951; Roche and Yagi, 1952; Shaw, 1960).

Iodine metabolism in the mammalian thyroid has been studied most thoroughly, and the rat in particular has been observed in this respect. An immense literature exists in which the metabolic fate of inorganic radioiodide is described in minute detail, and it has been summarized in many reviews and books (Roche and Michel, 1955; Pitt-Rivers and Tata, 1959). To compare the well-known mechanisms of mammalian iodine metabolism with the less well-known mechanisms in nonmammals, it is useful to characterize briefly the typical situation in mammals.

II. IODINE METABOLISM IN MAMMALS

Iodine which enters the animal through the digestive tract is quickly taken up by the thyroid gland. If radioiodine is used as a marker of the iodine of a particular time, then measurements of thyroid radioactivity may be seen to rise to a maximum, and then to decline. Since these gross changes in thyroid radioactivity are easily measured, they have been used with more or less scientific justification, as indices of the state of thyroid activity, or of the stimulation or depression of thyroid activity by changes in pituitary TSH secretion. Difficulties in the interpretation of thyroid

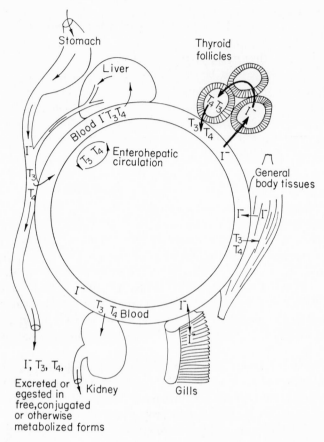

Fig. 1. Schema of iodine metabolism and distribution of iodine compounds in the organism. Symbols: I⁻, iodide; T₃, triiodothyronine; T₄, thyroxine.

radioactivity measurements are inherent in the fact that these measurements reflect a dynamic condition in which the thyroid gland is not the sole participant (Fig. 1). Thus, the rate of entry of radioiodine depends not only on the rate of iodide transport by the thyroid epithelium, but also on the rate of iodide absorption from the skin, intestine, or gills, and the rate of its excretion from the kidney, skin, or gills. The largest fraction of a given dose of radioiodine which may be found eventually in the thyroid (the maximum uptake) is determined not only by these same factors, but also by the rate of conversion of the iodide into organic, hormonal form. Another variable which affects the maximum uptake is the amount of stable iodine in the diet or in the environment (Perlman et al., 1941). If the environmental source of iodine is abundant, then only a small proportion of that which is available can be utilized by the thyroid. The radioiodine which is diluted in the large pool of stable iodine (i.e., present in low specific activity) is then taken up in a correspondingly small proportion, and low maximal uptakes are found. On the other hand, if the labeled radioiodine is administered when the animal's sources of iodine are meager, and the gland is "iodine hungry," then a large proportion of the radioiodine is taken up by the thyroid. For reasons such as this it is difficult to compare the levels of thyroid activity of animals living in environments which offer different iodine supplies. Finally, the rate of loss of radioactivity from the thyroid has been taken to represent the rate of release of the synthesized hormone. However, at any one time iodine enters as well as leaves the thyroid. Hence, hormonal secretion rate is probably higher than the observed rate of loss of radioactivity indicates, but the corrected rate is difficult to determine.

In general, after giving radioiodine to a mammal, a peak of radioactivity is reached in the thyroid in 12–24 hours. The maximum uptake, as indicated before, depends upon the dietary stable iodine level. In man maximum thyroid uptake values ordinarily are near 50–60%. In mice fed ordinary laboratory diets the maximum uptake is usually below 10% of the administered dose of I^{131}. In other mammals widely varying maxima have been reported, but usually they fall between these values (Kelsey *et al.*, 1960).

Chemical and radioautographic analysis of the thyroid during the period of accumulating radioactivity shows that iodoprotein (thyroglobulin) is formed quickly (Wollman and Wodinsky, 1955). In the early phases of thyroglobulin formation the largest proportion of labeled iodine is in the form of the iodotyrosines, monoiodotyrosine (MIT) and diiodotyrosine (DIT) (see review by Söderberg, 1959). In later phases of thyroglobulin formation the originally small proportion of thyroxine and triiodothyronine increases at the expense of the iodotyrosines. Wolff and Chaikoff have reported (1947) that in a number of mammalian species (guinea pig, rabbit, dog, rat, horse, cow, and sheep) and in sharks, turtles, chickens, and turkeys the final (equilibrium) proportion of thyroxine in the thyroid is about 30% (of all iodine-containing compounds).

Two classes of "antithyroid drugs" have been found to inhibit thyroid hormone formation (many reviews, see especially Pitt-Rivers and Tata, 1959). One group includes such ions as thiocyanate, nitrite, and perchlorate and appears to act by poisoning or immobilizing the iodide transport mechanism. Administering such substances not only prevents accumulation of iodide, but also causes discharge of that which is already present. The second class of antithyroid drugs includes thiourea, thiouracil, and their substituted derivatives, as well as some other sulfur-containing compounds.

These permit iodide accumulation but block formation of organic compounds. It has been thought that they prevent oxidation of iodide, and the immediately subsequent iodination of thyroid proteins. However, considerable amounts of MIT may form (Slingerland *et al.*, 1959) in the presence of thiouracil, so that a block in iodine metabolism between MIT and DIT is at least partly involved in the action of these substances.

Since thyroid hormones probably are formed while attached to a very large protein molecule, they remain undiffusable, trapped within the follicular membrane until the protein is hydrolyzed. Several proteolytic enzymes have been separated from the thyroid, or from crude thyroglobulin preparations; the one first demonstrated by De Robertis (1943) in the colloid of the mammalian thyroid has an optimal pH near 4.0 and falls into the catheptase class Thyroglobulin is never found normally in the blood, and when the protein is injected, or when the thyroid follicle is injured by disease or radiation, permitting some thyroglobulin to escape, it appears to be autoantigenic (Lilien, 1954; Rose and Witebsky, 1956).

Whereas the hormones are free to diffuse from the thyroid after hydrolysis of the thyroglobulin, the "immature forms" of the hormones, the iodotyrosines which are released at the same time, are destroyed specifically by a dehalogenating enzyme (Roche *et al.*, 1952).

In the blood the thyroid hormones circulate loosely bound to proteins. The strength of this binding determines in part the rate of diffusion of the hormones into the tissues (Robbins and Rall, 1960). Triiodothyronine in mammalian blood appears to be much more readily diffusible into the tissues than thyroxine.

In the tissues the hormones are subject to the action of dehalogenating and deaminating systems. It is not known, unfortunately, in which form the thyroid hormones are actually metabolically active in the responsive cells. The liver withdraws thyroid hormone from the blood and secretes it into the bile, partly in conjugation with glucuronic acid. Some of the hormone so secreted is reabsorbed from the intestine. This event of secretion and reabsorption is known as the enterohepatic circulation (Fig. 1).

Principal control over thyroid hormone formation depends upon thyrotropic hormone (TSH) output of the adenohypophysis. The relation between pituitary and thyroid function was first shown by P. E. Smith (1916) and Allen (1916) in hypophysectomized frog tadpoles. The relations of TSH to particular phases of mammalian thyroid function have been analyzed, and the following have been found to be stimulated by the hypophyseal factor: (a) rate of growth of the whole organ, (b) growth of individual follicle cells, (c) transport of iodide, (d) rate of thyroid hormone formation, (e) rate of release of the hormone, (f) concentration of the proteolytic enzyme(s), and (g) concentration of the dehalogenating enzyme.

A very low level of thyroid function persists after hypophysectomy (D'Angelo, 1955; Albert and Lorenz, 1951; Roche *et al.*, 1953a) and, indeed, thyroid slices *in vitro* can synthesize some thyroxine and triiodothyronine (Morton and Chaikoff, 1943). However, maintenance of a normal rate of thyroxinogenesis requires TSH stimulation. The interesting question of control over TSH secretion is still being explored. However, it is clear that to a large extent TSH secretion is regulated by nervous and neurosecretory mechanisms mediated through the hypothalamus (Harris, 1959; Knigge, 1960). It is through neuroendocrine mechanisms like this that the thyroid takes part in thermoregulatory responses (Knigge, 1960). It is well known, for example, that significant reduction of the normal environmental temperature of rats, rabbits, and other mammals, leads to stimulation of the thyroid. However, this response is blocked if lesions are made in the parts of the hypothalamus known to affect TSH secretion (Harris, 1959.)

III. THYROID FUNCTION IN NONMAMMALS

A. Birds

Surprisingly little study has been made of avian thyroid function despite the great interest in the use of the chick thyroid for the bioassay of TSH (Smelser, 1938). It is difficult to understand why animals as genetically uniform as inbred strains of chicks, even when of the same age and sex, should be so variable with respect to thyroid function. When used for the bioassay of TSH, the effect upon thyroid weight or histological features is commonly measured; the rate of loss of a tracer dose of I^{131} (Piotrowski *et al.*, 1953; Bates and Cornfield, 1957; Frey and Albert, 1959) has also been found to be a good index of TSH action. Thyroidal accumulation of I^{131} is rapid, a peak being reached before 6 hours after giving the tracer. The height of this peak has been variously reported to be between 5 and 60%. Some of this variability in the chick thyroid is seasonal (Piotrowski *et al.*, 1953). However, there are many possibilities, mostly untested, which might explain the differences between the results of different investigators or of the same investigators at different times: (a) differences in the hen's or chick's diet (particularly its iodine content), (b) degree of yolk resorption in young chicks, (c) differences in temperature experiences of the birds, (d) genetic stock. Roche and Desruisseaux (1951) and Roche *et al.* (1951) have shown that the laying hen concentrates iodine in the ovarian egg and that this iodine, partly organic and partly inorganic, is thereby transferred to the developing chick. At any rate, thyroidal iodine uptake in chicks is readily altered by changes in dietary iodine content (Kobayashi and Gorbman, 1960).

The iodotyrosines and iodothyronines formed by the chick and chicken and duck thyroids are the same as in mammals (Taurog *et al.*, 1950; Vlijm, 1958; Kobayashi and Gorbman, 1960; Tixier-Vidal and Assenmacher, 1960). In one respect thyroid hormone formation differs slightly in these birds from that in mammals; the proportion of MIT to DIT is unusually high (Taurog *et al.*, 1950; Vlijm, 1958). However, in tests made in different seasons Kobayashi and Gorbman found a variable MIT/DIT ratio in chick thyroids. Another interesting feature of thyroxinogenesis in chicks is that thiouracil blocks the process between the MIT and DIT step (Kobayashi and Gorbman, 1960). Most authors report that the thiouracil block in mammalian thyroids is between iodide and MIT (i.e., no organic compounds are formed). However in the previously mentioned work of Slingerland *et al.* (1959), it was shown that under stated circumstances goitrogens can block hormone synthesis in the rat thyroid between MIT and DIT. Iino (1960) has shed more light upon this interesting question by incubating rat thyroid *in vitro* with various concentrations of goitrogens. He found that the MIT–DIT step is inhibited at lower concentrations of goitrogen; at higher concentrations not even MIT is formed. Hence, it may be that thyroid hormone formation differs in no important way between domestic fowl and mammals.

The only nonmammalian thyroglobulin which has been isolated in a form pure enough for further study is that of the chicken. Hektoen *et al.* (1927) found that an antiserum prepared against chicken thyroglobulin does not cross-react with any of a variety of mammalian thyroglobulins. Numerous immunologic studies of mammalian thyroglobulin antibodies have shown that they cross-react to some degree with thyroglobulins from any other mammal (ungulate, rodent, primate) (Stokinger and Heidelberger, 1937; Witebsky, 1929; Rose and Witebsky, 1956).

Many studies of seasonal morphological changes of the thyroids of wild birds have shown that there is an annual cycle (Küchler, 1935; Elterich, 1936; Miller, 1939; Oakeson and Lilley, 1957). Generally, maxima in thyroid activity coincide with breeding activity and with the colder seasons. On the basis of experiments with caged migratory birds Merkel (1938) concluded that thyroid hormone is involved in stimulating a behavioral change, premigratory restlessness, or *Zugunruhe*. If it is indeed so, then it is important to know more about the seasonal variations in thyroid function in wild, particularly migratory birds. Unfortunately, there is but little such information available. Fink (1957) injected white-crowned sparrows (*Zonotrichia leucophrys pugetensis* and *Zonotrichia leucophrys gambelii*) and brown towhees (*Pipilio fuscus*) with radioiodine and found that a peak of thyroidal uptake occurred 15–17 hours afterwards. However, in all other avian species tested the maximal thyroid uptake has been found to be within 6 hours after I^{131} injection (Kobayashi and Tanabe, 1959; Kobayashi et al., 1960). The species so tested include (aside from chicks, cited above) bengalees (Uroloncha domestica), white-throated sparrows (Zonotrichia albicollis), and African weaver finches (Euplectes afer taha). The most remarkable feature of thyroidal I^{131} uptake aside from its rapidity is its intensity which amounts to between 60% and 80% of the injected dose. In the bengalees, addition of 200 μg of KI per 100 gm of diet reduced the mean 4-hour thyroid I^{131} uptake from 82% to 25%. On the other hand, adding 10 μg of KI per 100 gm to the diet of weaver finches did not significantly reduce the maximum uptake, but delayed attainment of the maximum (30 hours instead of 6 hours). However, thyroxine treatment reduced the thyroid I^{131} uptake to about 0.5%. Kobayashi et al. (1960) also found in the weaver finch seasonal variation in the maximum proportion of labeled thyroxine formed. In May (autumn for this species) only 2.4% of the thyroidal I^{131} was in the form of thyroxine. Such studies suggest interesting differences between avian thyroxinogenesis and that of other vertebrates, but a series of careful studies is needed for real understanding of the relation between thyroid function and seasonal events like breeding and migration.

In summary, the most unusual features of thyroid function in wild birds appear to be: (1) a rapid and strong uptake of tracer iodine, (2) a relatively slow release of this iodine, (3) a relatively low rate of conversion of I^{131} to labeled thyroxine, and (4) a high degree of responsiveness of the thyroid mechanism to additional circulating thyroxine.

B. Reptiles

As in most physiological comparisons among vertebrates, the least can be said about reptilian thyroid function. It has been shown that the reptile thyroid gland contains a substance similar to thyroxine (Wolff, and Chaikoff, 1947), and that it responds morphologically in a typical way to thiouracil and to TSH (Ratzersdorfer et al., 1949; Adams and Craig, 1951; Hellbaum, 1936; Evans and Hegre, 1940). Tests with radiodiodine have shown that maximum thyroidal uptake is relatively low, usually less than 10%, and that thyroidal radioactivity decreases very slowly (Shellabarger et al., 1956; Kobayashi and Gorbman, 1959). An interesting phenomenon was discovered in the turtle by Shellabarger et al. (1956). When kept away from water, they retain urine in the bladder and reabsorb excreted I^{131}. Over a period of eight days such reabsorbed radioiodine accumulates progressively in the thyroid until about 70%–80% is found there. In lizards (Kobayashi and Gorbman, 1959) this response to dehydration does not occur.

Another remarkable aspect of thyroid function in adult reptiles is the slowness of thyroxine production, as revealed by tracer experiments. In such tests (Shellabarger et al., 1956; Kobayashi and Gorbman, 1959) about 8–10 days after I^{131} administration usually less than 10% of the small fraction of I^{131} in the thyroid was in the form of thyroxine.

C. Amphibians

Although thyroid function in the Amphibia has been most intensively investigated, particularly with respect to its role in metamorphosis, until recently the amphibian thyroid hormones remained unidentified. In the toad *Bufo arenarum*, Donoso and Trivelloni (1958) found a maximum of 9.3% of an administered dose of radioiodine in the thyroid 72 hours after injection. Although it is relatively low, this is the most active thyroidal I^{131} accumulation that has been reported in any amphibian with the exception of tadpoles in the crisis of metamorphosis. Donoso and Trivelloni found that pituitary injections increased the uptake to 56% and hypophysectomy reduced it to 4%. Isotope-labeled thyroxine was produced in a proportion comparable to other vertebrate thyroids. Twenty-four hours after giving the radioiodine, 17% of it was in the form of thyroxine. For comparison it may be mentioned that most anuran tadpole thyroids (*Rana pipiens, R. clamitans, Xenopus laevis*) take up a very small proportion of injected tracer iodine, about 1–2% (Saxen et al., 1957; Kaye and LeBourhis, 1958; Kaye, 1961). However, at the height of metamorphosis this figure rises above 50% and then falls again. Berg et al. (1959) have reported that thyroids of both larval and adult leopard frogs (*Rana pipens*) form triiodothyronine as well as thyroxine. The same has been found in adult toads by Shellabarger and Brown (1959). Dundee and Gorbman (1960) have studied the fate of radioiodine in the thyroid of a neotenous salamander, *Eurycea tynerensis*. In this species radioiodine accumulation is very slight (maximum is about 2% of the injected dose of I^{131}) and very slow. Isotope-labeled thyroxine did not appear for several days. Kobayashi and Gorbman (unpublished) made a similar study of another species, *Amphiuma means*, which according to G. K. Noble, represents a "partly metamorphosed" type. Like *Eurycea*, the thyroid of *Amphiuma* takes up very little radioiodine. The only detectable radioactive thyroxine appeared 96 hours after the I^{131} was given, and at that time it accounted for only 1.4% of the small amount of radioiodine in the thyroid. It would be reasonable to question whether thyroxine produced so slowly, and in such slight proportion, can play an important physiological role in these amphibians. On the other hand, at least in *Amphiuma*, the lack of thyroxine cannot be held responsible for the failure of metamorphosis. Kobayashi and Gorbman found that the only visible effect of extremely large doses (more than 5 mg) of thyroxine was a slight stimulation of shedding of epidermis.

In several of the studies mentioned above, thyroidal iodine metabolism was found to be influenced by hypophyseal TSH (e.g., Donoso and Trivelloni, 1958; Kaye, 1961). Furthermore, when thyroxine or thyroxine analogs are given to larval or adult amphibians, thyroidal uptake of radioiodine is greatly reduced (Money et al., 1958; Kaye, 1961; Kobayashi and Gorbman, unpublished). This suggests that TSH is normally secreted in these animals, and that a thyroxine-sensitive negative feedback control mechanism for TSH secretion exists, as it does in other vertebrate groups.

The existence of hypothalamic centers which affect TSH secretion by neurosecretory pathways which end in the amphibian neurohypophysis (median eminence) is suggested by the investigations of Jørgensen and Larsen (1960a, b), Scharrer (1959), and Etkin and Lehrer (1959). Furthermore, it has long been known that the thyroid of frogs and salamanders is stimulated by lowering of the environmental temperature (Wolf, 1934; Morgan and Moyer, 1936; Morgan and Fales, 1942). More recently Cehovic (1957) showed that continued darkness similarly affects thyroid function (I^{131} uptake). Unless the thyroid is directly responsive to temperature or light, a more likely explanation is that the nervous phenomena generated by these environmental factors are mediated by the hypothalamic centers which affect TSH secretion.

Dent and Lynn (1958) and Lynn and Dent (1961) have contrasted the striking differences in the hypophyseal–thyroid relationships between two urodeles, *Triturus viridescens* and *Desmognathus fuscus*. Goitrogen treatment inhibits radioiodine metabolism in the thyroids of both species. Yet, only in the thyroid of *Desmognathus* can stimulation be shown histologically after such treatment (thus revealing a release of TSH from the pituitary). By giving exogenous TSH to either species these authors showed that the thyroids are equally responsive to hypophyseal stimulation. Thus, the failure of a goitrogen-induced histologically demonstrable response in *Triturus* must be due to a failure to release TSH from the pituitary. Similar examples of absence in the thyroid of histological responses to goitrogens have been found in elasmobranch and teleost fishes (Section III,D).

Shibusawa and his co-workers (1956; Shibusawa, 1960) have extracted a substance from dog hypothalamus and neurohypophysis which stimulates thyrotropic hormone release from the adenohypophysis of mammals. They have extracted a similar material from urine and claim that it accelerates metamorphosis of the frog tadpole. This substance has been named the TRF, or thyrotropin-releasing factor.

D. Fishes

Since the thyroid glands of teleosts are in almost all instances unencapsulated, diffusely distributed groups of follicles they cannot be dissected out as a unit, weighed, or analyzed as a relatively pure tissue. Despite this handicap, however, there have been numerous studies of thyroidal iodine metabolism of teleosts, elasmobranchs, and cyclostomes. The elasmobranchs have a consolidated thyroid gland, but for the others "thyroid" tissue samples usually have included large amounts of muscular, connective, and other tissues.

It is interesting that it was first shown in a fish, the brook trout, *Salvelinus fontinalis* (Marine and Lenhart, 1910, 1911) that goiter may be caused by a lack of iodine. Further data on iodine metabolism in fishes was slowly accumulated until recent years. Much of this research was summarized by Berg *et al.* (1959). There is great variation in the appetite of different species for iodine. In general, fishes in sea water, an environment high in iodine, exhibit a smaller uptake of tracer radioiodine (usually less than 10%) than fishes in fresh water (whose thyroids usually accumulate more than 20%–30% of a given dose of I^{131}). This is understandable on the basis of the principles expressed earlier. If the thyroids of two fishes, one in fresh water, and the other in sea water, take up the same total quantity of stable iodine, the uptake of tracer iodine may be quite different between the two. If the blood level of iodide reflects the external supply, then the sea water fish needs to take up only a relatively small fraction of the available iodide to satisfy its requirements. Therefore, it takes up only a correspondingly small fraction of the tracer iodine which is diluted in the stable iodine. If the environmental and blood levels of iodide are low, then by this reasoning, the thyroidal tracer uptake should be relatively high. This was, in fact, demonstrated by Gorbman and Berg (1955), and Berg *et al.* (1959), using a single species, *Fundulus heteroclitus* and varying separately the salinity and iodine content of its environmental water. A similar relation between thyroid I^{131} uptake and environmental stable iodine supply was shown in the flounder *Platichthys* by Hickman (1959), and in the goldfish, *Carassius auratus*, by Srivastava (1960). In the light of this discussion it seems peculiar that Baggerman (1960) has reported that young salmon have the same thyroidal I^{131} uptake in fresh water and sea water (of unknown iodine contents).

There are some interesting exceptions to the generalization that fresh water fishes have a high, and salt water fishes a low I^{131} uptake. Fresh water species with low thyroid uptakes (less than 5%) include the goldfish, *Carassius auratus* (Berg *et al.*, 1954), *Lepomis gibbosus* (Berg *et al.*,

1959), and the ammocete of *Petromyzon marinus* (Leloup and Berg, 1954). On the other hand, the shark *Scyliorhinus canicula*, in sea water, has been found to have a thyroidal I^{131} uptake of almost 30% (Gorbman *et al.*, 1952). The amphibious mudskipper, *Periophthalmus*, which lives in brackish water of varying salinity was found by Leloup (1958) to have a highly active thyroid with a high radioiodine uptake and rapid production of thyroid hormone.

In a qualitative sense, the same hormones and hormonal precursors have been found in the piscine thyroid as in other vertebrates (Berg *et al.*, 1959; Leloup and Berg, 1954; Leloup, 1952, 1956, 1958). A number of seemingly exceptional situations have been reported, but in most of these instances it requires further careful work to establish conclusively the extent of variation from the usual thyroidal pattern of iodine metabolism. For example, in the goldfish, and in *Lepomis*, radioactive labeled thyroxine either does not form at all, or it forms extremely slowly and in a small proportion (Berg *et al.*, 1959). Similarly, in *Petromyzon* larvae kept at 16°C no thyroxine could be demonstrated, but at 20°C it formed in good proportion (Leloup and Berg, 1954). In *Umbra limi* (a small minnow), triiodothyronine but no thyroxine forms at one time of the year (August), but at other times most of the labeled thyroid hormone is thyroxine (March, December) (Berg *et al.*, 1959). *Umbra* is another fish whose thyroid is more active at lower temperatures than at higher ones. However, aside from such variations, there has never been any reason to suspect (Pickford and Atz, 1957) that there may be a species specificity of thyroid hormones.

In general there is little difficulty in demonstrating that the teleostean thyroid is subject to adenohypophyseal control. Hypophysectomy results in thyroid involution and reduced iodine metabolism (see reviews by Olivereau, 1954; Pickford and Atz, 1957). The sensitivity of the goldfish thyroid to TSH has, in fact, suggested its use for the bioassay of this hormone (Gorbman, 1940). A feedback balancing system between thyroid and adenohypophysis is suggested by the histologically demonstrable depressing effect of thyroxine upon thyroid function (Robertson, 1949; Fontaine and Wurtz-Arlet, 1952; Honma and Murakawa, 1955) and upon radioiodine uptake (LaRoche, 1950; Berg and Gorbman, 1953; Fontaine *et al.*, 1955). Prolonged iodine deficiency, as originally shown by Marine and Lenhart (1910) leads to hypertrophy and hyperplasia of teleostean thyroid tissue (Berg *et al.*, 1954).

A different type of relationship between the brain and the thyroid is brought out in the experiments of Pflugfelder (1954, 1956). Pflugfelder removed or destroyed the epiphysis (pineal) of the guppy (*Lebistes*) and found that the thyroid became greatly hypertrophied, and even "adenomatous." Pflugfelder (1956) found, further, that injection of an extract of beef pineal gland prevented thyroid hyperplasia after epiphysectomy. Activation of the reptilian thyroid by cutting of the pineal stalk has been reported by Stebbins and Eakin (1958).

The interrelationship of thyroid and pituitary in the Agnatha and Elasmobranchii, on the other hand, is not so clear, nor has it been investigated so thoroughly. Young and Bellerby (1935) were unsuccessful in producing any changes in the larval thyroid (endostyle) or in the adult gland of *Lampetra planeri* with beef pituitary extract. Knowles (1941), using ammocetes of the same species, stimulated parts of the endostyle by injections of beef pituitary extract, but he found no effect from hypophysectomy. Klenner (1953) and Klenner and Schipper (1954) stimulated the endostyle of *Lampetra* ammocetes with various antithyroid drugs. These data suggest that in the Agnatha, the most primitive living vertebrates, a regulatory relationship of mutual responsiveness exists between thyroid and hypophysis.

In the elasmobranchs it appears possible that this relationship is different. Administration of pituitary extracts or purified TSH stimulates morphological and functional changes in the thyroid of the shark *Scyliorhinus* (Olivereau, 1954). In the same species, although Waring *et al.* (1942) and Dodd (unpublished, cited by Olivereau, 1960) found no histological change in the thyroid from 30 days up to 2 years after hypophysectomy of adults, hypophysectomy of embryos (Vivien, 1954; Vivien and Rechenmann, 1954) produced a detectable decrease in radioiodine metabolism. In contrast with this orthodox response by *Scyliorhinus* to TSH is the lack of a thyroidal hypertrophic response to antithyroid agents. In a series of studies (Leloup, 1952a, b; Olivereau, 1950, 1951, 1952, 1954) it was shown that although there is a blockage of thyroid hormone formation (failure of iodine metabolism), there appears to be no responsive secretion of TSH. Consequently, the thiourea- or thiouracil-treated shark thyroid undergoes no histological change. This may be a species peculiarity, since Tinacci (1947, 1948) has reported that in another shark (*Mustelus*) thiouracil produces thyroid hyperplasia. The inference to be drawn from the work with *Scyliorhinus* is that TSH secretion is not sensitive to the level of circulating thyroid hormone. If this is so, then *Scyliorhinus* resembles certain urodele amphibians in this respect (Lynn and Dent, 1961). A possibly similar case is that of the goldfish whose thyroid, according to Fortune (1956), is unresponsive to goitrogen treatment. Yet, Gorbman (1940) and others have found the goldfish thyroid to be very sensitive to relatively small amounts of injected TSH.

IV. ACTION OF THYROID HORMONE IN MAMMALS

The responses of mammals to thyroid hormones have been summarized from a very extensive literature in numerous recent reviews. Reference is made again to the excellent reviews by Werner (1962) and Pitt-Rivers and Tata (1959). For the purpose of later comparisons with nonmammals, a highly abbreviated outline is provided.

Treatment with thyroid hormones has been found to influence almost every organ system in the mammal to some extent. The effects of the hormones are expressed as (a) morphological changes, (b) alterations in the levels or rates of function of certain organs, or (c) alterations in the rate or pattern of utilization of certain basic metabolic substances like oxygen or carbohydrate.

The morphological changes which follow changes in thyroid hormone level usually have been of the type which may be called "maturational," and they are produced most strikingly in younger mammals. Thus, in the skeleton thyroxine hastens differentiation of the epiphyseal discs in long bones, and it accelerates eruption of teeth. Thyroxine treatment of late embryos or newborn mammals has a striking stimulatory influence upon the central nervous system with respect to mitotic rate, growth rate, and differentiation of specific centers and tracts. As in other vertebrate groups, thyroxine also acts upon the integument and its derivatives in mammals, stimulating hair growth and pigment deposition (Berman, 1960) and epidermal proliferation [but a thinning of the epidermis (Eartly and Leblond, 1954)]. Also there is a relation between thyroid state and mucopolysaccharide deposition and fluid infiltration of the dermis.

In the same organs in which morphological changes are induced by thyroxine there are, as might be expected, important functional changes as well, and these are not necessarily limited to developmental stages. Thus, a wide variety of nervous activities are stimulated by thyroid hormone: time of differentiation of specific reflexes (e.g., blink, ear twitch); threshold sensitivity to electrical, auditory, and other stimuli; rate of response to such stimuli; rate and pattern of emission of alpha waves in the brain; and level of performance in learning or intelligence tests (in children). Probably related are effects of thyroxine upon electrical properties of the muscle fiber plasma membrane (Laplaud et al., 1961) and upon cardiac function in general (Leblond and Hoff, 1944; van den Beld et al., 1959; Gargouil, 1960).

Secretory activity of the integumentary glands as well as that of the pancreas and perhaps other glands of the digestive tract is believed to be influenced by thyroid hormone. It has been claimed that thyroid hormone also controls the selective permeability of the digestive epithelium to different sugars and it increases the permeability of mammalian muscle cells to sugars (Norman and Hiestand, 1960).

In response to thyroid hormone treatment there is characteristically an increase in serum glucose and nitrogen content, and a reduction in lipids. These changes must, of course, reflect changes in metabolism in the peripheral tissues and in specific organs. For example, it has been demonstrated that thyroxine promotes glycogenolysis in the liver. Recent evidence seemingly indicates that it stimulates cellular utilization of glucose and production of lactic acid (Halevy and Avivi, 1960). It is well known that the thyroid hormone at different dosage levels has apparently different effects upon protein metabolism. At minimal doses it promotes growth of young mammals, apparently by synergistic action with growth hormone (Simpson et al., 1950). Under such circumstances there is a positive nitrogen balance. The hyperthyroid animal, on the other hand, loses weight and excretes large amounts of nitrogen. Not only is there a reduction in muscle mass in hyperthyroid animals, but also the muscle loses creatine phosphate, and becomes less efficient in terms of work capacity.

The best known action of thyroid hormone in mammals is its stimulation of oxygen consumption and thermogenesis. The mechanism of integration of this function in the regulation of body temperature has been studied intensively. The thyroid gland is clearly stimulated in most mammals by lowered temperatures through a mechanism involving the hypothalamus and pituitary (Knigge, 1960). There is little doubt that the thyroid hormones are involved in thermoregulatory calorigenesis, but recent evidence has raised the question of whether these hormones play the major role in this phenomenon (Carlson, 1960; Cottle, 1960). Similarly, it has been attractive to think that lack of the thyroid hormone is a factor in hibernation, particularly in those hibernating species which become hypothermic. Unfortunately, accumulating evidence has lent little or no support for this hypothesis (Lyman and Chatfield, 1955; Sadler and Tyler, 1960).

Closer examination of the nature of thyroid-stimulated respiration in mammals offers the basis for belief that this may be an indirect action. It is well known that there is a delay (latent period) before the increase in respiration after thyroid hormone injection. Oxygen consumption of tissue slices does not increase when thyroid hormones are added in vitro; however, under specified conditions (Barker, 1957; Lindsay and Barker, 1958) thyroxine may prevent the decrease in respiration of rat kidney slices for several days. An attractive theory of the cellular basis of action of thyroid hormone is based on the observation that it partly inhibits oxidative phosphorylation in mitochondrial preparations in vitro (Tapley et al., 1955). Thyroid hormone treatment induces a state in which a greater amount of metabolic oxidation is required to produce a given amount of

ATP (lowering of the P/O ratio), thus a larger than normal proportion of heat is produced. Unfortunately, to reproduce such results mitochondria must be isolated and fragmented according to exact procedures. If the procedure is varied, then other relationships between phosphorylation and oxygen consumption may be obtained (Bronk, 1960). If it is true that increased cellular oxygen consumption is an indirect or secondary effect of thyroid hormonal action, then it is perhaps unfortunate that so far respiration is the only aspect of thyroid function which has been investigated from the standpoint of cellular level of action (Tata *et al.*, 1962).

V. ACTION OF THYROID HORMONE IN BIRDS

It has been well established that surgical thyroidectomy of birds (fowl), destruction of their thyroid by radioactive iodine, or feeding of antithyroid drugs reduces oxygen consumption and interrupts growth. Thyroxine stimulates oxygen consumption and growth when given in proper doses. Whether the growth effect of thyroid hormone in birds (Glazener and Schaffner, 1949; Irwin *et al.*, 1943) is actually a result of synergistic action with growth hormone, as in mammals, has not been established. However, it is interesting that Singh *et al.* (1956) have found direct correlations between thyroxine secretion rates and characteristic rates of growth in different genetic strains of fowl. Apparent genetic control over the level of thyroid secretion has also been described in different inbred strains of mice (Barnett and Manly, 1958). It was established in earlier work by Riddle (1927) that in different races of pigeons the sizes of thyroid glands and presumably their secretion rates are characteristic of each race.

In mammals triiodothyronine is as much as five times as effective in stimulating respiration as thyroxine. In birds, on the other hand, they are approximately equally active in raising oxygen consumption (Shellabarger, 1955; Newcomer, 1957). Tata and Shellabarger (1959) have provided an explanation for this on the basis of their studies of binding of these two hormones to serum proteins in chickens and ducks (see also Robbins and Rall, 1960). In contrast with mammals, serum protein-binding is almost equal and the rate of escape of the hormones from the blood is similar.

Portet (1960) has shown that even during the embryonic life of chicks respiratory and other metabolic functions are responsive to thyroid hormone. This is of more than mere experimental interest since the hen's egg actively concentrates iodine and thyroid hormones from the maternal blood (Roche *et al.*, 1956, 1957; Blanquet *et al.*, 1957) so that early morphogenesis occurs in the presence of considerable quantities of such hormones.

Furthermore, the thyroid of the chick embryo itself begins to form hormone even before the midpoint of incubation (Wollman and Zwilling, 1953; Trunnell and Wade, 1955).

The avian integument is as responsive to changes in thyroid state as the mammalian skin. The principal phenomena in which thyroid responsiveness may be seen are pigmentation, feather color and structure, and frequency of molt. Many studies have been made of the relation of thyroid function to molting. Particularly the older work is summarized by von Buddenbrock (1950).

There is some disagreement in the published literature but, generally, in the hypothyroid state molting is inhibited, and it is stimulated by thyroxine injections. Species which have been tested include domestic birds (fowl, ducks, pigeons, geese) as well as tamed or wild birds (canary, bengalee, peacock, partridge, kestrel, owl, jay, bullfinch, crossbill, starling, siskin, crow, etc.). There is some difference in the readiness with which these birds respond to thyroid treatment by molting. Crows and ravens have been found to be particularly resistant to high doses of thyroid hormone (Zawadowsky and Rochlina, 1927; Zawadowsky, 1932). Pigeons and peacocks, on the other hand, are sensitive to small doses.

An altered thyroid state also influences morphogenesis of the feather, and the literature contains many references, particularly with respect to domestic fowl, of shifts toward cock-feathering in hypothyroidism and toward hen-feathering in hyperthyroidism (Torrey and Horning, 1925; Cole and Hutt, 1928). Regardless of how this is to be interpreted, or whether sex hormones are involved, it seems clear that differentiation of form of the feather is influenced by thyroid hormone. The hypothyroid feather is deficient in barbules so that it fails to form a flat vane (Parkes and Selye, 1937; Bruce et al., 1954). Furthermore, it is clear that the feathers of different body regions are not equally sensitive to thyroid hormone (Larionow and Kusmina, 1931). Also, in several species (starling, canary; Woitkewitsch, 1940; Takewaki and Mori, 1944) it has been shown that there is a seasonal cycle of sensitivity of the feather to changes in thyroid state.

It has long been believed, and often suggested, that a part of the apparent seasonal, sex, and species variability in feather sensitivity to thyroid hormone may be due to responsiveness of feathers to other hormones, particularly steroids. Recently Kobayashi (1958) has tested 19 species of birds and has found that certain of them will molt after injection with 17α-oxyprogesterone. He suggests that progestogens and perhaps other steroids may sensitize the feather follicle to thyroid hormones.

Horning and Torrey (1923), Cole and Hutt (1928), Parkes and Selye (1937), Juhn (1944), and Blivaiss (1947) all have found that in fowl blackness of feathers due to melanin is increased by proper dosage with thyroxine; in the hypothyroid state lighter colors (reds, browns, or white) are found. Lipochromes as well as melanins are affected by thyroid state, and Stadie (1938) has reported that thyroid hormone interferes with deposition of these pigments in feathers of wild species (siskins, crossbills, and orange weavers). In such species pale and unusual shades of color appear in regenerating feathers formed during a period of thyroid hormone treatment.

Aside from its effects upon growth and upon integumentary structures there has been relatively little study of the actions of thyroid hormone in avian species. A stimulatory action upon heart rate has been noted in chickens (Newcomer, 1957). Zawadowsky et al. (1928), and Asmundsen and Pinsky (1935), among others, have found that small doses of thyroid hormone increase the egg-productive capacity of hens and lower the ratio of yolk to albumen; higher doses of thyroxine are inhibitory for egg-laying. Possibly related to the thyroxine-induced reduction of yolk content of the hen's egg is the general reduction in liver and plasma lipid reported recently by Evans et al. (1961).

An important action of thyroid hormone upon the nervous system may be inferred from its induction of a type of restlessness in migratory birds which has been named Vogelzug or Zugunruhe (Merkel, 1938). This behavior has been interpreted to be the equivalent of premigratory restlessness, and, therefore, thyroid hormones may play a role in avian breeding migrations.

There has been very little investigation of cellular levels of action of thyroid hormone in birds. Haarmann (1936) has made the unconfirmed claim that very minute concentrations of thyroxine (10^{-14}–10^{-16}) may stimulate respiration in vitro of pieces of liver, cardiac, or skeletal muscle from hens or pigeons. Maruyama and Kobayashi (1956) found that treatment of canaries with thyroxine increased the latent apyrase (ATP-splitting) enzymatic activity in mitochondria preparations from liver tissue. The increased alkaline phosphatase concentration in the skin of thyroxine-treated pigeons is thought by Kobayashi et al. (1955) to be causally related to the cornification and molt elicited by the hormone in this species.

VI. ACTION OF THYROID HORMONE IN REPTILES

Only scattered and relatively inconsistent information exists concerning the role of thyroid hormone in reptilian physiology. The most extensive investigation, by Eggert (1936, 1938), deals principally with the lizard *Lacerta agilis*. In this species there is a distinct seasonal cycle of thyroid activity revealed by cyclic changes in histological structure. Thyroidectomy of *Lacerta* results in a period of slow decline of which anemia is a characteristic symptom, and which terminates in death after about 6–8 months. In thyroidectomized *Lacerta* normal cyclic molting is greatly inhibited or it is completely arrested (Drzewicki, 1928; Eggert, 1938). Failure or inhibition of the process of epidermal keratinization appears to be a characteristic feature, as well as a cessation of production of new epidermal cells. On the other hand, thyroidectomy of a gecko, *Hemidactylus brookei* (Noble and Bradley, 1933), or a snake, *Python bivittatus* (Krockert, 1941), merely reduces the frequency of molting. In contrast to these results Schaefer (1933) found that thyroidectomy of the garter snake precipitates a successive chain of molts. These can be arrested by thyroid feeding. Such differences in apparent relation of thyroidectomy to the epidermal molting process suggest that other endocrine mechanisms may also be concerned with this process. Such a possibility is illustrated in the work of Kobayashi (1958) and Jørgensen and Larsen (1960a, b) who found that adrenocorticoids are active in molting birds and amphibians.

The role of thyroid hormones in reptilian metabolic processes is similarly difficult to assess on the basis of published literature. Drechsler and von Issekutz (1935) found that prolonged feeding of thyroid to turtles produced no change in oxygen consumption. In contrast, Scott (1935) using isolated erythrocytes of thyroxine-injected *Alligator*, and Haarmann (1936) using isolated pieces of snake muscle tissue (thyroxine added *in vitro*) have reported respiratory stimulation. More recently, Maher and Levedahl (1959) observed that neither thyroidectomy nor the injection of thyroxine affected oxygen consumption in *Anolis* at 21°–24°C, but that these treatments were effective at 30°C. It is possible that such findings may be correlated with the reports of Stebbins and Eakin, 1958; and Eakin *et al.* (1959). These workers found that pinealectomy, or cutting of the pineal stalk of the lizard, *Sceloporus* results in thyroid hyperplasia (see also the results of Pflugfelder, 1954, 1956 in the fish *Lebistes*). Associated with this thyroid response is a behavioral change in which thermoregulation by choice of proper environmental locus is disturbed.

VII. ACTION OF THYROID HORMONE IN AMPHIBIANS

Studies of the effects of thyroid hormones in the Amphibia have been confined largely to four areas of research: (a) action upon metamorphosis, (b) action upon integumentary structure, (c) action upon nervous function, and (d) action upon oxidative and other metabolism.

Gudernatsch (1912) in experiments in which he fed raw glandular tissue to tadpoles discovered that thyroid tissue contains a potent metamorphosis-stimulating factor.

It is beyond the scope of this chapter to deal with the detailed and voluminous literature which has grown in connection with this topic since 1912. There are several recent reviews which are concerned with thyroid function in amphibian larvae (Etkin, 1955; Saxen et al., 1957; Kollros, 1959; Kaye, 1961). It has been shown that virtually all organ systems of the tadpole, but especially the integumentary and nervous systems, are sensitive to the "maturational" influence of thyroid hormone. Furthermore, not all tissues are equally responsive to thyroid hormone; normal metamorphosis and development of the larva require a progressive increase in thyroid hormone level coordinated with the appearance of target tissue sensitivity to the hormone. The extreme sensitivity of the metamorphic response to triiodothyropropionic acid, a deaminated form of triiodothyronine (Michel, 1956; Money et al., 1958; Truchot et al., 1960) suggests that at least one mechanism of "sensitizing" a tissue may be the development of its ability to metabolize thyroxine (in this case, by deamination). These workers have found triiodothyropropionic acid to be about 300 times as active as thyroxine itself.

In many urodele amphibians periodic shedding of cornified epidermis is inhibited or completely arrested after thyroidectomy. However, epidermal proliferation and some cornification continue slowly after thyroidectomy, to produce eventually a greatly thickened epidermis of characteristic color and texture (Adams et al., 1932; Adams, 1933). The accumulation of epidermal layers raises the question of whether thyroid state influences epidermal mitotic proliferation. Taylor (1937) has found in newts that thyroidectomy is followed by an initial period of accelerated epidermal mitosis. This is succeeded after 140 days by a period of retarded mitotic activity. Treatment with large doses of thyroxine stimulates sloughing of superficial cornified epidermis in all amphibians, even in those in which molting persists after thyroidecomy (Ungar, 1933). However, in Bufo bufo, one such exceptional species, even doses of 0.1 mg of thyroxine do not stimulate shedding of epidermis (Jørgensen and Larsen, 1960b). It is interesting that in Bufo a single injection of deoxycorticosterone (0.5 mg) results in sloughing. Similar results were obtained with Xenopus (Jørgensen and Larson, 1961). On the basis of such experiments Jørgensen and Larsen have concluded that both thyroxine and adrenal steroids may be involved in the molting process, and that the optimal proportions of these hormones for induction of molting may vary with the species. It has been observed by several workers that a single administration of about 50 μgrams of thyroxine or more may produce a "burst of molts," a rapid succession of sloughings of epidermis. This has led Jørgensen and Larsen (1960b) to conclude that periodicity of molting in amphibians is governed by absolute level of thyroid hormone, not by a periodic release or increase of the hormone. The burst of molts phenomenon has been observed in the author's laboratory (unpublished data) after thyroid treatment of *Triturus pyrrhogaster*. Scharrer (1959) has emphasized that an intact hypothalamo-hypophyseal neurosecretory relationship is necessary for normal molting in *Bufo*.

The action of thyroid hormone upon differentiation of the amphibian central nervous system has been investigated by Kollros and his collaborators by implanting thyroxine-containing agar pellets into specific sites in the tadpole's brain (Kollros, 1942, 1943, 1959; Kollros and Pepernik, 1952; Pesetsky and Kollros, 1956). Such treatment not only produces localized differentiation in the vicinity of the thyroxine pellet (mesencephalic V nucleus, Mauthner's cells), but also unilateral functional differentiation of reflexes (e.g., the blink reflex). May and Mugard (1955) have shown that thyroxine also stimulates mitosis in the differentiating brain of frog tadpoles. An effect upon basic electrical properties of peripheral nerves was shown by Le Grand and Ajoulat (1931) who found that thyroxine reduced both chronaxie and rheobase (increased sensitivity to minimal electrical stimuli) in frog nerve–muscle preparations.

Although Davis and Hastings (1935) claimed that oxygen consumption of the isolated frog heart is stimulated by added thyroxine, Warren (1940) found that such hearts are not stimulated *in situ* when the frog is treated with thyroxine. More recently Kleinfeld *et al.* (1958) have supported Davis and Hastings' finding. They showed that thyroxine or triiodothyronine, but not uniodinated thyronines, when added to the perfusion fluid stimulated the isolated perfused frog's heart.

It is generally agreed (Allen, 1918, 1929; Hoskins and Hoskins, 1919; Chang, 1955) that thyroidectomy of amphibians has relatively little effect upon reproductive development. Since complete neoteny and pedogenesis (ability to reproduce without completion of development) is characteristic of some amphibian species, it is important to note this relative independence of gonad and thyroid in this group. In other vertebrates gonadal maturation is more strictly dependent upon a euthyroid state. In a positive sense, Warren (1940) has noted that thyroid treatment of frogs accelerates spermatogenesis.

Regeneration of amputated limbs in young salamanders is known to be inhibited by hypophysectomy or thyroidectomy (Speidel, 1929; Richardson, 1940). Treatment of such animals with small doses of thyroid hormones restores regenerative capacity. Large doses of thyroid hormone, on the other hand, inhibit regeneration by causing premature differentiation of the indifferent tissue in the blastema which is required for successful regeneration. Regeneration of the lens of the salamander's eye has been found to be independent of thyroid state (Stone and Steinitz, 1953).

To the question of whether thyroid hormone influences respiratory oxidative metabolism in amphibians no clear answer can yet be given. The most general experience is that thyroid hormone does not stimulate oxygen consumption (Gayda, 1922; Henschel and Steuber, 1935; von Issekutz et al., 1943). However, it is impossible to dismiss the contradictory evidence. Taylor (1939) found a slow decline in oxygen consumption after thyroidectomy of Triturus, and a slow rise (after an initial decline) after thyroid implantation. Warren (1940) reported an increased oxygen consumption in Rana pipiens after thyroid hormone injection and Donoso and Trivelloni (1958) obtained a similar response in Bufo. Jankowsky (1960) recently described a significant decline in oxygen consumption of thyroidectomized Rana temporaria. Three weeks after thyroidectomy respiratory oxygen consumption had fallen 14% in frogs kept at 5°C, and 26% in frogs kept at 25°C.

Work with tissue slices has yielded apparently confusing results. Ahlgren (1924) stimulated oxygen consumption of pieces of frog tissue by adding thyroxine (10^{-14}) in vitro. In some older work von Euler (1933) found that incubating frog muscle tissue with thyroxine (about 10^{-15}) produced little change in tissue respiration (with respect to controls) unless the oxygen content of the atmosphere was reduced to about 10%. This suggested a stimulation of anaerobic metabolism. Haarmann (1936) incubated minced frog muscle in media containing very minute amounts of thyroxine. He reported the curious finding that oxygen consumption was stimulated at the remarkably low thyroxine concentration of 10^{-16}, but not at slightly higher or lower concentrations. More recently Donoso (1960) measured the respiration of tissues removed from thyroxine-injected (a very high dose of 1.0 mg was given) or thyroidectomized toads. Kidney and heart slices exhibited an increased rate of respiration, but the tissues which contribute most to the mass of the animal, muscle and liver, were not different from controls. There is a clear need for more study in this field to resolve the numerous apparent contradictions. It should be noted that most research of this type in recent years has involved the use of thyroxine concentrations of about 10^{-5}. However, Kollros (1959) has obtained minimal metamorphic effects in hypophysectomized tadpoles by keeping them in thyroxine solutions of 10^{-10} to 10^{-11}.

Thyroid hormone treatment has been found to increase nitrogen excretion in frogs. There are two interesting descriptions of "maturation" of biochemical systems in developing amphibians. Wald (1946) has found that differentiation of the larval visual pigment, porphyropsin, to the adult type, rhodopsin, is stimulated by thyroid hormone treatment. The synthesis of an enzyme in the tadpole's liver, carbamyl phosphate synthetase, has been reported (Paik and Cohen, 1960) to be accelerated by thyroid treatment. This enzyme, characteristic of adult metabolism in the frog, takes part in the Krebs–Henseleit urea cycle.

VIII. ACTION OF THYROID HORMONE IN FISHES

A large variety of morphological changes, mostly integumentary, have been described as the sequelae of an altered thyroid state in fishes. The skeletal and other systems as well as the skin appear to be responsive in some degree. The role of thyroid hormone in growth, one of the most easily observed expressions of thyroid hormone action, remains undetermined. The use of antithyroid drugs has been found to inhibit growth of young small aquarium teleosts (Lebistes, Gambusia) (Nigrelli et al., 1946; Hoar and Bell, 1950; Hopper, 1952; Gaiser, 1952; Smith et al., 1953; Scott, 1953; Dales and Hoar, 1954). La Roche and Leblond (1954) found that radio-thyroidectomy of young salmon did not affect growth. Similarly, Fortune (1955) found that a goitrogenic dose of thiourea had no effect on growth in Phoxinus or Lebistes. Frieders (1949) reported that Trichogaster "escapes" from the goitrogenic influence of an antithyroid drug and resumes growth after five weeks of treatment.

Thyroxine treatment of the guppy, Lebistes, was found to be growth-inhibiting by Grobstein and Bellamy (1939) and Svärdson (1943), but growth-stimulating by Hopper (1952). In the same species Vivien and Gaiser (1952a, b) found that thyroxine has a biphasic effect, at first inhibiting growth, and later permitting resumed growth. Dales and Hoar (1954) found that thyroxine inhibited growth of young salmon (Oncorhynchus) but Fontaine and Baraduc (1955) stimulated growth of trout by feeding thyroid. It is clear that somewhere within this confusing array of information there must be a proper answer to the question of the role of thyroid hormones in teleostean growth. In such experiments there must be proper evaluation of the factors of toxicity of treatment and of proper dosage levels of hormone.

There is better agreement concerning the role of thyroid hormones in morphogenesis, but some of the described effects of thyroid hormones are difficult to relate to normal morphological events. Accelerated growth and differentiation of fins has been reported after thyroxine treatment of salmon (Dales and Hoar, 1954), Lebistes and Aequidens (Krockert, 1936a, b), swordtails (Grobstein and Bellamy, 1939), and *Gambusia* (Buser and Bougis, 1951). Buser-Lahaye (1953) has found that thyroid treatment favors regeneration of fins in *Gambusia*. Abnormal types of growth and differentiation, particularly in the head region have been described in thyroxine-treated *Gambusia* (Rizzo, 1950a, b) and in salmon and trout (La Roche, 1950, 1953; and La Roche *et al.*, 1950). In these species the head becomes broad and blunt, the brain is somewhat enlarged, and proliferation of certain cranial bones and of orbital tissue produces exophthalmos.

In general, it has been found that the skin of fishes responds to thyroxine by epidermal thickening and by lightening of color due principally to increase in the number of guanophores (Fontaine *et al.*, 1952; Fontaine and Baraduc, 1955; La Roche and Leblond, 1954; Robertson, 1949, 1951a, b). In addition to thickening of the epidermis after thyroid treatment Harms (1929, 1935) noted that the skin in the mudskipper, *Periophthalmus* (an amphibious gobiid fish) became highly vascular, especially in the caudal region. Harms interpreted this as an adaptation for terrestrial integumentary respiration, and partly on the basis of such effects he proposed that thyroxine is the hormone for terrestrialization or "Landtierwerdung" of the vertebrates.

There is general agreement concerning the increased integumentary guanine, but Robertson (1951a, b) has proposed further that thyroid hormone inhibits the dispersion of melanophores. Prolonged thyroid feeding leads to extensive depigmentation, particularly demelanization, of the skin in goldfish or carp (Blacher, 1927; Müller, 1953). Melanophores of *Phoxinus* (Müller, 1953) and *Fundulus* (Pickford, in Pickford and Atz, 1957) do not respond to thyroid treatment. In salmon and trout La Roche and Leblond (1952) stated that thyroid treatment decreases integumentary pigment cells. The same authors (1954) found that radiothyroidectomy also caused depigmentation in salmon. Frieders (1949) and Patane (1949) also have produced depigmentation in smaller aquarium fishes after prolonged antithyroid drug treatment.

There is no evidence that thyroid hormone stimulates the piscine heart as it stimulates cardiac activity in other vertebrates (Dales and Hoar, 1954). On the other hand, there is reason to believe that the nervous system in this group responds to thyroid hormone. Hoar and his collaborators (1952, 1955) have shown in several species of fish that thyroid treatment increases spontaneous motor activity, decreases schooling behavior, and alters rheotactic behavior in a way which can be interpreted to favor migration (Fontaine, 1956a, b). In the earlier work of Harms (1929, 1935) thyroid treatment of *Periophthalmus* and of blennies was reported to produce behavioral changes marked by a progressive abandonment of aquatic in favor of terrestrial living. Baggerman (1959, 1960) has devised a technique by which another seemingly thyroid-related behavioral feature may be analyzed. In such tests the fishes are confronted with a choice of aquatic environments of different salinity (e.g., fresh water and sea water). In this way Baggerman has shown that thyroid hormone may influence salinity preference in adult sticklebacks or in young salmon, and thus it may play a role in anadromous or catadromous migrations. A more easily visualized effect upon central nervous function by thyroid hormone was demonstrated recently by Gorbman and Ishii (1960). They found that treatment of one-year old *Squalus* embryos resulted in rapid differentiation of the hypothalamic neurosecretory system and the appearance of stainable neurosecretion characteristic of two-year old full term embryos.

Students of the problem of fish migration have been concerned also with a possible role of thyroid hormone in regulating physiological tolerance and adjustment to variation in environmental salinity ("osmoregulation"). Unfortunately, the evidence on this point is relatively inconsistent (see reviews of the subject by Fontaine, 1956a, b; Smith, 1956; Hickman, 1959); various authors reported no effect by thyroid hormone upon salt metabolism, or conflicting effects. There appears to be no doubt that the thyroid gland of certain species of fish is activated at the time of migration. However, aside from Hoar's evidence showing that thyroid hormone elicits migration-predisposing behavior, there is still no reason to believe that the two phenomena necessarily are causally related. Properties like salinity tolerance and salinity preference may preadapt the fish to physiological problems which occur during migration, but these properties cannot be thought to predispose toward migration since the fish does not live in a gradient of salinity; it may even need to cross several gradients of salinity during its migratory run (Fontaine, 1956a, b).

It must be remembered that whatever the role of the thyroid may be in salt metabolism and osmoregulation in fish, there is another endocrine organ, the interrenal tissue secreting adrenocorticoids, whose role in this phenomenon is much less equivocal (Chester Jones *et al.*, 1959).

The possible influence of thyroid hormones upon respiratory metabolism in fishes has received much attention. Although the evidence is not all in agreement it now appears relatively unlikely that thyroid hormones are important regulators of oxygen consumption, if they have this function at all in fishes. Tests in the following species do not indicate that thyroid hormone influences oxygen consumption: goldfish (Etkin *et al.*, 1940; Hasler and Meyer, 1942; Punt and Jungbloed, 1945), guppies (Drexler and von Issekutz, 1935; Smith and Everett, 1943), *Opsanus tau* (Root and Etkin, 1937), *Rhodeus amarus* (Punt and Jungbloed, 1945), *Salmo gairdneri* (Baraduc, 1954, 1955). Smith and Matthews (1948) reported that white grunts of a minimum size responded to parrot fish thyroid by increased respiration. Matty (1957), on the other hand, found that changes in the thyroid state of the parrot fish did not affect its oxygen consumption. Müller (1953) reported that repeated injections of 1.0 mg of thyroxine in goldfish produced an increase in oxygen consumption. This result, which does not conform with the experience of others using the same species, may be based on the unphysiological high dose; neither did Müller control the variable factor of locomotor activity which is stimulated in goldfish by thyroxine (Hoar *et al.*, 1952), and which could cause a large error in measurements of basal respiration. Pritchard and Gorbman (1960) have reported more recently that repeated relatively small doses (10 μg to 50 μg) of tetraiodothyropropionic acid and, to a lesser extent, triiodothyronine provide a temporary stimulus for oxygen consumption in embryos of the shark *Squalus suckleyi* in observations over a 3-week period. The unsustained stimulation of respiration is difficult to interpret. Matty (1954) showed that thyroidectomy of the adult shark *Scyllium* has no effect on respiratory metabolism by three days after the operation. Since Matty found also that injected radioiodine remains detectable in the blood of *Scyllium* for long periods (at least 6 weeks), it is possible that a failure to note an effect of thyroidectomy may be due to the persistence of thyroid hormone in blood and tissues.

Nitrogenous metabolism seems to be affected by thyroxine injections. Hoar *et al.* (1955) have reported that treated goldfish excrete unusual amounts of urinary nitrogen.

References

Adams, A. E. (1933). *J. Exptl. Biol.* **10**, 247–255.

Adams, A. E., and Craig M. (1951). *J. Exptl. Zool.* **117**, 287–316.

Adams, A. E., Kuder, A., and Richards, L. (1932). *J. Exptl. Zool.* **63**, 1–14.

Ahlgren, G. (1924). *Klin. Wochschr.*, **1924**, 667–668.

Albert, A., and Lorenz, N. (1951). *Biol. Med.* **77**, 204–205.

Allen, B. M. (1916). *Science* **44**, 755–757.

Allen, B. M. (1918). *J. Exptl. Zool.* **24**, 499–520.

Allen, B. M. (1929). *Quart. Rev. Biol.* **4**, 325–352.

Asmundson, V. S., and Pinsky, P. (1935). *Poultry Sci.* **14**, 99–104.

Baggerman, B. (1959). *In* "Comparative Endocrinology" (A. Gorbman, ed.), pp. 24–37. Wiley, New York.

Baggerman, B. (1960). *J. Fisheries Research Board Can.* **17**, 295–322.

Baraduc, M. M. (1954). *Compt. rend. acad. sci.* **238**, 728–730.

Baraduc, M. M., and Fontaine, M. (1955). *Compt. rend. soc. biol.* **149**, 1327–1329.

Barker, S. B. (1957). *CIBA Foundation Colloq. Endocrinol.* **10**, 253–269.

Barnett, S. A., and Manly, B. M. (1958). *Physiol. Bohemosloven.* **8**, 19–28.

Bates, R. W., and Cornfield, J. (1957). *Endocrinology* **60**, 225–238.

Berg, O., and Gorbman, A. (1953). *Proc. Soc. Exptl. Biol. Med.* **83**, 751–756.

Berg, O., Gordon, M., and Gorbman, A. (1954). *Cancer Research* **14**, 232–236.

Berg, O., Gorbman, A., and Kobayashi, H. (1959). *In* "Comparative Endocrinology" (A. Gorbman, ed.), pp. 302–319. Wiley, New York.

Berman, A. (1960). *J. Endocrinol.* **20**, 288–292.

Blacher, L. J. (1927). *Trans. Lab. Exptl. Biol. Zoo-park Moscow* **3**, 79–81.

Blanquet, P., Stoll, R., Maraud, R., Mounier, J., and Meyniel, J. (1957). *Compt. rend. soc. biol.* **151**, 104–107.

Blivaiss, B. (1947). *Physiol. Zoöl.* **20**, 67–107.

Bronk, J. R. (1960). *Ann. N. Y. Acad. Sci.* **86**, 494–505.

Bruce, H., Pitt-Rivers, R., and Sloviter, H. A. (1954). *J. Endocrinol.* **10**, 340–341.

Buser, J., and Bougis, P. (1951). *Arch. zool. exptl. et gén. Notes et Rev.* **88** (3), 116–122.

Buser-Lahaye, J. (1953). *Ann. inst. océanog. (Paris)* **28**, 1–61.

Carlson, L. D. (1960). *Federation Proc.* **19**, Suppl. 5, 25–30.

Cehovic, G. (1957). *Compt. rend. acad. sci.* **244**, 2647–2650.

Chang, C. Y. (1955). *Anat. Record* **123**, 467–478.

Chester Jones, I., Philips, J. G., and Holmes, W. N. (1959). *In* "Comparative Endocrinology" (A. Gorbman, ed.), pp. 582–612. Wiley, New York.

Cole, L. J., and Hutt, F. B. (1928). *Poultry Sci.* **7**, 60–66.

Cottle, W. H. (1960). *Federation Proc.* **19**, Suppl. 5, 59–63.

Dales, S., and Hoar, W. S. (1954). *Can. J. Zool.* **32**, 244–251.

D'Angelo, S. A. (1955). *Brookhaven Symposia in Biol.* **7**, 9–27.

Davis, J. E., and Hastings, A. B. (1935). *Proc. Central Soc. Clin. Research* **104**.

Dent, J. N., and Lynn, W. G. (1958). *Biol. Bull.* **115**, 411–420.

De Robertis, E. (1943). *Arch. soc. biol. Montevideo* **11**, 35–56.

Dimond, Sister M. T. (1954). *J. Exptl. Zool.* **127**, 93–116.

Donoso, A. O. (1960). *Compt. rend. soc. biol.* **154**, 832.

Donoso, A. O., and Trivelloni, J. C. (1958). *Rev. soc. arg. biol.* **34**, 64–69.

Drechsler, E., and von Issekutz, B. (1935). *Arch. exptl. Pathol. Pharmakol. Naunyn-Schmiedeberg's* **177**, 435–441.

Drexler, E., and von Issekutz, B. (1935). *Arch. exptl. Pathol. Pharmakol. Naunyn-Schmiedeberg's* **177**, 435–441.

Drzewicki, S. (1928). *Wilhelm Roux' Arch. Entwicklungsmech. Organ.* **114**, 155–176.

Dundee, H., and Gorbman, A. (1960). *Physiol. Zoöl.* **33**, 58–63.

Eakin, R. M., Stebbins, R. C., and Wilhoft, D. C. (1959). *Proc. Soc. Exptl. Biol. Med.* **101**, 162–164.

Eartly, H., and Leblond, C. P. (1954). *Endocrinology* **54**, 249–271.

Eggert, B. (1936). *Z. wiss. Zool.* **149**, 280–322.

Eggert, B. (1938). "Morphologie und Histophysiologie der normalen Schilddrüse," *Zwanglose Abhandl. inneren Sekretion.* Barth, Leipzig (Reprinted by Edwards Brothers, Ann Arbor, Michigan, 1944).

Elterich, C. F. (1936). *Endokrinologie* **18**, 31–37.

Etkin, W. (1955). *In* "Analysis of Development" (B. H. Willier, P. A. Weiss, and V. Hamburger, eds.), pp. 631–663 Saunders, Philadelphia, Pennsylvania.

Etkin, W., and Lehrer, R. (1960). *Endocrinology* **67**, 457–466.

Etkin, W. N., Root, R. W., and Mofshin, B. P. (1940). *Physiol. Zoöl.* **13**, 415–429.

Euler, U. S. von. (1933). *Klin. Wochschr.* **1933**, 671–672.

Evans, L. T. (1939). *Anat. Record* **78**, Suppl., 113–114.

Evans, L. T., and Clapp, M. L. (1939). *Anat. Record* **75**, Suppl., 126–127.

Evans, L. T., and Hegre, E. (1940). *Endocrinology* **27**, 144–148.

Evans, J. D., Aleksyshyn, N. L., Middleton, P. J., and Schwartz, H. G. (1961). *Federation Proc.* **20**, Suppl. 1, 201 Abstr.

Fell, H. B., and Mellanby, E. (1955). *J. Physiol. (London)* **127**, 427–447.

Fink, B. A. (1957). *Auk* **74**, 487–493.

Fontaine, M. (1954). *Biol. Revs. Cambridge Phil. Soc.* **29**, 390–418.

Fontaine, M. (1956a). *Mem. Soc. Endocrinol. No.* **5**, 69–81.

Fontaine, M. (1956b). *In* "L'instinct dans le comportement des animaux et de l'homme." Fondation Singer-Polignac, Paris.

Fontaine, M., and Baraduc, M. M. (1955). *Bull. franc. piscic.* **179**, 89–97.

Fontaine, M., and Wurtz-Arlet, J. (1952). *Bull. muséum natl. hist. nat. (Paris)* **64**, 350–352.

Fontaine, M., Baraduc, M. M., and Fontaine, Y. A. (1955). *Compt. rend. soc. biol.* **149**, 1330–1332.

Fontaine, M., Leloup, J., and Olivereau, M. (1952). *Arch. sci. physiol.* **6**, 83–104.

Fortune, P. (1955). *J. Exptl. Biol.* **32**, 504–513.

Fortune, P. Y. (1956). *Nature* **178**, 98.

Frey, H. M., and Albert, A. (1959). *Acta Endocrinol.* **30**, 61–69.

Frieders, F. (1949). Ph.D. Dissertation, Catholic University, Washington, D. C.

Gaiser, M. (1952). *Compt. rend. soc. biol.* **146**, 496–498.

Gargouil, Y. M. (1960). *J. physiol. (Paris)* **52**, 104–106.

Gayda, T. (1922). *Arch. fisiol.* **20**, 209–224.

Glazener, E. W., Schaffner, C. S., and Jull, M. A. (1949). *Poultry Sci.* **28**, 834–849.

Gorbman, A. (1940). *Proc. Soc. Exptl. Biol. Med.* **45**, 772–773.

Gorbman, A. (1959). *In* "Comparative Endocrinology" (A. Gorbman, ed.), pp. 266–282. Wiley, New York.

Gorbman, A., and Berg, O. (1955). *Endocrinology* **56**, 86–92.

Gorbman, A., and Ishii, S. (1960). *Proc. Soc. Exptl. Biol. Med.* **103**, 865–868.

Gorbman, A., Lissitzky, S., Michel, O., Michel, R., and Roche, J. (1952). *Endocrinology* **51**, 311–321.

Grobstein, C., and Bellamy, A. W. (1939). *Proc. Soc. Exptl. Biol. Med.* **41**, 363–365.

Gudernatsch, J. F. (1912). *Wilhelm Roux' Arch. Entwicklungsemch. Organ.* **35**, 457–483.

Haarmann, W. (1936). *Arch. exptl. Pathol. Pharmakol. Naunyn-Schmiedeberg's* **180**, 167–182.

Halevy, S., and Avivi, L. (1960). *Exptl. Cell Research* **20**, 458–463.

Harms, J. W. (1929). *Z. wiss. Zool.* **133**, 211–397.

Harms, J. W. (1935). *Z. wiss. Zool.* **146**, 417–462.

Harris, G. W. (1959). *In* "Comparative Endocrinology" (A. Gorbman, ed.), pp. 202–222. Wiley, New York.

Hoskins, E. R., and Hoskins, M. M. (1919). *J. Exptl. Zool.* **29**, 1–69.

Hasler, A. D., and Meyer, R. K. (1942). *J. Exptl. Zool.* **91**, 391–404.

Hektoen, L., Fox, H., and Schulhof, K. (1927). *J. Infectious Diseases* **40**, 641–646.

Hellbaum, H. W. (1936). *Anat. Record* **67**, 53–68.

Henschel, H. (1931). *Z. ges. exptl. Med.* **77**, 689–692.

Henschel, H., and Steuber, M. (1930). *Klin. Wochschr.* **9**, 1442–1443.

Henschel, H., and Steuber, M. (1931). *Arch. exptl. Pathol. Pharmakol.* **160**, 401–427.

Hickman, C. P. (1959). *Can. J. Zool.* **37**, 997–1060.

Hoar, W. S., and Bell, G. M. (1950). *Can. J. Research* **D28**, 126–136.

Hoar, W. S., MacKinnon, D., and Redlich, A. (1952). *Can. J. Zool.* **30**, 273–286.

Hoar, W. S., Keenleyside, M. H. A., and Goodall, R. G. (1955). *Can. J. Zool.* **33**, 428–439.

Honma, Y., and Murakawa, S. (1955). *Japan. J. Ichtyol.* **4**, 83–93.

Hopper, A. F. (1952). *J. Exptl. Zool.* **119**, 205–217.

Horning, B., and Torrey, H. B. (1923). *Anat. Record* **24**, 395–396.

Iino, S. (1961). *Acta Endocrinol.* **36**, 212–220.

Irwin, M. R., Reineke, E. P., and Turner, C. W. (1943). *Poultry Sci.* **22**, 374–380.

Jankowsky, H. (1960). *Z. vergleich. Physiol.* **43**, 392–410.

Jørgensen, C. Barker, and Larsen, L. O. (1960a). *Proc. Soc. Exptl. Biol. Med.* **103**, 685–688.

Jørgensen, C. Barker, and Larsen, L. O. (1960b). *Nature* **185**, 244–245.

Jørgensen, C. Barker, and Larsen, L. O. (1961). *Gen. Comp. Endocrinol.* **1**, 145–153.

Juhn, M. (1944). *Endocrinology* **35**, 278–279.

Juhn, M., and Fraps, R. M. (1934). *Proc. Soc. Exptl. Biol. Med.* **31**, 1185–1187.

Kaye, N. W. (1961). *Gen. Comp. Endocrinol.* **1**, 1–19.

Kaye, N. W., and LeBourhis, E. E. (1958). *Zoologica* **43**, 73–76.

Kelly, S., and Bailey, N. A. (1951). *Biol. Bull.* **100**, 188–190.

Kelsey, F. O., Gullock, A., and Clausen, H. J. (1960). *Acta Endocrinol.* **35**, 495–500.

Kleinfeld, M. A., Rosenthal, A., and Stein, E. (1958). *Am. J. Physiol.* **195**, 63–65.

Klenner, J. J. (1953). *Proc. Indiana Acad. Sci.* **62**, 318.

Klenner, J. J., and Schipper, A. L. (1954). *Anat. Record* **120**, 790.

Knigge, K. M. (1960). *Federation Proc.* **19**, Suppl. 5, 45–51.

Knowles, F. G. W. (1941). *Proc. Zool. Soc. London* **111A**, 101–109.

Kobayashi, H. (1958). *Endocrinology* **63**, 420–430.

Kobayashi, H., and Gorbman, A. (1959). *Annotationes Zool. Japon.* **32**, 179–184.

Kobayashi, H., and Gorbman, A. (1960). *Endocrinology* **66**, 759–804.

Kobayashi, H., and Tanabe, Y. (1959). *Tori* **15**, 55–60.

Kobayashi, H., Maruyama, K., and Kambara, S. (1955). *Endocrinology* **57**, 129–133.

Kobayashi, H., Gorbman, A., and Wolfson, A. (1960). *Endocrinology* **67**, 153–161.

Kollros, J. J. (1942). *Proc. Soc. Exptl. Biol. Med.* **49**, 204–206.

Kollros, J. J. (1943). *Physiol. Zoöl.* **16**, 269–279.

Kollros, J. J. (1959). *In* "Comparative Endocrinology" (A. Gorbman, ed.), pp.340–350. Wiley, New York.

Kollros, J. J., and Pepernik, V. (1952). *Anat. Record* **113**, 527 Abstr.

Krockert, G. (1936a). *Z. exptl. Pathol. Therap.* **98**, 214–220.

Krockert, G. (1936b). *Z. exptl. Pathol. Therap.* **99**, 451–455.

Krockert, G. (1941). *Vitamine u. Hormone* **1**, 24–31.

Küchler, W. (1935). *J. Ornithol.* **83**, 414–461.

Laplaud, J., Rougier, O., and Gargouil, Y. (1961). *Compt. rend. acad. sci.* **252**,334–335.

Larionow, W. T., and Kusmena, N. (1931). *Biol. Zentr.* **51**, 81–104, 593–606.

La Roche, G. (1950). *Ann. Acfas* **16**, 134–137.

La Roche, G. (1953). *Rev. can. biol.* **11**, 431–438.

La Roche, G., and Leblond, C. P. (1952). *Endocrinology* **51**, 524–545.

La Roche, G., and Leblond, C. P. (1954). *Proc. Soc. Exptl. Biol. Med.* **87**, 273–276.

La Roche, G., Leblond, C. P., and Prefontaine, G. (1950). *Rev. can. biol.* **9**, 101–103.

Leblond, C. P., and Hoff, H. (1944). *Endocrinology* **35**, 229–233.

Le Grand, A., and Ajoulat, L. (1931). *Compt. rend.* **108**, 1263–1264.

Leloup, J. (1952a). *Compt. rend. acad. sci.* **234**, 1315–1317.

Leloup, J. (1952b). *Compt. rend. acad. sci.* **234**, 2485–2487.

Leloup, J. (1955). *J. Physiol. (Paris)* **47**, 671–677.

Leloup, J. (1956). *Compt. rend. acad. sci.* **242**, 1765–1767.

Leloup, J. (1958). *Compt. rend. acad. sci.* **246**, 474–477.

Leloup, J., and Berg, O. (1954). *Compt. rend. acad. sci.* **238**, 1069–1071.

Lilien, O. M. (1954). *Compt. rend. soc. biol.* **148**, 1572–1573.

Lindsay, R. H., and Barker, S. B. (1958). *Endocrinology* **62**, 513–521.

Ludwig, V., and von Mutzenbecher, P. (1939). *Hoppe-Seyler's Z. physiol. Chem.* **258**, 195–211.

Lyman, C. P., and Chatfield, P. O. (1955). *Physiol. Revs.* **35**, 403–425.

Lynn, W. G., and Dent, J. W. (1961). *Biol. Bull.* **120**, 54–61.

Maher, M. J., and Levedahl, B. J. (1959). *J. Exptl. Zool.* **140**, 169–189.

Marine, D., and Lenhart, C. H. (1910). *Bull. Johns Hopkins Hosp.* **21**, 95–98.

Marine, D., and Lenhart, C. H. (1911). *J. Exptl. Med.* **13**, 455–475.

Maruyama, K., and Kobayashi, H. (1956). *Endocrinology* **59**, 213–216.

Matty, A. J. (1954). *J. Marine Biol. Assoc. United Kingdom* **33**, 689–697.

Matty, A. J. (1957). *J. Endocrinol.* **15**, 1–8.

May, R. M., and Mugard, H. (1955). *Ann. endocrinol. (Paris)* **16**, 46–66.

Merkel, F. W. (1938). Zur Physiologie der Zugunruhe bei Vögeln. *Ber. Ver. schles. Ornithol.* **23**, Sonderabdruck 72.

Michel, R. (1956). *Am. J. Med.* **20**, 670–683.

Miller, D. S. (1939). *J. Exptl. Zool.* **80**, 259–286.

Money, W. L., Lucas, V., and Rawson, R. W. (1955). *J. Exptl. Zool.* **128**, 411–421.

Money, W. L., Meltzer, R. I., Young, J., and Rawson, R. (1958). *Endocrinology* **63**, 20–28.

Morgan, A. H., and Fales, C. H. (1942). *J. Morphol.* **71**, 357–390.

Morgan, A. H., and Moyer, E. K. (1936). *Anat. Record* **64**, 86–87.

Morton, M. E., and Chaikoff, I. L. (1943). *J. Biol. Chem.* **147**, 1–9.

Müller, J. (1953). *Z. vergleich. Physiol.* **35**, 1–12.

Nadler, N. J. (1960). *Proc. Soc. Exptl. Biol. Med.* **105**, 38–41.

Nadler, N. J., Carneiro, J., and Leblond, C. P. (1960). *Acta Endocrinol.* **35**, Suppl., 1209 Abstr.

Newcomer, W. S. (1957). *Am. J. Physiol.* **190**, 413–418.

Nigrelli, R. F., Goldsmith, E. D., and Charipper, H. A. (1946). *Anat. Record* **94**, 523.

Noble, G. K., and Bradley, H. T. (1933). *Biol. Bull.* **64**, 289–298.

Norman, D., and Hiestand, W. A. (1960). *Comp. Biochem. Physiol.* **1**, 167–179.

Oakeson, B., and Lilley, B. (1957). *Anat. Record* **128**, 699–714.

Olivereau, M. (1950). *Compt. rend. soc. biol.* **144**, 832–834.

Olivereau, M. (1951). *Ann. endocrinol.* *(Paris)* **12**, 98–107.

Olivereau, M. (1952). *Compt. rend. soc. biol.* **146**, 569–570.

Olivereau, M. (1954). *Ann. inst. oceanog.* *(Paris)* **29**, 95–296.

Olivereau, M. (1960). *Ann. soc. royale zool. belg.* **90**, 83–98.

Paik, W. K., and Cohen, P. P. (1960). *J. Gen. Physiol.* **43**, 683–696.

Parkes, A. S., and Selye, H. (1937). *J. Genet.* **34**, 297–306.

Patane, L. (1949). *Boll. soc. ital. biol. sper.* **25**, 1509–1510.

Perlman, I., Chaikoff, I. L., Morton, M. E. (1941). *J. Biol. Chem.* **139**, 433–456.

Pesetsky, I., and Kollros, J. J. (1956). *Exptl. Cell Research* **11**, 477–482.

Pflugfelder, O. (1954). *Wilhelm Roux', Arch. Entwicklungsmech. Organ.* **147**, 42–60.

Pflugfelder, O. (1956). *Wilhelm Roux' Arch. Entwicklungsmech. Organ.* **148**, 463–473.

Pickford, G., and Atz, J. W. (1957). "The Physiology of the Pituitary Gland of Fishes." New York Zoological Society, New York.

Piotrowski, L. J., Steelman, S. L., and Koch, F. C. (1953). *Endocrinology* **52**, 489–495

Pitt-Rivers, R., and Tata, J. R. (1959). "The Thyroid Hormones." Pergamon Press, New York.

Portet, R. (1960). *J. Physiol.* *(Paris)* **52**, 200–201.

Pritchard, A. W., and Gorbman, A. (1960). *Biol. Bull.* **119**, 109–119.

Punt, A., and Jungbloed, J. (1945). *Arch. néerl. zool.* **7**, 1–15.

Quastel, J. H. (1939). *Physiol. Revs.* **19**, 135–183.

Ratzersdorfer, C., Gordon, A. S., and Charipper, H. A. (1949). *J. Exptl. Zool.* **112**, 13–28.

Reineke, E. P. (1949). *Ann. N. Y. Acad. Sci.* **50**, 450–465.

Richardson, D. (1940). *J. Exptl. Zool.* **83**, 407–429.

Riddle, O. (1927). *Endocrinology* **11**, 161–172.

Rizzo, L. (1950a). *Boll. mus. instit. biol. Univ. Genova* **23**, 1–12.

Rizzo, L. (1950b). *Boll. mus. instit. biol. Univ. Genova* **23**, 23–29.

Robbins, J., and Rall, J. E. (1960). *Physiol. Revs.* **40**, 415–489.

Robertson, O. H. (1949). *J. Exptl. Zool.* **110**, 337–355.

Robertson, O. H. (1951a). *Physiol. Zoöl.* **24**, 309–323.

Robertson, O. H. (1951b). *Endocrinology* **48**, 658–668.

Roche, J., and Desruisseaux, A. (1951). *Compt. rend. soc. biol.* **145**, 1831–1833.

Roche, J., and Michel, R. (1955). *Physiol. Revs.* **35**, 583–610.

Roche, J., and Yagi, Y. (1952). *Compt. rend. soc. biol.* **146**, 642–645.

Roche, J., Michel, O., Michel, R., and Marois, M. (1951). *Compt. rend. soc. biol.* **145**, 1833–1836.

Roche, J., Michel, R., Michel, O., and Lissitzky, S. (1952). *Biochim. et Biophys. Acta* **9**, 161–169.

Roche, J., Deltour, G. H., Michel, R., and Velez, E. (1953a). *Compt. rend. soc. biol.* **147**, 270–274.

Roche, J., Michel, O., Michel, R., Gorbman, A., and Lissitzky, S. (1953b). *Biochim. et Biophys. Acta* **12**, 570–576.

Roche, J., Michel, R., and Volpert, E. (1956). *Compt. rend. soc. biol.* **150**, 2149–2153.

Roche, J., Michel, R., Volpert, E., and Sanz, B. (1957). *Compt. rend. soc. biol.* **151**, 225–228.

Root, R. W., and Etkin, W. R. (1937). *Proc. Soc. Exptl. Biol. Med.* **37**, 174–175.

Rose, N. R., and Witebsky, E. (1956). *J. Immunol.* **76**, 417–427.

Sadler, W. W., and Tyler, W. S. (1960). *Acta Endocrinol.* **34**, 586–604.

Saxén, L., Saxén, E., Toivonen, S., and Salimaki, K. (1957). *Endocrinology* **61**, 35–44.

Schaefer, W. H. (1933). *Proc. Soc. Exptl. Biol. Med.* **30**, 1363–1365.

Scharrer, E. (1959). *In* "Comparative Endocrinology" (A. Gorbman, ed.), pp. 233–249. Wiley, New York.

Schmidt, J. A. (1956). *J. Exptl. Zool.* **133**, 539–558.

Scott, A. H. (1935). *Am. J. Physiol.* **111**, 107–117.

Scott, J. L. (1953). *Zoologica* **38**, 53–62.

Shaw, T. I. (1960). *Proc. Roy. Soc.* **B152**, 109–117.

Shellabarger, C. J. (1955). *Poultry Sci.* **34**, 1437–1440.

Shellabarger, C. J., and Brown, J. R. (1959). *J. Endocrinol.* **18**, 98–101.

Shellabarger, C. J., Gorbman, A., Schatzlein, F. C., and McGill, D. (1956). *Endocrinology* **59**, 331–339.

Shibusawa, K. (1960). *Acta Endocrinol.* **35**, Suppl. 51, 89–90 Abstr.

Shibusawa, K., Saito, S., Nishi, K., Yamamoto, T., Tomizawa, K., and Abe, C.(1956). *Endocrinol. Japon.* **3**, 116–124.

Simpson, M. E., Asling, C. W., and Evans, H. M. (1950). *Yale J. Biol. Med.* **23**, 1–27

Singh, O. N., Henneman, H., and Reineke, E. P. (1956). *J. Animal Sci.* **15**, 625–630.

Slingerland, D. W., Graham, D. E., Josephs, R. K., Mulrey, P. F., Trakas, A. P., and Yamazaki, E. (1959). *Endocrinology* **65**, 178–188.

Smelser, G. K. (1938). *Endocrinology* **23**, 429–438.

Smith, D. C., and Everett, G. M. (1943). *J. Exptl. Zool.* **94**, 229–240.

Smith, D. C., and Matthews, S. A. (1948). *Am. J. Physiol.* **153**, 215–221.

Smith, D. C., Sladek, S. A., and Kellner, A. W. (1953). *Physiol. Zoöl.* **26**, 117–124.

Smith, D. C. W. (1956). *Mem. Soc. Endocrinol. No.* **5**, 83–98.

Smith, P. E. (1916). *Science* **44**, 280–282.

Söderberg, U. (1959). *Physiol. Revs.* **39**, 777–810.

Speidel, C. C. (1929). *Am. J. Anat.* **43**, 103–165.

Srivastava, P. N. (1960). *Physiol. Zoöl.* **33**, 277–280.

Stadie, R. (1938). *Z. wiss. Zool.* **151**, 445–466.

Stebbins, R. C., and Eakin, R. M. (1958). *Am. Museum Novitates No.* **1870**, 1–40.

Stokinger, H. E., and Heidelberger, M. (1937). *J. Exptl. Med.* **66**, 251–272.

Stone, L. S., and Steinitz, H. (1953). *J. Exptl. Zool.* **124**, 469–504.

Svärdson, G. (1943). Studien über den Zusammenhang zwischen Geschlechstsreife und Wachstum bei *Lebistes*. Medd. Undersökanst. Söttvatensfisk., Stockholm, (21), p.48

Takewaki, K., and Mori, H. (1944). *J. Fac. Sci. Univ. Tokyo* **6**, 547–575.

Tata, J. R., and Shellabarger, C. J. (1959). *Biochem. J.* **72**, 608–613.

Tata, J. R., Ernster, L., and Lindberg, O. (1962). *Nature* **193**, 1058–1060.

Taurog, A., Tong, W., and Chaikoff, I. L. (1950). *J. Biol. Chem.* **184**, 83–93.

Taylor, A. (1937). *J. Exptl. Zool.* **75**, 239–244.

Taylor, A. (1939). *J. Exptl. Zool.* **81**, 135–146.

Tinacci, F. (1947). *Boll. soc. ital. biol. sper.* **28**, 575–578.

Tinacci, F. (1948). *Publ. staz. zool. Napoli* **21**, 124–131.

Tixier-Vidal, A., and Assenmacher, I. (1960). *Compt. rend. soc. biol.* **154**, 98–101.

Torrey, H. B., and Horning, B. (1925). *Biol. Bull.* **49**, 275–287.

Truchot, R., Salvatore, G., and Michel, R. (1960). *Compt. rend. soc. biol.* **165**, 1393–1395.

Trunnell, J. B., and Wade, P. (1955). *J. Clin. Endocrinol. and Metabolism* **15**, 107–117.

Ungar, I. (1933). *Compt. rend. soc. Biol.* **112**, 504–506.

van den Beld, C. H., Douglas, R. R., and Talesnik, D. J. (1959). *Acta Physiol. Latinoam.* **9**, 273–285.

Vivien, J. H. (1954). *Arch. anat. Strasbourg* **37**, 163–174.

Vivien, J. H., and Gaiser, M. L. (1952a). *Compt. rend. soc. biol.* **234**, 1585–1587.

Vivien, J. H., and Gaiser, M. (1952b). *Compt. rend. acad. sci.* **234**, 1643–1645.

Vivien, J. H., and Rechenmann, R. (1954). *Compt. rend. soc. biol.* **148**, 170–172.

Vlijm, L. (1958). *Arch. néerl. zool.* **12**, 467–531.

von Buddenbrock, W. (1950). "Vergleichende Physiologie," Bd. IV: Hormone. Birkhäuser, Basel.

von Issekutz, B. (1935). *Wien. klin. Wochschr.* **48**, 1325–1330.

Wald, G. (1945–46). *Harvey Lectures*, Ser. **41**, 117–134.

Waring, H., Landgrebe, F. W., and Bruce, J. R. (1942). *J. Exptl. Biol.* **18**, 306–316.

Warren, M. R. (1940). *J. Exptl. Zool.* **83**, 127–159.

Werner, S., ed. (1962). "The Thyroid." Harper (Hoeber) and Row, New York.

Witebsky, E. (1929). *Z. Immunitätsforsch.* **62**, 35–73.

Woitkewitsch, A. A. (1940). *Compt. rend. acad. sci. U.R.S.S.* N.S. **26**, 511–519.

Wolf, O. M. (1934). *Anat. Record* **60**, Suppl. 83 Abstr.

Wolff, J., and Chaikoff, I. L. (1947). *Endocrinology* **41**, 295–298.

Wollman, S. H., and Zwilling, E. (1953). *Endocrinology* **52**, 526–535.

Wollman, S. H., and Wodinsky, I. (1955). *Endocrinology* **56**, 9–20.

Young, J. Z., and Bellerby, C. W. (1935). *J. Exptl. Biol.* **12**, 246–253.

Zawadowsky, B. (1932). *Endokrinologie* **10**, 23–36.

Zawadowsky, B., Liptschina, N., and Radiswon, E. N. (1928). *Wilhelm Roux' Arch. Entwicklungsmech. Organ.* **113**, 419–425.

Zawadowsky, B., and Rochlina, M. (1927). *Wilhelm Roux' Arch. Entwicklungsmech Organ.* **109**, 188–209.

~ 9 ~

Parathyroid Glands

ROY O. GREEP

Harvard School of Dental Medicine
Boston, Massachusetts

I. PROLEGOMENON

The biological background of the parathyroid glands as we know them in man and the common laboratory animals seems curiously obscure. It is not so much that information is lacking, as it is that in terms of interest and attention the parathyroids in general have played an off-stage role in the drama of endocrinological research. The parathyroids have not been called from the wings even by comparative endocrinologists; thus far in three international meetings dealing with the comparative aspects of endocrinology, the parathyroids have not been a topic of discussion. Physiological inconsequence cannot be the basis of this disregard. Life for the vast majority of vertebrates is either endangered or impossible without the parathyroids yet even recent treatises on the life of the vertebrates make little or no mention of the parathyroid glands. The parathyroids also have a respectable phylogenetic history; their ontogeny, likewise, reveals a lineage with the vertebrates that extends back to Devonian times. However, it would probably be an overstatement to assert that it is common knowledge among biologists that the parathyroids are not found among the fishes.

The comparative aspects of parathyroid research have been equally neglected. Much of the work that has been done on the parathyroid glands in the lower vertebrates has been colored by prior knowledge of the morphology and function of these glands in a very limited number of eutherian mammals. Similarly the only parathyroid hormone preparation that has been available for testing in submammalian orders is that extracted from the glands of a single species of mammal, the ox. There is much yet to be clarified concerning the parathyroids throughout the vertebrate kingdom but the gaps in our knowledge become increasingly broad as the phyletic scale is examined in descending order. Most of the early studies of the parathyroids in the lower vertebrates have dealt with their embryological origin and their morphological relationship with other derivatives of the primitive pharynx. The elucidation of these matters occupied the attention of many eminent morphologists at the turn of the century and comprised one of the great chapters in vertebrate embryology. Therein lies the background for much of our knowledge of the biology of the parathyroids.

II. INTRODUCTION

The early history of the parathyroids is connected very closely indeed with early discoveries in regard to the thyroid gland. Sandström's original description of the parathyroids published in 1880 was based on dissection of dog, cat, rabbit, horse, and ox and it is obvious that his observations were confined to the so-called internal pair of parathyroids which in these animals are in intimate contact with the thyroid gland. During the 1880's it was a common but not invariable experience that removal of the thyroid glands in dogs, cats, and man was frequently accompanied by severe if not fatal tetany of unknown cause. Gley's discovery in 1891 of the external pair of parathyroid glands in the rabbit and his conclusive demonstration that tetany did not follow thyroidectomy if one pair of the parathyroid glands was left intact delineated irrefutably the separate and different functions of the thyroid and parathyroid glands. Nonetheless, the close anatomical approximation of these glands and certain similarities in their histological structure were to muddy the water for another quarter century. Swale Vincent in his early textbook on the ductless glands lent credence as late as 1912 to a then-popular concept that the closed tubules of the parathyroids could give rise to the colloid-filled follicles of the thyroid, and vice versa, depending on relative need.

On the phyletic scale the parathyroid glands first appear as definitive structures in the Amphibia. Their origin is more precisely linked with the time when the ancestors of our modern amphibians were making their terrestrial debut. It seems to be generally agreed that the parathyroids arose, through whatever circumstances, at the time of the disappearance of the branchial apparatus. It is interesting that the parathyroids, originating as they do from pharyngeal epithelium that was originally concerned with respiration, came to subserve a function of the gills totally unrelated to the transfer of oxygen, namely the transfer of salts. If there is any purposive relation between the origin of the parathyroids and the coincident substitution of lungs for gills as a means of breathing it would seem more likely that this concerns the mechanics of breathing, i.e., the maintenance of a proper ionic environment for the neuromuscular control of the ventilating system.

What part the parathyroids may have played, if any, in the emergence of land forms is unknown. It is conceivable, as suggested by Waggener (1930), that the origin of the parathyroid glands may have some pertinent connection with the mode of respiration in land vertebrates. It is also an intriguing observation (Studitsky, 1945) that the ancestors of the amphibians, the fishes, although destitute of parathyroids, have an abundance of vitamin D (especially the Teleostei) which may have aided in the regulation of calcium metabolism. As the Amphibia became terrestrial the problems in control of calcium metabolism were undoubtedly amplified and Studitsky suggests that the parathyroids may have come into operation along with the vitamin D mechanism, aiding in the control of the calcium content of the internal environment through the mobilization of skeletal calcium. As we shall note later, the parathyroids in Amphibia do play a role, more critical in some species than others, in the control of calcium metabolism.

The term "parathyroid" implies a relationship with the thyroid gland which is in poor accord with the facts. It is only in man and certain of the laboratory animals that any relationship exists and even here it is strictly topographical. Actually, the parathyroid glands have a closer kinship with the thymus, which derives from the same pharyngeal pouches as do the parathyroids. This relationship, long a matter of contention among embryologists, is still unsettled and will be referred to in a later section. Be it noted here only that an early French worker (Aimé, 1911) termed these glands the *parathymique glandules* and Weller (1933) among other English writers has used the term "parathymus." It is small wonder that many alternative names have been proposed. The term *Epithelkörpchen* (epithelial body) proposed by Maurer (1886) and adopted by Kohn (1895, 1899) has been widely used and is still favored by many modern authors. Prenant used the term *glandule thyroidienne* and van Bemmelen (1886), mistaking one pair of the parathyroids in reptiles for carotid bodies, labeled them *Carotiskörperchen*. This gave rise to later designations such as "carotid body" and "carotid gland" for the parathyroid glands. Adams (1939, 1952) preferred the generic term "epithelial body." This too has its drawbacks in that it does not adequately describe the definitive gland except with respect to histogenetic origin. A new term is needed which would properly indicate the physiological role of these glands of internal secretion. Now that purified preparations of the parathyroid hormone are available and the functional role is rapidly being elucidated, perhaps the time is near when a suitable new name for the parathyroids will be forthcoming—a name that will accord them anatomic and functional individuality, a status that does, in fact, exist in nature.

III. FISHES

Parathyroid glands have not been found in fish (Vincent, 1912; Bargmann, 1939; Fontaine, 1956).[1] It would, however, be premature to conclude that no parathyroid-like functions are served in these animals. The absence of parathyroid hormone-secreting tissue in fish was first called into question by Rasquin and Rosenbloom (1954). They observed a striking hypertrophy and hyperplasia of the ultimobranchial body in an eyed form of *Astyanax mexicanus* (Filippi) maintained under stress of total darkness. They kept these fish in darkness for periods ranging from 1 week up to $2\frac{1}{2}$ years. Detectable hypertrophy of the ultimobranchial body was present after 2–4 weeks in a few specimens but the exaggerated type of response illustrated in Fig. 1 was not seen before 7 months or more.

---

[1] The identity of certain small bodies composed of compact masses of adenoidal and epithelial cells which Thompson (1910) described in the thyroid of an elasmobranch *Scyllium canicula* and which raised the question of their possibly being parathyroids cannot be established with any certainty from her published drawings and should be disregarded until more conclusive evidence is at hand.

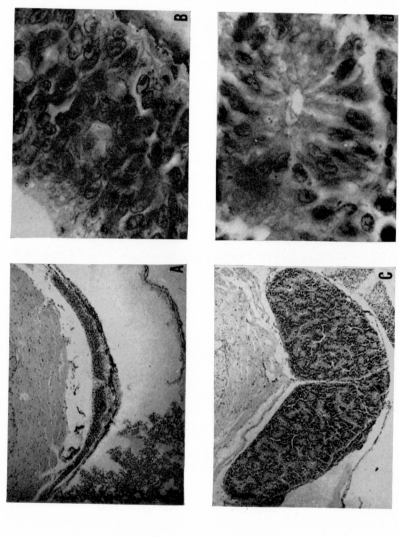

FIG. 1. Ultimobranchial body of *Astyanax mexicanus* raised in light (A, low and B, high magnification), and after 34 weeks in dark-ness (C, low and D, high magnification). (From Rasquin and Rosenbloom, 1954.)

According to Rasquin and Rosenbloom, the ultimobranchial body in untreated *Astyanax* "consists of a broad sac-like structure situated between the ventral wall of the esophagus and the sinus venosus. . . . A thin connective tissue membrane encloses a peripheral band of high columnar cells and also forms a septum dividing the gland into two parts. The peripheral cells appear foamy . . . as if some cytoplasmic elements had been dissolved out . . . The gland has a wide lumen within which are found lymphocytes." In the stimulated state the peripheral cells showed both hypertrophy and hyperplasia of an extreme sort. In sections the cells appeared to be arranged in cords and acini. The small lymphocytes completely disappeared. The histologic evidence is impressively suggestive of secretory activity.

Correlated with these changes in the ultimobranchial body, Rasquin and Rosenbloom found renal and skeletal defects. Some animals developed kyphosis of the vertebral column (Fig. 2). The kidneys showed coalescence, distension or hyalin degeneration of the tubules, adenomas, rupture of the capsule, and in some instances near total destruction of the organ. Of 87 dark-raised fish, 79% showed ultimobranchial hypertrophy and renal damage and 42% showed skeletal defects. The authors suggest that the sequence may be renal insufficiency, hypertrophy of the ultimobranchial body and secretion of a parathyroid hormone-like substance resulting in skeletal decalcification and fibrosis.

FIG. 2. Distorted vertebral column in *Astyanax* after living in darkness for a year. (From Rasquin and Rosenbloom, 1954.)

The evidence for a parathyroid type of involvement in these results is not, however, entirely clear-cut. It is important to note that slight hypertrophy was seen in the ultimobranchial body of 50% of the light-raised fish and that multiple endocrine imbalances were present in the animals raised in darkness. Changes were seen in the pituitary, interrenal, and thyroid glands. After long exposure to darkness a condition simulating hypophysectomy was in evidence. Moreover, the possibility of an existing vitamin D deficiency imposed by the absence of light must also be considered.

A positive response in fish to injections of extracts of mammalian parathyroid glands was first demonstrated in 1958 by Budde. This demonstration, coming as it did hard on the heels of the report of a negative finding, was rather surprising. In 1957, Hoar referred to the fact that his associate, A. J. Rampone, found no significant change in bone or muscle ash in 82 goldfish receiving 1–30 units Parathyroid Extract (Lilly). Budde injected both sexes of adult guppies (*Lebistes reticulatus*) with 0.5–1 unit Paroidin (Parke, Davis & Co.) every third day for periods up to 60 days. Some fish developed arched backs and many showed an actual decrease in body length (reminiscent of the noted case of shrinking stature in a man with hyperparathyroidism referred to by Albright and Reifenstein, 1948). The fish receiving a total dosage of 15–20 units Paroidin showed increased calcification and ossification. The bones became thicker and denser. The pharyngeal teeth were likewise wider and sturdier. The number of osteoblasts was increased. Lesser dosages or shorter term treatment with high dosage often had the effect of converting the osteoblasts to fibroblasts thereby interrupting bone formation and allowing concomitant excessive bone destruction. No significant histologic deviations were noted in the ultimobranchial body in these treated guppies. Although atrophy might have been anticipated, the organ was not favorable for study because in this species it is an extremely thin and attenuated structure.

Recently, Fleming and Meier (1961a,b) obtained a weakly positive response to mammalian parathyroid extract (PTE) in a second teleost, *Fundulus kansae*. The response to PTE was limited to a fleeting increase in serum calcium of estrogen-primed females or to an increase in serum Ca^{45} turnover in females during the breeding season. Similar tests in *F. catenatus* were entirely negative. The authors suggest that either the calcemic response to PTE is conditioned by estrogen or the estrogen provides an experimental situation which makes detection of the response possible. A rationale for the latter was given by Bailey (1957) who showed that estrogen induced in the serum of fish the formation of a calcium-binding protein similar to the phosphoprotein reported by Schjeide and Urist (1956) in birds. Thus the calcium mobilized by PTE may be trapped transiently and rendered detectable. The increase in serum calcium by estrogen alone was considerable in both males and females of *F. kansae* and *F. catenatus*. Inasmuch as only the females of *F. kansae* responded to PTE, Fleming and Meier conclude that in these two closely related species of killifish, a sex as well as a species difference in responsiveness to mammalian PTE has been demonstrated.

IV. AMPHIBIANS

Reference to structures in amphibians likely to have been the parathyroids were made in 1853 by Ecker and by Leydig. Toldt (1868) observed these structures, of reddish color and hempseed proportions, more closely and concluded that they should be regarded as accessory thyroids which led to their later designation as *Nebenschildrüsen*. It was Maurer (1888), however, who traced the embryological development of these glands in a number of amphibia and gave them the name *Epithelkörperchen* (epithelial bodies). Their homology with the "glandulae parathyroidienne" discovered earlier in higher vertebrates by Sandström (1880) was first established by Kohn (1895) and confirmed by Maurer (1899a).

In anurans and urodeles the anlage of the parathyroids arise from the third and fourth pharyngeal pouches (Maurer, 1888). It is generally stated that the parathyroids arise at the time of metamorphosis and this is in essence true. In anurans, as Maurer demonstrated, the anlage appear during the larval stage at the time of the formation of the inner gills whereas in urodeles they arise only at the time of transformation. Parathyroids are not found in the permanently neotenous amphibian such as the Mexican axolotl or in the Perennibranchiata, *Typhlomolge rathbuni*, the blind Texan cave salamander (Uhlenhuth, 1923); *Necturus maculosa* (Eycleshymer and Wilson, 1910) and *Proteus anguinus* (Klose, 1932).

The parathyroid glands in all the amphibians studied are quite similar in histological structure. It may, in fact, be remarked that the microscopic appearance of parathyroid tissue (Fig. 3) is notably constant through-

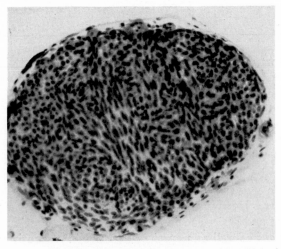

FIG. 3. Section of parathyroid gland of summer *Rana pipiens*. Whorls in parenchyma and subcapsular capillary network are evident. 200× (From Cortelyou *et al.*, 1960.)

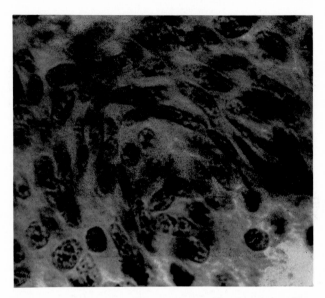

FIG. 4. Parenchymal cells of Fig. 3 at higher magnification. 840✕ (From Cortelyou *et al.*, 1960.)

out the vertebrates. The most distinguishing characteristic is the compact arrangement of the parenchymal cells, the so-called chief cells. The cells are typically elongated with round or ovoid nuclei (Fig. 4). In most, but not all amphibians (notably *Xenopus*, Shapiro, 1933), the cells are arranged in whorls. Romeis (1926) has provided an elegantly illustrated account of the parathyroids in *Rana temporaria*. Cytologically the cells are remarkable for the relative absence of granular constituents generally associated with secretory activity. In most cells the cytoplasm is virtually clear and the cell membranes are indistinct. In fact, the cells have been often categorized on the basis of their stainability as "clear" cells and "dark" cells. These almost certainly represent cells in different phases of cyclic secretory activity. Finally it is to be noted that in amphibians as in higher vertebrates the parathyroid glands are invariably encapsulated by fibrous connective tissue.

During the winter season, amphibian parathyroids undergo degenerative changes as noted in *R. temporaria* (Romeis, 1926); *R. catesbeiana* (Waggener, 1929) and *R. pipiens* (Cortelyou *et al.*, 1960). The changes are most severe in *R. catesbeiana* where all but a peripheral border of cells undergo a peculiar liquefaction and are replaced with the approach of summer by isolated subscapsular growth centers. In the other frogs studied, a similar dissolution of cytoplasm occurs (Fig. 5) but the cells do not lose their structural identity. Microscopically, such glands have a reticular appear-

334 R. O. GREEP

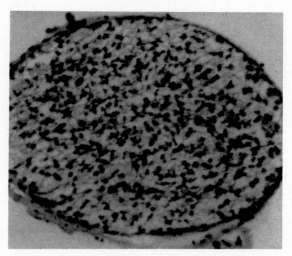

FIG. 5. Reticular type of degeneration seen in winter *Rana pipiens*. 860× (From Cortelyou *et al.*, 1960.)

ance. Studitsky (1945), with inadequate justification, regards the liquefaction as evidence of stimulation coinciding with critical phases of calcium metabolism. He claims to have found these changes in *R. temporaria* and *R. ridibunda* during metamorphosis and also during the spring and summer periods.

The parathyroids of *Bufo* as reported by Boschwitz (1961) require special comment in that they are said to be avascular, i.e., they have no internal capillaries (Fig. 6A,B). The dense network of vessels on the surface of the gland bulge into the parenchyma. Most striking is the fact that fine intercellular slits or spaces comparable to acellular bile ducts of mammals ramify through the parenchyma (Fig. 6). The lack of any internal blood supply has not been previously noted in Amphibia although a dense subscapular network of vessels is common. Krause (1923), Romeis (1926), and Studitsky (1945) described the presence of internal blood vessels in *Rana*.

A. Anura

There are a number of adequate descriptions of the parathyroid glands in adult Anura (*T. temporaria*, Romeis, 1926; *R. catesbeiana*, Waggener, 1929, 1930; *Xenopus laevis*, Shapiro, 1933 and *Bufo*, Boschwitz, 1961). There are ordinarily four glands, two on each side, designated parathyroid III and parathyroid IV. The two glands are usually fairly close together, especially in *R. pipiens*, and are located in the sinus sternalis (Fig. 7) close

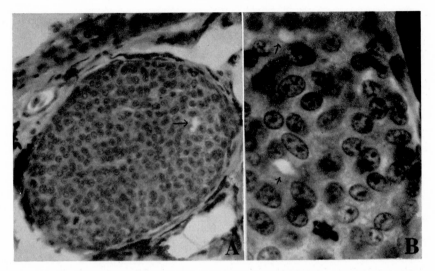

FIG. 6. Sections of parathyroid glands of *Bufo viridis* showing intercellular ducts. (A, low and B, high magnification.) (From Boschwitz, 1961.)

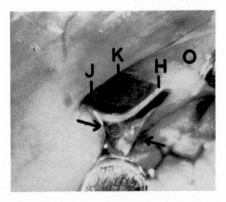

FIG. 7. Fresh dissection showing parathyroid glands in *Rana pipiens* in relation to kiemenrest (K), hypoglossal nerve (H), external jugular vein (J), and omohyoid muscle (O). Arrows point to parathyroid glands. 120× (From Cortelyou *et al.*, 1960.)

to the external jugular vein and just caudad of the kiemenrest or ventral branchial body (the *venträler Kiemenrest* of Maurer). In *R. catesbeiana* they are commonly situated one on each side of the external jugular; in *R. pipiens* they are dorsal to this vein. In any given species the number and position of the main glands may vary and the presence of accessory glands has been noted (Romeis, 1926; Pischinger, 1937). Although these variations do not alter the fundamental pattern in origin and development of the parathyroid glands, they are to be reckoned with whenever complete extirpation of parathyroid tissue is sought.

The glands themselves are minute and, in some instances, barely visible to the naked eye. Their dissection or surgical removal requires the aid of a binocular dissecting microscope. The parathyroids are ovate and roughly 0.5–1 mm in diameter. They are whitish to yellowish or greyish-red in color. They have a glistening appearance and firm consistency which helps in distinguishing them from fat globules with which they are often associated.

1. PARATHYROIDECTOMY

a. Neuromuscular symptoms. The effect of surgical extirpation of the parathyroids has been studied in *R. temporaria* (Romeis, 1926), *R. catesbeiana* (Waggener, 1930), *Hyla aurea* (Kuffler, 1945), *R. pipiens* (Cortelyou et al.,* 1960; Cortelyou, 1960a), and *Bufo viridis,* Laur. (Boschwitz, 1961). The reports are in poor agreement in respect to the appearance of neuromuscular symptoms including tetany. The operated *Rana catesbeiana* developed tetany and died in $1\frac{1}{2}$–$3\frac{1}{2}$ days (Waggener, 1930). Experience with other frogs has been quite different. Kuffler noted virtually no muscular tremors in *Hyla* but the animals did evince hyperexcitability when approached. Tetany could be precipitated by lesser doses of sodium citrate and it lasted longer in operated than in intact animals. In a series of over 300 operated *R. pipiens,* Cortelyou et al. (1960) reported that tetanic symptoms were never seen nor was there any evidence of behavioral change. Neuromuscular preparations from operated animals, however, did reveal a slight increase in excitability and a decrease in fusion frequency during the first 5 days after removal of the glands. Beyond the second week, preparations from operated and intact animals behaved in identical fashion. The season of the year in which the operation was carried out was of no consequence. The only report on parathyroidectomized toads is the very recent one on *B. viridis* by Boschwitz (1961). She states that the animals moved and leapt as usual on recovery from the anesthetic and "caught flies after 2 or 3 days . . . But after a variable period of apparent normality . . . the toad rolled on its back remaining in this position for several minutes (catalepsy). A certain weakness . . . carpopedal spasm and fibrillations indicated the outbreak of tetany. The first seizures started if the animal was touched or caught. Later, in addition, spontaneous violent convulsions took place: the eyes and lungs bulging. The floor of the mouth moved up and down rapidly, compensating for the lack of lung respiration . . ." During the attack (Fig. 8), respiration was via the skin and

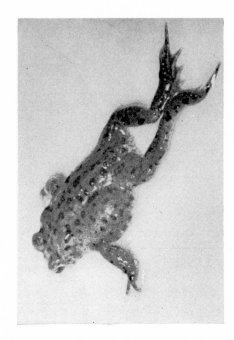

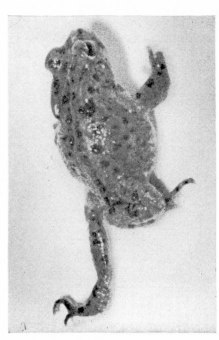

FIG. 8. Two views of parathyroidectomized *Bufo viridis* during seizure of tetany showing typical position of extremities and toes; note bulging eyes and distended lungs. (From Boschwitz, 1961.)

floor of the mouth. The duration of these fits ranged from a few seconds
to more than 9 hours. Between seizures the animals behaved normally.
The animals operated on in the fall suffered the first seizure in 2–8 days.
After mid-November the latency period was 20–40 days. In two exceptional
instances the first symptoms appeared at 98 and 138 days.

   b. Effect on calcium and phosphorus in blood and urine. The published
values for the calcium and phosphorus content of the blood of intact frogs
is given in Table I. It will be apparent that the calcium content of the
blood of amphibians is very nearly identical with that of the blood of
mammals. The variation noted between species is probably partly real
and partly a reflection of the use of different analytical methods.

TABLE I

CALCIUM AND PHOSPHORUS CONTENT OF THE BLOOD OF INTACT AMPHIBIA

Species	Whole blood Mean (and range)	Plasma Mean (and range)	References
	Calcium (mg/100 ml)		
Rana catesbeiana	11.9(9.7–13.0)	—	Waggener (1930)
Rana pipiens	10.3(9.4–12.5)	6.6(5.2–8.6)	Cortelyou *et al.* (1960)
Rana temporaria and *Rana ridibunda*	—	$8.41^a(5.25–7.45)^b$	Kovalsky (1941; quoted by Studitsky, 1945)
	Phosphorus (mg/100 ml)		
Rana pipiens[c]	—	3.62±0.11(—)	Cortelyou (1962)

[a] Spring.
[b] Winter.
[c] Eighty-two animals used.

   Irrespective of the fact that parathyroidectomy leads to the appearance
of neuromuscular symptoms in some species of Anura and not in others,
the operation has led to a decrease in the blood calcium in all species
studied. Waggener (1930) pioneering in this area took blood from *R.
catesbeiana* in severe tetany and found the calcium content to average 7.7
mg/100 ml as opposed to an average value of 11.9 mg/100 ml for intact
controls. Cortelyou and associates have underway a full-scale investigation
of the relationship of the parathyroid to calcium and phosphorus metabolism in the common frog *R. pipiens* and only the first results of this study
are available (Cortelyou *et al.*, 1960; Cortelyou, 1962). At 24 hours after
parathyroidectomy they found that the mean blood calcium had declined

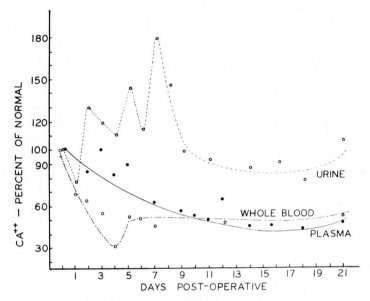

FIG. 9. Changes in calcium content of whole blood, plasma, and urine after removal of the parathyroid glands in the frog *Rana pipiens*. (From Cortelyou *et al.*, 1960.)

by 30% and at 96 hours had reached 3.3 mg, a decrease of 68% (Fig. 9). In frogs the depression in whole blood calcium reached its lowest point between 4 and 7 days, whereas in parathyroidectomized rats the maximal drop in blood calcium was observed very much sooner, i.e., 24–48 hours (Talmage *et al.*, 1953). The decline in plasma calcium was less precipitous reaching 4 mg/100 ml at 1–2 weeks, or one-third of the normal mean value of 6.6 mg/100 ml (Fig. 9). Since these animals showed no visible evidence of parathyroid deficiency it is quite clear that changes in blood chemistry are a more reliable and sensitive index of parathyroprivea. However, even these changes were by no means permanent; after several weeks, whether through natural readjustments or the action of accessory parathyroids, the values for blood and plasma calcium returned to the lower limits of the normal range (a similar phenomenon has often been described in mammals; reviewed by Greep, 1948).

Among the Amphibia, it is only in *R. pipiens* that observations on blood and urine phosphorus have been made (Cortelyou, 1960a,b, 1962). Hypophosphaturia is a constant finding in mammals after parathyroidectomy; frogs too show an initial slight decrease but this is followed by a pronounced upward trend that may exceed the normal value by as much as 78% within a week. The time relationships between the lowered plasma calcium and

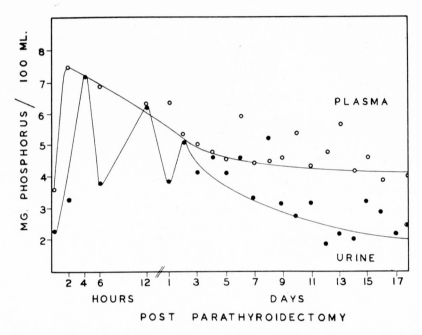

Fɪɢ. 10. Changes in phosphorus content of plasma and urine after removal of the parathyroid glands in the frog *Rana pipiens*. (Graphed from data in Table 1, Cortelyou, 1962).

increased urine calcium after parathyroidectomy suggest that the absence of the parathyroid hormone lessens the renal reabsorption of calcium. Unlike mammals, in which parathyroidectomy typically leads to hyperphosphatemia and hypophosphaturia, frogs show an increase in both blood and urine phosphorus after this operation. These elevated levels gradually decline to near normal values after 18 days (Fig. 10). In 1962 Cortelyou reported that the maximal increase in plasma phosphorus occurs at 2 hours, and the maximal urine phosphorus at 4 hours after removal of the parathyroids. Since the urine phosphorus was elevated at 2 hours as well, it will be obvious that the increase in plasma phosphorus cannot be accounted for by an increased reabsorption of phosphorus by the mesonephros. That the initial rapid increases in blood and urine phosphorus are not wholly due to the trauma of the operation is suggested by the high values persisting for a week or more. Since the blood calcium remained relatively unchanged during the first 12 hours after the operation it will be apparent that changes in calcium and phosphorus content of the plasma occurred independently which is in accordance with recent evidence in mammals (see Munson, 1960).

2. EFFECT OF MAMMALIAN PARATHYROID EXTRACT (PTE)

a. Intact animals. Waggener (1930) came to the conclusion that the calcemic response to PTE in the bullfrog was limited. The best he could obtain was an increase in blood calcium of some 2 or 3 mg/100 ml. Cortelyou (1960a) in a preliminary report on the use of Paroidin in unoperated *R. pipiens* found no significant alteration in plasma calcium in frogs given 5 or 10 units on alternate days for 2 weeks. A hypercalciuria, however, was maintained throughout the period of treatment. In a personal communication, Cortelyou, on the basis of additional observations at shorter intervals, has revised his estimate of the effectiveness of Paroidin in these animals. With 10 units there was an unequivocal rise in plasma calcium from 6.2 to 8.8 mg/100 ml at 2 hours, and a further rise to 9.0 mg/100 ml at 4 hours. The results with 30 units were similar. Graded calciuria was produced with 5, 10, and 30 units. The responses, maximal at 4 hours, were sustained for 24–48 hours.

It seems thoroughly established now that one of the sites of action of purified parathyroid hormone in mammals is the kidney. The hormone has a phosphaturic action but the mechanism has not been fully settled as between reduced tubular reabsorption and tubular secretion of phosphate (see Rasmussen, 1961, for review); the evidence strongly favors the former.

In frogs, 5 and 10 units Paroidin were surprisingly ineffective in respect to the urinary excretion of phosphorus (Cortelyou, 1960a). With 30 units, however (Cortelyou, personal communication), urine phosphorus increased from control values of 2.5 mg to 4.5–6 mg/100 ml; with continued injections on alternate days the hyperphosphaturia was sustained for 16 days. Lastly, and interestingly, with 50 units "the urine becomes bloody and has a greenish color after about the fourth injection. This would indicate mesonephric damage."

b. Parathyroidectomized animals. Injection of PTE into parathyroidectomized *R. catesbeiana* gave only slight and temporary relief from tetany (Waggener, 1930). In the absence of measurements of blood calcium, it is possible that the dose administered was inadequate.

B. Urodela

The embryology and topographical anatomy of the parathyroid glands has been well documented in several species. Maurer (1888, 1899a) in his classic study of the ontogeny of the pharynx in *Amphibia* was the first to show that in Urodela as in Anura, the parathyroids arise from the ventral portion of the third and fourth visceral pouches. His work was based mainly on *Tritunus taeniatus* but he also examined specimens of *Tr. alpestris*, *Tr. cristatus*, and *Salamandra maculosa*. His observations were confirmed by Baldwin (1918) working with *Ambystoma punctatum*. All workers agree that the parathyroids arise as the gills degenerate during metamorphosis and that they fail to appear in those species which do not naturally undergo metamorphosis. It would be interesting to know whether the parathyroids develop in these forms when metamorphosis is artificially induced by means of thyroid hormone (as occurs in the treated axolotl).

Although two pairs of glands are typical in the adult urodele, Thompson (1910), in a cursory examination of a single specimen of *Spelerpes ruber*, mentions finding only one gland on each side. Since the glands she found were not visible to the naked eye it is assumed that she may have missed a second pair but to my knowledge the point has never been clarified. The parathyroids in adult *Ambystoma* (Fig. 11) are located bilaterally as two yellowish glandules, 200–300 μ in diameter, medial to the distal tip of the first branchial cartilage, and are arranged in tandem (Baldwin, 1918).

In comparison with the anurans, very little experimental work has been done on the parathyroids in urodeles. Scholz (1935) removed the parathyroids (Fig. 12) from a number of adult *Salamandra atra* and *S. maculosa* without causing ill effects other than those attributable to the operation and loss of blood. Many of his animals were observed for periods up to a year without showing evidence of tetany or any muscular twitching. The operation had no influence on the skeleton, and cataracts were not observed. The liver glycogen and fat content was not altered and there was no change in the thymus or ultimobranchial bodies. Although the question of completeness of the removal of the parathyroids may be raised, considerable pains were taken to insure a total extirpation. Similar observations on parathyroidectomized *Tritons* (Studitsky, 1945) led to the same conclusions.

V. REPTILES

Parathyroid glands have been found in the few species of lizards, crocodiles, turtles, and snakes that have been examined and are presumed to be present in all the Reptilia. They have been studied mainly from the standpoint of their embryological origin and their morphological relationship with other pharyngeal derivatives. Excellent early accounts of the dissection of the cervical region in reptiles are to be found in the works of van Bemmelen (1886, 1887, 1888), Verdun (1898), de Meuron (1886), Maurer (1899b, c), Saint-Rémy and Prenant (1904).

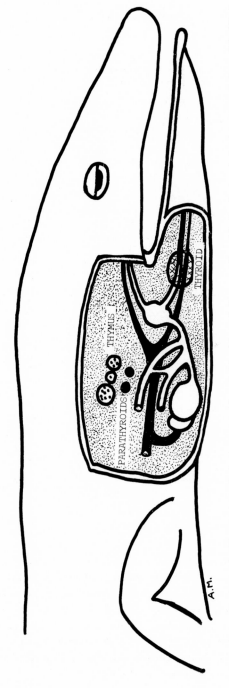

Fig. 11. A schematic illustration of the topographic relationships of the parathyroid glands in *Ambystoma punctatum*. (Modified after Baldwin, 1918.)

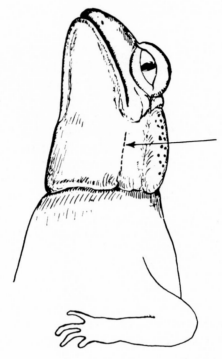

FIG. 12. Line of incision for removal of parathyroid glands in *Salamandra*. (From Scholz, 1935.)

Much of the information in the English literature stems, however, from a less thorough study of a few specimens of reptiles by Mrs. F. D. Thompson[2] in her 1910 account of "The thyroid and parathyroid glands throughout vertebrates" and Swale Vincent in one of the earlier textbooks on endocrinology (1912) based a brief account of the reptiles almost wholly on her report. In reptiles, as in vertebrates generally, the parathyroids are in most instances derived from the third and fourth visceral pouches. The usual situation in the adult is—with certain doubtful exceptions noted below—two parathyroid glands on each side, designated parathyroids III and IV. The number and location of glands in any given species is, however, subject to considerable variation. The definitive glands are structurally identical and clearly parathyroid in nature as determined by both histologic and functional criteria.

---

[2] Thompson's article being one of the first reports on this topic in the English language, coupled with the fact that it failed to cite important earlier literature, has tended to perpetuate a number of inaccuracies.

A. Sauria

The lizards are usually categorically stated to possess only one pair of parathyroid glands—parathyroid III. Saint-Rémy and Prenant (1904) studying two genera of lizards (*Anguis* and *Lacerta*) found parathyroid IV to be a transitory rudimentary structure seen only during early embryological stages. Exceptions have been noted, however. As long ago as 1898 Verdun recorded the finding of a second pair of glands in Lacertilia, and again in 1939 Adams reported the finding of a persisting parathyroid IV embedded in the thymus on the left in *Lacerta*. Underwood (1957) observed the presence of a parathyroid IV in the Australian pygopodid lizard *Delma fraseri* and confirms by personal communication[3] that he has found parathyroid IV in a number of Jamaican species of anoline lizards. Adams (1939) states that in *Lacerta* "these caudal epithelial bodies are usually seen to appear early in development, and to disappear again before birth; their occasional persistence, therefore, is not at all surprising, and closer observation may show that it is not unusual." The presence of accessory parathyroids has been noted by Peters (1940).

Van Bemmelen (1888) appears to have made the first observations on *Sphenodon*, a saurian representative of great phyletic interest. He found two bodies on each side (Fig. 13): a *Carotiskörperchen* (parathyroid III) in the arch of the carotid artery and an *Aortakörperchen* (parathyroid IV) in the aortic (systemic) arch. This truly primitive disposition of the parathyroid glands in *Sphenodon* is not unique among the Sauria as Adams (1953) has found the same situation prevailing in adult *Phrynosoma*.

The names *Carotiskörperchen* and *Aortakörperchen* which van Bemmelen gave to the parathyroid bodies recall the vascular relationship which the parathyroid glands as derivatives of pharyngeal pouches III and IV bear to the third (carotid) and fourth (aortic) arches in the Reptilia during early embryonic life. The term *Carotiskörperchen*, however, was particularly unfortunate as Trinci (1912) and Adams (1939) point out in that it suggests an homology with structures of similar vascular relationship and name but of entirely different nature in mammals. It is a peculiarity of

---

[3] "In *Anolis L. lineatopus* Gray I have observed parathyroid IV repeatedly in dissections, I have also confirmed it in serial sections of hatchlings. It is about half the diameter of parathyroid III. It is quite loosely attached to the systemic arch. I have verified the same condition by dissection in *Anolis g. grahami* Gray, *Anolis opalinus* Cope, *Anolis garmani* Stejneger, and *Xiphocercus valenciennii* Dumeril and Bibron . . . I have found no indication of a parathyroid IV in *Iguana i. iguana,* *Cyclura carinata* and *Cyclura macleayi caymanensis*. The anoline lizards are a very well-defined section of the family Iguanidae but I would hesitate to press the view that the parathyroid IV is a primitive feature because I believe that it normally appears in the course of the development of lizards generally, only to involute in the majority of cases."

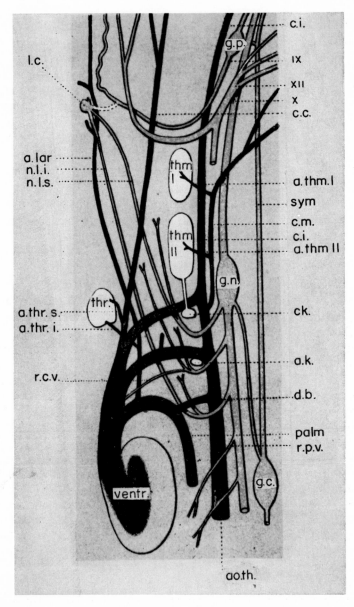

FIG. 13. Van Bemmelen's 1888 illustration of the location of the parathyroid glands in *Sphenodon*; a.k., *Aortakörperchen* or parathyroid IV, c.k. *Carotiskörperchen* or parathyroid III.

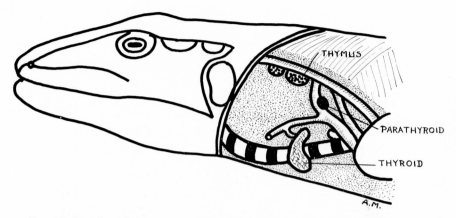

FIG. 14. Location of the parathyroid gland (III) in *Lacerta viridis*. (Modified after Peters, 1940.)

lizards that the parathyroids are in intimate contact with the carotid arteries (Figs. 14, 15, 16) and the structure of the latter is likewise out of the ordinary (Adams, 1952). Scattered through the adventitia are numerous small nests of epitheloid cells which Adams believes are homologues of the mammalian carotid sinus and carotid body. Their resemblance thereto is made obscure only by their diffuse arrangement.

The fact that parathyroid III in Lacertilia is situated at the carotid fork has led to its being sometimes mistakenly identified as the homologue of the mammalian glomus caroticum. For the clarification of two notable instances of such mistaken identity see Adams (1939, 1952).

PARATHYROIDECTOMY

Peters (1940) studied the effects of removal of the parathyroids in *Lacerta muralis, L. agilis*, and *L. viridis*, and has provided a detailed account of the operative procedure. The glands being barely visible, control of hemorrhage was requisite to a complete parathyroidectomy. Special precautions in respect to anesthesia and postoperative infection were found to be necessary. The operations were carried out in the spring and fall. Several of the operated animals developed cramping spasms followed by tetany. When the animals were operated in April or May the first spasm appeared after 7 weeks whereas when the parathyroids were removed in October spasms appeared much earlier, i.e., in 3 to 17 days. The operated animals showed excessive reaction to painful stimuli and percussion. Maximum survival was twelve weeks. Death was often preceded by atony and cachexia. Food was refused as soon as the neuromuscular symptoms

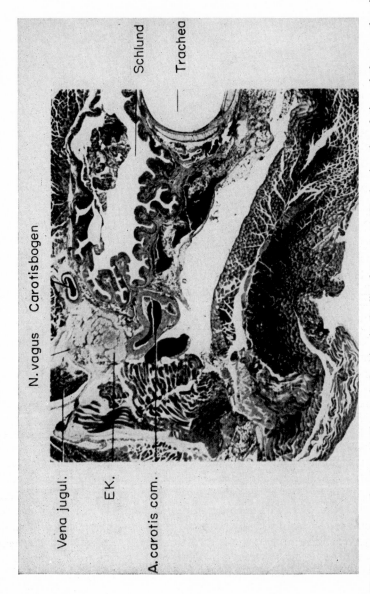

FIG. 15. Transverse section through the cervical region in the lizard *Lacerta viridis* showing the relation of the parathyroid gland (EK.) to the carotid artery and other pharyngeal structures. (From Peters, 1940.)

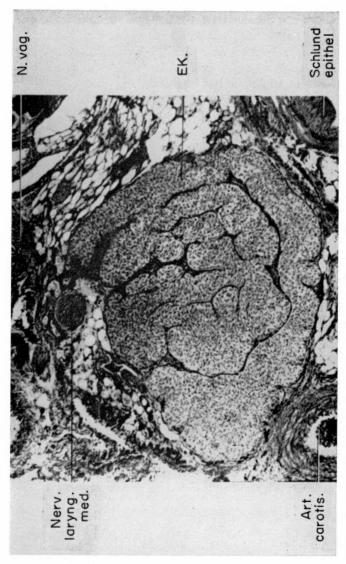

N. vag.

EK.

Schlund epithel

Nerv. laryng. med.

Art. carotis.

Fig. 16. Higher magnification of the parathyroid tissue shown in Fig. 15; note the proximity of the carotid artery.

appeared and this may have contributed to the severity of symptoms. Regrettably, no observations were made on the changes in blood calcium. The skeleton was examined and, as was to be expected, no morphological changes were found. Cataracts did not develop; a conjunctivitis, possibly not related to the experimental procedure, was common. In summary, lizards appear to respond to parathyroidectomy in much the same manner as the higher forms, the main difference being that it may take longer for the deficiency symptoms to appear. No report of the administration of parathyroid extract to lizards has been found.

B. Chelonia

Observations on the parathyroids in turtles have been made by van Bemmelen (1888), Doyon and Kareff (1904), Doyon (1907), Aimé (1911, 1912a,b), Shaner (1921) and Johnson (1922). Both Shaner and Johnson have reviewed the earlier literature as has Pischinger (1937). All authors seem to agree on the presence of parathyroid IV in adult Chelonia (Fig. 17) but parathyroid III which is enclosed in the anterior thymus appears to have been overlooked by Doyon (1907) and Thompson (1910).

In *Chrysemys* (Shaner, 1921 and Johnson, 1922) and *Chelydra* and *Trionyx* (Johnson, 1922), it has been established that parathyroids III and IV arise from the corresponding visceral pouches. In the adult state parathyroid III is deeply embedded in the thymus but parathyroid IV, as the result of a peculiarity in embryological development, is usually closely associated with or even embedded in the ultimobranchial body on the left. The fourth and fifth pouches and the ultimobranchial body originate on each side as a single evagination of the pharyngeal endoderm. The left ultimobranchial body becomes very much larger than that on the right and engulfs, as it were, the left parathyroid IV. On the right, parathyroid IV is often adjacent to III.

Doyon and Kareff (1904) attempted surgical removal of the parathyroids from turtles and noted that they all died in paralysis. Here again information is inconclusive, and it remains for further experimental study to define the functional role of the parathyroid glands in Chelonia.

C. Ophidia

Adult snakes typically have two pairs of parathyroids: a cranial pair situated at the bifurcation of the carotid artery and a caudal pair located between the anterior and posterior lobes of the thymus (Herdson, 1956). Although some variation is seen in the position of the left cranial gland it is nonetheless in close proximity to the carotid fork. The two glands on each

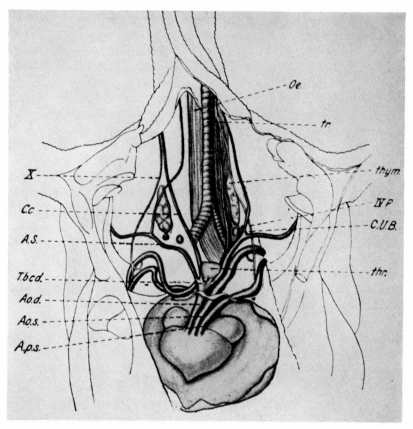

Fig. 17. Location of the parathyroid glands (IV P) in the turtle *Emys europaea*. (From Pischinger, 1937.)

side are of about equal size and very small (i.e. about 0.5 mm in *Thamnophis* and 1 mm in *Notechis*). The glands in any given species are identical in histological structure. Unlike the situation in lizards, the parathyroids in snakes are mobile and not in intimate contact with the walls of the vessels along which they rest.

There being poor agreement in respect to the pharyngeal pouches from which the parathyroid glands are derived in Ophidia, the designations "caudal" and "cranial" are preferred for the pairs of definitive structures. Epithelial proliferations from all five visceral pouches have been noted (van Bemmelen, 1888; Saint-Rémy and Prenant, 1904; Harrison and Denning, 1929). Ordinarily only two pairs survive but Verdun (1898) claims to have found five pairs in *Coluber*; some of these, of course, may have been accessory parathyroids. Harrison and Denning's study of

Thamnophis radix appears to establish conclusively that in this species the parathyroids derive from the fourth and fifth pouches. Snakes show a peculiarity of development in the area of the pharynx that is of considerable interest. The fourth and fifth pouches communicate with the pharynx by means of a common duct, the "ductus pharyngobranchialus communis." According to Harrison and Denning, "This places the reptiles in a unique position as to their phylogenetic history, since a similar common pharyngobranchial duct has not been described for earlier vertebrates, but has been described in certain members of the mammalian group, including man."

Information concerning the function of the parathyroids in snakes appears to be lacking. Snakes being mainly carnivorous, the response to parathyroidectomy might be expected to be severe.

D. Crocodilia

The available information concerning the parathyroid glands in the crocodiles and alligators is very limited. One of the finest accounts of the dissection of the cervical region of a crocodile is still that given by van Bemmelen in 1888. He found only one pair of glands which by reason of their location at the origin of the carotid (Fig. 18) were labeled *Carotis-körperchen*. We can accept these bodies as parathyroid III.

Reese (1931), in searching for the parathyroids in young specimens of *Alligator mississippiensis*, found a small mass of questionable parathyroid tissue embedded in the side of the thyroid and "several small, more or less spheroidal bodies, situated on each side of the neck, or even embedded in the thymus." He quotes a colleague as having observed two or three on one side. The confusion was dissipated by a careful study of the embryos of *Alligator mississippiensis* and *Crocodilus porosus* (Hammar, 1937). Irrespective of earlier embryological indications, by the time of hatching only parathyroid III could be found.

VI. BIRDS

Knowledge of the role of the parathyroids in birds is of particular interest for a variety of reasons. Being the oldest of the living warm-blooded vertebrates, birds may reveal attributes of parathyroid functions basic to this group. Birds, moreover, by having a higher specific gravity than the heterotherms, coupled with the need for a buoyant skeleton and the necessity of an adequate calcium reservoir for egg-shell formation, are confronted with some special mineral problems which might reasonably be expected to either affect or be affected by the parathyroid glands.

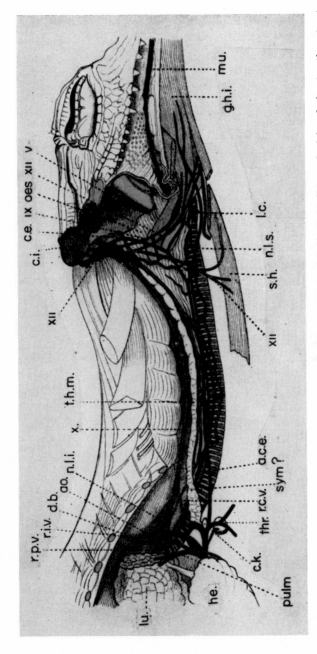

FIG. 18. Neck dissection of *Crocodilus biporcatus* showing parathyroid gland (c.k., *Epithelkörperchen*) in relation to other structures including the thyroid (thr.) and thymus (t.h.m.). (From van Bemmelen, 1888.)

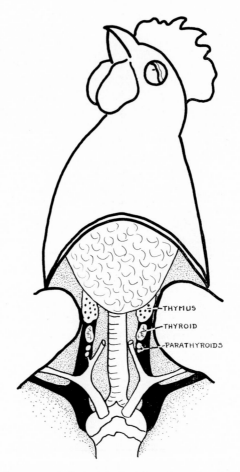

FIG. 19. Schematic representation of the location of parathyroid glands (III cephalad and IV caudad) in the chicken. (After Nonidez and Goodale, 1927.)

Adult birds characteristically have four parathyroids, two on each side, which originate from the third and fourth pouches (Pischinger, 1937; Schrier and Hamilton, 1952). In chickens, parathyroid IV is smaller than, and often connected with, parathyroid III (Fig. 19). They are located in the upper thorax, near the thyroid in chickens, but well removed from it in pigeons (Smith, 1945). Accessory parathyroids have been detected histologically by Nonidez and Goodale (1927) but not by Campbell and Turner (1942) or Smith (1945). Physiological evidence regarding the presence of remnant or accessory parathyroid tissue in experiments involving parathyroidectomy is likewise contradictory. Prevalence of such tissue in chickens is suggested by the work of Polin and Sturkie (1957, 1958); rarity, by that of Urist *et al.* (1960).

The parathyroids show no unusual microscopic features. Oxyphils are absent. The chief cells show some variations in granularity and stainability which are felt to be related to the degree of secretory activity (Benoit *et al.*, 1944; Benoit and Clavert, 1947).

The parathyroids in birds have an extraordinary capacity for enlargement. This first came to light as a result of the conspicuous overgrowth of these glands in rachitic chickens (Marine, 1913; Nonidez and Goodale, 1927; Higgins and Sheard, 1928; Dossel, 1960). The enlargement was first presumed to be due to vitamin D deficiency but in 1933, Oberling and Guérin rightly deduced that the actual stimulus was the accompanying mineral deficiency. Similar circumstances were later noted to produce enlargements of four- to six-fold in pigeons (Hollander and Riddle, 1945) and ten-fold in ducks (Benoit, 1950). Witschi (1940) also remarked on a peculiar type of parathyroid hyperplasia in caged African weaver finches.

In pigeons and ducks the changes in mineral metabolism which accompany the gonadal cycle are reflected in some seasonal changes in the parathyroid glands. Stimulation of the ovarian cycle by injecting estrogen induces enlargement of the parathyroids in ducks but not in fowl. Although it is well known that alterations in the skeleton correlate with the breeding cycle in birds, there is uncertainty as to the importance of the parathyroids in bringing these changes about (Sturkie, 1954; Höhn, 1961).

Experimental calcium deprivation in birds, as in laboratory mammals, results in an enlargement of the parathyroids, and there is histological evidence of heightened secretory activity (Benoit and Clavert, 1945; Urist, 1959).

A. Parathyroidectomy

1. NEUROMUSCULAR SYMPTOMS

By the turn of the century, considering the experience that had been gained regarding the effect of parathyroid ablation in mammals, curiosity as to its effect in birds was natural. In the context of the contemporary knowledge of comparative endocrinology and technique, however, it seems rather remarkable that in 1904 Doyon and Jouty were able to identify and destroy the parathyroids in hens and roosters. Since surgical removal was difficult because of the proximity of the glands to large vessels, they resorted to cauterization. Their results are strikingly "mammalian" in character. "On constate: des paralysies, des contractures, des tremblements fibrillaires, des secousses musculaires, des tremblements généralisés, de la dyspnée, de la diarrhée, des vomissements, une soif intense, de l'hyper-excitabilité. L'animal présente au début une démarche très incertaine, ataxique, puis ne tarde pas à rester étendu. La crête des coqs est par moments très congestionnée et violacée." Some animals did not respond and were presumed to have accessory parathyroid tissue. It was some time, however, before these findings were pursued. In 1927, Nonidez and Goodale mentioned under "unpublished observations" that parathy-roidectomy in chickens was not attended by severe tetanic symptoms—rather, they often showed a profound depression lasting 7–10 days. They criticized the cauterization technique of Doyon and Jouty and questioned whether it may not have involved injury to the vagal nerves. The sketchy information given by Nonidez and Goodale must also leave some doubt concerning their own operative technique. In 1935, Hutt and Boyd observed tetany in a laying hen believed to have idiopathic hypoparathy-roidism. Next came demonstrations that operative removal of the para-thyroids in ducks (Benoit et al., 1941a) and pigeons (Smith, 1945) resulted in severe tetany and death of the animals within a day or two unless some maintenance therapy was supplied.

It is only in recent years that full-scale investigations of the effects of altered parathyroid states in chickens have been undertaken. Even so, constant findings regarding the consequences of parathyroidectomy have not been obtained. In a large series of operated birds Polin and Sturkie (1957, 1958) found that tetany and early deaths were infrequent except in the case of laying hens, where 8 out of 30 animals died within 4 days. The outcome was greatly influenced by food intake. If the birds resumed eating on the day of operation few signs of hypoparathyroidism appeared; recovery was spontaneous and complete usually within 6 days. These authors regard the response of chickens to parathyroidectomy as extremely variable, and dependent upon the presence or absence of accessory para-thyroid tissue. In the experience of Urist et al. (1960) the operative sequelae are more severe and of greater incidence. Out of 15 laying hens and 10 roosters only 4 females and 6 males survived beyond 48 hours and all showed marked evidence of hypoparathyroidism.

2. Changes in Blood Chemistry

A sharp decrease in total blood calcium follows parathyroidectomy within 24 hours in ducks (Benoit et al., 1941a) and pigeons (Riddle et al., 1945). The total blood calcium in female birds varies tremendously due to the changes brought on in connection with the egg-laying cycle. The level of total blood calcium in males and in nonlaying females is generally in the range 10–12 mg/100 ml whereas during the breeding season the calcium level in females may reach 30 mg/100 ml or more. Polin and Sturkie (1957) give a mean value of 27.0 ± 1.6 mg/100 ml for a group of 14 laying hens; at 18–24 hours after operation, the mean level was 10.9 ± 1.6 mg/100 ml.

In birds, as in mammals, parathyroidectomy also causes a consistent small decrease in the ultrafilterable calcium as shown in pigeons by Riddle and McDonald (1945) and in chickens by Polin and Sturkie (1957, 1958) and Urist et al. (1960). By and large, however, it is the fall in non-ultra-filterable plasma calcium that accounts for the major part of the drop in total blood calcium. Polin and Sturkie doubt, however, that this response can be attributed to an influence of the parathyroids since they found a similar decrease in sham-operated and starved controls. They believe that the effect is attributable to reduced food consumption and that only the diffusible calcium is under the influence of the parathyroids.

Few studies have been reported on the effect of parathyroidectomy on the blood phosphorus in birds and these are mostly in good general agreement with the findings in mammals—namely, the operation is followed by a modest increase in total inorganic (Benoit et al., 1941a) and in ultra-filterable phosphorus (Riddle and McDonald, 1945).

B. Parathyroid Hormone Injections

1. INTACT BIRDS

Early tests of the effect of mammalian PTE in birds were not dramatic but it must be noted that the doses used were often small. Negative or inconsequential results were reported by Collip (1931), Macowan (1932) Knowles et al. (1935), Avery et al. (1940a), Landauer et al. (1941), and Campbell and Turner (1942). With higher dosages and single injections, modest elevations in total blood calcium were obtained in pigeons (Riddle and Dotti, 1934) and actively laying hens (Deobald et al., 1936). Continued treatment of laying hens starved of calcium had, however, no beneficial effect on the blood calcium, bone ash, or egg production (Deobald et al., 1936).

Results of more recent date attest to an indisputable effectiveness of PTE in chickens. Polin et al. (1957) examined the changes in total blood calcium by serial sampling soon after the injection of 100 units PTE. The results are shown in Fig. 20. The maximal response occurred at $3\frac{1}{2}$ hours and was quite transient. Laying hens responded better than cocks (8 mg % increase vs. 2 mg %). Urist et al. (1960) administered PTE in doses of 500 and 1000 units and induced marked calcemia in chickens of all ages and both sexes; increments in total blood calcium ranged up to 10 mg % in males and 19 mg % in laying hens. Increases in ultrafilterable calcium were of lesser magnitude. In this study the changes in total blood organic phosphorus were minor and inconsistent.

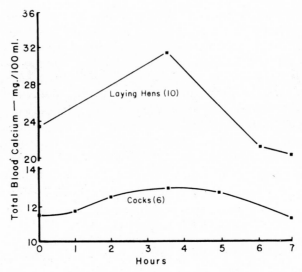

Fig. 20. Effect on total blood calcium in laying hens and roosters of 100 units PTE injected subcutaneously. (From Polin *et al.*, 1957.)

2. Parathyroidectomized Birds

The only reference to the use of PTE in parathyroidectomized birds is the mention by Polin and Sturkie (1957) of unpublished observations that "parathyroid extract injected into parathyroidectomized birds causes a remission of symptoms and increases in blood calcium."

C. The Parathyroids and Estrogen in Relation to Blood Calcium

It is well known that in female birds the calcium content of the blood is conspicuously increased during the egg-laying season and that this phenomenon can be duplicated by exogenous estrogen. Interest, for the purpose of the present discussion, centers primarily on the possibility that the parathyroids may be involved in this calcemic reaction. The first-held and obvious supposition that the estrogen-induced calcemia may be part of a mechanism for the mobilization of calcium for eggshell formation has not been borne out by recent studies.

Exogenously administered estrogens evoke a phenomenal rise in total blood calcium in birds. Peak elevations to approximately 100 mg/100 ml are not uncommon. The effect is greater in females but by no means confined to one sex. In terms of blood calcium fractions, the response is limited entirely to the non-ultrafilterable or bound calcium. The question naturally arises whether the estrogen-induced increases in total blood calcium are mediated in any manner by the parathyroids. When this possibility was first put to test by administering estrogen to parathyroidectomized ducks (Benoit *et al.*, 1941b), a complete blocking of the response was seen. However, when the same experiment was repeated in parathyroidectomized pigeons (maintained on aluminum hydroxide) the estrogen effect was undiminished (Riddle *et al.*, 1945 and Riddle and McDonald, 1945). Polin and Sturkie (1958) found that the ability of estrogen to augment the plasma calcium in parathyroidectomized cocks and capons was dependent upon the level of ultrafilterable calcium. When this was low the effectiveness of the estrogen was impaired. They claimed that the parathyroids by maintaining a normal level of ionized calcium exert an indirect or facilitating action that allows the estrogen-induced calcemic response to occur. Urist *et al.* (1960) found that estrogen had a marked calcemic action in parathyroidectomized birds but, as might be anticipated, it offered no protection from tetany or death, since the incremental calcium was all in the bound form. These authors hold the opinion that it is not the parathyroid hormone *per se* which is important to the calcemic action of estrogen but the availability of calcium ions, however achieved. This view is in accord with the accepted generalization that in birds the diffusible blood calcium is largely controlled by the parathyroids, and the nondiffusible calcium by estrogen. Although the observation of Benoit *et al.* (1941b) that estrogen is ineffective in parathyroidectomized ducks is at variance with the explanation offered by Urist *et al.*, there are circumstances in connection with the experiments of Benoit *et al.* (1941b) that may have militated against a positive result; for example, their ducks did not survive beyond 8–20 postoperative hours. The work needs to be repeated using some palliative that would prolong survival.

In these connections it is necessary to consider the capacity of estrogen to induce the formation of a calcium-binding phosphoprotein complex in the females of all vertebrates below the mammals (Urist *et al.*, 1958). This phosphoprotein, found naturally only in the blood of sexually mature females, is synthesized in the liver. In males the neoformation of this substance can be experimentally induced by exogenous estrogen. It is the presence of this calcium-binding protein that makes possible the up-to-eighteen-fold elevation in blood calcium in estrogen-treated birds. This calcemic action of estrogen appears to be a very ancient physiological mechanism. Because of its occurrence in birds, first thoughts were that it must be related to mobilization of calcium for eggshell formation. However, the same protein complex is now known to occur in other oviparous forms including fish, amphibians, and reptiles which do not deposit calcium in the covering of their eggs. Urist and associates have marshalled strong evidence for their belief that estrogen-induced calcemia is a mechanism for the transport of materials used in yolk formation. It is perhaps pertinent, and certainly of interest, that in mammals, in which the ova are notably poor in yolk, a calcium-binding phosphoprotein does not occur and no elevation in bound calcium has been achieved with exogenous estrogen.

D. The Parathyroids and Shell Deposition

Shell deposition during egg-laying imposes a severe cyclic drain on calcium which does not, however, appear to be reflected by any notable disturbances in calcium homeostasis. Study of the total blood calcium during the egg-cycle by Knowles et al. (1935), Deobald et al. (1936), Avery et al. (1940b), and Polin and Sturkie (1957) suggested that only minor variations occur. On pinpointing the measurements to the time of actual shell deposition, Polin and Sturkie (1959) found an appreciable drop in total calcium, and Winget and Smith (1957, 1958) and Urist (1959) found a small decrease in both bound and diffusible calcium—hence also of total calcium—during the period of shell formation. Although the changes in diffusible calcium were of the order of only 1–2 mg/100 ml, they are possibly significant in that it is primarily the diffusible calcium which contributes to shell calcium. Winget and Smith doubt that the normal daily fluctuations in bound and diffusible calcium are mediated in any way by parathyroid activity whereas Polin and Sturkie (1957) hold to the contrary that the parathyroids by their influence on ionic calcium exert a direct influence on shell deposition. The resolution of this interesting point will likely have to await refinement in methods of assessing parathyroid secretory activity.

E. The Parathyroids in Relation to Egg-Laying

Inasmuch as removal of the parathyroids results in a marked decline in blood calcium in nonlaying hens, an even greater decline was to be expected when actual shell deposition was in progress. Data bearing on this expectation were obtained by Polin and Sturkie (1957). Of 30 parathyroidectomized laying hens there were 8 deaths within 4 days. Eggs present in the uterus were expelled prematurely (in 3–5 hrs) with little or no evidence of shell formation. The abortive expulsion of eggs was presumed to be due to hyperirritability of the uterine muscle as a result of the decrease in diffusible calcium. The expulsion of eggs and the removal therewith of the stimulus for shell deposition undoubtedly favored survival of some of the operated hens. After periods of 6–32 days the parathyroidectomized hens resumed laying and the eggs were of normal shell weight and shell calcium content. Egg production and shell weight were not disturbed in sham-operated hens. Urist *et al.* (1960) removed the parathyroids from 15 laying hens and 11 died within 48 hours. They note only that the amount of egg yolk in the ovaries was greatly reduced in the operated animals.

As regards the relation of these results to possible mechanisms in the intact laying hen, Polin and Sturkie (1957) suggest that the demand for shell calcium may exceed the rate of calcium mobilization and thus diminish the plasma-diffusible calcium level. There is firm ground for believing that the latter would stimulate the parathyroids to mobilize additional ionic calcium. The views of Polin and Sturkie are supported by the fact that administered PTE evokes an elevation of the blood calcium and brings about a remission of symptoms in parathyroidectomized laying hens. Furthermore, chickens on calcium starvation for periods longer than 4 weeks develop tetany which can be interrupted by intramuscular injections of 1000 units PTE (Urist, 1959). Thus the available evidence tends to support the view that the daily drain on ionic calcium in normal, laying birds effects in turn a rhythmic daily upswing in parathyroid hormone output. That the parathyroids play no critical role in egg-laying is indicated, however, by the resumption of normal egg-laying within 1–5 weeks after removal of the parathyroids.

VII. MAMMALS

A. Prototheria

Observations of the parathyroids in the Monotremata are exceedingly limited. Maurer (1899b,c) showed that in echidna (*Tachyglossus aculeatus*) parathyroids derive from the third and fourth pharyngeal pouches and that parathyroid III remains attached to or embedded in thymus III (Fig. 21). Both pairs of glands were shown to migrate to the thorax. This probably accounts for the fact that MacKenzie and Owen (1919), reporting on some exploratory dissections of glands in the neck in the monotremes, made no mention of parathyroids in echidna.

In the platypus (*Ornithorhynchus anatinus*), MacKenzie and Owen found one pair of glands lying near the commencement of the trachea and showing "histologically typical parathyroid structure." The dimensions of these bodies were given as 3 mm long and 2 mm across. Both the size and the location raise doubt as to the true nature of these glands. These authors also describe a body of obscure nature near the thymus. They refer to it

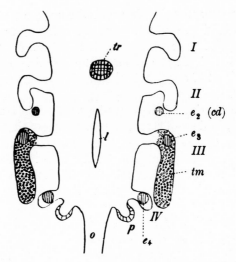

Fig. 21. Schematic representation of the origin of pharyngal derivatives in echidna. Parathyroids III (e_3) and IV (e_4) originate from visceral pouches III and IV, respectively; (e_2), epithelial body, anlage of the carotid gland; (P), postbranchial body (Maurer's preferred designation) or ultimobranchial body. (From Maurer, 1899b.)

as parathymus and illustrate its histologic structure as that of a tubular gland. Their observations on these highly interesting animals need confirmation.

B. Metatheria

The marsupials typically have two pairs of parathyroid glands, parathyroid III and parathyroid IV, with parathyroid III being much the larger. Parathyroid III is invariably located at or near the bifurcation of the common carotid. Parathyroid IV is found in the thorax in association with the thoracic thymuses and may be fragmented or absent. Neither parathyroid gland has ever been found to be situated in association with the thyroid in the marsupials.

Some interesting anatomical features of parathyroid III have been observed. Zuckerkandl (1902) described an annular "external *Epithelkörper*," (parathyroid III) completely surrounding the origin of the internal carotid in *Didelphis azarea*. Similarly, in *Perameles obescula* and *P. nasuta* (Fraser, 1915) and *D. virginiana* (Kingsbury, 1940; McCrady, 1941) parathyroid III has been found molded to, but only partially surrounding, the internal carotid at the same location. Parenthetically, a similar situation has been described in the calf (Hägström, 1921). That such annular or partially annular forms are not characteristic of parathyroid III in the marsupials

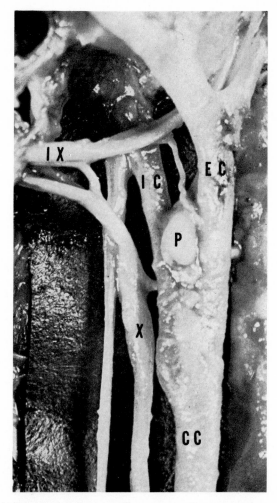

FIG. 22. Neck dissection of the Australian opossum *Trichosurus vulpecula* showing the normal relationship of parathyroid III(P) to the bifurcation of the common carotid artery(CC); IX, hypoglossal nerve, X, vagus nerve. (From Adams, 1955.)

was made evident by the observations of Fraser (1915) and Fraser and Hill (1915) who found parathyroid III to be an ovoid and mobile organ in *Trichosurus vulpecula, Phaseolarctus cinereus*, and *Phascolomys mitchelli*. Similarly, Adams (1955) found parathyroid III in *Trichosurus* a "small solid-looking ovoid nodule with a smooth, regular surface" lying in the fork of the carotid (Fig. 22). Other accounts of parathyroid tissue in the phalanger (*Trichosurus*) by Forsyth (1908), and in the Tasmanian devil and kaola bear by MacKenzie and Owen (1919) are wholly inadequate.

Parathyroid IV is variable in presence. It has been identified in the pouch young of *D. virginiana* (Kingsbury, 1940) but not in adult specimens (McCrady, 1941). In adult *T. vulpecula*, Adams (1955) made positive identification of parathyroid IV embedded in or near thymuses III and IV within the thorax.

Although some unusual features in the histology and vascularization of the marsupialian parathyroids have been noted by Fraser and Hill (1915), Adams (1955) in a careful study of one of the same species, *T. vulpecula*, found "no obvious peculiarities." All the glands showed the usual compact cell arrangement.

Of special interest were Adams' (1955) observations on the relationship of parathyroid III and thymic tissue. He often found a thymic nodule or accessory thymus in close association with parathyroid III and in some instances the two adjacent tissues were enclosed within a common capsule. "Indeed, in one animal . . . there was a quite remarkable conjunction of the two: for instead of lying side-by-side, the thymic nodule—in this case a highly-organized miniature thymus—was actually embedded deeply with the parathyroid . . . forming a composite organ. . . ." (Fig. 23). Similar associations, including the intermingling of these tissues, have been noted in a variety of animals (see Adams for a full review of the literature). These naturally occurring abnormalities have led to controversial considerations. The questions raised have involved metaplastic potentialities of the two tissues, cell migrations, and intermingling of embryologic rests. Suffice it to say that a satisfactory explanation of the thymo-parathyroid tissue continuity as depicted in Fig. 24 has not been reached.

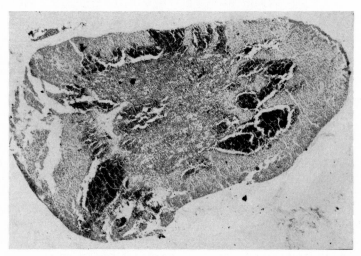

Fig. 23. Section of parathyroid III from *Trichosurus* showing, as an unusual feature, a thymic nodule enclosed within the parathyroid gland. (From Adams, 1955.)

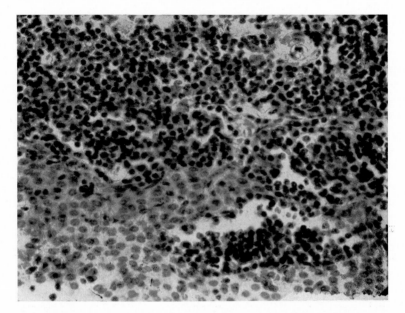

FIG. 24. A higher magnification of the intermingling of parathyroid and thymic tissue shown in Fig. 23; note on the extreme right the presence of a Hassall's corpuscle. (From Adams, 1955.)

These considerations are of practical importance in the study of parathyroid physiology especially when ablation of all parathyroid tissue is desired. Until one can be certain that parathyroid tissue cannot be generated from the thymus or primitive embryonic elements associated with the thymus, the possibility of such an occurrence will remain.

C. Eutheria

Although the work done on the eutherian mammals is obviously encompassed in the scope of comparative endocrinology, the literature covering the anatomy, physiology, and clinical aspects of the parathyroid glands in man, and a few of the higher mammals, has been reviewed repeatedly (see Greep, 1948; Bartter, 1954, among others). Only a very brief summay of the status of this area will be attempted here in that the recent and rapid progress in the purification of parathyroid hormone and in the clarification of its mechanisms of action has been amply reviewed by Munson (1960, 1961), Rasmussen (1961), and Munson et al. (1963). Also, the proceedings of the 1960 Houston conference on the parathyroids have been made available (Greep and Talmage, 1961).

The parathyroids in mammals are typically four; the reported variations in number and location have been summarized elsewhere (Greep, 1948). Most of our present day knowledge covering the physiology of these glands derives from work on mammals, mainly rats, dogs, and man. The only commercially available extract of the parathyroids is prepared from the glands of cattle. Extracts of sheep, horse, and human glands have been shown to have activity (reviewed by Munson et al., 1963).

The consequences of parathyroid ablation in most mammals studied are severe and often fatal; the adult rat and cow (Stott and Smith, 1957) are notable exceptions. The primary defect is a lowering of the blood calcium concentration leading to involuntary, disordered, violent contractions of the skeletal musculature (tetany). These symptoms are relieved immediately by the intravenous administration of calcium salts and as dramatically, though less swiftly, by extracts containing parathyroid hormone.

Collip and Clark described the preparation of an active extract of bovine parathyroid glands in 1925 and despite continuous efforts at purification by many workers little headway was made in more than thirty years. Over the past five years, however, tremendous progress has been made. Through the work of Rasmussen and Westall (1957), Friedman and Munson (1958), and Aurbach (1959), differing purification procedures have led to stepwise increases in potency of the active principle. In 1959 Rasmussen and Craig reported the isolation of a homogeneous protein having a specific activity approximately 200 times that of the U.S.P. preparation. The active protein is a simple unbranched polypeptide chain containing no cysteine and with alanine as the N-terminal group. Using different purification procedures, Rasmussen (1961) has obtained three active polypeptides with different molecular weights designated Parathormone A (mol wt 3700), Parathormone B (mol wt 6500) and Parathormone C (mol wt 8500). The specific activities in U.S.P. units per milligram are roughly: A, 1000; B, 2000; C, 3000. It is assumed that A and B are degradation products of C.

The major function of parathyroid hormone (PTH) is to maintain the plasma calcium at the physiological norm. Toward the maintenance of this homeostatic constant, the parathyroid hormone is believed to have at least two major sites of action, namely, bone and kidney. In bone, PTH stimulates the proliferation of osteoclasts resulting in an increased bone resorption; in kidney, it interferes with the reabsorption of phosphorus by the proximal convoluted portion of the nephron. Contrary to an earlier hypothesis the alterations in blood calcium are now known to be neither dependent upon nor necessarily related to changes in the blood phosphorus.

Tubular secretion of phosphate is well known to occur in lower marine vertebrates and birds but it has not been conclusively demonstrated in mammals. In 1959 Nicholson and Shepherd advanced evidence that PTH may stimulate tubular secretion of phosphate in the dog, but the weight of present evidence is against this possibility. A number of discordant observations on the action of PTH on calcium absorption from the gut suggests that if any effect exists at all it is at best of minor significance. Other possible peripheral actions of PTH, reviewed by Munson et al. (1963), include reduction in the calcium loss in urine and in milk.

An interesting new contribution to parathyroid research is the demonstration of the production in rabbits of an antibody to bovine parathyroid hormone (Tashjian et al., 1962), an observation that could lead to the development of a sensitive immunological assay of PTH. Recently, too, evidence has been presented by Copp et al. (1962) indicating the presence of a second parathyroid hormone termed "calcitonin." This second principle is held to aid in the maintenance of blood calcium homeostasis by exerting a fast-acting calcium lowering effect. The evidence on which the existence of calcitonin is postulated is largely physiological, and identification of the hormone as a chemical entity has not yet been achieved.

I am greatly indebted to Dr. W. E. Adams of New Zealand for his continued interest and helpful correspondence during the preparation of this article.

References

Adams, W. E. (1939). *J. Anat.* **74**, 57–71.

Adams, W. E. (1952). *Anat. Record* **113**, 1–27.

Adams, W. E. (1953). *J. Morphol.* **92**, 115–155.

Adams, W. E. (1955). *Am. J. Anat.* **97**, 1–58.

Aimé, P. (1911). *Compt. rend. soc. biol.* **70**, 209–210.

Aimé, P. (1912a). *Compt. rend. soc. biol.* **72**, 889–890.

Aimé, P. (1912b). *Compt. rend. soc. biol.* **73**, 115–116.

Albright, F., and Reifenstein, E. C., Jr. (1948). "The Parathyroid Glands and Metabolic Bone Disease," Williams & Wilkins, Baltimore, Maryland.

Aurbach, G. D. (1959). *J. Biol. Chem.* **234**, 3179–3181.

Avery, T. B., Scott, H. M., and Conrad, R. M. (1940a). *Poultry Sci.* **19**, 321–323.

Avery, T. B., Scott, H. M., and Conrad, R. M. (1940b). *Poultry Sci.* **19**, 324–325.

Bailey, R. E. (1957). *J. Exptl. Zool.* **136**, 455–469.

Baldwin, F. M. (1918). *J. Morphol.* **30**, 605–680.

Bargmann, W. (1939). *In* "Handbuch der mikroskopischen Anatomie des Menschen" (W. von Möllendorf, ed.), Vol. VI/2, pp. 137–196. Springer, Berlin.

Bartter, F. C. (1954). *Ann. Rev. Physiol.* **16**, 429–444.

Benoit, J. (1950). *In* "Traité de Zoologie" (P. P. Grassé, ed.), Vol. XV, pp. 297–305. Masson, Paris.

Benoit, J., and Clavert, J. (1945). *Compt. rend. soc. biol.* **139**, 737–740.

Benoit, J., and Clavert, J. (1947). *Acta Anat.* **4**, 49–53.

Benoit, J., Stricker, P., and Fabiani, G. (1941a). *Compt. rend. soc. biol.* **135**, 1600–1602.

Benoit, J., Fabiani, G., Grangaud, R., and Clavert, J. (1941b). *Compt. rend. soc. biol.* **135**, 1606–1609.

Benoit, J., Clavert, J., and Cabannes, R. (1944). *Compt. rend. soc. biol.* **138**, 1074–1075.

Boschwitz, D. (1961). *Herpetologica* **17**, 192–199.

Budde, M. L. (1958). *Growth* **22**, 73–92.

Campbell, I. L., and Turner, C. W. (1942). *Missouri Univ. Research Bull. No.* **352**, 1–134.

Collip, J. B. (1931). *Can. Med. Assoc. J.* **24**, 646–653.

Collip, J. B., and Clark, E. P. (1925). *J. Biol. Chem.* **66**, 133–137.

Copp, D. H., Cameron, E. C., Cheney, B. A., Davidson, G. F., and Henze, G. K. (1962). *Endocrinology* **70**, 638–649.

Cortelyou, J. R. (1960a). *Anat. Record* **137**, 346.

Cortelyou, J. R. (1960b). *Anat. Record* **138**, 341.

Cortelyou, J. R. (1962). *Endocrinology* **70**, 618–621.

Cortelyou, J. R., Hibner-Owerko, A., and Mulroy, J. (1960). *Endocrinology* **66**, 441–450.

de Meuron, P. (1886). *Rec. zool. suisse* **3**, 517–628.

Deobald, H. J., Lease, E. J., Hart, E. B., and Halpin, J. G. (1936). *Poultry Sci.* **15**, 179–185.

Dossel, W. E. (1960). *In* "McGraw-Hill Encyclopedia of Science and Technology" (William H. Crouse, ed.,), Vol. IX, pp. 557–560. McGraw-Hill, New York.

Doyon, M. (1907). *J. physiol. et pathol. gén.* **9**, 457–459.

Doyon, M., and Jouty, A. (1904). *Compt. rend. soc. biol.* **56**, 11.

Doyon, M., and Kareff, N. (1904). *Compt. rend. soc. biol.* **56**, 719.

Ecker, A. (1853). *Wagners Handwörterbuch Physiol.* **4**, 1853.

Eycleshymer, A., and Wilson, J. (1910). *In* "Normentafeln zur Etwicklungsgeschichte der Wirbeltiere" (F. K. J. Keibel, ed.). Fischer, Jena, Germany.

Fleming, W. R., and Meier, A. H. (1961a). *Comp. Biochem. Physiol.* **2**, 1–7.

Fleming, W. R., and Meier, A. H. (1961b). *Comp. Biochem. Physiol.* **3**, 27–29.

Fontaine, M. (1956). *Mem. Soc. Endocrinol. No.* **5**, 69–82.

Forsyth, D. (1908). *J. Anat.* **42**, 141–169, 302–319.

Fraser, E. A. (1915). *Phil. Trans. Roy. Soc. London* **B207**, 87–112.

Fraser, E. A., and Hill, J. P. (1915). *Phil. Trans. Roy. Soc. London* **B207**, 1–85.

Friedman, S., and Munson, P. L. (1958). *Biochim. et Biophys. Acta* **28**, 204–205.

Gley, E. (1891). *Compt. rend. soc. biol.* **43**, 841–847.

Greep, R. O. (1948). *In* "The Hormones" (G. Pincus and K. V. Thimann, eds.), Vol. I, pp. 255–299. Academic Press, New York.

Greep, R. O., and Talmage, R. V., eds. (1961). "The Parathyroids." C. C. Thomas, Springfield, Illinois.

Hägström, M. (1921). *Anat. Anz.* **53**, 545–566.

Hammar, J. A. (1937). *Z. mikroskop.-anat. Forsch.* **41**, 75–87.

Harrison, B. M., and Denning, N. E. (1929). *Anat. Record* **44**, 101–116.

Herdson, P. B. (1956). "The Cervical Region of the Ophidia with Special Reference to the Parathyroids and Carotid Arteries." Unpublished thesis for Bachelor of Medical Science in Anatomy, University of Otago, New Zealand.

Higgins, G. M., and Sheard, C. (1928). *Am. J. Physiol.* **85**, 299–310.

Hoar, W. S. (1957). *In* "The Physiology of Fishes" (M. E. Brown, ed.), Vol. I, pp. 245–277. Academic Press, New York.

Höhn, E. O. (1961). *In* "Biology and Comparative Physiology of Birds" (A. J. Marshall, ed.), Vol. II, pp. 87–114. Academic Press, New York.

Hollander, W. F., and Riddle, O. (1945). *Am. Naturalist* **79**, 451–463.

Hutt, F. B., and Boyd, W. L. (1935). *Endocrinology* **19**, 398–402.

Johnson, C. E. (1922). *J. Morphol.* **36**, 299–329.

Kingsbury, B. F. (1940). *Am. J. Anat.* **67**, 393–435.

Klose, W. (1932). *Z. Zellforsch u. mikroskop. Anat.* **14**, 385–449.

Knowles, H. R., Hart, E. B., and Halpin, J. G. (1935). *Poultry Sci.* **14**, 83–89.

Kohn, A. (1895). *Arch. mikroskop. Anat. u. Entwicklungsmech.* **44**, 366–422.

Kohn, A. (1899). *Ergeb. Anat. u. Entwicklungsgeschichte* **9**, 194–252.

Krause, R. (1923). "Microskopische Anatomie de Wirbettiere in Einzeldarostellungen." Vol. III, p. 598. de Gruyter, Berlin & Leipzig.

Kuffler, S. W. (1945). *J. Physiol.* **103**, 403–411.

Landauer, W., Pfeiffer, C. A., Gardner, W. U., and Shaw, J. C. (1941). *Endocrinology* **28**, 458–464.

Leydig, F. (1853). "Anatomisch-Histologische Untersuchungen über Fische u. Reptiliens." Von Georg Reimer, Berlin.

McCrady, E. (1941). *Anat. Record* **79**, Suppl., 45.

MacKenzie, W. C., and Owen, W. J. (1919). "The Glandular System in Monotremes and Marsupials." Jenkin, Buxton & Co., Melbourne.

Macowan, M. M. (1932). *Quart. J. Exp. Physiol.* **21**, 383–392.

Marine, D. (1913). *Proc. Soc. Exptl. Biol. Med.* **11**, 117–118.

Maurer, F. (1886). *Morphol. Jahrb.* **11**, 129–175.

Maurer, F. (1888). *Morphol. Jahrb.* **13**, 296–382.

Maurer, F. (1899a). *Morphol. Jahrb.* **27**, 119–172.

Maurer, F. (1899b). *Verhandl. anat. Ges.* **13**, 88–101.

Maurer, F. (1899c). *Semon's Zool. Forschungsreisen* **3**, 405–444.

Munson, P. L. (1960). *Federation Proc.* **19**, 593–601.

Munson, P. L. (1961). *Ann. Rev. Pharmacol.* **1**, 315–350.

Munson, P. L., Hirsch, P. F., and Tashjian, A. H., Jr. (1963). *Ann. Review Physiol.* **25** (in press).

Nicholson, T. F., and Shepherd, G. W. (1959). *Can. J. Biochem. Physiol.* **37**, 103–111.

Nonidez, F. J., and Goodale, H. D. (1927). *Am. J. Anat.* **38**, 319–347.

Oberling, C., and Guérin, M. (1933). *Compt. rend. Assoc. Anat.* **28**, 489–500.

Peters, H. (1940). *Z. microskop.-anat. Forsch.* **49**, 1–40.

Pischinger, A. (1937). *Handbuch vergleich. Anat. Wirbeltiere* **3**, 279–348.

Polin, D., and Sturkie, P. D. (1957). *Endocrinology* **60**, 778–784.

Polin, D., and Sturkie, P. D. (1958). *Endocrinology* **63**, 177–182.

Polin, D., and Sturkie, P. D. (1959). *Poultry Sci.* **38**, 166–170.

Polin, D., Sturkie, P. D., and Hunsaker, W. (1957). *Endocrinology* **60**, 1–5.

Rasmussen, H. (1961). *Am. J. Med.* **30**, 112–128.

Rasmussen, H., and Craig, L. C. (1959). *J. Am. Chem. Soc.* **81**, 5003.

Rasmussen, H., and Westall, R. G. (1957). *Biochem. J.* **67**, 658–663.

Rasquin, P., and Rosenbloom, L. (1954). *Bull. Am. Museum Nat. Hist.* **104**, 365–420.

Reese, A. M. (1931). *Smithsonian Inst. Publs. Misc. Collections* **82/116**, 1–14.

Riddle, O., and Dotti, L. B. (1934). *Proc. Soc. Exptl. Biol. Med.* **32**, 507–509.

Riddle, O., and McDonald, M. R. (1945). *Endocrinology* **36**, 48–52.

Riddle, O., Rauch, V. M., and Smith, G. C. (1945). *Endocrinology* **36**, 41–47.

Romeis, B. (1926). *Z. Anat. u. Entwicklungsgeschichte* **80**, 547–578.

Saint-Rémy, G., and Prenant, A. (1904). *Arch. Biol. Paris* **20**, 145–216.

Sandström, I. (1880). *Upsala Läkarefören. Förh.* **15**, 635–639.

Schjeide, O. A., and Urist, M. R. (1956). *Science* **124**, 1242–1244.

Scholz, J. (1935). *Wilhelm Roux' Arch. Entwicklungsmech. Organ.* **132**, 752–762.

Schrier, J. E., and Hamilton, H. L. (1952). *J. Exptl. Zool.* **119**, 165–182.

Shaner, R. F. (1921). *Am. J. Anat.* **29**, 407–429.

Shapiro, B. G. (1933). *J. Anat.* **68**, 39–44.

Smith, G. C. (1945). *Anat. Record* **92**, 81–86.

Stott, G. H., and Smith, V. R. (1957). *J. Dairy Sci.* **40**, 897–904.

Studitsky, A. N. (1945). *Compt. rend. acad. sci. U.R.S.S.* **47**, 444–447.

Sturkie, P. D. (1954). "Avian Physiology," Comstock (Cornell Univ. Press), Ithaca, New York.

Talmage, R. V., Kraintz, F. W., Frost, R. C., and Kraintz, L. (1953). *Endocrinology* **52**, 318–323.

Tashjian, A. H., Jr., Levine, L., and Munson, P. L. (1962). *Biochem. Biophys. Research Communs.* **8**, 259–265.

Thompson, F. D. (1910). *Phil. Trans. Roy. Soc. London* **B201**, 91–132.

Toldt, C. (1868). *Sitzber. Akad. Wiss. Wien Math.-naturw. Kl. Abt. III* **58**, 171–187.

Trinci, G. (1912). *Arch. ital. anat. e embriol.* **10**, 197–260.

Uhlenhuth, E. (1923). *Biol. Bull.* **45**, 303–324.

Underwood, G. (1957). *J. Morphol.* **100**, 207–268.

Urist, M. R. (1959). *Recent Progr. in Hormone Research* **15**, 445–481.

Urist, M. R., Schjeide, O. A., and McLean, F. C. (1958). *Endocrinology* **63**, 570–585.

Urist, M. R., Deutsch, N. M., Pomerantz, G., and McLean, F. C. (1960). *Am. J. Physiol.* **199**, 851–855.

van Bemmelen, J. F. (1886). *Zool. Anz.* **9**, 528–532; 543–548.

van Bemmelen, J. F. (1887). *Zool. Anz.* **10**, 88–96.

van Bemmelen, J. F. (1888). *Koninkl. Zool. Genoot. Amsterdam* **16**, 101–146.

Verdun, P. (1898). "Contribution à l'étude des dérivés branchiaux chez les vertébrés supérieurs," Thesis, Toulouse.

Vincent, S. (1912). "Internal Secretion and the Ductless Glands." Arnold, London.

Waggener, R. A. (1929). *J. Morphol. and Physiol.* **48**, 1–44.

Waggener, R. A. (1930). *J. Exptl. Zool.* **57**, 13–56.

Weller, G. L. (1933). *Contribs. to Embryol., Carnegie Inst. Wash. Publ. No.* 141, **24**, 93–138.

Winget, C. M., and Smith, A. H. (1957). *Poultry Sci.* **37**, 1169.

Winget, C. M., and Smith, A. H. (1958). *Poultry Sci.* **38**, 509–512.

Witschi, E. (1940). *Endocrinology* **27**, 437–446.

Zuckerkandl, E. (1902). *Ergeb. Anat. u. Entwicklungsgeschichte* **19**, 59–84.

$$\sim 10 \sim$$

Pancreatic Hormones: Insulin

F. G. YOUNG

Department of Biochemistry, University of Cambridge, England

I. INTRODUCTION

Insulin is the hormone secreted by the β-cells of the islets of Langerhans of the pancreas, and by analogous cells in some lower species which lack a pancreas. The parenteral administration of this hormone can control the symptoms of the disease in a human being suffering from diabetes mellitus; therefore extraction has been done on a commercial scale of insulin from pancreas of oxen, pigs, sheep, and some other species, which makes such insulin easily available for both chemical and biological investigation.

371

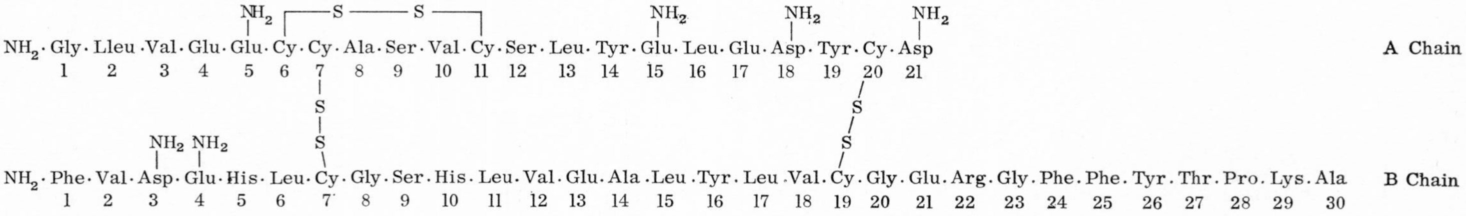

A Chain

NH_2·Gly·Lleu·Val·Glu·Glu·Cy·Cy·Ala·Ser·Val·Cy·Ser·Leu·Tyr·Glu·Leu·Glu·Asp·Tyr·Cy·Asp
1 2 3 4 5 6 7 8 9 10 11 12 13 14 15 16 17 18 19 20 21

B Chain

NH_2·Phe·Val·Asp·Glu·His·Leu·Cy·Gly·Ser·His·Leu·Val·Glu·Ala·Leu·Tyr·Leu·Val·Cy·Gly·Glu·Arg·Gly·Phe·Phe·Tyr·Thr·Pro·Lys·Ala
1 2 3 4 5 6 7 8 9 10 11 12 13 14 15 16 17 18 19 20 21 22 23 24 25 26 27 28 29 30

FIG. 1. The structure of ox insulin. (Based on Sanger, 1959.)

372

Chemically, insulin is a protein and its chemical structure was the first of any protein to be completely understood. The feat of elucidation by Sanger (1959, 1960) and his colleagues, has led to an understanding of the differences in chemical structure between the insulins prepared from the glands of different species of animals.

The chemical structure of insulin from ox pancreas is given in Fig. 1, and the variations in this structure so far encountered in the insulins from different species are illustrated in Table I. In Table II, the amino acid composition of separated A and B chains of insulins from ox, cod fish, (*Gymnosarda alleterata*) are compared; Table III illustrates the species variations in the terminal amino acids in insulins so far encountered.

The existence of variations in the chemical structure of insulin which can involve at least seven of the fifty-one amino acid residues in the molecule, and also the preparation from the pancreas of the rat and of the bonito fish of two chemically different insulin molecules, pose a number of

TABLE I

SPECIES DIFFERENCES IN THE AMINO ACID SEQUENCE OF THE INSULIN MOLECULE

	A chain[b]				B chain[c]		
Animal[a]	4	8	9	10	3	29	30
Ox (1)	Glu	Ala	Ser	Val	Asp(NH₂)	Lys	Ala
Sheep (2)	Glu	Ala	Gly	Val	Asp(NH₂)	Lys	Ala
Horse (3)	Glu	Thr	Gly	Ileu	Asp(NH₂)	Lys	Ala
Sei whale (4)	Glu	Ala	Ser	Thr	Asp(NH₂)	Lys	Ala
Pig (2)	Glu	Thr	Ser	Ileu	Asp(NH₂)	Lys	Ala
Sperm whale (3)	Glu	Thr	Ser	Ileu	Asp(NH₂)	Lys	Ala
Dog (5)	Glu	Thr	Ser	Ileu	Asp(NH₂)	Lys	Ala
Human (6)	Glu	Thr	Ser	Ileu	Asp(NH₂)	Lys	Thr
Rabbit (5)	Glu	Thr	Ser	Ileu	Asp(NH₂)	Lys	Ser
Rat 1 (5)	Asp	Thr	Ser	Ileu	Lys	Lys	Ser
Rat 2 (5)	Asp	Thr	Ser	Ileu	Lys	Met	Ser

[a] Numbers in parentheses refer to References as follows:
  (1) Sanger and Tuppy (1951).
     Sanger and Thompson (1953).
  (2) Brown et al. (1955).
  (3) Harris et al. (1956).
  (4) Ishihara et al. (1958).
  (5) Smith, L. F. Unpublished.
  (6) Nicol and Smith (1960).
[b] Numbers of column heads refer to positions indicated in Fig. 1, A chain.
[c] Numbers of column heads refer to positions indicated in Fig. 1, B chain.

TABLE II

AMINO ACID COMPOSITION OF SEPARATED A AND B CHAINS OF INSULIN FROM OX, COD
FISH, AND BONITO FISH (BONITO FISH INSULIN II)[a]

Amino acid	A Chain			B Chain		
	Ox	Cod[b]	Bonito[c]	Ox	Cod[b]	Bonito[c]
Ala	1	*0*	*0*	2	2	*3*
Arg	0	*1*	0	1	1	1
Asp	2	*5*	*3*	1	*3*	1
Cys	4	4	4	2	2	2
Glu	4	*2*	4	3	*2*	3
Gly	1	1	1	3	3	3
His	0	*1*	*2*	2	2	2
Ileu	1	*2[d]*	1	0	0	0
Leu	2	*1[d]*	2	4	4	4
Lys	0	0	*1*	1	1	1
Met	0	0	0	0	*1*	0
Phe	0	*1*	*1*	3	*2*	*2*
Pro	0	*1*	*1*	1	*3*	*2*
Ser	2	*0*	*0*	1	1	1
Thr	0	0	0	1	*0*	*0*
Try	0	0	*0?*	0	0	*0?*
Tyr	2	*1*	*1*	2	2	2
Val	2	*1*	*0*	3	*2*	*2*
	21	21	21	30	*31*	*29*

[a] Figures which differ from those for ox insulin are in italic type.
[b] Wilson and Dixon (1961).
[c] Kotaki (1961).
[d] These figures have been corrected from Table 1 of Wilson and Dixon (1961) as the result of correspondence with Dr. G. H. Dixon.

questions. Can we be sure that in a given species only one type of insulin molecule normally exists? The isolation of adrenaline and noradrenaline from the adrenal medulla, of thyroxine and triodothyronine from the thyroid gland, and of the numerous physiologically active steroids from the adrenal cortex, has made the belief that only one hormone is secreted by each endocrine gland certainly not now tenable, although such an idea did linger on even after the multiplicity of the hormones secreted by the anterior lobe of the pituitary gland had been well substantiated. If, in fact, more than one type of molecule is secreted by β-cells in a number of animal species, the information now available about the nature of the hormone of the islets of Langerhans may clearly be incomplete.

TABLE III

THE N-TERMINAL AND C-TERMINAL AMINO ACID RESIDUES OF INSULINS FROM
DIFFERENT SPECIES

Insulin	A Chain		B Chain	
	N-Terminal	C-Terminal	N-Terminal	C-Terminal
Ox[a]	Gly	Asp(NH₂)	Phe	Ala
Human[b]	Gly	Asp(NH₂)	Phe	Thr
Rabbit[c]	Gly	Asp(NH₂)	Phe	Ser
Rat (1 and 2)[c]	Gly	Asp(NH₂)	Phe	Ser
Cod[d]	Gly	Asp(NH₂)	Ser	Lys
Bonito II[e]	Gly	Asp(NH₂)	Ala	Lys
Bonito I[f]	Gly	—	Leu	—

[a] Sanger and Tuppy (1951); Sanger and Thompson (1953).
[b] Nicol and Smith (1960).
[c] L. F. Smith, unpublished.
[d] Wilson and Dixon (1961).
[e] Kotaki (1961).
[f] Yamamoto et al. (1960).

In comparative studies the effect on animals of the administration of the types of insulin available industrially, mainly those from ox, pig, and sheep, is so far the only area to have been explored and this could mean that significantly different biological results might be obtained if the effects of the homologous insulins were investigated. The fact that insulin from one species may be antigenic in another (Stavitsky and Arquilla, 1953; Arquilla and Stavitsky, 1956; Moloney and Coval, 1955) is relevant in this respect. Nevertheless, industrially available insulin is usually highly effective in controlling the symptoms of diabetes mellitus which develop in most species (though not in all) when the pancreas is experimentally removed. This suggests that, in a given species of animal, biological activity is not highly or specifically related to the primary structure of the insulin molecule characteristic of that species. Therefore, the available evidence about the control of carbohydrate metabolism by insulin, admittedly based largely on experiments with commercial insulin, is not necessarily of doubtful value. Nevertheless, much research remains to be done to clarify the possible biological significance of the known and expected species differences in the chemical structure of insulin. Until clarification of this sort has been effected one should at least be cautious in interpreting the results of experiments in which industrially available insulin is injected into an animal of a species widely different from those domesticated types from which insulin is usually obtained.

Because of the medical importance of insulin much of the research designed to elucidate the mechanism of action of this hormone has been carried out on higher vertebrates, particularly on man, the dog, and the cat. Nevertheless, a rising interest is evident in the effect of experimental removal of the pancreas, or of damage by various means, of the pancreatic islets from different species of animals. Some survey of these results and of those concerned with replacement therapy in pancreatectomized animals can usefully be made. But first a brief survey of the comparative morphology of the pancreas is needed.

II. COMPARATIVE MORPHOLOGY OF THE ISLETS OF LANGER-HANS OF THE PANCREAS (Hill, 1926; Barrington, 1942; Willmer, 1951; Miller and Wurster, 1959; Frye, 1959).

The pancreas is a complex, fairly constant and uniformly distributed organ found only in vertebrates; no directly comparable organ has been found in the invertebrates.

Embryologically both the pancreas and the liver develop at a point just caudad to the pylorus, the pancreas arising typically from three main buds or rudiments, two ventral and one dorsal. These buds give rise to the parts of the adult pancreas in mammals and to three completely or partially separated pancreatic glands in birds.

In all mammals and in most other types of vertebrates the islets of Langerhans (Langerhans, 1869) are scattered throughout the substance of the exocrine pancreas, constituting altogether about 1% of the weight of the whole organ in man (Ogilvie, 1937; Maclean and Ogilvie, 1955). In certain fish, notably teleosts, the tissue of the islets is gathered together in discrete nodules or "principal islets" which may be quite separate from the main bulk of the pancreas (McCormick, 1924; Mosca, 1960; Falkmer, 1961).

The islets develop embryologically as abortive outgrowths of the ducts of the pancreas, and in some ways they can be regarded as composed of modified duct epithelial cells. Moreover the ducts are outgrowths of the wall of the duodenum, and from some points of view the islets can be regarded as the result of specialization of the glands of the duodenal mucosa (Willmer, 1951).

In the ammocete larva of the lamprey, an organism which is regarded as an extremely primitive vertebrate and which does not possess a true pancreas, groups of cells are found in the submucosa of the alimentary canal at the junction of the foregut and the midgut. These cells were first described by Langerhans (1873) and have been named "follicles of Langerhans." These follicles can be regarded as a primitive stage in the evolution of the endocrine component of the vertebrate pancreas (Barrington, 1942).

In mammals the islets of Langerhans of the pancreas contain at least two types of secretory cells. The α-cells of the pancreatic islets are believed to secrete glucagon, while there is good evidence that the β-cells secrete insulin. An increase in the amount of glucose in the blood flowing through the islets results in a rise in the rate of secretion of insulin. The evidence is satisfactory that, where they can be unequivocably identified, the β-cells are the place of manufacture of the insulin secreted by the pancreatic islets (Macleod, 1922, 1926; Lazarow, 1957). Although the evidence is good that at least the major part of the insulin present in the animal is secreted by the pancreas, there is no adequate proof that all the insulin comes from this source. The idea has been put forward that insulin, like other hormones, may be a metabolite liberated in small amounts by many different types of cells (Young, 1959). The problem of the possible extrapancreatic secretion of insulin has not yet been investigated with modern, sensitive methods for the detection and assay of this hormone.

Types of cells similar to those seen in the islets of mammals have been identified in fish (Bowie, 1924; Thomas, 1940; Falkmer, 1961) and in amphibians and lizards (Miller and Wurster, 1959; Miller, 1960). These observations, together with the fact that in most vertebrates experimental removal of the pancreas results in a condition resembling diabetes mellitus, indicate that the insulin-secreting mechanism of pancreatic islets is widespread throughout the Vertebrata.

III. EFFECTS OF REMOVAL OF, OR DAMAGE TO, THE ISLETS OF LANGERHANS OF THE PANCREAS

The pancreas is a complex organ, and the islets of Langerhans secrete at least two hormones, insulin and glucagon. The effect of the surgical removal of the pancreas as a whole might be expected to differ according to the species of animal under investigation. The fact that extirpation of the pancreas nevertheless induces a condition of experimental diabetes mellitus in most species therefore suggests that the secretion of insulin by the pancreas is normally of dominating importance. Means whereby the β-cells of the islets of Langerhans can be selectively damaged have been developed during the past 25 years and the metabolic results of such selective destruction are usually not greatly different from those which follow removal of the pancreas as a whole, although some differences in detail are seen. In toads, reptiles, and birds the differences tend to be greater than are found otherwise (Section C, 4, 5, 6).

A. The Effects of Damage to the β-Cells of the Pancreatic Islets

1. Means Whereby Selective Damage to the β-Cells of the Pancreatic Islets May Be Effected

The first example of an animal in which damage to the β-cells of the pancreatic islets was selectively induced was provided by the investigations of Young (1937, 1938) and Richardson and Young (1938) in which a permanent diabetes was induced in dogs by a short period of daily injections of an extract of ox anterior pituitary tissue. This persisting diabetes (sometimes called metahypophyseal diabetes) was associated with gross damage to the β-cells of the islets (Richardson and Young, 1938; Richardson, 1940). The activity of the extract used was subsequently attributed to the pituitary growth hormone it contained (Cotes et al., 1949; Young, 1953). Diabetes may also be induced by those adrenal corticosteroids which have a ketonic oxygen atom or a hydroxyl group at position 11 of the molecule (Ingle, 1941, 1948), or by pituitary corticotropin (Conn et al., 1948).

Subsequently, Dunn and his colleagues (Dunn et al., 1943; Dunn and McLetchie, 1943) found that the simple chemical substance alloxan could cause damage to the β-cells of the pancreatic islets associated with persisting diabetes in rabbits and other species, and these observations were rapidly extended to many different types of animal. Reducing substances chemically related to alloxan, such as dehydroascorbic acid (Patterson, 1950) were subsequently found also to damage the insulin-secreting cells of the pancreatic islets, and a number of unrelated substances such as oxine (8-hydroxyquinoline) and dithizon (diphenylthiocarbazone) have also been reported to induce necrosis of the β-cells, along with diabetes (Kadota, 1950).

In the cat repeated intraperitoneal injections of glucose-saline may induce persisting diabetes associated with damage to the β-cells of the pancreatic islets (Dohan and Lukens, 1947a, b). These and other means of inducing damage to the pancreatic islets have been reviewed by Ogilvie (1952).

2. The Mechanism of Action of Damage to the Islet Cells

Clearly the mechanism of action of all these different means of inducing damage to the pancreatic islets, and of thus causing the development of experimental diabetes mellitus, are unlikely to be the same. The action of the hormones, and of glucose, is probably the induction of a physiological overstrain in the insulin-secreting mechanism of the pancreatic islets, which ultimately leads to its damage. Alloxan and other substances exert a toxic action on the β-cells of the pancreatic islets which brings about their rapid necrosis. Although this toxic action is most strikingly seen in the β-cells of the islets it is probably not lacking, though less severe, in cells of other tissues (Lukens, 1948). The action of alloxan and of related oxidizing substances has been attributed to an oxidation of essential sulfhydryl groups in the β-cells of the islets, and the action of chelating agents such as oxine has been ascribed to a sequestering action on the zinc believed to be associated with insulin in the islet cells (see Ogilvie, 1952 for references).

Although damage to the pancreatic islets by the agents discussed above is most strikingly seen in the β-cells, usually not all the β-cells are damaged (see, however, Young, 1948) while a varying proportion of the α-cells are also affected. The variable action on the α-cells may be a result of the extensive though not necessarily complete damage to the β-cells, and its subsequent effect on the blood supply to the islets. Because of these varying local effects on the islets the metabolic influence of the damaging agents may differ significantly from one animal to another within a given species.

3. THE METABOLIC EFFECTS OF DAMAGE TO THE ISLET CELLS

Since all the insulin-secreting cells of the islets are usually not damaged by the agents under discussion, the diabetes mellitus induced under their influence is usually less severe than that which follows total pancreatectomy. Indeed in some instances an initially severe alloxan diabetic may show slow but ultimate complete remission (Lukens, 1948; Ogilvie, 1952). The same is true of the cat made persistently diabetic by treatment with growth hormone (Young, 1948; Lever et al., 1961) though not of the similarly treated dog (Young, 1938, 1953).

In general the animal from which the pancreas has been surgically removed is more liable to develop fatal ketosis and ketonuria than is an animal of the same species in which diabetes-inducing islet damage has recently been effected. This observation is consonant with the fact that usually only a proportion of the β-cells of the islets are irreparably damaged by the agents discussed above. The dog in which damage to the β-cells of the islets has been induced by treatment with growth hormone-containing pituitary extract may survive in good health with minimal ketonuria for a year or more in the absence of insulin therapy, though an untreated depancreatized dog dies in 1–2 weeks with severe ketonuria (Young, 1938; Marks and Young, 1939). Nevertheless the animal with pituitary-induced diabetes may need significantly more insulin for the control of its diabetic condition than does a completely depancreatized dog

(Young, 1938; Campbell and Best, 1938; Marks and Young, 1939) even though adequate precautions are taken to ensure that the absorption of food by the gut of the depancreatized animal is similar to that of the intact dog. In such instances the insulin requirement may diminish when the animal with diabetes resulting from damage to the islets is depancreatized (Marks and Young, 1939). Thorogood and Zimmermann (1945), Candela (1945), and Candela et al. (1947) observed a similar fall in insulin requirement when alloxan diabetic dogs were depancreatized, though the adequacy of the absorption of food from the gut of the depancreatized animals was not always ensured (see Mirsky et al., 1951; Candela, 1952). These results suggest that in animals with damaged islets sufficient insulin is being secreted to depress ketosis and to make survival possible, at least for a time, where otherwise it would not occur. Nevertheless sensitivity to the action of exogenous insulin is lower in the animal with pituitary-induced diabetes than in the depancreatized animal, presumably because of the presence of the tissues of the pancreas other than the β-cells of the islets (Young, 1939). The most likely candidate for the role of a depressant in sensitivity to the action of insulin which originates in the pancreas is glucagon, although other possibilities cannot be ruled out.

B. The Effects of Complete or Partial Surgical Removal of the Pancreas

The accidental and important discovery of von Mering and Minkowski (1890) that total surgical removal of the pancreas from the dog induces a condition which resembles severe diabetes mellitus in the human being, was the first of many investigations all over the world directed to an examination of the metabolic derangement induced by pancreatectomy in different species, and to the preparation of an extract of the pancreas which would prevent or cure it. The way in which the discovery of von Mering and Minkowski came to be made has been recently interestingly illuminated by the publication by Houssay (1952) of a letter from Minkowski written in 1926.

The condition of experimental diabetes mellitus which follows total extirpation of the pancreas from the dog is severe, reasonably stable, and without treatment is usually fatal in 1–2 weeks. The fact that von Mering and Minkowski (1890) happened to choose a dog for their epoch-making discovery is a good example of serendipity. Because of its severity, stability, and its historical importance, pancreatic diabetes in the dog will be described in some detail; the conditions in other species will be less closely outlined later.

The depencreatized dog on a mixed diet excretes 3–10 gm/kg of body weight of glucose in its urine each day, and its blood sugar varies from 300 to 500 mg/100 ml. It suffers from polyphagia, polydipsia, polyuria, hyperlipemia, hypercholesterolemia, ketonemia, and ketonuria (50–500 mg/kg per day).

The administration of glucose to the depancreatized dog leads to prolonged elevation of the blood sugar level, and the whole of the administered sugar may be lost in the urine. The respiratory quotient does not rise after the administration of the sugar, and although the tissues may absorb some glucose from the blood passing through them, they take up much less than do those of a normal dog. The animal is continually in negative nitrogen balance and rapidly loses weight despite the polyphagia, becoming emaciated and asthenic. Acidosis with a gross diminution of the alkali reserve of the blood arises from a progressively increasing ketonemia, and this in turn leads to an increase in urinary excretion of ammonia. Dehydration with loss of electrolytes from the body occurs (Sunderman and Dohan, 1941) and coma may develop which is attributable to a specific intoxication by the acetoacetate accumulating in the tissues (Schneider and Droller, 1938). The animal ultimately dies in coma, with emaciation, dehydration, and asthenia as outstanding features.

In the depancreatized dog the glycogen stores of the liver and skeletal muscles are much diminished, though that of the heart and of the leucocytes (Minkowski, 1893) is usually above normal. Restoration of the glycogen stores after their depression by muscular contraction is usually slow. Depletion of the fat stores is a striking feature, though the liver usually shows marked fatty infiltration.

The condition is mainly due to the inability of the tissues to utilize sufficient glucose for metabolic purposes (oxidation, conversion to fat, conversion to glycogen) and to the excessive catabolism of protein and fat. It is completely and indefinitely alleviated by the continued administration of commercial insulin, as such or in one of its long-acting forms, provided that disturbances which can arise from the absence of pancreatic digestive enzymes are avoided. The fasting depancreatized dog requires 0.1–0.8 units/kg body weight per day of insulin for control of the diabetic condition (Houssay et al., 1929; Greeley, 1937a) while on a mixed diet 3–6 units/kg per day may be needed (Marks and Young, 1939).

Hédon (1893a), Minkowski (1893), and Sandmeyer (1895), observed that if only a small portion of the pancreas (about one ninth of the whole organ) of the dog is left in situ, the diabetic condition is mild, nonexistent, or grossly delayed in appearance. Subsequently Langfeldt (1920) found that when puppies are surgically deprived of such a proportion of the pancreas as might be expected to induce diabetes in the adult animal, diabetes may not develop for 10 months or more, during which period the sugar tolerance of some of the animals may be enhanced rather than depressed. Likewise, it is a common observation that young growing rats treated with alloxan may not become diabetic until many months later (see Lukens, 1948; Lazarow, 1949); moreover puppies do not develop diabetes in response to treatment with a dose of diabetes-inducing pituitary extract which is effective in the adult dog (Young, 1941) though a diabetic condition may develop after 9–12 months of continuous treatment (Young, 1944).

In the discussion of species variations in pancreatic diabetes which follows, no attempt will be made to segregate the effects of surgical removal of the pancreas from those of damage to the islets, though in general the means whereby the diabetic condition was induced will be noted. In some instances the existence of naturally occurring diabetes is noted (Meier, 1960).

C. Species Variations in Pancreatic Diabetes

1. PANCREATIC DIABETES IN PRIMATES

a. *Man.* The successful therapeutic removal of the whole pancreas from man was first carried out in 1942 (Priestley *et al.*, 1944) and since then many instances have been recorded, recent examples being given by McCullagh *et al.* (1958). The diabetic state is generally less severe than that seen in the depancreatized dog, and in a person receiving a moderate mixed diet the insulin needed for control of the condition may range from 0.2 to 1.0 units/kg per day. This is significantly less than that needed by the depancreatized dog and also by many human patients with spontaneous diabetes mellitus. Human beings who develop diabetes mellitus are often overweight when the condition is first observed, and since many appear to need more insulin for the control of the condition than do depancreatized patients, the suggestion has been made that in some instances at least the diabetes arises because of an excess of insulin antagonists in the circulation, and that this condition may relate to an oversecretion of pituitary growth hormone (see Young, 1953). This view cannot be taken as proved, though it seems very likely that human diabetes does not always develop primarily because of a diminished supply of insulin by the pancreas.

There is evidence that susceptibility to diabetes mellitus is inherited as a recessive Mendelian character in the human being, but again the evidence for such a simple relationship is by no means complete.

b. *Monkey.* The depancreatized baboon exhibits a moderately severe diabetic condition in which the insulin requirement is about 0.5 units/kg per day (Gillman *et al.*, 1958).

Although discrepancies exist in the literature about severity of the diabetic condition of the depancreatized Macaque monkey, particularly in respect to the degree of the ketonuria which develops on fasting, there is general agreement that a moderately severe diabetes exists in the totally depancreatized monkey (*Macaca mulatta* and *Macacus rhesus*) receiving adequate food (Hédon, 1898; Collip *et al.*, 1937; Mirsky *et al.*, 1942; Chapman and Fulton, 1938).

2. PANCREATIC DIABETES IN CARNIVOROUS MAMMALS

Spontaneous diabetes in the domestic dog has been described (Bloom and Handelsmann, 1937; Waddington 1937; Wilkinson, 1957, 1958; Meier, 1960), and experimentally induced alloxan diabetes has been extensively investigated in this species (Goldner and Gomori, 1943; Covian and de Oya, 1944; Houssay *et al.*, 1946). The diabetes which persists after a short period of treatment with pituitary extract (Young, 1937) has also been closely examined (Marks and Young, 1939; Haist *et al.* 1940; Dohan *et al.*, 1941). These conditions are usually less severe initially than that after total pancreatectomy even though the insulin requirement may be slightly greater. However, the diabetes usually increases in severity with time until it ultimately may come to resemble that due to pancreatectomy.

Diabetes in the depancreatized cat is severe and resembles that seen in dog after pancreatectomy (Epstein and Baehr, 1916; Aszódi, 1928; Long and Lukens, 1936). Naturally occurring diabetes in the cat has been described (Bloom, 1937; Lande, 1944; Meier, 1960); alloxan diabetes (Lukens, 1948) and persisting diabetes induced by a short period of treatment with pituitary extract (metahypophyseal diabetes) (Lukens and Dohan, 1942; Young, 1948, 1951; Lever *et al.*, 1961) have also been described for this species. In the cat, unlike the dog, metahypophyseal diabetes shows a tendency to spontaneous remission. The insulin requirement of the depancreatized cat and of the cat with metahypophyseal diabetes is about 0.5–2 units/kg per day.

3. PANCREATIC DIABETES IN OMNIVOROUS AND HERBIVOROUS MAMMALS

Minkowski (1893) observed the development of diabetes in a partially depancreatized pig. In many omnivorous or herbivorous mammals total pancreatectomy, or treatment with alloxan, induces a relatively mild diabetes and insulin is usually not needed for survival. Glycosuria and ketonuria are often only slight, and the blood sugar level may fall on fasting although it may be quite high (200–400 mg/100 ml) after food. This is generally true for the rabbit after pancreatectomy (Hédon, 1893b; Greeley, 1937b, 1947) and after alloxan treatment (Bailey and Bailey, 1943; Dunn *et al.*, 1944; Kennedy and Lukens, 1944), for the depancreatized goat (Lukens, 1938; Greeley, 1947), for the alloxan-diabetic goat (Saviano and De Francisis, 1946; De Moor and Vuylsteke, 1948), and for the calf either depancreatized (Cook *et al.*, 1949) or made diabetic with alloxan (McCandless and Dye, 1949). In the depancreatized pig ketonuria can be severe but serious acidosis or coma do not develop (Lukens, 1937). In alloxan-diabetic piglets ketosis was absent (Lukens, 1937).

In the adult sheep complete pancreatectomy induces a moderately severe diabetes with ketosis which may be marked but is usually mild (Jarrett *et al.*, 1956), while alloxan diabetes (Jarrett, 1946; McCandless *et al.*, 1948) is sometimes associated with an initially severe ketosis which may later decline. In the sheep the amount of insulin needed to control the diabetes produced by pancreatectomy (0.5–0.8 units/kg per day) is much less than that needed by the alloxan-diabetic animal, which may be 5–10 times as much (Jarrett, 1946; McCandless *et al.*, 1948).

In the rat alloxan diabetes is relatively easily produced (Dunn and McLetchie, 1943; Gomori and Goldner, 1943; Lazarow and Palay, 1946; Gitter, 1947; Lukens, 1948) and it has been extensively studied. The diabetes is certainly not complete; it may develop only slowly, especially in young animals, and it sometimes shows spontaneous remission. In nonacidotic alloxan-diabetic rats the deposition of liver glycogen from administered sugars is not obviously depressed, and the liver glycogen content rises above normal after 24 hrs of starvation (Tuerkischer and Wertheimer, 1948).

Complete pancreatectomy in the rat is difficult because of certain anatomical peculiarities in this species. When 95% of the pancreas is removed diabetes may develop 1–2 months later and then slowly progress until it is quite severe (Foglia, 1953). Scow (1957) has described a method for surgically removing 99.5% of the pancreas from the rat. Under these conditions an intense diabetes develops within 18 hrs, with hyperglycemia (350–400 mg/100 ml), glycosuria (about 50 mg/100 gm body weight), and ketonuria (30 mg/100 gm body weight). If the animal is not treated with insulin it usually dies within 48 hrs in diabetic coma. When food is given the insulin requirement is high (2.5 units/gm food eaten, or about 100 units/kg body weight per day) although the starving animal may respond well to a very small dose of insulin (0.0033 units) (Scow, 1957).

Alloxan diabetes (Nace *et al.*, 1956) and spontaneous hereditary diabetes (Meier and Yerganiau, 1961) have been observed in the hamster. Those animals with hereditary diabetes could be maintained by suitable insulin therapy but were not very sensitive to it, needing as much as 500 units/kg body weight for reduction of the blood sugar to normal. Alloxan diabetes in the mouse has been studied by Lazarow (1947).

The herbivorous marsupial *Trichosurus vulpecula* (common brush-tailed phalanger) appears to have a low renal threshold and the urine frequently contains reducing sugars. Alloxan can produce a persisting diabetes, and insulin must sometimes be administered to prevent wasting and coma (Adams and Bollinger, 1954).

4. EFFECT OF PANCREATECTOMY IN BIRDS

The β-cells of the pancreatic islets of birds in general appear to be relatively resistant to the damaging action of alloxan (Lukens, 1948). Minkowski (1893) found that removal of the pancreas from ducks and pigeons did not produce glycosuria, though some later observers found that in ducks and geese only mild hyperglycemia and glycosuria usually occurred (Sprague and Ivy, 1936; Mirsky *et al.*, 1941). On the other hand, Mialhe (1955, 1956) believes that pancreatectomy was incomplete in the earlier researches on the duck, and he reports that if all of the pancreas is removed the duck becomes hypoglycemic and drowsy, and may die in convulsions 2–24 hrs after the operation. Glucose can keep the animal alive during this critical period after which therapy can be stopped and the animal can survive with a low blood sugar level. When the depancreatized duck feeds, the blood sugar level rises to normal or supernormal values, but if it starves the blood sugar falls to low levels. The condition is ascribed to the absence of insulin and of glucagon, the latter of which in this species appears to be necessary for the avoidance of starvation hypoglycemia (Mialhe, 1960). In agreement with such a view is the fact that in the pancreatic islets of the duck there are 6–10 times more α-cells than there are in mammalian pancreatic islets (Mialhe, 1958) and the pancreas of the duck is particularly rich in glucagon (Vuylsteke and de Duve, 1953). Suitable treatment with both glucagon and insulin can maintain both a starving blood sugar value and a sugar tolerance curve at normal levels in the depancreatized duck (Mialhe, 1957a).

Removal of the pancreas from the chicken is sometimes followed by hyperglycemia (Giaja, 1912; Mirsky and Gitelson, 1957); ketosis may be seen (Mirsky *et al.*, 1941). Since the pancreas of the chicken is very rich in glucagon (Vuylsteke and de Duve, 1953) circumstances similar to those for the duck may hold in part for the chicken (compare Beekman, 1956). Diabetes does not develop in the pancreatectomized pigeon (Janes, 1939).

386 F. G. YOUNG

In carnivorous birds, nevertheless, pancreatectomy usually induces hyperglycemia and some glycosuria. This is true for hawks (Minkowski, 1893; Weintraud, 1894), buzzards and ravens (Weintraud, 1894), and for the carnivorous horned owl *Bubo virginianus virginianus* (Nelson *et al.*, 1942).

The general conclusion may tentatively be drawn that in noncarnivorous birds the glucagon-secreting function of pancreatic islets is at least as important as their insulin secreting function, though carnivorous birds more closely resemble mammals in that the secretion of insulin by the pancreas is of dominant importance.

5. EFFECT OF PANCREATECTOMY IN REPTILES

In fluvial turtles (*Chrisemis d'orbignyi* and *Phrynops hilarii*) total pancreatectomy (Foglia *et al.*, 1955) and alloxan (Garcia Ramos, 1944; Lopes, 1955; Cardeza, 1957b) produce diabetes; partial pancreatectomy (Cardeza, 1957a) may induce diabetes more easily in the male turtle (*Phrynops hilarii*) than in the female (Marques, 1955). In the tortoise total pancreatectomy induces an intense diabetes (Aldehoff, 1891; Nishi, 1910; Foglia *et al.*, 1955).

Total pancreatectomy of the snake *Xenodon merremii* produces a slight lowering of the blood sugar level for 1–3 days and then a rise to 5–6 times the normal value (Houssay and Penhos, 1960). Treatment with alloxan, on the other hand, induces an initial hyperglycemia after which there is a substantial and lasting hypoglycemia (Houssay and Penhos, 1960). Glucagon has a powerful and lasting hyperglycemic action in this snake (Houssay and Penhos, 1960). Treatment with alloxan induces hyperglycemia in several species of snake according to Saviano (1955).

In lizards treatment with alloxan induces first a fall in the blood sugar level and then a rise (Miller and Wurster, 1956) but pancreatectomy induces only a fall (Miller and Wurster, 1958).

In the pancreatic islets of snakes and lizards α-cells are much more numerous than in mammalian pancreatic islets (Miller and Wurster, 1956, 1958). It may well be that the tendency for the blood sugar level to fall after damage to the β-cells of the islets or after removal of the pancreas, may relate to the predominant importance of the secretion of glucagon by the islets. In this respect snakes and lizards, perhaps not surprisingly, resemble certain birds, notably the duck (Mialhe, 1957a). The turtle, on the other hand, which immediately becomes hyperglycemic on pancreatectomy, has pancreatic islets which appear morphologically much less rich in α-cells than do those of snakes and lizards (Miller, 1960).

6. Effects of Pancreatectomy in Amphibians

Total pancreatectomy produces a diabetic condition, albeit slowly, in all species of amphibians which have been examined, with a typical fall in liver and muscle glycogen. This is true for *Rana esculenta* and other European frogs (Marcuse, 1894; Loewit, 1910; Houssay, 1959), many types of *Bufo* toad (Houssay and Biasotti, 1933) and for *Rana pipiens* (Houssay, 1950). Salamanders also exhibit severe diabetes after removal of the pancreas (Miller and Wurster, 1956, 1959; Wurster and Miller, 1960). The pancreas of amphibians in general is relatively poor in islet tissue as compared with those of other types of vertebrates, and α-cells may be sparse or completely missing from the islets of the frog and of the salamander, though those of the toad are richer in α-cells than those of other amphibians examined (Miller, 1960). In agreement with this is the observation that in the toad treatment with alloxan induces an initial hyperglycemia followed by prolonged hypoglycemia (Houssay *et al.*, 1945), although Biasotti and Porto (1945) have seen the development of long term hyperglycemia in alloxan-treated toads.

7. Effects of Pancreatectomy in Fishes

Removal of the pancreas from the eel was found by Caparelli (1894) to induce an inconstant glycosuria but in selachian fishes pancreatectomy regularly results in hyperglycemia (Diamare, 1906, 1911; Orias, 1932; Abramowitz *et al.*, 1940). In the sculpin (*Myoxocephalus*) in which the islet tissue usually is gathered together in two separate and discrete islets, removal of the principal islets results in substantial hyperglycemia. (McCormick and Macleod, 1925; Simpson, 1926). The administration of alloxan produces hyperglycemia in certain selachian fishes (Saviano, 1947a, b; Grosso, 1950; Lazarow *et al.*, 1957, 1959). In the toadfish *Opsanus tau*, alloxan produces hyperglycemia and severe lesions in the giant islet (Lazarow and Berman, 1948). There is good evidence that glucagon is present in the islets of fishes (Mosca, 1951, 1960; Lazarow, 1957; Lazarow *et al.*, 1957, 1959).

When the follicles of Langerhans in the alimentary canal wall of the lamprey ammocete larva (*Petromyzon marinus unicolor*) are destroyed by cautery a significant rise in blood sugar level occurs, which is consistent with the existence of an insulin-secreting mechanism in these analogues of pancreatic islets (Barrington, 1942).

8. Insulin Therapy in Pancreatectomized Animals

Despite significant species variations in the chemical structure of insulin (Table I), where it has been tested, commercial insulin has usually been found to be capable of controlling the diabetes which follows pancreatectomy. Insulin can be administered intravenously, or more commonly, subcutaneously or intramuscularly. For subcutaneous or intramuscular therapy insulin mixed with protamine or some other agent designed to slow its absorption from the tissues, is sometimes used. Considerable variations in sensitivity exist among the species examined, and in general poikilothermic vertebrates respond much more slowly to the blood sugar lowering action of insulin than do homeothermic animals (see Prado, 1947 for experiments with the snake and Stevenson et al., 1957 for experiments with the alligator).

Except in special instances, of which the duck is the best examined (Mialhe, 1957a), glucagon therapy does not appear to be important in depancreatized animals. Nevertheless, the interesting differences, in some cases, between the effects of damage to the islet β-cells and those of pancreatectomy indicate that in other species also the secretory activity of the α-cells of the islets should not be ignored.

D. Influence of Ablation of Endocrine Organs on the Course of Pancreatic Diabetes

In nearly all species in which the investigation has been made, removal of the pituitary gland, or of its pars glandularis alone, alleviates the resultant diabetic condition after pancreatectomy and prolongs the life of an animal in which untreated pancreatic diabetes may be fatal (Houssay and Biasotti, 1931; Houssay, 1936, 1959). A possible exception to this rule is the salamander, in which hypophysectomy subsequent to pancreatectomy will not immediately alleviate the hyperglycemia; only several weeks after hypophysectomy, when substantial inter-renal atrophy has occurred, is the hyperglycemia of pancreatectomy reduced (Miller, 1960; Wurster and Miller, 1960).

In many species removal of the adrenal glands also depresses the severity of diabetes resulting from pancreatectomy, although some therapy with adrenal hormones may be needed to maintain the adrenalectomized-depancreatized animal in good condition. Extensive observations of this sort were first made on the cat by Long and Lukens (1936) and have subsequently been extended to many different species (see Chester Jones (1957), Houssay (1959), and Miller (1960) for references).

In hypophysectomized-depancreatized animals the potentially diabetic condition can be manifested or exacerbated by the administration of pituitary growth hormone, pituitary adrenocorticotropin, or of adrenal 11-oxy steroids. The diabetic condition of the adrenalectomized-depancreatized animal is exacerbated by certain adrenal steroids or by pituitary growth hormone (Lockett et al., 1953).

Removal of the thyroid gland will also alleviate existing pancreatic diabetes in many species of animal (Houssay, 1948) and thyroid hormones will exacerbate the condition. The influence of the thyroid gland is less striking than that of the pituitary or adrenal glands.

All these observations indicate that the action of insulin is to some extent antagonized by secretions of the pituitary, adrenal, and thyroid glands. The relevant hormones from the pituitary gland are growth hormone (or something formed from it or under its influence) (Cotes *et al.*, 1949; Young, 1953) and corticotropin (Conn *et al.*, 1948); adrenaline and noradrenaline play a less important role than the adrenal steroids with an oxygen atom at position 11.

Since glucagon also acts antagonistically to insulin in some ways, we can infer that the control of the blood sugar level is the result of balanced antagonism between the action of insulin on the one hand, and certain actions, direct or indirect, of glucagon, growth hormone, corticotropin, adrenaline and noradrenaline, and adrenal 11-oxy steroids, on the other.

IV. MECHANISM OF ACTION OF INSULIN

In its ability to alleviate, single-handedly, the metabolic disturbances after pancreatectomy, insulin influences many different aspects of metabolism. It not only lowers the blood sugar level and abolishes glycosuria, but also converts the negative nitrogen balance of the depancreatized animal into a positive one, and promotes the synthesis of protein in the tissues. The action of insulin also abolishes diabetic ketosis and ketonuria, and in promoting the synthesis and storage of the fatty acids in the body, exerts an important effect on fat metabolism.

The question has been much debated as to how far these many actions of insulin may be explicable in terms of a single effect on a specific metabolic process, and no final answer has yet been given. Before this question is discussed the influence of insulin on the metabolism of carbohydrate, protein, and fat will be considered. The action of insulin in general has recently been reviewed by Randle and Young (1960) and Tepperman and Tepperman (1960).

A. The Action of Insulin on the Utilization of Glucose

There is good evidence that insulin promotes the uptake of glucose from the blood by muscle tissue, though any action in depressing the rate of sugar formation and secretion by the liver is less certain.

1. The Hexokinase Theory

According to this theory, put forward by Carl and Gerty Cori and their collaborators between 1945 and 1950, the enzyme hexokinase is a focus of insulin activity. Hexokinase catalyzes the formation of glucose-6-phosphate from glucose at the expense of the formation of adenosine diphosphate from adenosine triphosphate:

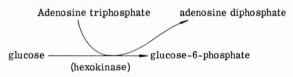

According to this view insulin is active in releasing hexokinase from a depressive action exerted by substances from the pituitary gland and from the adrenal cortex. Since the phosphorylation of glucose under the influence of hexokinase is probably an obligatory step in the utilization of glucose by all tissues of the body, an action of insulin in relieving this enzyme from a depressed state might explain the influence of insulin on carbohydrate metabolism in general (Fig. 2). Nevertheless, since insulin exerts an enhanced action in animals from which both the pituitary gland and adrenal glands have been removed (Bornstein, 1950) it seems unlikely that the inhibitors from whose action insulin may relieve hexokinase can come only from these glands.

This idea has stimulated both controversy and experiment, but the balance of evidence at present available suggests that it is almost certainly not valid in the terms in which it was put forward (Randle and Young, 1960).

2. The Permeability Theory

Levine and Goldstein (1955) and Park (1955) have been the strongest proponents of this theory in recent years (see Randle and Young, 1960 for references). According to this view insulin aids the transport of glucose across the cell membrane, particularly that of skeletal muscle cells, which the sugar would not be able to traverse in its absence. Once in the cell the glucose can be phosphorylated or otherwise used for any relevant metabolic process (Fig. 2). This idea has been widely accepted, though Chain and his colleagues (Chain, 1959) reject this view because in their experiments the promotion of entry of glucose into muscle cells brought about simply by a rise in the external concentration of this sugar gives a pattern of glucose metabolites different from that seen under the influence of insulin. Apart from the opposition of Chain and his colleagues, this view has gained wide acceptance (Fisher, 1960; Randle and Young, 1960).

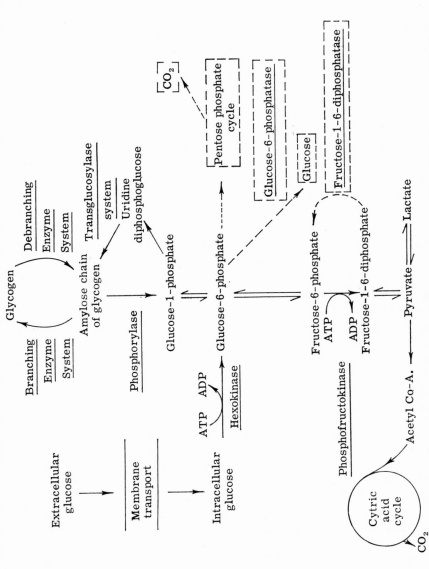

FIG. 2. The main metabolic pathways for the utilization of carbohydrate in muscle and liver. The pathways which occur mainly or solely in liver are indicated by labels enclosed by dotted lines.

3. The Influence of Insulin on Carbohydrate Metabolism in Muscle

When insulin is added *in vitro* to isolated rat diaphragm the uptake of glucose can be enhanced by as much as 300%, and the addition of insulin to the fluid perfusing an isolated rat heart also stimulates the utilization of glucose. When insulin acts on diaphragm *in vitro* there is no substantial change in the oxygen consumption; the production of carbon dioxide may be slightly, though inconsistently, raised but there is no indication of any substantial enhancement of the oxidation of carbohydrate. Some of the glucose which disappears under the influence of insulin is converted to glycogen, but saccharides such as maltose, maltotriose, and other similar substances are also formed (Chain, 1959). Lactic acid production may also rise. The formation of glycogen probably does not involve the direct formation of glycogen from glucose-1-phosphate under the influence of the enzyme phosphorylase. Uridine diphosphoglucose arises from the interaction of uridine triphosphate and glucose-1-phosphate, and then glycogen ultimately is formed from the uridine diphosphoglucose (Leloir and Cardini, 1957). An *in vitro* action of insulin on this pathway has been described (Larner *et al.*, 1959).

These effects of insulin can all be explained in terms of a primary action on the permeability of the cell membrane to glucose, with the possible exception of an *in vitro* action of insulin on the uridine diphosphoglucose pathway of glycogen formation (Fig. 2).

4. The Influence of Insulin on Carbohydrate Metabolism in the Liver

Ashmore *et al.* (1956) find that although insulin acts rapidly in reducing the blood sugar level, the impairment of metabolic processes in the liver of the diabetic animal is only slowly restored under the influence of insulin. No effect is discernible less than 6 hours after the administration of insulin, which suggests the possibility that the effect here of insulin is a secondary one. Insulin may thus act indirectly in depressing the activity of the enzyme glucose-6-phosphatase (Ashmore and Weber, 1959) but this is not likely to be the sole mechanism whereby insulin depresses the rate of liberation of glucose into the bloodstream by the liver (Hastings *et al.*, 1955; Fisher, 1960) if indeed it does so.

5. The Influence of Insulin on Carbohydrate Metabolism in Adipose Tissue

An important difference between muscle on the one hand, and liver and adipose tissue on the other, is the prominence in the latter of the hexose-monophosphate–oxidative pathway of glucose utilization. In this process, the first carbon atom of glucose is more rapidly converted to CO_2 than is the sixth carbon atom, while in the classical Embden-Meyerhof pathway of the utilization of glucose, CO_2 is formed from carbon atoms 1 and 6 of the glucose molecule with equal rapidity. Winegrad and Renold (1958) find that when glucose labeled with radioactive carbon either in the first or the sixth position is metabolized *in vitro* by the rat epididymal fat pad, the addition of insulin markedly increases the amount of carbon atom 1 converted to CO_2 and stimulates the oxidation of carbon atom 6 to a much lesser degree. On the other hand, insulin stimulates lipogenesis from carbon atom 1 and carbon atom 6 to the same extent. If insulin stimulates selectively the hexosemonophosphate-oxidative pathway of glucose oxidation in adipose tissue the point of action of the hormone is far from clear, and the interpretation of the experimental results is by no means unequivocal (Winegrad and Renold, 1958).

Barrnett and Ball (1959), and Ball and Barrnett (1960), have observed the stimulation of pinocytosis in isolated rat adipose tissue under the influence of insulin, and suggest that this agrees with the view that insulin acts on cell permeability. However, it is hard to see how a selective action of insulin on glucose utilization would be explicable on this basis.

B. Insulin and Fat Metabolism

In the normal animal much of the carbohydrate taken in as such is converted, in the liver and in adipose tissue (Wertheimer and Shapiro, 1948; Wertheimer and Shafrir, 1960), to neutral fat, which is the form in which the energy of the carbohydrate is stored. This process of lipogenesis from carbohydrate depends on the availability of insulin, and is conspicuously deficient in diabetes mellitus.

Fat can be mobilized from the stores and in particular from the adipose tissue in the form of "non-esterified fatty acids" which are particularly associated with the albumin fraction of plasma proteins. This mobilization is stimulated by certain hormones, growth hormone being noteworthy in this respect, and is depressed under the influence of insulin, an effect which can be demonstrated with adipose tissue *in vitro* (Wertheimer and Shafrir, 1960; Olson and Vester, 1960).

In diabetes the total fat content of the blood plasma rises, this being associated with elevated amounts in the blood of lipoproteins, cholesterol, phospholipid, and nonesterified fatty acids. In diabetes there appears to be a deficiency of synthesis of fatty acids from carbohydrate and a greater mobilization of fat for oxidation, both of which deviations are corrected by the suitable administration of insulin (Butterfield and Schless, 1959). In a diabetic liver, cholesterol synthesis from acetate apparently occurs at an abnormally high rate (Hotta *et al.*, 1954); this high rate is depressed under the influence of treatment with insulin.

In the normal animal the synthesis of fatty acids from acetyl coenzyme A (and therefore from many different sources) is linked, at least in some tissues, with the catabolism of carbohydrate (Fig. 3). When carbohydrate utilization is depressed, as occurs in insulin deficiency, the rate of synthesis of fatty acids is therefore also subnormal. Clearly, the link could be one involving the early stages of the utilization of glucose, or a specific point at the later stages. Brady and Gurin (1950a, b) observed that the incorporation of labeled acetate into the fatty acids of liver slices was accelerated by the simultaneous addition of insulin and glucose *in vitro*, but not by the addition of glucose or of insulin alone. Similar observations were made by Balmain *et al.* (1952) with mammary gland slices. The existence of the link thus receives direct *in vitro* support.

The availability of nicotinamide adenine dinucleotide phosphate (NADPH),[1] produced in the hexosemonophosphate-oxidative pathway and the tricarboxylic acid cycle (Fig. 3), and needed for reduction of crotonyl coenzyme A to butyryl coenzyme A in the biosynthesis of fatty acids (Fig. 4) could be an important limiting factor in the rate of biosynthesis of fatty acids. The action of insulin in promoting the utilization of glucose by enhancing the permeability of cell membranes to it, could increase the production of the reduced coenzyme and might thus influence the biosynthesis of fatty acid.

But this is almost certainly not the only way that insulin exerts its effect on fat metabolism. Matthes *et al.* (1960) find that in the liver tissue of alloxan-diabetic rats the NADP-linked reductase, which reduces crotonyl coenzyme A to butyryl coenzyme A, is diminished in activity and that insulin may well exert a specific action on this enzyme.

The glycerol that is needed for the laying down of neutral fat is made available from carbohydrate, and the utilization of carbohydrate is, of course, dependent upon the activity of insulin. The influence of insulin on the synthesis of fats may therefore be exerted through a number of points (see Fig. 3) (Folley and Greenbaum, 1960).

The acetyl coenzyme A formed from carbohydrate and other sources can be reduced to acetoacetic acid, and this, together with β-hydroxybutyric acid which, with acetone, can be formed from the acetoacetic acid, constitute the ketone bodies. The acetyl coenzyme A is normally oxidized through the operation of the tricarboxylic acid cycle (Fig. 3) and if the latter declines in activity, as occurs in diabetes, the accumulating acetyl coenzyme A may give rise to excess ketone bodies. But the precise reason

---

[1] Formerly known as coenzyme II or triphosphopyridine nucleotide.

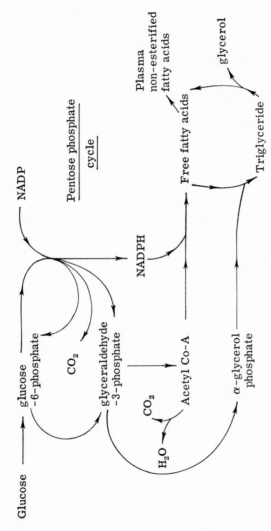

FIG. 3. The main lines of integration of the metabolism of carbohydrate and fat in adipose tissue. In liver the integration is similar but neutral fat, rather than nonesterified fatty acid, is liberated into the blood by the liver.

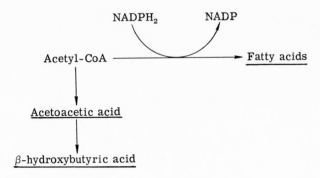

Fig. 4. The biosynthesis of fatty acids and ketone bodies from acetyl coenzyme A.

why such an accumulation of ketone bodies occurs in diabetes is still not clear (Krebs, 1960).

C. Insulin and Protein Metabolism

In diabetes the negative nitrogen balance and loss of protein from the body is a striking feature, and the suitable administration of insulin will correct this deviation from normal metabolism. However, the administration of insulin to a normal animal does not normally induce a positive nitrogen balance even if the complicating effects on nitrogen metabolism of an insulin-induced hypoglycemia are avoided. Nevertheless, Manchester and Young (1961), in reviewing the relevant evidence including the results of their own investigations, conclude that insulin exerts an important action on protein metabolism and support the view that the growth-promoting action of growth hormone depends upon the availability of insulin in the body. The evidence quoted in support of this conclusion includes the fact that, (1) the administration of insulin to hypophysectomized rats can induce growth and nitrogen retention provided that hypoglycemia is avoided by the administration of glucose (Salter and Best, 1953; Salter *et al.*, 1957) or glucagon (Smith and Young, 1953, 1954), and (2) that insulin *in vitro* can stimulate the incorporation of amino acids into protein by a process which does not depend upon the power of insulin to enhance the utilization of carbohydrate (Manchester and Young, 1958, 1959, 1960a, 1961). The action of insulin in this respect appears not to be analogous to its effect on glucose transport, since insulin does not stimulate the movement of amino acids into the cell (Manchester and Young, 1960b).

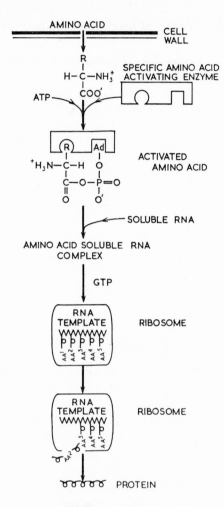

FIG. 5. Outline of some steps in the biosynthesis of protein. (Based on Korner, 1960c).

Insulin can apparently influence the activity of intracellular structures such as ribosomes, which are intimately concerned in the mechanism of protein biosynthesis (Korner, 1960a, b; Korner and Manchester, 1960) (Fig. 5). It is possible that insulin assists this process by increasing the availability of high energy phosphate to the intracellular structures concerned in the biosynthesis of protein (Tepperman and Tepperman, 1960; Manchester and Young, 1961).

D. The Mechanism of Action of Insulin on Metabolic Processes

In discussing the mechanism of action of insulin Randle and Smith (1958a, b) point out that anoxia and certain cell poisons which depress oxidative phosphorylation act like insulin in that they accelerate the movement of glucose into the muscle cell. They suggest that the transport of glucose across the cell membrane is normally inhibited when high-energy phosphate-containing substances are easily available, perhaps because the latter can phosphorylate and thus inactivate the carrier in the cell membrane which is normally active in glucose transport. The action of insulin could be interpreted in terms of activating the glucose carrier in the cell membrane either by inhibiting its phosphorylation or by dephosphorylating it. Manchester and Young (1961), taking into account the fact that protein biosynthesis depends on the availability of high-energy phosphate-containing substances, suggest that the action of insulin which directs energy-rich phosphate-containing substances away from the carrier involved in sugar transport, might direct such substances to the site of protein biosynthesis, at which their access may be limited in the absence of insulin. A similar idea has been put forward by Tepperman and Tepperman (1960).

If the action of insulin on carbohydrate utilization is sufficient also to promote lipogenesis by the mechanisms discussed above, a single point of action of insulin with respect to its effects on the metabolism of carbohydrate, protein, and fat might exist, but such a theory of the unitary action of insulin is not safely based at the present time and judgment must be suspended.

The biological activity of the insulin molecule as a whole has so far been considered. The question can now be asked, are there any qualitative changes in biological activity after chemical alteration of the molecule? The existence of naturally occurring variations in the structure of insulin have already been considered (Section I) and the general statement seems justified that these natural variations are not yet known to be associated with qualitative differences in biological activities. Nicol (1960) could find no relative differences in activity with respect to carbohydrate metabolism when insulin was partially degraded by the enzymatic removal of 8 of the 51 amino acid residues, to yield a molecule with only about 15% of the biological activity of the insulin itself (see however Young and Carpenter, 1961). In experiments in which the enzymatic removal of the first 6 residues from the N-terminal end of the B chain of ox insulin was believed to be effected Smith et al. (1958) concluded that these amino acid residues are not essential for the biological activity of insulin.

Some biological activity has been reported for the separated A and B chains of the insulin molecule (Nicol, 1959; Fisher and Zachariah, 1960; Langdon, 1960). Langdon believes that the B chain in the sulfhydryl form alone possesses biological activity (Langdon, 1960). Dixon and Wardlaw (1960) have been able to regenerate insulin which is biologically active by reduction of a mixture of the A and B chains separated from insulin by sulfite cleavage. Unless one chain is shown to be substantially free from the other (which was not the case in Langdon's experiments) the evidence for biological activity in one chain or the other on its own, must be regarded as inconclusive.

The general conclusions may be drawn that chemical degradation of the insulin molecule has not revealed the existence of any qualitative differences in relative potencies with respect to the different biological activities of insulin, and that the existence in the molecule of areas associated predominantly with one type or another of biological activity has not yet been demonstrated.

V. INSULIN SUBSTITUTES

In 1942 Loubatières observed the hypoglycemic action in patients of certain sulfonamide drugs, and found that this could be produced in animals provided that some portion of the pancreas was present (Loubatières, 1944, 1957, 1960). Subsequently Franke and Fuchs (1955) described the use of a simple sulfonamido-urea derivative (BZ 55 or carbutamide = N^1-sulfanilyl-N^2-butylcarbamide) in the treatment of human diabetes mellitus by oral administration. Subsequently the use of other simple chemical substances, active by mouth, in the treatment of diabetes, has been described (see Young, 1956a; Forsham, 1959; Goldner, 1959; Loubatières, 1960; Mahler, 1960). The effectiveness of these substances appears to depend upon the presence of some insulin in the pancreas (Loubatières, 1960). In some instances treatment with these substances apparently permanently cures a diabetes of moderate severity (Loubatières, 1960; Lever et al., 1961), and their use as a prophylactic measure in susceptible individuals has been investigated, with encouraging results (Loubatières, 1960).

The mechanism of action of these substances is far from clear but it seems probable that they enhance and perhaps prolong the effectiveness of any insulin that may be present in the body, and they are therefore not truly substitutes for insulin. It is possible also that they stimulate islets to secrete insulin and to hypertrophy (Lever et al., 1961).

Many other simple substances are known which mimic the action of insulin in that they induce a fall in blood sugar, but a discussion of them is outside the scope of this book.

VI. ANTIBODIES TO INSULIN

In addition to the existence of hormonally dependent antagonists or inhibitors of insulin action, immunological antibodies which can depress the physiological activity of insulin have been described (Moloney and Coval, 1955; Arquilla and Stavitsky, 1956; Wright, 1959, 1960). In a small proportion of insulin-resistant diabetic patients, insulin-neutralizing antibodies have been found in the blood serum, but these are exceptional, and insulin resistance is more usually associated with the presence of hormonally induced antagonists or inhibitors. Nevertheless, the experimentally induced production of antibodies to insulin, presumably dependent upon the existence of species differences in the chemical structure of insulin, has made possible the development of sensitive immunological methods for the assay of insulin (Yalow and Berson, 1957, 1960; Wright, 1959, 1960). Insulin antibodies of the immunological type have also been used for the experimental induction of insulin deficiency in animals (Moloney and Coval, 1955; Moloney and Goldsmith, 1957; Armin et al., 1960, 1961). In the rat, symptoms similar to those following pancreatectomy are observed when suitable treatment with insulin antibodies is instituted (Armin et al., 1960, 1961).

VII. THE ASSAY OF INSULIN

This subject can be only briefly considered in the space available.

The fall of the blood sugar level, induced by the administration of insulin to animals, was the first and is the most widely used method for the assay of insulin. The stimulation of glucose uptake when insulin is added to isolated tissues in vitro has also been much used in recent years, and immunological methods are now being widely developed. Recently chemical methods for the estimation of insulin have been based on chromatography and on fibril formation in a solution of insulin. These methods have been reviewed by Stewart (1960) and by Randle and Taylor (1960).

Although different investigators have found significantly different values it can be said that the insulin activity of the blood plasma of a normal human being in the post-absorptive state is of the order of 1 milliunit/ml. In terms of solid insulin this is about 0.05 μg/ml, or about 1 part in 20,000 of plasma proteins.

VIII. THE CONTROL OF THE SECRETION OF INSULIN

There can be little doubt that the rate of secretion of insulin is largely determined by the amount of glucose in the blood passing through the islets of Langerhans. Complete denervation of the pancreas has only a very small effect on the rate of secretion of insulin under physiological conditions (Houssay, 1937), and the control of insulin secretion appears to be largely humoral (Foà, 1956).

The possibility that growth hormone stimulates the secretion of insulin cannot be taken as proved (Young, 1953; Ketterer *et al.*, 1957), although some such process is at least likely (Young, 1961). In the hypophysectomized duck the hyperglycemic effect of glucagon is much diminished, and the administration of glucagon induces a substantial and prolonged fall in the blood sugar level. The latter effect is not seen in the depancreatized-hypophysectomized duck and probably indicates that the secretion of insulin by the islets has been evoked by glucagon (Mialhe, 1957b, c). If growth hormone evokes the secretion of glucagon among that of other blood sugar-raising substances (Bornstein *et al.*, 1951; Foà *et al.*, 1957), any influence of growth hormone on the secretion of insulin might well be mediated by the secretion of glucagon by the α-cells of the pancreatic islets (Young, 1953). In any case, the rate of secretion of insulin by the β-cells of the islets is presumably determined by the amount of sugar in the blood passing through the islets, which may not itself be directly or simply related to the peripheral blood sugar level (Young, 1956b). If growth hormone, acting through the secretion of glucagon, were able to raise the blood sugar level locally in the islets the secretion of insulin might be stimulated even though the peripheral blood sugar level was not raised.

Almost nothing is known about the biochemistry of insulin production in the islet cells. Lazarow (1957) believes that sulfhydryl groups are of importance in the biosynthesis of insulin but the evidence for this is not unequivocal.

IX. CONCLUSION

The pancreas is important as a regulator of metabolism in nearly all the vertebrates which have been studied. The insulin-secreting function of the islets is of special importance in all carnivorous animals. In some species of bird, notably the duck, and in certain reptiles and amphibians the glucagon-secreting function of the pancreas appears to outweigh in importance that concerned with the secretion of insulin. In such species pancreatectomy, or damage to the β-cells of the pancreatic islets, is followed by a tendency of the blood sugar level to fall seriously during a short fast although the level may rise substantially after food. These animals resemble hypophysectomized-depancreatized mammals in this respect and it may be surmised that their anterior pituitary glands are less active, possibly with respect to the secretion of growth hormone, than are those of most mammals.

The action of insulin in stimulating the utilization of carbohydrate for the synthesis of glycogen and of fat, and the formation of protein from amino acids, illustrates the importance of this hormone in biosynthetic processes. Under its influence the storage of the energy of foodstuffs is promoted and prolonged. The carnivore, which usually gorges itself with food, may particularly depend upon the availability of insulin to foster the retention of the amino acids which rapidly enter the blood stream after meat is consumed, since the quick conversion of a substantial part of the amino acids to carbohydrate in the liver might well exceed the storage capacity for glycogen of the liver, and an undesirably great rise of blood sugar could follow.

The activity of insulin is held in check by numerous hormonal or hormone-dependent antagonists so that a dangerous overactivity, which could lead to hypoglycemic coma and death, is guarded against. The control of the secretion of insulin is largely humoral and is the result of a sensitive response of the pancreatic islet cells to a rise in blood sugar level.

Insulin is clearly of great importance in the control of metabolic processes and it is disappointing that we still know so little detail about its mechanism of action.

References

Abramowitz, A. A., Hisaw, F. L., Boettiger, E., and Papandrea, D. N. (1940). *Biol. Bull.* **78**, 189.

Adams, D. M., and Bollinger, A. (1954). *Australian J. Exptl. Biol. Med. Sci.* **32**, 101–111.

Aldehoff, G. (1891). *Z. Biol.* **28**, 293–304.

Armin, J., Grant, R. T., and Wright, P. H. (1960). *J. Physiol. (London)* **153**, 146–165.

Armin, J., Cunningham, N. F., Grant, R. T., Lloyd, M. K., and Wright, P. H. (1961). *J. Physiol. (London)* **157**, 64–73.

Arquilla, E. R., and Stavitsky, R. B. (1956). *J. Clin. Invest.* **35**, 458–466 and 467–474.

Ashmore, J., and Weber, G. (1959). *Vitamins and Hormones* **17**, 91–132.

Ashmore, J., Hastings, A. B., Nesbett, F. B., and Renold, A. E. (1956). *J. Biol. Chem.* **218**, 77–78.

Aszodi, Z. (1928). *Biochem. Z.* **192**, 26–35.

Bailey, C. C., and Bailey, O. T. (1943). *J. Am. Med. Assoc.* **122**, 1165–1166.

Ball, E. G., and Barrnett, R. J. (1960). *Diabetes* **9**, 70–71.

Balmain, J. H., Folley, S. J., and Glascock, R. F. (1952). *Biochem. J.* **52**, 301–306.

Barrnett, R. J., and Ball, E. G. (1959). *Science* **129**, 1282.

Barrington, E. J. W. (1942). *J. Exptl. Biol.* **19**, 45–55.

Beekman, B. E. (1956). *Endocrinology* **59**, 708–712.

Biasotti, A., and Porto, J. (1945). *Rev. soc. arg. Biol.* **21**, 63.

Bloom, F. (1937). *New Engl. J. Med.* **217**, 395.

Bloom, F., and Handelsmann, M. B. (1937). *North Am. Veterinarian* **18**, 39.

Bornstein, J. (1950). *Australian J. Exptl. Biol. Med. Sci.* **28**, 87–91.

Bornstein, J., Reid, E., and Young, F. G. (1951). *Nature* **168**, 903–905.

Bowie, D. J. (1924). *Anat. Record* **29**, 57–73.

Brady, R. O., and Gurin, S. (1950a). *J. Biol. Chem.* **186**, 461–469.

Brady, R. O., and Gurin, S. (1950b). *J. Biol. Chem.* **187**, 589–596.

Brown, H., Sanger, F., and Kitai, R. (1955). *Biochem. J.* **60**, 556–565.

Butterfield, W. J. H., and Schless, G. (1959). *Diabetes* **8**, 450–450.

Campbell, J., and Best, C. H. (1938). *Lancet* **i**, 1444.

Candela, J. L. R. (1945). *An. Acad. méd-quir.* **29**, 283.

Candela, J. L. R. (1952). *J. Clin. Endocrinol. and Metabolism* **12**, 245–246.

Candela, J. L. R., Goni, P. M., Caldero, M. R., and Gonzalez-Carreras, P. (1947). *Trabajos inst. nacl. cienc. méd. (Madrid)* **9**, 89.

Caparelli, A. (1894). *Arch. ital. biol.* **21**, 398.

Cardeza, A. F. (1957a). *Rev. soc. arg. biol.* **33**, 67–73.

Cardeza, A. F. (1957b). *Rev. soc. arg. biol.* **33**, 74–79.

Chain, E. B. (1959). *Brit. Med. J.* **II**, 709–719.

Chapman, S. W., and Fulton, J. F. (1938). *Am. J. Physiol.* **123**, 35.

Chester Jones, I. (1957). "The Adrenal Cortex." Cambridge Univ. Press, London and New York.

Collip, J. B., Selye, H., and Neufeld, A. (1937). *Am. J. Physiol.* **119**, 289–290.

Conn, J. W., Louis, L. H., and Wheeler, C. E. (1948). *J. Lab. Clin. Med.* **33**, 651–661.

Cook, E. T., Dye, J. A., and McCandless, E. L. (1949). *Am. J. Physiol.* **156**, 349–354.

Cotes, P. M., Reid, E., and Young, F. G. (1949). *Nature* **164**, 209–211

Covian, F. G., and de Oya, J. C. (1944). *Rev. clin. españ.* **15**, 262–270.

De Moor, P., and Vuylsteke, C. A. (1948). *Arch. intern. pharmacodynamie* **75**, 459–461.

Diamare, V. (1906). *Zentr. Physiol.* **20**, 617.

Diamare, V. (1911). *Arch. ital. biol.* **55**, 97.

Dixon, G. H., and Wardlaw, A. C. (1960). *Nature* **188**, 721–724.

Dohan, F. C., and Lukens, F. D. W. (1947a). *Am. J. Med. Sci.* **213**, 122.

Dohan, F. C., and Lukens, F. D. W. (1947b). *Science* **105**, 183.

Dohan, F. C., Fish, C. A., and Lukens, F. D. W. (1941). *Endocrinology* **28**, 341–357.

Dunn, J. S., and McLetchie, N. G. B. (1943). *Lancet* **ii**, 384–387.

Dunn, J. S., Sheehan, H. L., and McLetchie, N. G. B. (1943). *Lancet* **i**, 484–487.

Dunn, J. S., Duffy, E., Gilmour, M. K., Kirkpatrick, J., and McLetchie, N. G. B. (1944). *J. Physiol. (London)* **103**, 233–243.

Epstein, A. A., and Baehr, G. (1916). *J. Biol. Chem.* **24**, 1–16.

Falkmer, S. (1961). *Acta Endocrinol.* **37**, Suppl. 59, 3–122.

Fisher, R. B. (1960). *Brit. Med. Bull.* **16**, 224–227.

Fisher, R. B., and Zachariah, P. (1960). *Biochem. J.* **76**, 155.

Foà, P. P. (1956). *Ciba Foundation Colloq. on Endocrinol.* **9**, 55–71.

Foà, P. P., Galansino, G., and Pozza, G. (1957). *Recent Progr. in Hormone Research* **13**, 473–503.

Foglia, V. G. (1953). *Acta Physiol. Latinoam.* **3**, 96.

Foglia, V. G., Wagner, E. M., de Barros, M., and Marques, M. (1955). *Rev. soc. arg. biol.* **31**, 87–95.

Folley, S. J., and Greenbaum, A. L. (1960). *Brit. Med. Bull.* **16**, 228–232.

Forsham, P. (1959). *Ann. N. Y. Acad. Sci.* **82**, 508–639.

Franke, H., and Fuchs, J. (1955). *Deut. med. Wochschr.* **80**, 1449.

Frye, B. E. (1959). *In* "Comparative Endocrinology" (A. Gorbman, ed.), pp. 681–696. Wiley, New York.

Garcia Ramos, J. (1944). *Rev. soc. mex. hist. nat.* **5**, 25.

Giaja, J. (1912). *Comp. rend. soc. biol.* **73**, 102.

Gillman, J., Gilbert, C., and Epstein, E. (1958). *Brit. Med. J.* **II**, 1260–1263.

Gitter, S. (1947). *Rev. soc. arg. biol.* **23**, 255–263.

Goldner, M. (1959). *Ann. N. Y. Acad. Sci.* **74**, 407–1028.

Goldner, M. G., and Gomori, G. (1943). *Endocrinology* **33**, 297–308.

Gomori, G., and Goldner, M. G. (1943). *Proc. Soc. Exptl. Biol. Med.* **54**, 287–290.

Greeley, P. O. (1937a). *Am. J. Physiol.* **120**, 345–349.

Greeley, P. O. (1937b). *Proc. Soc. Exptl. Biol. Med.* **37**, 309–312.

Greeley, P. O. (1947). *Am. J. Physiol.* **150**, 46–51.

Grosso, L. L. (1950). *Zoologica* **35**, 169.

Haist, R. E., Campbell, J., and Best, C. H. (1940). *New Engl. J. Med.* **223**, 607–615.

Harris, J. I., Sanger, F., and Naughton, M. A. (1956). *Arch. Biochem. Biophys.* **65**, 427–438.

Hastings, A. B., Renold, A. E., and Ching-Tseng, T. (1955). *Recent Progr. in Hormone Research* **11**, 381–397.

Hédon, E. (1893a). *Arch. Physiol. norm. Pathol.* **5**, 154–163.

Hédon, E. (1893b). *Comp. rend. acad. sci.* **116**, 649–651.

Hédon, E. (1898). "Travaux de Physiologie du Laboratoire de M. Hédon." Doin, Paris.

Hill, W. C. O. (1926). *Proc. Zool. Soc. (London)* 581–631.

Hotta, S., Hill, R., and Charkoff, I. L. (1954). *J. Biol. Chem.* **206**, 835–844.

Houssay, B. A. (1936). *New Engl. J. Med.* **214**, 961–971.

Houssay, B. A. (1937). *Am. J. Med. Sci.* **193**, 581–610.

Houssay, B. A. (1948). *Recent Progr. in Hormone Research* **2**, 277–291.

Houssay, B. A. (1950). *Rev. soc. arg. biol.* **26**, 43.

Houssay, B. A. (1952). *Diabetes* **1**, 112–116.

Houssay, B. A. (1959). *In* "Comparative Endocrinology" (A. Gorbman, ed.), pp. 639–667. Wiley, New York.

Houssay, B. A., and Biasotti, A. (1931). *Endocrinology* **15**, 511–523.

Houssay, B. A., and Biasotti, A. (1933). *Compt. rend. soc. biol.* **113**, 469.

Houssay, B. A., and Penhos, J. C. (1960). *Acta Endocrinol.* **35**, 313–323.

Houssay, B. A., Lewis, J. T., and Foglia, V. G. (1929). *Compt. rend. soc. biol.* **101**, 241.

Houssay, B. A., Houssay, A. B., and Sara, J. G. (1945). *Rev. soc. arg. biol.* **21**, 74–80.

Houssay, B. A., Brignone, R. F., and Mazzocco, P. (1946). *Rev. soc. arg. biol.* **22**, 195–231.

Ingle, D. J. (1941). *Endocrinology* **29**, 649–652.

Ingle, D. J. (1948). *Recent Progr. in Hormone Research* **2**, 229–253.

Ishihara, Y., Saito, T., Ito, Y., and Fujino, M. (1958). *Nature* **181**, 1468–1469.

Janes, J. M. (1939). *J. Lab. Clin. Med.* **24**, 1210.

Jarrett, I. G. (1946). *Australian J. Exptl. Biol. Med. Sci.* **24**, 95–102.

Jarrett, I. G., Potter, B. J., and Packham, A. (1956). *Australian J. Exptl. Biol. Med. Sci.* **34**, 133–142.

Kadota, I. (1950). *J. Lab. Clin. Med.* **35**, 568–591.

Ketterer, B., Randle, P. J., and Young, F. G. (1957). *Ergeb. Physiol. biol. Chem. u. exptl. Pharmakol.* **49**, 127–211.

Kennedy, W. B., and Lukens, F. D. W. (1944). *Proc. Soc. Exptl. Biol. Med.* **57**, 143–149.

Korner, A. (1960a). *Biochem. J.* **74**, 471–478.

Korner, A. (1960b). *J. Endocrinol.* **20**, 256–265.

Korner, A. (1960c). *In* "The Mechanism of Action of Insulin" (W. A. Broom, F. W. Wolff, and F. G. Young, eds.), p. 129, Fig. 2. Blackwell, Oxford.

Korner, A., and Manchester, K. L. (1960). *Brit. Med. Bull.* **16**, 233–236.

Kotaki, A. (1961). *J. Biochem. (Japan)* **50**, 256–263.

Krebs, H. A. (1960). *Proc. Roy. Soc. Med.* **53**, 71–80.

Lande, K. E. (1944). *Am. J. Clin. Pathol.* **14**, 590–591.

Langdon, R. G. (1960). *J. Biol. Chem.* **235**, PC15–PC16.

Langerhans, P. (1869). "Beiträge zur Mikroskopischen Anatomie der Bauchspeicheldrüse." Gustav Lange, Berlin.

Langerhans, P. (1873). *Ber. naturforsch. Ges. Freiburg Breisgau* **6**.

Langfeldt, E. (1920). *Acta Med. Scand.* **53**, 1–189.

Larner, J., Villar-Palasi, C., and Richman, D. (1959). *Ann. N. Y. Acad. Sci.* **82**, 345–353.

Lazarow, A. (1947). *J. Lab. Clin. Med.* **32**, 1258–1261.

Lazarow, A. (1949). *Physiol. Revs.* **29**, 48–74.

Lazarow, A. (1957). *Diabetes* **6**, 222–232.

Lazarow, A., and Berman, J. (1948). *Anat. Record* **100**, 688.

Lazarow, A., and Palay, S. (1946). *J. Lab. Clin. Med.* **31**, 1004–1015.

Lazarow, A., Cooperstein, S. J., Bloomfield, D. K., and Fritz, C. T. (1957). *Biol. Bull.* **113**, 414.

Lazarow, A., Makineu, P., and Cooperstein, S. J. (1959). *Biol. Bull.* **117**, 418.

Leloir, L. F., and Cardini, C. E. (1957). *J. Am. Chem. Soc.* **79**, 6340–6341.

Lever, J. D., Jeacock, M. K., and Young, F. G. (1961). *Proc. Roy. Soc.* **B154**, 139–150.

Levine, R., and Goldstein, M. (1955). *Recent Progr. in Hormone Research* **11**, 343–375.

Lockett, M. F., Reid, E., and Young, F. G. (1953). *J. Physiol. (London)* **121**, 28–34.

Loewit, M. (1910). *Arch. exptl. Pathol. Pharmakol. Naunyn Schmiedeberg's* **62**, 47–91.

Long, C. N. H., and Lukens, F. D. W. (1936). *Trans. Assoc. Am. Physicians* **51**, 123–127.

Lopes, N. (1955). *Acta Physiol. Latinoam.* **5**, 39.

Loubatières, A. (1944). *Compt. rend. soc. biol.* **138**, 766–767.

Loubatières, A. (1957). *Diabetes* **6**, 408–417.

Loubatières, A. (1960). *Proc. Roy. Soc. Med.* **53**, 595–599.

Lukens, F. D. W. (1937). *Am. J. Physiol.* **118**, 321–327.

Lukens, F. D. W. (1938). *Am. J. Physiol.* **122**, 729–733.

Lukens, F. D. W. (1948). *Physiol. Revs.* **28**, 304–330.

Lukens, F. D. W. and Dohan, F. C. (1942). *Endocrinology* **30**, 175–202.

McCandless, E. L., and Dye, J. A. (1949). *Am. J. Physiol.* **156**, 355–360.

McCandless, E. L., Woodward, B. A., and Dye, J. A. (1948). *Am. J. Physiol.* **154**, 94–106.

McCormick, N. A. (1924). *Trans. Roy. Can. Inst.* **15**, 57–81.

McCormick, N. A., and Macleod, J. J. R. (1925). *Proc. Roy. Soc.* **B98**, 1–29.

McCullagh, E. P., Cook, J. R., and Shirey, E. J. (1958). *Diabetes* **7**, 298–307.

Maclean, N., and Ogilvie, R. F. (1955). *Diabetes* **4**, 367–376.

Macleod, J. J. R. (1922). *J. Metabolic Research.* **2**, 149–172.

Macleod, J. J. R. (1926). "Carbohydrate Metabolism and Insulin." Longmans, Green, New York.

Mahler, R. F. (1960). *Brit. Med. Bull.* **16**, 250–254.

Manchester, K. L., and Young, F. G. (1958). *Biochem. J.* **70**, 353–358.

Manchester, K. L., and Young, F. G. (1959). *J. Endocrinol.* **18**, 381–394.

Manchester, K. L., and Young, F. G. (1960a). *Biochem. J.* **77**, 386–394.

Manchester, K. L., and Young, F. G. (1960b). *Biochem. J.* **75**, 487–495.

Manchester, K. L., and Young, F. G. (1961). *Vitamins and Hormones* **19**, 95–132.

Marcuse, W. (1894). *Z. klin. Med.* **26**, 225.

Marks, H. P., and Young, F. G. (1939). *J. Endocrinol.* **1**, 470–510.

Marques, M. (1955). *Rev. brasil. biol.* **15**, 349.

Matthes, K. J., Abraham, S., and Charkoff, I. L. (1960). *Biochim. et Biophys. Acta* **37**, 180–181.

Meier, H. (1960). *Diabetes* **9**, 485–489.

Meier, H., and Yerganiau, G. (1961). *Diabetes* **10**, 19–21.

Mialhe, P. (1955). *Compt. rend. acad. sci.* **241**, 1621.

Mialhe, P. (1956). *J. physiol. (Paris)* **48**, 647.

Mialhe, P. (1957a). *Compt. rend. acad. sci.* **244**, 385.

Mialhe, P. (1957b). *Compt. rend. acad. sci.* **249**, 312.

Mialhe, P. (1957c). *Ann. endocrinol. (Paris)* **18**, 609.

Mialhe, P. (1958). *Acta Endocrinol.* **28**, Suppl. 36, 9–134.

Mialhe, P. (1960). *Compt. rend. soc. biol.* **154**, 1867–1868.

Miller, M. R. (1960). *Diabetes* **9**, 318–323.

Miller, M. R., and Wurster, D. H. (1956). *Endocrinology* **58**, 114–120.

Miller, M. R., and Wurster, D. H. (1958). *Endocrinology* **63,** 191–200.

Miller, M. R., and Wurster, D. H. (1959). *In* "Comparative Endocrinology" (A. Gorbman, ed.), pp. 668–680. Wiley, New York.

Minkowski, O. (1893). *Arch. exptl. Pathol. Pharmakol. Naunyn Schmiedeberg's* **31,** 85–189.

Mirsky, I. A., and Gitelson, S. (1957). *Endocrinology* **61,** 148–152.

Mirsky, I. A., Nelson, N., Grayman, I., and Korenberg, M. (1941). *Am. J. Physiol.* **135,** 223–229.

Mirsky, I. A., Nelson, N., Grayman, I., and Elgart, S. (1942). *Endocrinology* **31,** 264–271.

Mirsky, I. A., Futterman, P., Wachman, J., and Perisutti, G. (1951). *Endocrinology* **49,** 73–81.

Moloney, P. J., and Coval, M. (1955). *Biochem. J.* **59,** 179–185.

Moloney, P. J., and Goldsmith, L. (1957). *Can. J. Biochem. and Physiol.* **35,** 79.

Mosca, L. (1951). *Boll. soc. ital. patol.* **2,** 6–11.

Mosca, L. (1960). "Istofisilogia delle isole Pancreatiche." Fondaz. Ganassini, Milano.

Nace, P. F., House, E. L., and Tassoni, J. P. (1956). *Endocrinology* **58,** 305–308.

Nelson, N., Elgart, S., and Mirsky, I. A. (1942). *Endocrinology* **31,** 119–123.

Nicol, D. S. H. W. (1959). *Biochim. et Biophys. Acta* **34,** 257–258.

Nicol, D. S. H. W. (1960). *Biochem. J.* **75,** 395–401.

Nicol, D. S. H. W., and Smith, L. F. (1960). *Nature* **187,** 483–485.

Nishi, N. (1910). *Arch. exptl. Pathol. Pharmakol. Naunyn Schmiedeberg's* **62,** 170–179.

Ogilvie, R. F. (1937). *Quart. J. Med.* **6,** 287–300.

Ogilvie, R. F. (1952). *Vitamins and Hormones* **10,** 183–215.

Olson, R. E., and Vester, J. W. (1960). *Physiol. Revs.* **40,** 677–733.

Orias, O. (1932). *Biol. Bull.* **63,** 477–483.

Park, C. R. (1955). *In* "The Hypophyseal Growth Hormone, Nature and Actions" (R. W. Smith, O. H. Gaebler, and C. N. H. Long, eds.), pp. 394–405. McGraw-Hill, New York.

Patterson, J. W. (1950). *J. Biol. Chem.* **183,** 81–88.

Prado, J. L. (1947). *Rev. can. biol.* **6,** 255–263.

Priestley, J. T., Comfort, M. W., and Radcliffe, J., Jr. (1944). *Ann. Surg.* **119,** 211–221

Randle, P. J., and Smith, G. H. (1958a). *Biochem. J.* **70,** 490–500.

Randle, P. J., and Smith, G. H. (1958b). *Biochem. J.* **70,** 501–508.

Randle, P. J., and Taylor, K. W. (1960). *Brit. Med. Bull.* **16,** 209–213.

Randle, P. J., and Young, F. G. (1960). *Brit. Med. Bull.* **16,** 237–241.

Richardson, K. C. (1940). *Proc. Roy. Soc.* **B128,** 153–169.

Richardson, K. C., and Young, F. G. (1938). *Lancet* i, 1098–1101.

Salter, J. and Best, C. H. (1953). *Brit. Med. J.* **2,** 353–356.

Salter, J. M., Davidson, I. W., and Best, C. H. (1957). *Can. J. Biochem. and Physiol.* **35,** 913–922.

Sandmeyer, W. (1895). *Z. Biol.* **31,** 12.

Sanger, F. (1959). *In* "Les Prix Nobel en 1958," pp. 134–146. Kungl. Boktr. P. A. Norstedt und Söner, Stockholm.

Sanger, F. (1960). *Brit. Med. Bull.* **16,** 183–188.

Sanger, F., and Thompson, E. O. P. (1953). *Biochem. J.* **53**, 366–374.

Sanger, F., and Tuppy, H. (1951). *Biochem. J.* **49**, 463–481; 481–490.

Saviano, M. (1947a). *Boll. soc. ital. biol. sper.* **23**, 1290.

Saviano, M. (1947b). *Boll. soc. ital. biol. sper.* **23**, 1300.

Saviano, M. (1955). *Arch. sci. biol. (Bologna)* **39**, 671.

Saviano, M., and De Francisis, P. (1946). *Arch. sci. biol. (Bologna)* **22**, 1239.

Schneider, R., and Droller, H. (1938). *Quart. J. Exptl. Physiol.* **28**, 323–333.

Scow, R. O. (1957). *Endocrinology* **60**, 359–367.

Simpson, W. W. (1926). *Am. J. Physiol.* **77**, 409–418.

Smith, E. L., Hill, R. L., and Borman, A. (1958). *Biochim. et Biophys. Acta* **29**, 207.

Smith, R. H., and Young, F. G. (1953). *Ciba Foundation Colloq. on Endocrinol.* **6**, 218–219.

Smith, R. H., and Young, F. G. (1954). *In* "Experimental Diabetes" (J. F. Delafresnaye and G. Howard Smith, eds.), p. 261. Blackwell, Oxford.

Sprague, R., and Ivy, A. C. (1936). *Am. J. Physiol.* **115**, 389–394.

Stavitsky, A. B., and Arquilla, E. R. (1953). *Federation Proc.* **12**, 461.

Stevenson, O. R., Coulson, R. A., and Hernandez, T. (1957). *Am. J. Physiol.* **191**, 95–102.

Stewart, G. A. (1960). *Brit. Med. Bull.* **16**, 196–201.

Sunderman, F. W., and Dohan, F. C. (1941). *Am. J. Physiol.* **132**, 418–425.

Tepperman, J., and Tepperman, H. M. (1960). *Pharmacol. Revs.* **12**, 301–353.

Thomas, T. B. (1940). *Anat. Record* **76**, 1–13.

Thorogood, E., and Zimmermann, B. (1945). *Endocrinology* **37**, 191–200.

Tuerkischer, E., and Wertheimer, E. (1948). *J. Endocrinol.* **5**, 229–235.

von Mering, J., and Minkowski, O. (1890). *Arch. exptl. Pathol. Pharmakol. Naunyn Schmiedeberg's* **26**, 371–387.

Vuylsteke, C. A., and de Duve, C. (1953). *Arch. intern. physiol.* **61**, 273–274.

Waddington, F. W. (1937). *Vet. Record* **49**, 859.

Weintraud, W. (1894). *Arch. exptl. Pathol. Pharmakol. Naunyn Schmiedeberg's* **34**, 303–312.

Wertheimer, E., and Shafrir, E. (1960). *Recent Progr. in Hormone Research* **16**, 467–490.

Wertheimer, E., and Shapiro, B. (1948). *Physiol. Revs.* **28**, 451–464.

Wilkinson, J. S. (1957). *Vet. Revs. and Annotations* **3**, 69–96.

Wilkinson, J. S. (1958). *Vet. Revs. and Annotations* **4**, 93–117.

Willmer, E. N. (1951). *In* "Cytology and Cell Physiology" (G. H. Bourne, ed.), 2nd ed., pp. 444–493. Oxford Univ. Press, London and New York.

Wilson, S., and Dixon, G. H. (1961). *Nature* **191**, 876–879.

Winegrad, A. I., and Renold, A. E. (1958). *J. Biol. Chem.* **233**, 273–276.

Wright, P. H. (1959). *Biochem. J.* **71**, 633–638.

Wright, P. H. (1960). *Brit. Med. Bull.* **16**, 219–223.

Wurster, D. H., and Miller, M. R. (1960). *Comp. Biochem. Physiol.* **1**, 101–109.

Yalow, R. S., and Berson, S. A. (1957). *J. Clin. Invest.* **36**, 648–655.

Yalow, R. S., and Berson, S. A. (1960). *J. Clin. Invest.* **39**, 1157–1175.

Yamamoto, M., Kotaki, A., Tsuneo, O., and Sataki, K. (1960). *J. Biochem. (Japan)* **48**, 84–92.

Young, F. G. (1937). *Lancet* **ii**, 372–374.

Young, F. G. (1938). *Proc. Roy. Soc. Med.* **31**, 1305–1316.

Young, F. G. (1939). *New Engl. J. Med.* **221**, 635–646.

Young, F. G. (1941). *Brit. Med. J.* **II**, 897–901.

Young, F. G. (1944). *Brit. Med. J.* **II**, 715–718.

Young, F. G. (1948). *Lancet* **ii**, 955–961.

Young, F. G. (1951). *Brit. Med. J.* **II**, 1167–1173.

Young, F. G. (1953). *Recent Progr. in Hormone Research* **8**, 471–510.

Young, F. G. (1956a). *Brit. Med. J.* **II**, 431–432.

Young, F. G. (1956b). *Ciba Foundation Colloq. on Endocrinol.* **9**, 74.

Young, F. G. (1959). *Ciba Foundation Symposium on Significant Trends in Med. Research*, pp. 135–157.

Young, F. G. (1961). *Brit. Med. J.* **II**, 1449–1454.

Young, J. D., and Carpenter, F. H. (1961). *J. Biol. Chem.* **236**, 743–748.

~ *11* ~

Pancreatic Hormones:
Glucagon

J. BERTHET

Laboratory of Physiological Chemistry, University of Louvain, Belgium

I. INTRODUCTION

Glucagon was discovered in pancreatic extracts by Murlin and his collaborators in 1923. It was investigated fairly extensively during the following years, particularly by Bürger and his co-workers (for historical reviews see Bürger, 1937; de Duve, 1953; Foa, 1954; von Holt, 1955; Schulze, 1956), but this work did not succeed in attracting general interest, and glucagon was almost forgotten until 1945, when various observations led to its rediscovery and to a new era of active investigation of this hypothetical hormone. The proof that glucagon originates in the α-cells of the islets of Langerhans gave a new impetus to histological research on these structures. Purified preparations of glucagon were obtained and allowed detailed studies of its chemical and biological properties, especially since 1953 when highly purified crystalline glucagon became available (Staub *et al.*, 1953, 1955). However, despite the rapid advances of the last years, the fundamental problems of the physiology of glucagon remain unsolved. A conclusive proof of its hormonal nature is still lacking and its possible role in metabolic regulations remains entirely conjectural.

Most of the experimental work on glucagon has been performed on mammals commonly used as laboratory animals. A few scattered observations reveal that an extensive study on other vertebrates would not only be very rewarding from a comparative point of view, but might also supply the answers to some general questions in glucagon physiology. However, the data presently available on the comparative aspects are much too limited to provide the framework for this review. The author feels rather that they should be included in a general discussion of what is known and what is unknown about the hormone in order to present a coherent picture of the present state of the problem and to suggest where further research of the comparative endocrinology of glucagon would be most interesting.

On many particular aspects, the lack of space has forced the author to make a selection amongst the published data, or to summarize the conclusions of many different investigators. The reader is referred to other reviews for a more extensive survey of the literature (see the reviews on particular aspects mentioned: Bergen and Van Itallie, 1959; Berthet, 1959; Best, 1959; Cavallero *et al.*, 1957; de Duve and Berthet, 1957; Foa *et al.*, 1957, 1959; Lazarow, 1957; Makman *et al.*, 1960; M. R. Miller, 1960; Miller and Wurster, 1959).

II. NATURE, IDENTIFICATION, AND ORIGIN OF GLUCAGON

A. Chemical Nature

Glucagon from pork pancreas is a small peptide (molecular weight, 3482) containing 29 amino acids. The sequence has been determined (Bromer *et al.*, 1957); it presents no apparent similarities to insulin or to any other known peptide.

Glucogon has also been purified from cattle pancreas. Although the products obtained from pork and cattle appear to be similar, their identity has not been definitely proved. It should be noted in this connection that many samples of purified glucagon supplied to investigators for pharmacological experiments were until recently mixtures of pork and cattle glucogon.

The peptide has no unusual chemical or physical properties (Staub *et al.*, 1955), but two of its properties deserve to be mentioned. Glucagon is almost insoluble between pH 6 and 8; this probably explains the prolonged action which is obtained when glucagon is injected subcutaneously as a suspension in saline rather than as a solution in acid or alkaline buffers. Another peculiarity is that glucagon does not contain any cystine residues, which makes it very resistant to treatments which destroy disulfide bridges. Some of these procedures are used to inactivate the insulin (where disulfide bridges are essential for activity) which sometimes contaminates glucagon preparations.

B. Identification and Assay

So far, no purely chemical assay for glucagon seems feasible. Most of the biological methods described are based on the blood sugar raising and glycogenolytic properties of the hormone. Although many procedures have been used as crude assay methods for glucagon, a quantitative determination requires an experimental design suitable for statistical analysis. The assays on anesthetized cats (Staub *et al.*, 1954), on rabbit liver slices (Vuylsteke and de Duve, 1957), or on dog liver homogenates (Berthet *et al.*, 1957) fulfill this requirement.

It will be seen later that some fundamental questions of glucagon physiology could only be answered if a very sensitive and specific assay method were available for its detection in blood. Although the liver slice or homogenate methods are accurate and possibly sensitive enough for this purpose, they lack specificity or are subject to interference by other plasma components. It is doubtful whether recovery of glucagon and removal of interfering substances have been achieved successfully in any of the concentration and purification procedures devised so far (Tyberghein and Williams, 1958; Makman *et al.*, 1958; Maggi, 1960; Maggi and Andreis, 1960a, b).

An immunological assay recently described (Unger *et al.*, 1959) is a promising new approach to this important problem since it should be insensitive to interferences by glycogenolytic substances unrelated to glucagon.

C. Site of Origin

1. THE PANCREAS

The work of Sutherland and de Duve (1948) suggested that in mammals glucagon was present in the α-cells of the islets of Langerhans. Although this assumption was sometimes disputed, it seems to be generally accepted now and it has usually been extended to include the α-cells of other vertebrates.

It is not feasible to include here a complete discussion of the morphology of the α-cells (see Ferner, 1952; Van Campenhout and Cornelis, 1953; Korp and Le Compte, 1955; Mosca, 1955; Lazarow, 1957; Cavallero *et al.*, 1957; Verne, 1957; Miller and Wurster, 1959; M. R. Miller, 1960) and only the main conclusions on their distribution in various animal groups will be mentioned here: α-cells seem to be present in all vertebrates except urodele amphibians (Miller and Wurster, 1959; M. R. Miller, 1960; Wurster and Miller, 1960). They are particularly numerous in the giant islets of many birds (Van Campenhout and Cornelis, 1953), lizards, and snakes (Thomas, 1942; Miller and Wurster, 1956, 1958). They seem less abundant in turtles and toads and even less in frogs (De Robertis and Primavesi, 1939; M. R. Miller, 1960). The ratio of α- to β-cells is very variable in some fishes, and is subject to considerable seasonal variations (Pallot and Schältze, 1953; Schältze, 1954). It should be pointed out that serious difficulties are encountered with some animal species in devising a staining procedure which would allow a conclusive identification of α-cells (Barrington, 1951, 1953). Moreover, the number of species examined so far is so small that the distribution pattern of α-cells summarized above should be considered as being provisional.

In vertebrates other than mammals, the morphological observations have rarely been supplemented by the demonstration of the presence of glucagon. However, glucagon has been found in large amounts in the pancreas of birds (Vuylsteke and de Duve, 1953) and it has been detected in the endocrine pancreas of some teleosts (Malandra and Mosca, 1952; Planas and Lluch, 1956; Lluch and Planas, 1956, Audy and Kerly, 1952).

2. OTHER TISSUES

Sutherland and de Duve (1948) reported the presence of glucagon in certain parts of the digestive tract, especially gastric mucosa of dogs and rabbits. Negative results were obtained with similar tissue extracts from pig, cattle, and sheep. Although a complete chemical comparison is still to be made, there is strong evidence that the hyperglycemic substance from dog gastric mucosa is indeed glucagon, since it shows many of its chemical and biological properties (Sutherland and de Duve, 1948; Sutherland *et al.*, 1949).

III. BIOLOGICAL PROPERTIES OF GLUCAGON

In most of the recent studies, glucagon from cattle or pork has been used; it is not known whether glucagon from other animal sources would exhibit identical biological properties. However, when glucagon was assayed in tissue extracts from birds or fishes, mammals or mammalian organs were used as assay systems, and were found to be responsive. Conversely, cattle glucagon induces hyperglycemia in vertebrates other than mammals. Nevertheless, before the question of class or species specificity can be answered, quantitative experiments should be performed with purified glucagon from various sources, and biological reactions other than hyperglycemia should be utilized.

It is generally assumed that only metabolic changes occur after glucagon administration. This is probably correct on the whole but some vascular actions have also been described (Shoemaker et al., 1959; Shoemaker and Teel, 1960; Shoemaker and Van Itallie, 1960; Farah and Tuttle, 1960) and renal function is known to be influenced (Staub et al., 1957; Butturini and Bonomini, 1957; Elrick et al., 1959; Serratto and Earle, 1959).

A. Metabolic Actions

1. CARBOHYDRATE METABOLISM

a. *Hyperglycemia and liver glycogen breakdown.* Glucagon raises the blood sugar level in all mammals so far investigated; the character of the response is, however, variable from species to species and depends to some degree on the route of administration. Intravenous administration is usually more effective than subcutaneous, intramuscular, or intraperitoneal injection. This is to be expected since glucagon acts rapidly but is also rapidly destroyed. In general, the blood sugar starts to increase a few minutes after the injection; unless a large dose has been given subcutaneously as a suspension of poorly soluble glucagon, the blood sugar returns to the normal level within 1 or 2 hours. It seems that, in the rat at least, the action on the liver is more prolonged and frequently more pronounced than the hyperglycemia may indicate (Sokal, 1960; Sokal and Sarcione, 1958).

Cats are extremely sensitive to glucagon; 0.05 μg of glucagon per kg of body weight by intravenous injection gives a definite response (Staub et al., 1955). Dogs and rabbits seem somewhat less sensitive, and rats and especially mice are rather insensitive. The action of glucagon on the blood sugar of other vertebrates has been much less investigated. If one may generalize from a few scattered observations, it seems that birds (Hazelwood and Lorenz, 1957; Mialhe, 1958; Snedecor et al., 1956) and reptiles (Miller and Wurster, 1958; Stevenson et al., 1957) are sensitive to glucagon, but urodeles are not (Miller and Wurster, 1959; Wurster and Miller, 1960).

The physiological mechanism of the glucagon hyperglycemia has only been investigated in mammals. There is little doubt that it results essentially from an overproduction of glucose by the liver mainly at the expense of glycogen. For this reason, the intensity of the response to glucagon is closely related to the amount of glycogen in the liver. Many investigators have observed depletion of the liver glycogen stores shortly after glucagon administration; it is followed within 12–24 hours by an increase above the normal level. This rebound phenomenon probably results from complex endocrine reactions (Foa *et al.*, 1957).

b. *Peripheral utilization of glucose.* The possibility of an action of glucagon on the utilization of glucose by the peripheral tissues has been a very controversial subject during the last ten years. The problem was raised by investigators who had estimated the peripheral glucose utilization by arterio-venous difference. These experiments, performed mostly on humans or on dogs, led the authors to widely differing conclusions. According to some investigators glucagon has no effect which could not be fully explained by the hyperglycemia, but others found that glucagon stimulated the peripheral utilization of glucose and acted as a synergist of insulin. On critical examination, it appears that none of these experiments provides a valid demonstration of a peripheral effect because (1) in some cases glucagon may have been contaminated by unknown and significant amounts of insulin, (2) the experiments performed on humans or intact dogs do not allow us to rule out an effect through a direct stimulation of the secretion of insulin by the pancreas, (3) when the blood sugar is changing rapidly, the arterio-venous difference in glucose concentration represents not only the peripheral consumption of glucose but also the exchanges between the vascular and extravascular spaces, and (4) the significance of the method rests on the assumption that the peripheral blood flow does not change appreciably during the experiments. However, recent work (Shoemaker and Teel, 1960) suggests that glucagon decreases the peripheral blood flow.

Other approaches to the problem have failed to yield definite conclusions. In most cases, no effect of glucagon was found on the glucose utilization by the rat diaphragm *in vitro* or by depancreatized or eviscerated animals, although in some instances glucagon seemed to depress the action of insulin (see review, by Berthet, 1959). However, recently glucagon has been demonstrated to stimulate the uptake and the oxidation of glucose by rat adipose tissue *in vitro*. The effects may, therefore, be quite different according to the peripheral tissue considered. The overall effect on the carbohydrate metabolism in the intact animal is difficult to evaluate, but it seems that large doses of glucagon impair the utilization of glucose. During chronic treatment with glucagon, rats show intense glucosuria and nitrogen loss but the negative nitrogen balance explains only part of the urinary loss of glucose and it appears that the glucosuria reflects an inability of the rat to utilize glucose normally (Best, 1959). Part of this deficiency could be accounted for by the inability of the liver to accumulate glycogen after the animal has been fed.

2. Fatty Acid Metabolism

Glucagon inhibits the incorporation of various labeled precursors into fatty acids and it increases the production of ketone bodies by rat or rabbit liver slices *in vitro* (Haugaard and Stadie, 1953; Haugaard and Haugaard, 1954; Berthet, 1958a). There is little doubt that the same catabolic actions obtain *in vivo*, since glucagon raises the level of ketone bodies in the blood (Salter *et al.*, 1960).

It was mentioned in Section III, A, 1, b that glucagon stimulates the uptake of glucose by the epididymal fat pad *in vitro* (Froesch *et al.*, 1960; Lee *et al.*, 1960; Vaughan, 1960a, b). Though glucagon resembles insulin in this respect, the metabolic pattern it induces in adipose tissue is very different; glucagon decreases the respiratory quotient and the incorporation of various precursors into fatty acids, and it seems that a large part of the extra glucose taken up is oxidized and converted to glycerol (Froesch *et al.*, 1960). Glucagon also has a lipolytic effect on adipose tissue, similar to the action of adrenaline or ACTH (Orth *et al.*, 1960; Vaughan, 1960a, b). However, glucagon administered *in vivo* does not raise the level of nonesterified fatty acids of the blood as would be expected in view of results *in vitro*. It seems that glucagon is not as potent a lipolytic agent as adrenaline, and that in the intact organism its effect is efficiently counteracted by insulin (Bierman *et al.*, 1957; Laurell and Christensson, 1958; Lipsett *et al.*, 1960).

A direct proof that a chronic treatment with glucagon effectively prevents the storage of fats in the intact animal was recently provided by the experiments of Salter (1960). The same effect had already been noticed by Cavallero (1956).

3. Cholesterol Metabolism

In vitro experiments have provided the main information in this field. The incorporation of labeled precursors in the cholesterol of rat or rabbit liver slices is inhibited by glucagon; this observation can probably be interpreted as a decrease in cholesterol synthesis (Berthet, 1958b). Some experiments on intact animals are consistent with this hypothesis since they indicate that glucagon can lower blood cholesterol. (Caren and Carbo, 1956, 1960; Salter, 1960).

4. PROTEIN METABOLISM

It has been known for some time (Kalant, 1954; Tyberghein, 1953) that glucagon influences the metabolism of proteins, but the importance of this action has been realized only since Salter and his co-workers (1957) showed that chronic treatment with the peptide induces a negative nitrogen balance in rats.

The liver certainly plays an important role in this effect. In the isolated liver, glucagon stimulates the production of urea (L. L. Miller, 1960) and inhibits the incorporation of labeled precursors into the proteins (Pryor and Berthet, 1960a). When labeled amino acids are injected into intact animals, glucagon has a similar effect on liver proteins (Pryor and Berthet, unpublished data). The latter result may be interpreted as a true inhibition of protein synthesis, since it is known that glucagon promotes the uptake of the circulating amino acids by the liver (Shoemaker and Van Itallie, 1960).

Certainly glucagon exerts some influence on the protein metabolism of peripheral tissue, since continued treatment inhibits the accumulation of protein in growing rats (Salter, 1960). The mechanism of this effect is not clear. It could be accounted for by the decrease in blood amino acids (Shoemaker and Van Itallie, 1960); no effect was obtained on protein synthesis by the rat diaphragm *in vitro* (Manchester and Young, 1959).

5. BASAL METABOLIC RATE

Glucagon increases the metabolic rate (Davidson *et al.*, 1957, 1960). This effect is not linked to its actions on the blood sugar or on liver glycogen and it does not seem that it can be accounted for by a secondary secretion of adrenaline (Davidson *et al.*, 1960). The fact that glucagon can increase the metabolic rate of rats by as much as 50% without the utilization of glucose being apparently much stimulated, indicates that its catabolic action on proteins and lipids is indeed a quantitatively important phenomenon.

6. DIABETOGENIC ACTION, INSULIN ANTAGONISM, AND THE EFFECT ON GROWTH

The diabetogenic action of glucagon was difficult to prove (Cavallero and Malandra, 1953; Cavallero *et al.*, 1954) and numerous investigators reported negative results (Berthet, 1959). It appears now that the failures to induce diabetes resulted mainly from the use of glucagon solutions which has an evanescent effect and were not injected frequently enough or at sufficient doses. Salter and co-workers (1957) succeeded in producing a diabetes-like state in rats by repeatedly injecting large doses of a glucagon suspension; these experiments have been repeated in various mammals and important physiological and morphological observations have been made (Van Itallie *et al.*, 1959; Salter *et al.*, 1960; Logothetopoulos and Salter, 1960; Logothetopoulos *et al.*, 1960; Volk and Lazarus, 1960).

Resistance to the diabetogenic action varies according to the animal species (Best, 1959). Rabbits and humans seem more sensitive than rats or guinea pigs; dogs are rather resistant. The main symptoms resulting from chronic glucagon treatment are qualitatively similar to those of a true diabetes; hyperglycemia, negative nitrogen balance, ketosis, and loss of weight. It is important to decide to what extent these effects are due to a direct action of glucagon or to an insulin deficiency. The histological examination of the pancreas indicates that at the early stage of the treatment the β-cells react by hyperactivity and mitosis, but the degenerative changes observed later in some cases suggest that the β-cells may become exhausted (Logothetopoulos and Salter, 1960; Logothetopoulos *et al.*, 1960; Volk and Lazarus, 1960). The latter interpretation is confirmed by the occasional development of metaglucagon diabetes lasting a few weeks in the rabbit and in the partially depancreatized dog. It is unlikely, however, that all the symptoms of early glucagon diabetes can be quantitatively accounted for by insulin deficiency, since they correspond very well with the pharmacological actions of glucagon observed *in vitro* or in acute experiments on intact animals.

The relationship between glucagon and insulin can be summarized as follows: (a) By its own metabolic properties glucagon antagonizes some of the actions of insulin; it raises the blood sugar, prevents the synthesis of liver glycogen, protein, and fat, and of peripheral fat and accelerates the production of urea and of ketone bodies. In some cases the antagonism has been directly demonstrated in acute experiments *in vivo* or *in vitro* (de Duve *et al.*, 1946; Tyberghein, 1952; L. L. Miller, 1960; Merlevede and De Wulf, 1960); (b) In the intact animal, glucagon stimulates the secretion of insulin, probably by the hyperglycemia which it produces; (c) A sustained treatment with glucagon may exhaust the β-cells and bring about a true insulin deficiency.

The increased oxygen consumption and nitrogen excretion during treatment with glucagon should by itself induce weight loss or prevent the growth of young animals. This is in fact observed if the dosage of the peptide is high enough. In recent experiments on pair-fed animals, Salter (1960) has confirmed that the growth of rats is effectively impeded by subdiabetogenic doses of glucagon; the protein and fat content of the carcass of the treated animal was reduced. These observations show clearly that the effects of a chronic treatment are not simply the result of an insulin deficiency.

7. Other Hormonal Interactions

Beside the important relationship between glucagon and insulin, other endocrine interactions have been discovered, namely with the adrenal cortex and medulla, and with the thyroid gland.

Since the discovery of the influence of glucagon on protein metabolism, its similarity with the action of cortisone has been frequently pointed out. The basal metabolic rate and the nitrogen excretion of adrenalectomized animals are not much influenced by glucagon. Since a normal response can be restored by treatment with cortisone, it appears that the adrenal cortex is not required as a mediator in these actions of glucagon, but only plays a "permissive role" (Davidson et al., 1960; Salter et al., 1957). Similar conclusions emerge from in vitro experiments (L. L. Miller, 1960).

Recent observations indicate that glucagon promotes the release of catecholamines by the adrenal medulla (Scian et al., 1960) and this phenomenon has been stated to play an important part in determining hyperglycemia in the rat (Sarcione et al., 1960). This can hardly apply to all mammals, for the hyperglycemic response to glucagon in rabbits or dogs is not influenced by substances like dihydroergotamine which effectively block the blood sugar-raising action of adrenaline (Ellis, et al., 1953; Sirek et al., 1957; Galansino et al., 1960).

The thyroid is essential for glucagon to influence the basal metabolic rate. Here again, the gland has a permissive role (Davidson et al., 1960). Contrary to a previous report (Davidson et al., 1957), recent investigations (Davidson et al., 1960) suggest that the adrenal medulla is not involved in this action.

Complex hormonal interactions probably explain why glucagon stimulates the growth of the pituitary dwarf mouse (Cavallero, 1956; 1959). As mentioned before (Section III, A, 6), the peptide has the opposite effect on normal rats and rabbits.

B. Biochemical Mechanism of Action

Space does not permit a complete discussion of the mechanism of action of glucagon. However, some aspects of this question should be mentioned here since it appears now that various hormones in different organs and in diverse animal groups may act by initiating similar sequences of events.

The main discovery of the recent years relates to the role of the cyclic nucleotide 3′,5′-adenosine-monophosphate (3′,5′–AMP) as an intracellular mediator of some hormonal actions. Since an extensive discussion of this question has recently been published elsewhere (Sutherland and Rall, 1960), only the main conclusions will be summarized here. It seems well established that 3′,5′-AMP is the mediator of the actions of glucagon and adrenaline on the liver. This applies not only to the glycogenolytic effect resulting from phosphorylase activation, but also to the independent effects on protein and lipid metabolism (Pryor and Berthet, 1960b; Berthet, unpublished data). The same mechanism seems to be involved in the activation of phosphorylase by adrenaline in heart and striated muscle where glucagon has little or no effect. The most surprising discovery has been that 3′,5′-AMP apparently plays a similar role in the action of ACTH on the adrenal cortex and in that of 5-hydroxytryptamine on the trematode *Fasciola hepatica*. These findings have opened an entirely new field in the comparative biochemistry of hormones.

IV. GLUCAGON AS A HORMONE

The hormonal status of glucagon remains so incertain that the main problem consists much more in deciding whether it is ever secreted by the α-cells than in evaluating its importance in metabolic regulations. Although the two questions are usually linked in the various theories so far proposed, they will be discussed here, as far as is possible, under separate headings.

A. The Secretion of Glucagon

1. INDIRECT EVIDENCE

A large number of morphological studies have revealed that the α-cells are influenced by various hormonal and metabolic factors. In many cases these observations are difficult to interpret but they suggest at least that these cells participate in some way in the control of metabolism, probably by regulating their secretion of glucagon. One of the most significant findings in this respect was made by Kracht (1955) and confirmed later by other authors (Logothetopoulos and Salter, 1960; Logothetopoulos *et al.*, 1960): in some mammals, repeated glucagon administration may produce an atropy of the α-cells. This phenomenon which suggests the existence of a feedback control seems to be a good indication that glucagon secretion occurs and that is is adjusted to the physiological state of the animal.

In human pathology or in experimental investigations on other mammals, no syndrome has been discovered which could be unequivocally attributed to insufficient or excessive glucagon secretion. The physiological consequences of the destruction of the α-cells by various substances such as cobalt salts can not be evaluated; these agents have other toxic effects and the damaged cells recover or regenerate too rapidly. When it is possible, as in the dog, to remove all the α-cells by partial pancreatectomy, leaving a fragment containing β-cells only, the syndrome obtained does not differ substantially from typical prediabetes (Bencosme et al., 1957; Paloyan et al., 1960). It has been frequently suggested that the presence of the α-cells explains why the need of insulin is usually smaller after pancreatectomy than in severe spontaneous or alloxan diabetes, but this interpretation has not been accepted by all authors. Moreover, since the consequence of pancreatectomy in mammals can apparently be fully compensated by the administration of insulin, it would seem that glucagon plays at the most a minor role in hormonal regulations. It should be noted, however, that as other parts of the digestive tract also elaborate glucagon, the hormone would not be entirely lacking in depancreatized animals. In any case, insulin deprivation after pancreas removal produces such serious metabolic imbalance that the consequences of glucagon deprivation would be undetectable, especially if glucagon acts predominantly as an insulin antagonist.

Investigations performed on birds and reptiles have given more encouraging results. In ducks (Mialhe, 1958) and some lizards or snakes (Miller and Wurster, 1958; Houssay and Penhos, 1960) pancreatectomy results in a more or less prolonged hypoglycemia which has usually been attributed to the lack of glucagon. This difference from many other vertebrates (see the review by Houssay, 1959) may be related to the large amount of glucagon in the bird pancreas and to the great number of α-cells in the islets of many birds and squamate reptiles. It suggests that glucagon may play a more important role in these animals.

2. GLUCAGON IN BLOOD

Most authors have not accepted the facts reported in Section IV, A, 1 to be fully convincing proof of the hormonal nature of glucagon. Unless an entirely new and different type of experimental evidence becomes available, the ultimate demonstration will have to rest on the identification of glucagon in blood. During the last ten years, hopes of solving the problem by this approach have periodically been raised but, as is apparent in a recent review by Makman et al. (1960), this goal has not yet been reached.

It appears now that a large number of controls are necessary before a blood sugar raising principle found in blood can be identified as glucagon. For instance, the hypothesis that growth hormone stimulates glucagon secretion collapsed when the substance responsible was identified as a sympathicomimetic substance released in the duodenal area but not from the pancreas (Sirek *et al.*, 1957; Colombo *et al.*, 1960 Galansino *et al.*, 1960). The protein or peptide isolated from dog plasma by Sutherland and his co-workers (Makman *et al.*, 1958) showed many intriguing similarities with glucagon but turned out to act by a substantially different mechanism (Makman *et al.*, 1960). Moreover, it was not found in higher concentration in the blood originating from the pancreatico-duodenal area. Tyberghein and Williams (1958) obtained similarly negative results in experiments on rabbits.

A group of Italian workers (Maggi, 1960; Maggi and Andreis, 1960a, b) have recently proposed a new extraction procedure for the detection and assay of glucagon in the blood of various mammals. However, not all the necessary controls were performed and it may well be that a glucagon-like substance rather than glucagon itself was involved. Whatever its nature, the substance disappears from rat blood within an hour after pancreatectomy (Maggi and Rodari, 1960). The principle in question could be identical with the blood sugar raising factor liberated by the pancreas under the influence of deserpidine (Colombo, *et al.*, 1960; Galansino *et al.*, 1960).

B. The Position of Glucagon in the Hormonal Regulation of Metabolism

As long as glucagon was only known as a hyperglycemic–glycogenolytic factor it was tempting to assume that it was exclusively involved in the regulation of the blood sugar concentration. Experiments on mammals have not provided much support for this theory. It may be significant in this respect that α-cells degenerate under the influence of large doses of glucagon, but that this does not occur as a result of prolonged and intense hyperglycemia. If α-cell degeneration is correctly interpreted as due to inactivity, the blood sugar cannot be the only regulating factor of glucagon secretion. Moreover, it would be rash to regard the various catabolic actions of glucagon on the liver and the adipose tissue as being without physiological importance. Recent research indicates that the earlier concept of the antagonism of glucagon to insulin with regard to blood sugar concentration should be extended to many other aspects of metabolism.

The few investigations on reptiles and birds suggest that glucagon may be physiologically much more important in both of these vertebrate classes, but it is not yet known whether protein or lipid metabolism are also influenced. If the differences between vertebrates turn out to be only of a quantitative nature in the amount of glucagon secreted or in the sensitivity of the tissues to the hormone, the choice of the animal species for further experiments could be an essential factor for obtaining clearcut results which could shed light on the whole field of glucagon physiology. The antagonism between insulin and glucagon may be sufficiently well-adjusted in nearly all mammals to allow an almost similar equilibrium to be reached by decreasing insulin secretion or increasing glucagon secretion. Under these conditions, a deficiency in the latter hormone would be difficult to recognize, especially when severe metabolic imbalance sets in almost immediately after insulin deprivation. In some reptiles and birds insulin is apparently not indispensable for the control of carbohydrate utilization, or else its action persists longer than in mammals after pancreatectomy. Whatever the ultimate reasons, the differences between animal species offer interesting opportunities to investigate fundamental aspects of the glucagon problem.

Even if the above hypotheses supply a satisfactory explanation of some of the experimental findings, they do not indicate the physiological role of glucagon in mammals. As long as the physiological stimuli for its secretion remain unidentified, teleological considerations based on the properties of the hormone will have to serve as the starting point for speculations. The best hint so far seems to be the antagonism between insulin and glucagon. However, if the latter is to be of any use to the animal, it is obvious that the two hormones should not neutralize each other perfectly. Various theories could be built by elaborating on situations in which the antagonism is known or suspected to fail; e.g., the peripheral utilization of glucose by muscles. Account may also be taken of the fact that glucagon is probably more rapidly destroyed or may be more specifically bound by the liver than insulin. Although a detailed theory would undoubtedly be premature, the possibility that glucagon acts as a modulator of the action of insulin seems to be a fruitful and stimulating hypothesis.

References

Audy, G., and Kerly, M. (1952). *Biochem. J.* **52**, 77–78.
Barrington, E. J. W. (1951). *Quart. J. Microscop. Sci.* **92**, 205–220.
Barrington, E. J. W. (1953). *Quart. J. Microscop. Sci.* **92**, 281–291.
Bencosme, S. A., Mariz, S., and Frei, J. (1957). *Endocrinology* **61**, 1–11.
Bergen, S. S., and Van Itallie, T. B. (1959). *Metabolism, Clin. and Exptl.* **9**, 132–156.

Berthet, J. (1958a). *Proc. Intern. Congr. Biochem.*, *4th Congr.*, *Vienna, 1958*, p. 107.

Berthet, J. (1958b). *In* "Radioisotopes in Scientific Research," Vol. III, pp. 179–184. Pergamon Press, New York.

Berthet, J. (1959). *Am. J. Med.* **26**, 703–714.

Berthet, J., Rall, T. W., and Sutherland, E. W. (1957). *J. Biol. Chem.* **229**, 351–361.

Best, C. H. (1959). *Ciba Foundation Symposium on Significant Trends in Med. Research*, pp. 164–190.

Bierman, E. L., Dole, V. P., and Roberts, T. N. (1957). *Diabetes* **6**, 475–479.

Bromer, W. W., Sinn, L. G., Staub, A., and Behrens, O. K. (1957). *Diabetes* **6**, 234–238.

Bürger, M. (1937). *Klin. Wochschr.* **16**, 361–363.

Butturini, U., and Bonomini, V. (1957). *Boll. soc. ital. biol. sper.* **33**, 960–963 and 963–965.

Caren, R., and Carbo, L. (1956). *J. Clin. Endocrinol. and Metabolism* **16**, 507–516.

Caren, R., and Carbo, L. (1960). *Metabolism, Clin. and Exptl.* **9**, 938–945.

Cavallero, C. (1956). *CIBA Foundation Colloq. on Endocrinol.* **9**, 266–284.

Cavallero, C. (1959). *Lancet* **i**, 521.

Cavallero, C., and Malandra, B. (1953). *Acta Endocrinol.* **13**, 79–88.

Cavallero, C., Malandra, B., and Galansino, G. (1954). *Nature* **173**, 585–586.

Cavallero, C., Malandra, B., and Mosca, L. (1957). "Isole pancreatiche e glucagone" (7th natl. congr. ital. soc. endocrinol). Belforte, Livorno.

Colombo, J. P., Weber, J. W., Kanameishi, D., and Foa, P. P. (1960). *Endocrinology* **67**, 248–251.

Davidson, I. W. F., Salter, J. M., and Best, C. H. (1957). *Nature* **180**, 1124.

Davidson, I. W. F., Salter, J. M., and Best, C. H. (1960). *Am. J. Clin. Nutrition* **8**, 540–546.

de Duve, C. (1953). *Lancet* **i**, 99–104.

de Duve, C., and Berthet, J. (1957). *In* "Diabète sucré, Diabète insipide, Régulation électrolytique" (Publication des Annales d'Endocrinologie), pp. 333–397. Masson, Paris.

de Duve, C., Hers, H. G., and Bouckaert, J. P. (1946). *Arch. intern. pharmacodynamie* **72**, 45–61.

De Robertis, E., and Primavesi, L. (1939). *Rev. soc. arg. biol.* **15**, 474–481.

Ellis, S., Anderson, H. L., and Collins, M. C. (1953). *Proc. Soc. Exptl. Biol. Med.* **84**, 383–386.

Elrick, H., Whipple, N., Arai, Y., and Hlad, C. J. (1959). *J. Clin. Endocrinol. and Metabolism* **19**, 1275–1281.

Farah, A., and Tuttle, R. (1960). *J. Pharmacol. Exptl. Therap.* **129**, 49–55.

Ferner, H. (1952). "Das Inselsystem des Pankreas." Thieme, Stuttgart.

Foa, P. P. (1954). *Advances in Internal Med.* **6**, 29–58.

Foa, P. P., Galansino, G., and Pozza, G. (1957). *Recent Progr. in Hormone Research* **13**, 473–510.

Foa, P. P., Galansino, G., and D'Amico, G. (1959). *In* "Modern Problems in Pediatrics" (E. Rossi, E. Gautier, and J. W. Weber, eds.), Vol. IV, pp. 237–248. Karger, Basel.

Froesch, E. R., Bally, P., Guhl, V., Ramseier, E., and Labhart, A. (1960). *Schweiz. med. Wochschr.* **90**, 1329–1332.

Galansino, G., D'Amico, G., Kanameishi, D., Berlinger, F. G., and Foa, P. P. (1960). *Am. J. Physiol.* **198**, 1059–1062.

Haugaard, E. S., and Haugaard, N. (1954). *J. Biol. Chem.* **206**, 641–645.

Haugaard, E. S., and Stadie, W. C. (1953). *J. Biol. Chem.* **200**, 753–757.

Hazelwood, R. L., and Lorenz, F. W. (1957). *Endocrinology* **61**, 520–527.

Houssay, B. A. (1959). *In* "Comparative Endocrinology" (A. Gorbman, ed.), pp. 639–667. Wiley, New York.

Houssay, B. A., and Penhos, J. C. (1960). *Acta Endocrinol.* **35**, 313–323.

Kalant, N. (1954). *Proc. Soc. Exptl. Biol. Med.* **86**, 617–619.

Korp, W., and LeCompte, P. M. (1955). *Diabetes* **4**, 347–366.

Kracht, J. (1955). *Naturwissenschaften* **42**, 50–51.

Laurell, S., and Christensson, B. (1958). *Acta Physiol. Scand.* **44**, 248–254.

Lazarow, A. (1957). *Diabetes* **6**, 222–233.

Lee, H. M., Ellis, R. M., and Bromer, W. W. (1960). *Proc. Soc. Exptl. Biol. Med.* **104**, 4–6.

Lipsett, M. B., Engel, H. R., and Bergenstal, D. M. (1960). *J. Lab. Clin. Med.* **56**, 342–354.

Lluch, M., and Planas, J. (1956). *Rev. españ. fisiol.* **12**, 21–27.

Logothetopoulos, J., and Salter, J. M. (1960). *Diabetes* **9**, 31–37.

Logothetopoulos, J., Sharma, B. B., Salter, J. M., and Best, C. H. (1960). *Diabetes* **9**, 278–285.

Maggi, G. (1960). *Arch. sci. med.* **109**, 9–22.

Maggi, G., and Andreis, G. (1960a). *Arch. sci. med.* **109**, 223–229.

Maggi, G., and Andreis, G. (1960b). *Arch. sci. med.* **110**, 406–408.

Maggi, G., and Rodari, T. (1960). *Boll. soc. med. chir. Pavia* **40**, 1–2.

Makman, M. H., Makman, R. S., and Sutherland, E. W. (1958). *J. Biol. Chem.* **233**, 894–899.

Makman, M. H., Makman, R. S., and Sutherland, E. W. (1960). *In* "Hormones in Human Plasma" (H. N. Antoniades, ed.), pp. 119–137. Little, Brown, Boston, Massachusetts.

Malandra, B., and Mosca, L. (1952). *Rass. fisiopatol. clin. e terap.* **24**, 43–48.

Manchester, K. L., and Young, F. G. (1959). *J. Endocrinol.* **18**, 381–394.

Merlevede, W., and De Wulf, H. (1960). *Arch. Intern. pharmacodynamie* **125**, 222–223.

Mialhe, P. (1958). *Acta Endocrinol. Suppl.* **36**, 1–134.

Miller, L. L. (1960). *Nature* **185**, 248.

Miller, M. R. (1960). *Diabetes* **9**, 318–323.

Miller, M. R., and Wurster, D. H. (1956). *Endocrinology* **58**, 114–120.

Miller, M. R., and Wurster, D. H. (1958). *Endocrinology* **63**, 191–200.

Miller, M. R., and Wurster, D. H. (1959). *In* "Comparative Endocrinology" (A. Gorbman, ed.), pp. 668–680. Wiley, New York.

Mosca, L. (1955). *Biol. Latina* **8**, 756–775.

Murlin, J. R., Clough, H. G., Gibbs, C. B., and Stokes, A. M. (1923). *J. Biol. Chem.* **56,** 253–296.

Orth, R. D., Odell, W. D., and Williams, R. H. (1960). *Am. J. Physiol.* **198,** 641–644.

Paloyan, E., Harper, P. V., and Watkins, H. B. (1960). *Federation Proc.* **19,** 223.

Pallot, G., and Schältze, W. (1953). *Compt. rend. soc. biol.* **147,** 1440–1444.

Planas, J., and Lluch, M. (1956). *Rev. españ. fisiol.* **12,** 295–300.

Pryor, J., and Berthet, J. (1960a). *Arch. intern. physiol. et biochem.* **68,** 277–278.

Pryor, J., and Berthet, J. (1960b). *Biochim. et Biophys. Acta* **43,** 556–557.

Salter, J. M. (1960). *Am. J. Clin. Nutrition* **8,** 535–539.

Salter, J. M., Davidson, I. W. F., and Best, C. H. (1957). *Diabetes* **6,** 248–252.

Salter, J. M., Ezrin, C., Laidlaw, J. C., and Gornall, A. G. (1960). *Metabolism, Clin. and Exptl.* **9,** 753–768.

Sarcione, E. J., Sokal, J. E., and Gerszi, K. E. (1960). *Endocrinology* **67,** 337–346.

Schältze, W. (1954). *Ann. Univ. Saraviensis* **2,** 19–56.

Schulze, W. (1956). *Ciba Foundation Colloq. on Endocrinol.* **9,** 147–166.

Scian, L. F., Westermann, C. D., Verdesca, A. S., and Hilton, J. G. (1960). *Am. J. Physiol.* **199,** 867–870.

Serratto, M., and Earle, D. P. (1959). *Proc. Soc. Exptl. Biol. Med.* **102,** 701–704.

Shoemaker, W. C., and Teel, P. (1960). *Endocrinology* **67,** 132–137.

Shoemaker, W. C., and Van Itallie, T. B. (1960). *Endocrinology* **66,** 260–268.

Shoemaker, W. C., Van Itallie, T. B., and Walker, W. F. (1959). *Am. J. Physiol.* **196,** 315–318.

Sirek, O. V., Sirek, A., and Best, C. H. (1957). *Am. J. Physiol.* **188,** 17–20.

Snedecor, J. G., Matthews, H., and Macgrath, W. B. (1956). *Poultry Sci.* **35,** 355–360.

Sokal, J. E. (1960). *Endocrinology* **67,** 774–783.

Sokal, J. E., and Sarcione, E. J. (1958). *Proc. Soc. Exptl. Biol. Med.* **98,** 879–882.

Staub, A., Sinn, L., and Behrens, O. K. (1953). *Science* **117,** 628–629.

Staub, A., Behrens, O. K., Ellis, J. T., and Kennedy, R. W. (1954). *J. Clin. Invest.* **33,** 1629–1633.

Staub, A., Sinn, L., and Behrens, O. K. (1955). *J. Biol. Chem.* **214,** 619–632.

Staub, A., Stoll, F., and Elrick, H. (1957). *Proc. Soc. Exptl. Biol. Med.* **94,** 57–60.

Stevenson, O. R., Coulson, R. A., and Hernandez, T. (1957). *Am. J. Physiol.* **191,** 95–102.

Sutherland, E. W., and de Duve, C. (1948). *J. Biol. Chem.* **175,** 663–674.

Sutherland, E. W., and Rall, T. W. (1960). *Pharmacol. Revs.* **12,** 265–299.

Sutherland, E. W., Cori, C. F., Haynes, R., and Olsen, N. S. (1949). *J. Biol. Chem.* **180,** 825–837.

Thomas, T. B. (1942). *Anat. Record* **82,** 327–347.

Tyberghein, J. (1952). *Arch. intern. physiol.* **60,** 113–115.

Tyberghein, J. (1953). *Arch. intern. physiol.* **61,** 104–107.

Tyberghein, J., and Williams, R. H. (1958). *Metabolism, Clin. and Exptl.* **7,** 635–645.

Unger, R. H., Eisentraut, A. M., McCall, M. S., Keller, S., Lanz, H. C., and Madison, L. L. (1959). *Proc. Soc. Exptl. Biol. Med.* **102,** 621–623.

Van Campenhout, E., and Cornelis, G. (1953). *Compt. rend. assoc. anat. (Paris)* **40,** 462–466.

Van Itallie, T. B., Felber, J. P., Hoet, J., and Renold, A. E. (1959). *Diabetes* **8,** 112–115.

Vaughan, M. (1960a). *Federation Proc.* **19,** 224.

Vaughan, M. (1960b). *J. Biol. Chem.* **235,** 3049–3052.

Verne, J. (1957). *In* "Diabète sucré, Diabète insipide, Régulation électrolytique" (Publication des Annales d'Endocrinologie), pp. 281–298. Masson, Paris.

Volk, B. W., and Lazarus, S. S. (1960). *Diabetes* **9,** 53–62.

von Holt, C. (1955). *Z. Vitamin- Hormon- u. Fermentforsch.* **7,** 138–152.

Vuylsteke, C. A., and de Duve, C. (1953). *Arch. intern. physiol.* **61,** 273–274.

Vuylsteke, C. A., and de Duve, C. (1957). *Arch. intern. pharmacodynamie* **111,** 437–469.

Wurster, D. H., and Miller, M. R. (1960). *Comp. Biochem. Physiol.* **1,** 101–109.

~12~

Comparative Biochemistry of Adenohypophyseal Hormones

CHOH HAO LI

Hormone Research Laboratory, University of California, Berkeley, California

I. INTRODUCTION

The adenohypophyseal hormones are either proteins or peptides. Only very recently the complete or partial structures of various of these hormones from different animal species have become known, and one of them has even been synthesized. Accompanying these advances, information about the relationship of chemical structure to biological activity in connection with these hormones has also gradually been accumulated, and from this information, it has become increasingly evident that a pure hormone can exhibit more than one hormonal activity. Indeed, it is rare for a hormone molecule to possess only one kind of biological action. Conversely, protein or peptide hormones may take the form of more than one chemical species, and a hormone may exercise a specific activity that is characteristic of another hormone with a different composition and structure; thus, it is not surprising that there is some overlapping of biological activities among pituitary hormones. This phenomenon of overlapping may be partly explained by the occurrence of common structures in these hormones, and it furnishes an example of how biological observations can give new insight into the structural problems encountered fn protein chemistry. In this chapter, certain aspects of recent developments in the comparative biochemistry of anterior pituitary hormones[1] are reviewed.

II. INTERSTITIAL CELL-STIMULATING HORMONE

Early investigations culminating in the purification and characterization of hypophyseal ICSH yielded highly active purified products from sheep and pig pituitary glands (Li, 1949). Two chromatographically distinct fractions, designated α- and β-ICSH, were recently detected and one of these, β-ICSH, was obtained in a state of high molecular homogeneity as shown by column chromatography, zone electrophoresis on starch, and sedimentation velocity analysis (Squire and Li, 1959; Ward et al., 1959). The molecular weight of β-ICSH calculated from sedimentation velocity and diffusion measurements is approximately 30,000 and the isoelectric point is between 7.0 and 7.5 when mono-monovalent buffers are used. Bioassays designed to detect contamination of known pituitary hormones showed that preparations of β-ICSH contained less than 0.1% of these impurities.

Attempts to purify ICSH from the human pituitary have been seriously hampered by the difficulty of obtaining human glands in quantity; however, certain side fractions obtained during the purification of human pituitary growth hormone serve as suitable starting materials for the purification of ICSH (and FSH, see Section III) (Li et al., 1960c; Steelman et al., 1959). The fractionation procedure is based upon fractional precipitation with ammonium sulfate, chromatography on IRC–50 resin in 0.45 M ammonium sulfate, chromatography on the same resin in a 0.2 M phosphate buffer, and zone electrophoresis on cellulose columns. Even though the products obtained are by no means pure by physical, chemical, or biological criteria, marked physicochemical and biological differences between human and ovine ICSH are apparent (Li et al., 1960c). The critical pH value above which the ICSH activity is no longer adsorbed onto IRC–50 resin from 0.2 M phosphate buffers is located at pH 5.6 for human ICSH and 6.2 for the ovine hormone. Moreover, bioassays indicate that human ICSH has a biological behavior different from the ovine hormone.

---

[1] Throughout this paper the following abbreviations are used: ACTH, adrenocorticotropin; TSH, thyrotropic hormone; FSH, follicle-stimulating hormone; ICSH, interstitial cell-stimulating hormone; MSH, melanocyte-stimulating hormone or melanotropin.

III. FOLLICLE-STIMULATING HORMONE

The purification of ovine FSH on a large scale has been outlined by Ellis (1958). In addition, the purification of ovine FSH on diethylamino-ethyl-cellulose (DEAE-cellulose) after ammonium sulfate fractionation has been described (Woods and Simpson, 1960); the product showed a high specific FSH potency, and very low ICSH activity. Studies of the electrophoretic behavior of sheep pituitary FSH on starch (Raacke et al., 1958) revealed the presence of an inert protein contaminant with the same isoelectric point (pH 4.5) as the FSH, but with a different mobility at higher pH values. A ten-fold purification of the FSH could be achieved by zone electrophoresis on starch in a borate buffer of pH 7.9.

The purification of FSH from porcine glands has also been described (Steelman et al., 1956); it was claimed that the preparation was homogeneous as shown by ultracentrifugation and also according to the results of paper electrophoresis. The molecular weight of porcine FSH was reported to be 29,000. A partial purification of this hormone from human pituitaries by methods similar to those used for human ICSH, including chromatography on DEAE-cellulose, has been reported (Li et al., 1960c; Steelman et al., 1959).

The presence of a carbohydrate moiety in ICSH and FSH (Li, 1949) has been abundantly confirmed by recent investigations of preparations obtained by the newer procedures (Ward et al., 1959; Gröschel and Li, 1960), and the content of hexose, fucose, hexosamine and sialic acid in highly purified preparations of human and sheep pituitary ICSH and FSH has recently been determined (Gröschel and Li, 1960). Gottschalk et al. (1960) demonstrated that the enzymic release of sialic acid by a highly purified receptor-destroying enzyme (neuraminidase) resulted in the complete inactivation of a sample of purified sheep FSH; considerations of the enzyme's specificity led these investigators to conclude also that the sialic acid residues are terminal, are linked α-ketosidically to their partner, and are accessible to the enzyme.

The action of periodate on ICSH and FSH has been found to result in markedly diminished biological activity (Geschwind and Li, 1958); this treatment causes oxidative destruction of the carbohydrate moiety as well as of any NH_2-terminal hydroxyamino acids that may be present. It is of interest, however, that 5–10% of the gonadotropic activity is retained after this treatment with periodate even when the periodate concentration is increased or the reaction is prolonged; this suggests that a residual inherent activity remains after the removal of the carbohydrate residues by oxidation with periodate.

IV. LACTOGENIC HORMONE

Until recently all the published methods for the isolation of lactogenic hormone (Li, 1957a; White, 1949) involved fractional precipitation which always had necessitated submitting the main fraction to the procedure several times in order to obtain a highly purified active preparation. A procedure of this kind is both tedious and time-consuming. In the course of purity studies involving countercurrent distribution of the hormone a simplified and convenient isolation procedure was developed whereby a yield of approximately 2 gm of lactogenic hormone could be obtained from 1 kg of whole sheep pituitaries (Cole and Li, 1955). When the hormone isolated by this procedure was assayed in one-month-old pigeons it was found to possess a crop-sac stimulating potency of approximately 35 international units per mg. Luteotropic activity was also detected by the deciduoma test in hypophysectomized–oophorectomized rats. All the studies discussed in this section were performed with this ovine hormone, except in those instances where special mention of the bovine hormone is made.

The published results concerning the molecular weight of prolactin are not in complete agreement (Li, 1957a; White, 1949). By various methods of determination values between 22,000 and 32,000 have been obtained. Recent molecular kinetic investigations (Li *et al.*, 1957) showed the molecular weight of the hormone to be 24,200.

Identification of threonine as the sole NH$_2$-terminal residue of prolactin (Cole *et al.*, 1957) was definitively confirmed by stepwise degradation of the hormone by the phenylisothiocyanate procedure, which also revealed the N-terminal amino acid sequence, Thr.Pro.Val.Thr.Pro. From these results, it might have been expected that the COOH-terminus, like the NH$_2$-terminus, would also consist of a single amino acid residue. However, when intensive studies gave no sign of the presence of any COOH-terminal residue, it was concluded that either prolactin did not possess a COOH-terminal residue at all, or that the residue was not identifiable by either of the two procedures used, namely, digestion with carboxypeptidase and hydrazinolysis. But after lactogenic hormone had been oxidized by treatment with performic acid, it was concluded, on the basis of the reaction of the oxidized product with carboxypeptidase and hydrazine, that cysteic acid was the sole COOH-terminal residue of the oxidized molecule (Li, 1957b).

The nature of the COOH-terminus was further investigated by subjecting the hormone protein to reduction with mercaptoethanol and performing C-terminal residue analyses of the reduced product (Li and Cummins, 1958) by means of the carboxypeptidase procedure. From these studies, the C-terminal sequence Tyr.Leu.Asp(NH$_2$)CyS—CH$_2$CONH$_2$ was postulated for the reduced, alkylated hormone. Therefore, it was finally concluded that the prolactin molecule consists of a single peptide chain with the sequence Thr.Pro.Val.Thr.Pro. at the NH$_2$-terminus and with an interchain disulfide loop at the COOH-terminus.

Table I summarizes the known physical and chemical properties of lactogenic hormone from beef and sheep pituitary glands. The tyrosine content is definitely higher for the bovine hormone than for the ovine. Both hormones have a molecular weight of approximately 26,000 and an isoelectric point at pH 5.73, and they both consist of a single peptide chain with threonine as the NH$_2$-terminal amino acid. The hormones from both species are structurally similar and have identical biological activity.

One of the unusual chemical properties of prolactin is the stability of its biological activity at high temperatures. It has been demonstrated that a 1% solution of the hormone at pH 7.6 can be kept at 100°C for 20 minutes with no loss of potency. Other investigators have reported that the hormone is more stable toward heat in acid than it is in alkaline solutions (Li, 1957a; White, 1949). In the presence of urea, the relative viscosity of the hormone solution is greatly increased; when the urea is removed by dialysis, the viscosity returns to that of the untreated hormone, and no loss of biological activity is found to have been incurred (Li, 1957a). Despite this unusual stability, some modification of the hormone protein, resulting in decreased activity, may be produced by certain specific reagents.

TABLE I

SOME PHYSICAL AND CHEMICAL CHARACTERISTICS OF PROLACTIN
FROM SHEEP AND BEEF PITUITARY GLANDS

Physicochemical characteristics	Sheep	Beef
Molecular weight	24,200	(26,000)
Isoelectric point, pH	5.73	5.73
Specific optical rotation, $[\alpha]_{D}^{25°}$	−40.5°	−40.5°
Partition coefficient^a	1.58	2.07
Tyrosine, % (by weight)	5.3	6.6
Tryptophan, % (by weight)	1.7	—
Cystine, % (by weight)	3.0	—
NH$_2$-terminal threonine (mole/mole)	1	1
COOH-terminal residue after performic acid oxidation	Cysteic acid	Cysteic acid

^{a} Solvent system, 2-butanol/0.4% aqueous dichloroacetic acid.

Earlier studies (Li, 1957a; White, 1949) showed that iodination, esterification, and acetylation of the hormone caused a loss of biological activity. Recently, it was noted that reaction of prolactin with *o*-methylisourea did not alter the hormonal potency even though all the lysine residues were converted to homoarginine (Geschwind and Li, 1957). End-group analysis of the hormone after this treatment revealed that the N-terminal threonine was unmodified; furthermore, no evidence of the presence of any guanidino compounds other than arginine and homoarginine was revealed by paper chromatography of the acid hydrolyzate of the guanidinated hormone. Even though complete conversion of the ε-amino groups to guanidino groups had been effected, the biological activity remained unimpaired. On the other hand, acetylation of the amino groups in the hormone protein with acetic anhydride as well as with ketene causes a marked loss of activity (Li, 1957a; White, 1949) although no inactivation has been found to result from acetylation of the guanidinated hormone. The results of these investigations indicate that the α-amino groups apparently are not essential for the biological activity of prolactin (Geschwind and Li, 1957). What is necessary for maintenance of the activity is conservation of the positive charge on the lysine residues, regardless of whether this charge is due to the presence of ε-amino or of guanidino groups.

V. GROWTH HORMONE (Somatotropin)

There are now growth hormone preparations from the pituitary glands of six different species, namely, ox, sheep, whale, pig, monkey, and man (Li *et al.*, 1945; Wilhelmi *et al.*, 1948; Li, 1958) that can be obtained in a high degree of purity for physicochemical characterization. The homogeneity of these preparations has been established by their behavior in the ultracentrifuge and by electrophoresis and chromatography, as well as by NH_2-terminal group analysis. In a few cases, purity on the basis of immunological behavior has also been established. Some physical and chemical data for the six pituitary growth hormones are summarized in Table II.

Although amino acid analysis has disclosed differences in chemical composition among the six somatotropins, they have an identical amino acid (phenylalanine) at both the COOH- and NH_2-termini. The bovine and ovine hormones, however, have two NH_2-terminal residues whereas the other four somatotropins possess only one. Further investigations on the sequences adjacent to the two termini have revealed additional differences among these hormones. The known NH_2-terminal sequences for the somatotropins from the various species are as follows: bovine somatotropin, alanyl-phenylalanyl-alanyl . . . and phenylalanyl-threonyl-alanyl

TABLE II

SOME PHYSICOCHEMICAL PROPERTIES OF PITUITARY GROWTH HORMONE
FROM VARIOUS SPECIES

Physicochemical characteristics	Ox	Sheep	Pig	Whale (Humpback)	Monkey (*Macacus*)	Man
Sedimentation[a] coefficient, $s_{20,w}$	3.19	2.76	3.02	2.84	1.88	2.18
Molecular weight	45,000	48,000	42,000	39,000	25,000	29,000
Isoelectric point, pH	6.85	6.8	6.3	6.2	5.5	4.9
Cystine[b]	4	5	3	3	4	3
Tyrosine[b]	12	13	13	12	10	9
Tryptophan[b]	3	3	3	3	1	1
NH$_2$-terminal residue	Phe, Ala[c]	Phe, Ala	Phe	Phe	Phe	Phe
COOH-terminal residue	Phe	Phe	Phe	Phe	Phe	Phe

[a] $s_{20,w}$ (in S) determined in pH 9.9 borate buffer.

[b] As residues per mole.

[c] Phe, phenylalanine; Ala, alanine.

. . ., and human, phenylalanyl-prolyl-threonyl . . . At the COOH-terminus, the respective sequences are: bovine somatotropin, . . . leucyl-alanyl-phenylalanyl-phenylalanine; ovine, . . . alanyl-leucyl-phenylalanine; cetacean, . . . leucyl-alanyl-phenylalanine; simian, . . . alanyl-glycyl-phenylalanine, and human, . . . leucyl-phenylalanine. It is evident that even the protein hormones isolated from species as closely related as man and monkey are not identical.

It is now well established by immunological investigations that bovine and human growth hormones induce production of antibodies that are specific to the species (Hayashida and Li, 1958; Li *et al.*, 1960b). In the case of the primate hormones, it has been shown that antibodies to human somatotropin cross react almost completely with the simian hormone but give no reaction with the bovine, ovine, porcine, or cetacean hormones. In similar studies with rabbit antiserum to bovine somatotropin, it was observed that the bovine and ovine somatotropins appear to be closely related antigenically, whereas bovine somatotropin and the primate hormones behave very differently from one another in this respect. These observations of species specificity as manifested by immunological reactions were further supported when it was demonstrated that antibodies to bovine somatotropin can completely neutralize the biological activity of bovine somatotropin but not that of the human hormone. Moreover, it was observed from results of the Ouchterlony double-diffusion test in agar gel that, of the growth hormones obtained from pituitary extracts of the rat, guinea pig, horse, cat, deer, rabbit, fish (cod), bullfrog (*Rana catesbeiana*), woodchuck (*Marmata monax*), camel (*Camelus bactrianus*), ant-eater (*Myrmecophaga jubata*), chicken, lizard (*Anolis carolinensis*), and sea lion (*Zalophus californianus*), only that of the deer contains a component which cross reacts completely with bovine growth hormone (Moudgal and Li, 1961a).

It is of considerable interest with respect to biological specificity that growth is elicited in the rat by injection of pituitary somatotropin from practically all the species studied so far, including ox, sheep, whale, pig, monkey, and man, the only exception being the hormone from fish glands. In view of the fact that there are marked differences among these various growth hormones in chemical structure and physicochemical characteristics, it is remarkable that the rat is capable of such a wide response. On the other hand, although it has been demonstrated that man can respond to the growth-promoting activity in primate somatotropins, practically all attempts so far to obtain a response in man with the bovine hormone have failed. The question has been raised whether a common biologically active core (Li, 1957c) or nucleus (Russell and Wilhelmi, 1958) might possibly exist in the somatotropin molecules derived from various species, and further, whether the explanation for the rat's almost universal responsiveness might not be that this animal possesses the necessary enzyme system to utilize the whole hormone protein from nonprimate sources, whereas man does not (Li, 1957c). In order to explore this hypothesis, it is necessary to establish with certainty the primary assumption that the complete integrity of the protein molecule is not needed for its biological action. This was found to be the case for bovine somatotropin (Li, 1956a), when the hormone was partially hydrolyzed with chymotrypsin, trypsin, and carboxypeptidase. Similar studies with ovine, porcine, cetacean simian, and human somatotropins have also shown that limited digestion of the hormone with chymotrypsin does not cause loss of growth-promoting potency (Li, 1958, 1957c). Indeed, a fraction (alpha core) prepared from a chymotryptic digest of bovine somatotropin (Li *et al.*, 1959a) in preliminary studies was shown to produce nitrogen retention in human subjects (Forsham *et al.*, 1958). It should be pointed out that these observations are not sufficient to verify with finality the assumption that the same active core occurs in various somatotropins, but they do encourage further investigation along the lines of the "common core" hypothesis.

VI. ADRENOCORTICOTROPIC HORMONE

Polypeptides possessing ACTH activity have been isolated in a highly
purified state from sheep (Li *et al.*, 1954), pig (Bell, 1954), beef (Li and
Dixon, 1956), and human (Lee *et al.*, 1959) pituitaries. Although all of
these ACTH preparations possess similar biological properties, there are
slight differences among them in amino acid composition and in chemical
structure. The ovine, porcine, and bovine adrenocorticotropins are single
chain polypeptides composed of 39 amino acids with a molecular weight of
approximately 4,500 and with serine and phenylalanine as NH_2- and
COOH-terminal residues respectively (Li *et al.*, 1955, 1958, 1961 and
Howard *et al.*, 1955).

The only difference in amino acid composition between the porcine and
ovine hormones appears to be that there is one more leucine in the former
and one more serine in the latter; this difference is manifested at positions
31 and 32 of the amino acid sequence, where alanine and serine appear in
the ovine hormone and leucine and alanine in the porcine. Although
there are no differences in amino acid composition between the ovine and
bovine hormones, a difference in amino acid sequence in a small portion of
the polypeptide chain appears, thus supporting the conclusion that sheep
and beef adrenocorticotropins are distinct chemical entities. Figure 1 summarizes the structural differences between these adrenocorticotropins.

From the structural data relating to these differences, it may be inferred that the removal of that portion of the COOH-terminal sequence

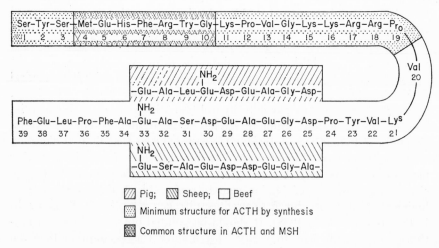

FIG. 1. A summary of structural differences among pig, sheep, and beef adrenocorticotropins.

which includes positions 25–39 does not impair the adrenal-stimulating activity. Indeed, it has recently been demonstrated that a synthetic non-adecapeptide (Li *et al.*, 1960a) with a structure identical to the first nineteen NH_2-terminal amino acid sequence, namely,

H-Ser-Tyr-Ser-Met-Glu-His-Phe-Arg-Try-Gly-
 1   2   3   4   5   6   7   8   9   10

Lys-Pro-Val-Gly-Lys-Lys-Arg-Arg-Pro-OH
 11 12 13 14 15 16 17 18 19

not only possesses adrenal-stimulating potency but also has other biological activities characteristic of the hormone in its natural state. When assayed on the basis of capacity to deplete adrenal ascorbic acid, the synthetic nonadecapeptide was found to have an ACTH potency of 74.2 USP units/mg if the injection was given subcutaneously, and a potency of 34.6 units/mg by the intravenous route. This synthetic peptide was also shown to possess MSH activity by both the *in vivo* and *in vitro* bioassay methods.

By the criterion of adrenal ascorbic acid depletion in hypophysectomized rats, the biological potency of ACTH peptides has been estimated to be in the range of 80–150 IU/mg (Li, 1956a). Forsham *et al.* (1955) have re-reported that when α_s-ACTH (the main component of sheep ACTH) was assayed in man, on the basis of steroidogenesis elicited by intravenous injections, an activity equivalent to 150 IU/mg of the peptide was obtained. The adrenocorticotropic activity of α_p-ACTH (the main component of porcine ACTH) as determined by the *in vitro* corticoidogenesis assay procedure was found to be 95 USP units/mg (Guillemin, 1960).

It is now well known that ACTH possesses melanocyte-stimulating (MSH) activity although the MSH potency of this hormone is only a fraction of that possessed by highly purified MSH preparations. Since the synthetic nonadecapeptide (Li *et al.*, 1960a) has both ACTH and MSH activities, there now can be no doubt that the melanocyte-stimulating activity of ACTH is an intrinsic property of the hormone.

The effect of ACTH in darkening frog skin *in vitro* is clearly an extra-adrenal property of the hormone. Moreover, this is not the sole extra-adrenal effect of ACTH. Lipolytic activity exerted by adrenocorticotropin on rat adipose tissue *in vitro* (Lopez *et al.*, 1959) and the *in vitro* release of nonesterified fatty acids from adipose tissues of adrenalectomized rats under the stimulation of ACTH (Schotz *et al.*, 1959) provide additional evidence that ACTH is biologically active in the absence of the adrenal glands. This stresses a misconception that has been prevalent arising from the name originally coined for the major biological activity of the hormone, i.e., adrenocorticotropic hormone. It had been assumed for a long time that any ACTH preparation which can elicit a biological response in adrenalectomized animals is contaminated with some active component or components other than the ACTH itself. A similar confusion arising from terminology has recently been discussed in connection with pituitary growth hormone (Li, 1956b).

One of the most fruitful ways to investigate the relationship between the structure of proteins or polypeptides and their biological behavior is to study the effect of alteration of the hormone molecule by means of substitution reactions with specific reagents or, in other words, the chemical modification of a certain functional group or groups in the molecule by means of reaction with a certain agent. The adrenocorticotropins furnish the ideal molecule for this type of study since they have the form of a random coil with no secondary or tertiary structures (Li, 1956a; Léonis and Li, 1959) to complicate the interpretation of results. In one such study on the effect of guanidination on the adrenocorticotropic molecule, it was found that under none of the conditions employed could this protein hormone be completely guanidinated, since only three of the four lysine residues present in the hormone were converted to homoarginine (Geschwind and Li, 1957). Albeit incomplete, guanidination of ACTH produced a derivative whose biological activity was similar to that of the control preparation. As with most of the other pituitary hormones, acetylation of adrenocorticotropin resulted in complete loss of activity. However, unlike the results obtained with other hormones, acetylation of the guanidinated derivative of ACTH also resulted in complete loss of activity. These results are consonant with the findings that the N-terminal serine of the hormone is necessary for biological activity (Li, 1956a).

Another such investigation dealt with the effect of acid methanol esterification of the free carboxyl groups in α_b-ACTH (the main component of bovine ACTH) (Li, 1960). It was found that esterification of adrenocorticotropin does not reduce its melanophore-stimulating activity but does diminish its adrenocorticotropic potency. This means that the free carboxyl groups in adrenocorticotropin are essential for its ACTH activity but are not implicated in its intrinsic melanocyte-stimulating effect. These observations make it quite clear that the structural requirements for these two biological activities in ACTH peptides are different.

VII. THYROTROPIC HORMONE

The biochemistry of TSH has recently been reviewed by several investigators (Sonenberg, 1958; Pierce et al., 1960; Bates and Condliffe, 1960). Thyrotropin has been detected in the pituitaries of the frog, sole, rat, mouse, dog, pig, sheep, toad, beef, turkey, man, horse, rabbit, guinea pig, cat, pigeon, and chick (Adams, 1946). Beef glands mainly have been used in purification studies.

Earlier work (Ciereszko, 1945) with organic solvent and isoelectric precipitation methods yielded a product with a potency of about 5 USP units/mg. After the observation of Heideman in 1953 that TSH could be purified by chromatography on Amberlite IRC-50, further purification studies on various ion exchangers have been carried out by Pierce et al. (1960) and by Bates and Condliffe (1960). Crude bovine TSH preparations have been subjected to chromatography on cellulose ion-exchangers such as DEAE-cellulose, and fractions have been obtained with potencies of 30–40 USP units/mg. The active material, however, emerges from the column as a complex peak, and in starch-gel electrophoresis a multitude of components are evident, many of which possess TSH activity. Indeed, at least six closely related components all possessing thyrotropic activity have been obtained (Pierce et al., 1960). It is not clear at present whether these six thyroid-stimulating components actually occur in the gland, whether they are artificially formed during the purification, or whether they represent six different inert proteins contaminated with equal amounts of TSH. Future investigations should answer this question.

Ultracentrifugation experiments as well as membrane electrodialysis carried out with these highly potent TSH preparations support the conclusion that the molecular weight of the hormone is in the range of 26,000–30,000 rather than 10,000 which was proposed by earlier workers for cruder preparations. Chemical analyses indicate that TSH contains the usual amino acid components with an unusually high content of cystine. Thyrotropin has long been thought to be a glycoprotein; carbohydrate analysis of the most potent fractions indicates the presence of glucosamine, galactosamine, mannose, and fucose. Sialic acid could not be detected.

With respect to species variation, Pierce et al. (1960) have reported that sheep concentrates exhibit the same chromatographic behavior on DEAE-cellulose columns as do the beef thyrotropins, with the biological activity appearing in the same fractions. This has also been found in the case of a thyrotropin preparation obtained from the humpback whale. The hormones from all three species were found by a membrane electrodialysis technique to be of approximately the same molecular weight. On the other hand, in studies on the TSH produced by transplantable tumors in mice, Bates and Condliffe (1960) have shown that the tumor-produced hormone differs chemically from purified bovine TSH, particularly in its behavior in starch-gel electrophoresis and in chromatography. These investigators also found that circulating TSH in plasma has different physicochemical properties from pituitary TSH.

440 CHOH HAO LI

VIII. CONCLUSIONS

During the past decade of progress in the biochemistry of the anterior pituitary hormones, the discovery which is perhaps the most intriguing in its implications is that the biological effects of several of these hormones are not always what they were at first supposed to be. For example, it was thought initially that ACTH acted only in the presence of the adrenals. The finding that ACTH has the capacity to exercise extra-adrenal functions has inspired speculations about hormonal activity in general. Along the same lines we could assume, for instance, that a highly purified TSH preparation might possibly be biologically active in the absence of the thyroid. This latter instance is, of course, no more than speculation but we now have to be aware of such a possibility. Since ACTH was found to have this quite unexpected intrinsic extra-adrenal activity, there is a chance that other peptide hormones of the adenohypophysis may behave in the same way.

The actual proof that this extra-endocrine stimulation by the "tropic" hormones is intrinsic can come only from synthesis, for there is always the possibility in naturally occurring hormones that they might contain very minute amounts of contaminating substances, amounts too small to be detected by chemical or biochemical means. For example, ACTH is now known to have intrinsic melanocyte-stimulating potency of the order of 0.1% of that of α-MSH, and it is certainly true that if this were a contamination, the amount would be so minute that it would be undetectable. Now, however, that the synthetic nonadecapeptide (Li et al., 1960a) with an amino acid sequence identical with that of the first 19 amino acids of native ACTH has been shown to possess MSH activity, it is established beyond doubt that this is an inherent property and not a contamination.

With respect to growth hormone, we are now convinced that human growth hormone in a highly purified state possesses crop-sac stimulating potency in pigeons, exercises a luteotropic effect in hypophysectomized rats, and a lactogenic effect in the rabbit and monkey.[2] In other words, it appears that human growth hormone can exert, as intrinsic properties, all the biological effects supposed to be exerted by animal lactogenic hormone. The human growth hormone does not possess these activities to the same degree as animal lactogenic hormone, only to the extent of 10% or less of the latter; nonetheless, no matter how we modify human growth hormone, it still has these activities side-by-side with the growth-promoting potency so long as the latter persists. If the growth-promoting activity is destroyed, the other activities are abolished also.

---

[2] Lyons and Li, unpublished observations.

It would thus appear that these are intrinsic properties of the human growth hormone molecule, although we cannot conclude with finality, despite all the criteria that we have applied thus far, that human growth hormone is pure. It was emphasized previously that final proof must be furnished by synthesis, but the problem is that synthesis of such a large molecule as growth hormone, with a molecular weight of 29,000, would be very difficult indeed, if not impossible, by the techniques known at the present time. Furthermore, we are ignorant of its primary structure, which must be known before synthesis can be attempted. What, under these circumstances, can the biochemist do, and how can he assure the biologist of the purity of the hormone? Without synthesis it is impossible to furnish the final unequivocal proof that the observed biological activities are not due to contaminants; yet, if one rejected the possibility that one were dealing with the pure hormone no progress could be made at all. The only possible course of action for the biochemist is to proceed as though the assumptions he makes about biological activity were correct, and to continue to establish proofs of the purity of the product in terms of physicochemical behavior, homogeneity, and other criteria, and to observe at every step whether the activities remain closely associated with the growth-promoting activity, as they do in the case of human growth hormone.

Another notable achievement during this decade has been the demonstration that the whole molecule is not essential for hormonal activity. Growth hormone preparations from various species have been found to retain their growth-promoting activity after hydrolysis with chymotrypsin; of the whole ACTH molecule consisting of 39 amino acid residues, as small a fragment as 19 amino acids has been found to be active. In view of these observations with growth hormone and ACTH, we might well infer that lactogenic hormone, TSH, or other adenohypophyseal hormones may not require the entire molecule for their biological activity.

Another interesting finding has been the observation of marked variation in structure among hormones from various species, which, although they all possess analogous biological activity, are chemically and immunochemically distinct. In the case of growth hormone, the primate preparations are very different from the non-primate preparations, and even their biological behavior has been found to differ in some respects, as attested by the results of long-term experiments with growth hormone in young hypophysectomized female rats. After 10 days of primate hormone administration growth reached a plateau, whereas with the bovine hormone the animals continued to gain weight (Li et al., 1959b). Furthermore, the growth hormone is a very potent antigen in the rat (Moudgal and Li, 1961a, b), whereas the bovine hormone cannot elicit antibodies in this species.

Indeed, the fact that the rat produces antibodies to the human hormone but not to the bovine brings up the very interesting question of the receptivity of various species to hormonal agents from the same or other species. One may take the case of lactogenic hormone isolated from ovine pituitaries. This preparation is luteotropic in the rat (Evans *et al.*, 1941) but not in the sheep itself (Duncan *et al.*, 1961). We do not actually know what this means. We can speculate, however, that somehow the rat is able to modify the sheep lactogenic hormone to a luteotropic agent, although the sheep itself cannot utilize it in this way, and that possibly this may mean that something in the environment of the corpus luteum in the sheep ovary is different from that in the rat ovary. This difference may involve the presence of a certain enzyme, or some aspect of cellular structure, or the participation of cofactors.

This kind of question emphasizes the importance of comparative investigations in connection with protein hormones. For the biochemist one of the chief values of comparative studies involving species differences is that such studies can lead to information about the active centers of peptide hormones. The finding that the first 24 amino acid residues of all ACTH preparations are identical in sequence and that any differences appear after this portion, carries the implication that the active core must lie within this common segment. Similarly, if we knew the complete structures of porcine and human growth hormone, these two might also be found to have a common core; if this were so and if the porcine core should prove to be active in man, this would be of tremendous clinical value. This type of comparative study can also be used to gain structural insight from the biochemical point of view. Assuming that there is a common core in preparations of a single hormone from various species, we may begin to ask certain questions such as, what makes molecules with a common central sequence behave so differently with respect to their biological potency in different animal hosts, and what is the biological role of the unessential portions of the molecule adjacent to the central core?

ADDENDUM

Since the writing of this chapter there have been new developments in all the fields discussed. They cannot be covered completely in anything short of a new chapter, but we wished to include in this addendum certain highlights of particular interest to the writer.

Recently, a human ICSH preparation with a higher biological potency than previous preparations and with a high degree of physiochemical and biological homogeneity was isolated [P. G. Squire, C. H. Li, and R. N.

Andersen, *Biochemistry* **1,** 412(1962)] by a procedure that included purification by chromatography on carboxymethylcellulose and column zone
electrophoresis. The yield of this highly purified product from the starting
material is very low: 1 mg from 10 gm of lyophilized glands or approximately 100 fresh pituitaries. It is of interest to note the differences between
the human ICSH and the ovine hormone. The molecular weights, as determined by sedimentation equilibrium, are identical, 25,000 for both, and
the sedimentation coefficients are virtually identical (2.70 S for the ovine
hormone and 2.71 S for the human). The isoelectric points, on the other
hand, differ markedly, with that of the human hormone at pH 5.4, as
compared with 7.3 for the ovine. This difference in isoelectric point was
predictible from the chromatographic behavior of the two hormones on
IRC-50 resin, when it was observed that the "leak point," or the critical
pH above which the biological activity is no longer absorbed by the resin
from a 0.2 *M* phosphate buffer, was 5.6 for the human ICSH and 6.2 for
the ovine hormone. The specific activity of human ICSH, as determined
on the basis of the ventral prostate test, is about 5 times greater than that
of the ovine ICSH.

After the synthesis of a nonadecapeptide ACTH was first published by
Li *et al.* (1960a), investigators from two other laboratories have reported
the synthesis of ACTH analogs with chain lengths of 19, 24, 23, and 20
residues [R. Schwyzer, W. Rittel, H. Kappeler, and B. Iselin, *Angew. Chem.*
23, 915 (1960); H. Kappeler and R. Schwyzer, *Helv. Chim. Acta* **44,** 1136
(1961); K. Hofmann, H. Yajima, T. Y. Liu, and S. Lande, *J. Am. Chem.
Soc.* **83,** 487 (1961); and K. Hofmann, T. Y. Liu, H. Yajima, N. Yanaihara,
C. Yanaihara, and J. L. Humes, *ibid.* **84,** 1054 (1962)]. Much can be learned
about the relationship of structure to activity by the varying proportions
in which the different activities occur in peptides of various lengths. The
nonadecapeptide reported by the California group has been shown to
have not only ACTH activity in a potency of about 50% of the native
ACTH, but also full MSH activity [C. H. Li, J. Meienhofer, E. Schnabel,
D. Chung, T. B. Lo, and J. Ramachandran, *J. Am. Chem. Soc.* **83,** 4449
(1961)]; in addition, it has been demonstrated to be clinically active in
man [P. H. Forsham, V. C. Di Raimondo, E. G. Biglieri, and C. H. Li,
Metabolism, Clin. and Exptl. **10,** 335 (1961)], with a potency of approximately 80% of the naturally occurring product. To date no detailed data
on biological activities have been published by either Schwyzer *et al.* or
Hofmann *et al.* Very recently, the synthesis of a heptadecapeptide consisting of the first 17 amino acid residues of ACTH was reported [C. H. Li,
D. Chung, J. Ramachandran, and B. Gorup, *J. Am. Chem. Soc.* **84,** 2460
(1962)]. This synthetic peptide has potency as assayed *in vitro* on the rat
adrenal, and is also active in steroidogenesis when injected intravenously

in man. Its ACTH potency is 6 U.S.P. units/mg, its MSH potency is identical with that of the native hormone, and it is as fully active as natural ACTH as a lipolytic agent.

Since the first report of the isolation and partial characterization of human growth hormone (HGH) [C. H. Li and H. Papkoff, *Science* **124,** 1293 (1956); C. H. Li (1957c)], other methods for the purification of HGH have been described [including reports by M. S. Raben, *Science* **125,** 883 (1957); A. E. Wilhelmi, *Canad. J. Biochem. and Physiol.* **39,** 1659 (1961); A. L. C. Wallace and K. A. J. Ferguson, *Endocrinology* **23,** 285 (1961)]. A modified isolation procedure has recently been developed in this laboratory [C. H. Li, W.-K. Liu, and J. S. Dixon, *Arch. Biochem. Biophys.*, Suppl. 1, 327 (1962)], a procedure which provides a consistently homogeneous product suitable for structural investigations of the human hormone. The NH_2-terminal amino acid sequence has been investigated and shown to be Phe.Pro.Thr.Leu.Asp.Leu. An amino acid analysis by chromatography on resin columns has also been carried out [J. S. Dixon and C. H. Li, *J. Gen. Physiol.* **45,** 176 (1962)]. On the basis of 29,000 for the molecular weight, the empirical formula of the hormone was obtained: $Lys_{13}His_5Arg_{14}Asp_{27}Thr_{14}Ser_{23}Glu_{34}Pro_{12}Gly_{13}Ala_{12}$ - $(Cys)_6Val_{12}Met_4Ileu_{10}Leu_{31}Tyr_{10}Phe_{15}Try_1$. Peptic digestion of HGH [C. H. Li, *J. Gen. Physiol.* **45,** 169 (1962)] to an extent of 40% did not diminish the biological activities of the hormone. It is of especial interest that the crop-sac stimulating activity of HGH responded in an identical fashion to the enzymic treatment as did the growth-promoting activity. More extensive peptic digestion caused a total loss of both activities.

References

Adams, A. E. (1946). *Quart. Rev. Biol.* **21,** 1–32.

Bates, R. W., and Condliffe, P. G. (1960). *Recent Progr. in Hormone Research* **16,** 309–352.

Bell, P. H. (1954). *J. Am. Chem. Soc.* **76,** 5565–5567.

Ciereszko, L. S. (1945). *J. Biol. Chem.* **160,** 585–592.

Cole, R. D., and Li, C. H. (1955). *J. Biol. Chem.* **213,** 197–201.

Cole, R. D., Geschwind, I. I., and Li, C. H. (1957). *J. Biol. Chem.* **224,** 399–405.

Duncan, G. W., Bowerman, A. M., Anderson, L. L., Hearn, W. R., and Melampy, R. M. (1961). *Endocrinology* **68,** 199–207.

Ellis, S. (1958). *J. Biol. Chem.* **233,** 63–68.

Evans, H. M., Simpson, M. E., and Lyons, W. R. (1941). *Proc. Soc. Exptl. Biol. Med.* **46,** 586–590.

Forsham, P. H., Di Raimondo, V., Island, D., Rinfret, A. P., and Orr, R. H. (1955). *CIBA Foundation Colloq. on Endocrinol.* **8,** 279–308.

Forsham, P. H., Li, C. H., Di Raimondo, V., Kolb, F. O., Mitchell, D., and Newman, S. (1958). *Metabolism, Clin. and Exptl.* **7**, 762–764.

Geschwind, I. I., and Li, C. H. (1957). *Biochim. et Biophys. Acta* **25**, 171–178.

Geschwind, I. I., and Li, C. H. (1958). *Endocrinology* **63**, 449–459.

Gottschalk, A., Chittin, W. K., and Graham, E. R. B. (1960). *Biochim. et Biophys. Acta* **38**, 183–184.

Gröschel, U., and Li, C. H. (1960). *Biochim. et Biophys. Acta* **37**, 375–376.

Guillemin, R. (1960). *Endocrinology* **66**, 819–823.

Hayashida, T., and Li, C. H. (1958). *Science* **128**, 1276–1277.

Heideman, M. L. (1953). *Endocrinology* **53**, 640–652.

Howard, K. S., Shepherd, R. G., Eigner, E. A., Davis, D. S., and Bell, P. H. (1955). *J. Am. Chem. Soc.* **77**, 3419–3420.

Lee, T. H., Lerner, A. B., and Buettner-Janusch, V. (1959). *J. Am. Chem. Soc.* **81**, 6084.

Léonis, J., and Li, C. H. (1959). *J. Am. Chem. Soc.* **61**, 415–419.

Li, C. H. (1949). *Vitamins and Hormones* **7**, 223-252.

Li, C. H. (1956a). *Advances in Protein Chem.* **11**, 101–190.

Li, C. H. (1956b). *Science* **123**, 617–619.

Li, C. H. (1957a). *Advances in Protein Chem.* **12**, 269–317.

Li, C. H. (1957b). *J. Biol. Chem.* **229**, 157–163.

Li, C. H. (1957c). *Federation Proc.* **16**, 775–783.

Li, C. H. (1958). *Symposium on Protein Structure, Paris* **1957** pp. 302–329.

Li, C. H. (1960). *J. Biol. Chem.* **235**, 1383–1385.

Li, C. H., and Cummins, J. T. (1958). *J. Biol. Chem.* **233**, 73–76.

Li, C. H., and Dixon, J. S. (1956). *Science* **124**, 934.

Li, C. H., Evans, H. M., and Simpson, M. E. (1945). *J. Biol. Chem.* **159**, 353–366.

Li, C. H., Geschwind, I. I., Levy, A. L., Harris, J. I., Dixon, J. S., Pon, N. G., and Porath, J. O. (1954). *Nature* **173**, 251–253.

Li, C. H., Geschwind, I. I., Cole, R. D., Raacke, I. D., Harris, J. I., and Dixon, J. S. (1955). *Nature* **176**, 687–689.

Li, C. H., Cole, R. D., and Coval, M. J. (1957). *J. Biol. Chem.* **229**, 153–156.

Li, C. H., Dixon, J. S., and Chung, D. (1958). *J. Am. Chem. Soc.* **80**, 2587.

Li, C. H., Papkoff, H., and Hayashida, T. (1959a). *Arch. Biochem. Biophys.* **85**, 97–102.

Li, C. H., Papkoff, H., and Jordan, C. W., Jr. (1959b). *Proc. Soc. Exptl. Biol. Med.* **100**, 44–45.

Li, C. H., Meienhofer, J., Schnabel, E., Chung, D., Lo, T. B., and Ramachandran, J. (1960a). *J. Am. Chem. Soc.* **82**, 5760–5761.

Li, C. H., Moudgal, N. R., and Papkoff, H. (1960b). *J. Biol. Chem.* **235**, 1038–1042.

Li, C. H., Squire, P. G., and Gröschel, U. (1960c). *Arch. Biochem. Biophys.* **86**, 110–116.

Li, C. H., Dixon, J. S., and Chung, D. (1961). *Biochim. et Biophys. Acta* **46**, 324–334.

Lopez, E., White, J. E., and Engel, F. L. (1959). *J. Biol. Chem.* **234**, 2254–2258.

Moudgal, N. R., and Li, C. H. (1961a). *Arch. Biochem. Biophys.* **93**, 122–127.

Moudgal, N. R., and Li, C. H. (1961b). *Endocrinology* **68**, 704–709.

Pierce, J. G., Carsten, M. E., and Wynston, L. K. (1960). *Ann. N. Y. Acad. Sci.* **86,** 612–624.

Raacke, I. D., Lostroh, A. J., and Li, C. H. (1958). *Arch. Biochem. Biophys.* **77,** 138–146.

Russell, J. A , and Wilhelmi, A. E. (1958). *Ann. Rev. Physiol.* **20,** 43–66.

Schotz, M. C., Masson, G. M. C., and Page, I. H. (1959). *Proc. Soc. Exptl. Biol. Med.* **101,** 159–161.

Sonenberg, M. (1958). *Vitamins and Hormones* **16,** 205–261.

Squire, P. G., and Li, C. H. (1959). *J. Biol. Chem.* **234,** 520–525.

Steelman, S. L., Kelly, T. L., Segaloff, H., and Weber, G. F. (1956). *Endocrinology* **59,** 256–257.

Steelman, S. L., Segaloff, A., and Andersen, R. N. (1959). *Proc. Soc. Exptl. Biol. Med.* **101,** 452–454.

Ward, D. N., McGregor, R., and Griffin, A. C. (1959). *Biochim. et Biophys. Acta* **32,** 305–314.

White, A. (1949). *Vitamins and Hormones* **7,** 253–292.

Wilhelmi, A. E., Fishman, J. B., and Russell, J. A. (1948). *J. Biol. Chem.* **176,** 737–744.

Woods, M. C., and Simpson, M. E. (1960). *Endocrinology* **66,** 575–584.

~13~

The Physiology of the Adenohypophyseal Hormones

E. KNOBIL AND R. SANDLER

Department of Physiology, The University of
Pittsburgh School of Medicine, Pittsburgh, Pennsylvania

I. INTRODUCTION

While all vertebrates share in the possession of a pituitary gland, its role in the regulation of the bodily economy among the members of this vast and diverse group is not always amenable to clear generalization. Yet functional homologies course broadly along the length of the vertebrate scale, although the main stream often escapes from full view in areas not adequately penetrated by the light of factual information.

As with physiology generally, the exploration of adenohypophyseal function has been most extensive in a few mammalian species which, as a result, have become the reference point for the comparative approach to the problem. This has, inevitably, led to some confusion in the interpretation of information gathered from forms whose modes of existence and reproduction bear little resemblance to the mammalian schema. Another unhappy consequence of the widely accepted use of the mammalian reference point, covert as it may be, has been the propagation of the impression, especially among the uninitiated, that the problems of mammalian pituitary physiology have been essentially solved except for some details of questionable biological importance. Unfortunately, such is not the case and, in the broad view, the nature, mode, and mechanism of action of the mammalian adenohypophyseal hormones are scarcely better understood than those of the lower vertebrates which have been subjected to more than casual study. Unfortunately, however, this brief survey does not permit a detailed and critical review of the enormous subject implied by its title and the discussions of mammalian adenohypophyseal physiology will be particularly slighted by cursory summarization. Whenever possible, comprehensive reviews will be cited for sources of the literature and for more extensive consideration of the topic at hand. Further, no attempt will be made to discuss the fascinating subject of the comparative anatomy of the adenohypophysis, the assignation of different functions to homologies of the gland in various vertebrate groups, or the cellular origins of the adenohypophyseal hormones.

II. THE REGULATION OF REPRODUCTIVE FUNCTION

A. Mammals

The current status of the role of the adenohypophyseal hormones in reproductive processes with especial reference to mammals has been expertly and extensively reviewed by Greep (1961) and by Simpson (1959). The rat has been most intensively investigated in this regard, largely because of the early development of a simple and reliable method for pituitary ablation in this species by Smith (1927), which, as a result, has been the source of a large body of information upon which most generalizations regarding this subject are based. Many of these are applicable to all mammalian forms studied to date, but some require modification as other species are examined.

Removal of the pituitary gland in sexually immature individuals of both sexes prevents subsequent maturation of the gonads and all its functions. The reproductive tract remains in the infantile state although other bodily functions may be returned to normal by appropriate replacement therapy. When the operation is performed in animals which have reached reproductive competence one finds, in the male, a reduction in the size of the testes and an atrophy of the accessory organs of reproduction quite comparable to that effected by castration. This indicates, drastic reduction, if not cessation, in the secretion of androgen by the interstitial cells of Leydig, which can be observed to be reduced in size and number and to exhibit other morphological manifestations of curtailed activity. Spermatogenesis essentially ceases, the seminiferous tubules decrease in diameter, and, in time, only spermatogonia and Sertoli cells remain in the epithelium lining the empty lumina.

In the female of reproductive age, hypophysectomy entrains homologous sequelae. The reproductive tract and mammary glands regress to a state approaching that engendered by ovariectomy because of the severe reduction in ovarian hormone secretion. Follicular maturation, ovulation, and corpus luteum formation are completely interrupted, follicular atresia occurs, the interstitial tissue undergoes regression, and the ovary decreases in size. The formation of immature follicles, some with small antra, is not curtailed by the operation, however, but these are incapable of further functional and structural development in the absence of the adenohypophysis (see Young, 1961).

1. THE GONADOTROPIC HORMONES

The implantation of pituitary tissue and the injection of relatively crude extracts of the gland into hypophysectomized animals will restore gonadal hormone secretion in varying degrees, depending upon the nature and dose of the extract given. In the male gametogenesis can be restored by such treatment, but orderly ovarian cyclic phenomena culminating in repeated ovulation and corpus luteum formation can be achieved but rarely by such indiscriminate therapy. Multiple ovulations and corpus luteum formation as isolated phenomena can, however, be produced with relative ease.

The isolation, preparation, and chemical characteristics of the active principles of the adenohypophysis which maintain gonadal function have been discussed in detail in the preceding chapter. They are two glycoprotein hormones which because of their preponderant physiological activities are referred to as the follicle stimulating hormone (FSH) and the luteinizing hormone (LH) or, synonymously, the interstitial cell stimulating hormone (ICSH).

In the female, FSH, as its name implies, appears to act on the Graafian follicle which has autonomously developed to the point of having several layers of granulosa cells enveloping the oocyte and in which small antra may be present. At this stage the follicle responds to FSH by the secretion of liquor folliculi, proliferation of the granulosa cells, and development of the thecal layers, resulting in a general enlargement of the structure. There is, at present, no general agreement concerning the action of FSH on estrogen secretion when it is administered alone to hypophysectomized animals. Greep and co-workers (1942) have reported that the administration of a highly purified porcine FSH preparation to hypophysectomized rats, while promoting follicular maturation to a point short of the preovulatory stage, will not stimulate estrogen secretion. Whether or not FSH alone can effect some estrogen secretion by the stimulated follicle, the consensus is that full maturation of the follicle and optimal estrogen secretion require the concerted action of both FSH and LH (see Hisaw, 1947).

Prolonged and excessive treatment of hypophysectomized animals with FSH preparations not totally devoid of LH activity leads to the production of cystic follicles in supernormal numbers, which, while extremely large on occasion, do not ovulate. In time these follicles become refractory to continued FSH administration and decrease in size. This has been demonstrated in a number of mammals including the primates (Knobil et al., 1959).

In the male, it is generally held that the sole action of FSH is on the germinal epithelium of the seminiferous tubules where it promotes full spermatogenesis. The studies of Woods and Simpson (1961), however, have adduced evidence which leads them to the conclusion that FSH alone will not restore spermatogenesis in hypophysectomized rats and that LH or ICSH is the major gametogenic gonadotropin in the male. In the hypophysectomized rhesus monkey, however, massive LH therapy which effected extensive Leydig cell stimulation with testosterone production had no significant effect on spermatogenesis (Knobil and Josimovich, 1961). FSH, on the other hand, has no demonstrable effect on testicular function other than gametogenesis as far as can be ascertained at present.

The administration of LH alone to hypophysectomized females has little influence beyond the repair of the ovarian interstitial cells. Hormone production is not initiated by this procedure. The more striking physiological effects of this hormone become evident only if the ovarian follicle has been under the prior influence of FSH. Under the synergistic action of these two hormones the follicle rapidly reaches full maturation, secretes maximal quantities of estrogen, and ovulation occurs followed by the formation of a corpus luteum. Observations of this kind have led to the assignment of ovulating and luteinizing activity to LH in the presence of optimal quantities of FSH which in itself does not possess these physiological properties.

More recently, however, Simpson and her colleagues (Carter et al., 1961) have demonstrated that FSH preparations minimally contaminated with LH activity can provoke ovulation in hypophysectomized rats and intact monkeys. Clearly, the exact hormonal conditions for ovulation in mammals remain to be determined.

In the male the principal action of LH is on the interstitial cells of Leydig, there promoting the secretion of androgen which secondarily stimulates the accessory organs of reproduction and may, under certain circumstances, play a role in spermatogenesis. As mentioned earlier, the role of LH in spermatogenesis in the rat is not settled and must await further investigation. At the moment, however, it may be concluded that the finely integrated synergistic action of FSH and LH requisite for the development of the ovarian follicle leading to estrogen secretion, ovulation, and corpus luteum formation does not appear to be necessary in the male, although the concerted action of both hormones for both testicular functions has not been ruled out and is in fact suggested by some experiments.

A third adenohypophyseal hormone usually grouped with the gonadotropins is prolactin or the luteotropic hormone (LTH). The role of this hormone in the growth of the mammary gland as well as the initiation of milk secretion has been the subject of several recent reviews to which the reader is referred for detailed discussions (Cowie and Folley, 1955; Meites, 1959; Cowie, 1961).

In intact animals with fully developed mammary glands, the administration of prolactin will initiate lactation. This action of the hormone is rather specific as far as can be determined and is demonstrable by local application in the vicinity of the alveoli. Prolactin of mammalian pituitary origin also initiates secretion of crop milk in pigeons (Riddle et al., 1932). More pertinent to the context of the present discussion, this hormone is required for luteal function in the rat. In its absence the corpus luteum, while seemingly normal by histological criteria, fails to secrete progesterone, a process which can be initiated by the administration of purified prolactin preparations. The luteotropic action of prolactin, however, is not clearly demonstrable in other mammals investigated in this regard and the pituitary factors responsible for the survival and normal function of the corpus luteum during the ovarian cycle remain to be elucidated. The availability of homospecific prolactin preparations may do much to solve these problems. The function of LTH in the male, if any, is completely unknown.

2. GONADAL-ADENOHYPOPHYSEAL RELATIONSHIPS AND CYCLIC GONADAL ACTIVITY

The widely documented and thoroughly confirmed observation that gonadal steroids generally inhibit the release of pituitary gonadotropins and, conversely, that their removal from the circulation stimulates gonadotropin secretion has given rise to the "negative feedback" concept of gonadal-adenohypophyseal interaction. Yet attempts to establish clear relationships between circulating levels of individual gonadal hormones and the secretion of any one gonadotropic hormone, thus providing a hormonal basis for the cyclic and orderly functioning of the adenohypophyseal-gonadal axes, have led to highly conflicting results and interpretations which have shed more obscurity than light onto the problem (see Greep, 1961). It is becoming increasingly evident that the action of the gonadal hormones on pituitary gonadotropic function is not a direct one, but rather serves to modulate the activity of centers in certain regions of the brain which ultimately determine the cyclic release of the gonadotropins. This subject is discussed in detail in another chapter in this volume. For that matter, the evidence of cyclic discharge of gonadotropins by the pituitary is mostly of an indirect nature and full clarification of this problem must await the availability of sensitive and specific assay methods which will permit their detection and quantitation in the body fluids.

It may be concluded that while a massive literature dealing with the role of the mammalian adenohypophyseal hormones involved in reproduction has been accumulated in the past decades, current understanding of their function, interactions, and secretion is, at best, fragmentary. Much work remains to be done before the seemingly enormous complexities involved are unravelled and the physiology of the gonadotropic hormones can be discussed in a more than tentative manner.

B. Birds

As in mammals, hypophysectomy in several avian genera (domestic animals such as the pigeon, chicken, and duck have been the most extensively studied) leads to a regression of the gonads accompanied by a cessation of gonadal hormone production, which in turn leads to an atrophy of the accessory organs of reproduction and secondary sexual characteristics. In laying hens, for example, Nalbandov (1959) reports a decrease of 99% in ovarian weight, of 97% in oviduct weight, and of 94% in comb area 40 days after hypophysectomy. Similar observations have been made on the genital tract of the male pigeon (Schooley et al., 1941) and in the cockerel (Baum and Meyer, 1956), as well as on the comb size of the growing male chick (Nalbandov and Card, 1943) following pituitary ablation.

Histologically, hypophysectomy in the white Leghorn male effects a decrease in tubular diameter while the tubular lumina become filled with lipid material, a phenomenon resembling a similar tubular lipid deposition in wild birds at the end of the breeding season (Coombs and Marshall, 1956). In the ovary of the laying hen, Nalbandov (1961) noted progressive atresia of follicles, which first became evident at 6 hours after hypophysectomy. The smallest follicles became atretic first, followed by the largest ones, whereas the medium-size follicles underwent atresia last; but by 24 hours nearly all follicles of measurable size were atretic.

1. THE GONADOTROPIC HORMONE COMPLEX OF THE AVIAN ADENO-HYPOPHYSIS

All available evidence strongly suggests that the avian pituitary gland secretes gonadotropic hormones functionally homologous to those in mammals (see Witschi, 1937; Nalbandov, 1953; Sturkie, 1954; Breneman, 1955; Fraps, 1961, for review). Thus, avian pituitary extracts contain FSH and LH activities, as assayed in mammals, as well as prolactin, the action of which on the pigeon crop sac has already been mentioned. While most studies dealing with the effects of avian gonadotropins in birds have been performed with relatively crude preparations, such as pituitary powder, it can be inferred from the information available that the primary function of LH is the stimulation of the interstitial cells in the male, while in the female it acts synergistically with FSH to produce maximal estrogen, androgen, and perhaps progesterone secretion, as well as stimulation of follicular development culminating in ovulation.

The administration of chicken pituitary powder to hypophysectomized cockerels elicited sustained testicular growth and androgen production (Nalbandov et al., 1951). In immature and mature hypophysectomized hens the same treatment stimulated ovarian and comb growth and follicular development resulting in ovaries closely resembling those of intact controls (Das and Nalbandov, 1955; Taber et al., 1958). Taber and coworkers (1958) made the interesting observation that the ovaries of pullets younger than 35 days are refractory to treatment with chicken gonadotropin, a situation reminiscent of the situation in very young rats (see Greep, 1961). Treatment of such animals with relatively purified mammalian gonadotropins was less effective than with the chicken pituitary preparations in that the response of the hypophysectomized male was not sustained and refractoriness was generally observed in the female; but where a response did occur, the resultant ovarian stimulation was not an orderly one and was characterized by hyperplastic cystic follicles (Nalbandov et al., 1951; Nalbandov and Card, 1946; Das and Nalbandov, 1955; Taber et al., 1958; Opel and Nalbandov, 1961). These results have been interpreted in terms of a qualitative difference between avian and mammalian gonadotropins, but other factors must also be considered before this conclusion can be drawn. These include immunological inactivation, the propriety of the ratio of mammalian FSH and LH administered, and the completeness of replacement, in that a full complement of pituitary hormones was given in one instance and purified fractions in another. It may also be recalled that the continued treatment of hypophysectomized female monkeys with crude monkey pituitary extract, while initially eliciting a massive ovarian response, leads in time to ovarian refractoriness with decreased estrogen secretion and reduction in ovarian size (Knobil et al., 1959), and that hypophysectomized hens may be induced to ovulate, under appropriate conditions, by the injection of mammalian LH (Opel and Nalbandov, 1961).

2. Pituitary-Gonadal Interrelationships

Extremely large seasonal variations in gonadal function associated with fluctuations in pituitary gonadotropin content, especially in the male, clearly indicate that the pituitary-gonadal axes are influenced in major fashion by external stimuli. These have been analyzed in detail by several groups of workers (see Marshall, 1955; Benoit, 1961, 1962) with the conclusion that environmental factors influence adenohypophyseal gonadotropic function via the central nervous system. During the sexually quiescent phase following the breeding season a massive regression in testicular size and function occurs, which can be attributed to a failure of gonadotropin secretion rather than to a refractoriness of the testes (Lofts and Marshall, 1958; Benoit, 1961, 1962). Similar observations have been made in the female, but in this instance a refractoriness at the level of the ovary is superimposed on a decreased release of gonadotropins from the pituitary (see Breneman, 1955; Benoit, 1961, 1962, for review).

Although cyclic release of gonadotropin in the absence of the testes has been unequivocally demonstrated in the weaver finch (Witschi, 1937), the influence of gonadal hormones, direct or indirect, on cyclic adenohypophyseal function under physiological conditions may be of importance, particularly with reference to ovulation.

3. OVULATION

The humoral and attendant mechanisms regulating ovulation in fowl have been thoughtfully reviewed and discussed by Benoit (1962), Nalbandov (1961), and Fraps (1961). As indicated above, a region of the central nervous system, perhaps the hypothalamus, appears to generate the signal for a consequent release of ovulating hormone (LH) from the adenohypophysis, which in turn impinges on a suitably developed follicle causing it to rupture and release the ovum. The analysis of the intricate neurohumoral integration mechanisms involved in this process is beyond the scope of this chapter but they are discussed elsewhere in this volume.

Nalbandov (1961) has made the unexpected observation that the follicles of hypophysectomized hens are more readily ovulated by exogenous LH administration than those of intact animals, and that the rate of ovulation increases as the interval from hypophysectomy to LH injection is lengthened. On the basis of these and other observations dealing with the normal follicular hierarchy in the fowl ovary, Nalbandov proposed the theory that predisposition to ovulation in response to the ovulating stimulus is the "nonsupport" of the follicle by the gonadotropic complex of the pituitary. He further proposed that an ovulating dose of LH may cause follicular rupture by engendering a local ischemia, which in turn leads to necrosis of the stigma.

The above postulate is based in turn on the hypothesis that the fowl pituitary usually secretes a "steady and unvarying stream" of gonadotropin which is distributed to all the follicles within the ovary. On this flow are superimposed peaks of additional LH secretion which trigger ovulation (Nalbandov, 1959). In the view of Nalbandov (1961) the largest follicles, those which have reached ovulatory size, can no longer be adequately maintained by the constant level of circulating gonadotropin and begin to undergo "physiological atresia," at which time they can respond to the ovulating stimulus of LH. The smaller follicles still receive adequate gonadotropic hormone support and hence do not respond to the ovulatory stimulus. This concept of the mechanism of ovulation at the level of the follicle, controversial as it may be, will do much to stimulate much needed work in this area.

The rhythmicity of egg laying in the hen, both in terms of individual ovulations and spacing of egg clutches, has received considerable attention. This involves nervous as well as humoral components. The former seems to be the major determinant of cyclic LH release and is modulated by such stimuli as the photoperiod. In addition, it is acted upon by signals from the oviduct. When an egg is present in the magnum or in the isthmus the secretion of ovulating hormone by the pituitary is inhibited. This inhibition, of undoubted neurogenic nature, is released when the egg leaves the oviduct, the circulating level of the ovulating gonadotropin rises once again, and a new follicle is ovulated (Nalbandov, 1961).

Progesterone appears to facilitate endogenous LH release and ovulation (Rothchild and Fraps, 1949). That this action of progesterone is on the hypothalamus rather than on the pituitary itself has been demonstrated by studies of Ralph and Fraps (1960). The physiological importance of progesterone in the excitation of central mechanisms, which lead to LH release by the pituitary and ovulation, is suggested by the finding that although the bird does not possess a corpus luteum, progesterone or substances with the same physiological activity are formed in the ovary of the hen and are secreted into the circulation (see Fraps, 1961). The gonadotropic stimulus for this progesterone secretion or its cyclic nature is, however, not established. Furthermore, the possibility that LH itself, released in response to a central stimulus, may act on the "ovulating center" and temporarily inhibit further ovulating signals to the pituitary, as has been suggested in the rabbit by Kawakami and Sawyer (1959), cannot be excluded.

4. PROLACTIN

In addition to its effect on the crop sac of the pigeon as demonstrated by Riddle and his colleagues (Riddle and Braucher, 1931; Riddle et al., 1932, 1933), prolactin induces broodiness or incubation behavior in a variety of birds. This effect is accompanied by a reduction in all phases of gonadal function (see Breneman, 1955). Whether the induction of incubation behavior by prolactin can be attributed to a direct action of the hormone on the central nervous system or whether it may be due to a reduction in the secretion of gonadal hormones is still unsettled. That the latter possibility may be a distinct one is suggested by the observation of Nalbandov (1945) that broody behavior induced in cocks by prolactin administration could be reversed by the administration of FSH and methyltestosterone, and by the experiments of Godfrey and Jaap (1950) which showed the ability of stilbestrol to interrupt broodiness in the hen. More recently Lehrman and Brody (1961) have reported that prolactin does not initiate incubation behavior in ring doves. In contrast, these authors found that progesterone consistently did so and advanced the suggestion that in the ring dove incubation behavior is produced by progesterone, and that participation in incubation provides the stimulus for prolactin secretion which then acts upon the crop sac.

Space does not permit the discussion of the numerous studies devoted to the extragonadal action of avian gonadotropic hormones on the coloration of plumage and bill pigmentation or the role of the pituitary in bird migration. For these the reader is referred to the volume edited by Marshall (1961).

C. Reptiles

The little information available suggests quite strongly that the gonads in this group are dependent upon the pituitary for their functional integrity (see Kehl and Combescot, 1955; Dodd, 1960, for detailed review). Schaefer (1933) hypophysectomized male garter snakes (*Thamnophis sirtalis* and *Thamnophis radix*) and noted an atrophy of the testes and degenerating spermatocytes in the atretic seminiferous tubules. He also recorded a decrease in the size of the interstitial cells. These findings are in accord with the more recent observations of Wright and Chester Jones (1957), who studied the effects of hypophysectomy in the lizard *Agama agama*. Thirty days after the operation the testes lost 90% of their weight with severe degeneration of the seminiferous tubules. Spermatogonia and spermatocytes could be distinguished but spermatozoa were never observed. The description by these authors is strongly reminiscent of the picture presented by the testis of the hypophysectomized rat. In the female garter snake (*Thamnophis sirtalis*) hypophysectomy led to follicular atresia (Bragdon, 1952).

Hypophysectomy of the pregnant viviparous snakes *Thamnophis*, *Natrix*, and *Storeria* led Clausen (1940) to the conclusion that the pituitary is necessary for gestation, at least in its later stages. Clausen's results, however, were not confirmed by Bragdon (1951), who found that hypophysectomy performed in any stage of pregnancy in *Thamnophis sirtalis* and *Natrix sipedon* did not interrupt gestation. These findings are in harmony with those of Panigel (1956), who failed to influence gestation of the viviparous lizard *Zootoca vivipara* by pituitary ablation. A "luteotropic" activity cannot, therefore, be ascribed to the reptilian pituitary gland at present, especially since the secretory function of the "corpus luteum" present in these forms remains to be established.

Homotransplantation of pituitary tissue to hypophysectomized *Thamnophis* stimulated spermatogenesis, increased the size of the tubules and of the interstitial cells, as well as elevating testicular weight (Schaefer, 1933; Cieslak, 1945). Hypophyses of the snake *Xenodon merremi* implanted into females of the same species resulted in oviposition (Houssay, 1931).

That the reptilian gonad can respond to mammalian gonadotropin preparations has been soundly established. Human chorionic gonadotropin (HCG), a preparation with a predominant LH activity, when administered to male lizards in winter when their testes normally undergo involution, resulted in stimulation of spermatogenesis accompanied by an increase in the size of the organ which attained the appearance normally seen during the breeding season. The epididymis was stimulated, exhibiting increased secretory activity, and other manifestations of increased androgen secretion also became evident (Evans, 1935a; Turner, 1935). Since in these experiments the animals' own pituitaries were present it is difficult to assign a specific site of action to HCG with reference to the tubules or the interstitial cells or both. The possibility remains that the stimulus acted primarily on the interstitial cells, resulting in enhanced androgen secretion which secondarily stimulated spermatogenesis (see Simpson, 1959). Similar results have been obtained in the horned lizard *Phrynosoma cornutum* following the administration of crude hog anterior pituitary extract (Mellish, 1936).

In the female lizard (*Anolis carolinensis* and *Phrynosoma cornutum*), which is also sexually quiescent during the winter months, the administration of HCG and sheep pituitary extract and other mammalian preparations resulted in ovarian hypertrophy and stimulation of the oviduct (Evans, 1935b; Mellish, 1936; Mellish and Meyer, 1937), but only whole sheep pituitary extract led to ovulation and oviposition (Evans, 1935b).

Alkaline extracts of whole sheep pituitary glands have been reported to accelerate the sexual development of immature alligators of both sexes, but spermatogenesis and ovulation were not achieved (Forbes, 1937). It is of interest that the responses were more pronounced in older immature animals than in younger ones, a situation reminiscent of the refractoriness to gonadotropins in young rats and chickens.

The hypophysectomized turtle *Emys leprosa* responds to the administration of HCG and pregnant mare serum (PMS), a placental gonadotropin rich in FSH activity, in a manner not entirely unlike that of the hypophysectomized rat. Combescot (1955, 1958) reported that PMS stimulates spermatogenesis while HCG acts upon the interstitial cells. If treatment with HCG was delayed some 40 days after hypophysectomy, spermatogenesis was not stimulated whereas early institution of therapy accelerated spermatogenesis, suggesting an indirect androgenic effect on the tubules. In the sexually immature turtle (*Emys leprosa*) with intact pituitaries, PMS accelerated testicular development, inducing full spermatogenesis and androgen production. Prolonged HCG treatment, on the other hand, feminized the gonad (Stefan, 1961).

Prolactin activity has not been identified with certainty in extracts of reptilian pituitaries (Leblond and Noble, 1937).

These studies indicate, despite the paucity of information regarding the nature of gonadotropins in the reptilian pituitary or their physiological actions, that the general scheme of pituitary gonadal interaction in this class probably does not differ in fundamental fashion from that to be found in the birds and mammals.

D. Amphibia

The role of the pituitary in the regulation of reproductive processes in the amphibia has been reviewed by Houssay (1949), Smith (1955), van Oordt and van Oordt (1955), van Oordt (1960), and Greep (1961).

Gonadal function in the amphibia, as in the forms discussed heretofore, is dependent upon the presence of the adenohypophysis. The effects of adenohypophyseal ablation on the testis and the ovary have been detailed in a vast literature dating back to the early 1920's and the classic experiments of Houssay and his school. In brief, this operation results in testicular atrophy and the prevention of compensatory hypertrophy following unilateral orchidectomy, indicating the presence of a negative feedback mechanism for release of pituitary gonadotropins, analogous to that described in higher forms. Spermatogenesis is impaired or arrested. The interesting observation has been made by van Oordt that in the common frog the development of spermatocytes and spermatids into spermatozoa does not appear to be under pituitary control, whereas the earlier stages of spermatogenesis are (see van Oordt, 1960), a situation quite dissimilar to the one usually ascribed to mammals or the one described in the toad (*Bufo arenarum*) by Burgos (1950), in which hypophysectomy occasions degeneration of the spermatids and spermatozoa first of all, followed by regressive changes in the spermatocytes and lastly in the spermatogonia.

In the female, hypophysectomy in a number of amphibia results in ovarian atrophy, atresia of follicles of a critical size, and the formation of corpora atretica. In the larva of *Ambystoma tigrinum* Burns (1932) described atresia of all follicles exceeding 400 μ in diameter, whereas those with smaller dimensions appeared to survive indefinitely.

The administration of whole pituitary tissue or pituitary extracts as well as purified mammalian gonadotropic preparations to hypophysectomized or sexually quiescent amphibia supports, in most convincing fashion, the concept of gonadal dependence upon the pituitary. The earlier literature dealing with this subject has been reviewed by Rugh (1935). Thus, homoimplantation of pituitaries into hypophysectomized *Bufo arenarum* by Houssay and his colleagues (1929) stimulated testicular growth and spermatogenesis and enhanced androgen secretion as evidenced by the development of secondary sexual characteristics and reproductive behavior. In the female, the same treatment led to ovulation and oviposition 2–3 days after implantation.

As in birds, the amount of gonadotropic activity in the pituitary fluctuates with the breeding season as does the responsiveness of the gonad to exogenous gonadotropic hormones, the gonads of male and female *Rana* being more sensitive to a given dose of pituitary extract as the breeding season is approached (Rugh, 1935; Witschi and Chang, 1959; van Oordt, 1960). The role of ambient temperature as a major regulating factor in both the secretion of pituitary gonadotropins and the responsiveness of the germinal epithelium in the frog has been discussed at length by van Oordt (1960). This author has also reviewed the evidence which favors the view that the influence of some external stimuli which affect spermatogenesis and spermiation in amphibia may be, at least in part, relayed to the pituitary by nervous pathways as has been demonstrated in birds and mammals.

While the identity of the gonadotropic complex of the amphibian pituitary in terms of its composition relative to LH and FSH and their respective functions is not known, suggestive attempts to clarify the problem by the use of mammalian hormones have been made. Wright and Hisaw (1946) found that FSH alone failed to produce ovulation in hypophysectomized *Rana pipiens*, whereas a combination of FSH and LH was effective whether administered *in vivo* or added to ovarian fragments *in vitro*. Comparable results were obtained in *Triturus viridescens* by Mayo (1937). More recently Burgers and Li (1960), using ovarian fragments of frogs pretreated with a frog pituitary extract to sensitize the ovary, observed that highly purified sheep LH preparations added *in vitro* promoted ovulation, whereas FSH, at all concentrations used, did not. Curiously, growth hormone was as effective as LH in this regard but ovine prolactin was inactive. Frog pituitary extracts were also fully effective. These workers further observed that progesterone in concentrations as low as 0.6 μg/ml of medium also promoted ovulation, demonstrating a direct effect of this steroid on the ovarian follicle.

In the male, numerous studies devoted to the administration of mammalian gonadotropic hormones lead to the inference that FSH is primarily concerned with spermatogenesis, while LH acts principally on the interstitial cells promoting androgen production and is also the factor responsible for spermiation (see van Oordt *et al.*, 1951; Burgos and Ladman, 1955; 1957; Lopez-Wille, 1959; Delsol and Blond-Fayolle, 1961; Lofts, 1961). The latter phenomenon can be homologized with ovulation which also appears to be triggered by LH (Witschi and Chang, 1959).

Witschi and Chang (1959) and Greep (1961) have reviewed the current status of taxonomic specificity of gonadotropins with especial reference to amphibia, a phenomenon first described by Houssay *et al.* (1929), who found that *Bufo arenarum* is less sensitive to pituitary extracts of mammalian origin than to pituitaries obtained from Anura. Such specificity can be demonstrated even among the Anura (see Creaser and Gorbman, 1939; Greep, 1961). Although this phenomenon is quantitative rather than absolute, it nevertheless suggests structural variations in the gonadotropic hormones from species to species. Conversely, amphibian pituitaries are singularly ineffective in promoting gonad stimulation in mammals (Adams and Tukey, 1937; see also Witschi, 1937; Gorbman, 1941).

Prolactin activity as assayed in the pigeon crop sac has been detected in the toad (Foglia, 1940) and in the frog pituitary (Keaty and Stanley, 1940). The administration of mammalian prolactin to male amphibia has no effect on the gonads (Burgos and Ladman, 1955; 1957 and Delsol and Blond-Fayolle, 1961), but it does stimulate the secretory activity of the oviduct in the female toad (*Bufo arenarum*), an effect observed even after ovariectomy (Houssay, 1949). Other pituitary hormones tested were ineffective in this regard, whereas progesterone or other progestational substances had a similar action. Subsequent work by Galli Mainini (1950, 1951) has suggested that in response to pituitary stimulation the ovary elaborates an ether-soluble substance, possibly progesterone, which also has the property of stimulating the secretory activity of the oviduct (see Smith, 1955, for a detailed discussion of this problem).

Another physiological activity of prolactin in amphibia is its apparent involvement in the "water drive" in the eft stage of *Diemictylus viridescens*. This water drive, which culminates in sexual maturation, is initiated prematurely by the administration of minute quantities of mammalian prolactin, all other adenohypophyseal hormones being inactive in this regard (Grant and Grant, 1958; Grant, 1959).

E. Fish

For purposes of convenience, this and subsequent sections similarly entitled include the cyclostomes and elasmobranchs as well as the teleosts. Limitations of space obviate discussion of the morphological correlated of the problem and allow but the briefest summary of the role of the piscine pituitary gland in reproduction. This is further justified by the appearance of the superb monograph by Pickford and Atz (1957) and the comprehensive review by Dodd (1960), which have amassed and critically reviewed the vast literature devoted to the physiology of the pituitary gland in fish. The reader is also referred to the reviews by Hoar (1955), Pickford (1959), Dodd *et al.* (1960), and Ball (1960).

1. HYPOPHYSECTOMY

This operation has been carried out in a large number of teleostean species and, while but a few of these have been studied in detail with reference to reproductive function, it is nevertheless clear that the gonads of both sexes are under the control of the pituitary gland. Dodd (1960) has summarized the effects of pituitary ablation in these forms as follows: "In the male, all stages of spermatogenesis other than spermatogonia are affected by hypophysectomy, though the nature of the effect is not clear. In the female, eggs below a certain size can apparently persist indefinitely in the absence of the pituitary, and oocyte development appears to come under its control from the onset of vitellogenesis. In the few cases in which the secondary sexual characteristics have been studied after hypophysectomy, these also appear to be affected, presumably indirectly, by pituitary removal."

While elasmobranchs have been subjected to hypophysectomy by many workers, the most detailed analysis of the sequelae of this operation on gonadal function has been made in the dogfish *Scylliorhinus caniculus* by Dodd and co-workers (1960). In the mature male this operation led to disorganization of testicular zonation and derangements in spermatogenesis, which could be localized as occurring between the spermatogonia and primary spermatocytes. Of particular interest and importance was the finding that removal of the ventral lobe of the pituitary, a structure unique to the elasmobranchs, was responsible for the observed effects. Ablation of the other hypophyseal lobes was without untoward consequence to the testes. Similarly, in the female, removal of the ventral lobe alone appeared to account for the degenerative changes observed in the ovary after the operation (Dodd *et al.*, 1960). These were characterized by a cessation of oviposition, atresia of all eggs in which vitellogenesis was well advanced with the development of corpora atretica. Similar observations have been made by Hisaw and Abramowitz (1938, 1939) in *Mustelus canis* and *Squalus acanthias*.

Information about the effects of hypophysectomy in cyclostomes on the gonads and reproductive processes is limited to the work of Dodd *et al.* (1960) in but five specimens of *Lampetra fluviatilis*, one female and four males. These animals were devoid of the secondary sexual characteristics noted in appropriate controls, "the gonads were immature, the eggs of the female were small and firmly held together with connective tissue, and the testes produced no milt." The authors tentatively conclude from their preliminary observations that pituitary ablation in the lamprey disrupts the spermatogonial stage of spermatogenesis and possibly also the generation of primary spermatocytes. Further maturation of the gametes appears to proceed unhindered in the absence of the pituitary, a situation quite comparable to that described by van Oordt in the frog.

2. THE ACTION OF GONADOTROPIC SUBSTANCES

In the teleosts, there can remain little doubt that the injection or implantation of fish pituitary glands or extracts therefrom can restore gonadal function in hypophysectomized individuals or accelerate gonadal development in sexually quiescent or immature animals. Evidence for this statement has been exhaustively documented in the reviews alluded to above and need not be elaborated here. Reports on the effects of mammalian gonadotropic preparations have been somewhat contradictory, but seem to lead to the conclusion that while LH can induce spermiation and ovulation as well as stimulation of the germinal tissue, FSH, if LH contaminants are taken into account, appears to be relatively inert (Pickford and Atz, 1957; Dodd, 1960).

Exceedingly little reliable information concerning the action of exogenous gonadotropins in elasmobranchs is extant. Carlisle (1954) reported that various mammalian gonadotropin preparations and prolactin induced spermiation in the male dogfish. Dodd (1955) described a small increase in ovarian and oviduct weight in immature *Raia radiata* in response to PMS treatment, and Hisaw and Albert (personal communication to Dodd, 1955) were able to reinstate ovulation in hypophysectomized dogfish (*Mustelus canis*) by implanting pituitary glands of the same species.

In the cyclostomes (*Lampetra*), both larval and metamorphosed, various effects on the secondary sexual characteristics were observed following administration of gonadotropin preparations without significant microscopic alterations in the gonads (see Dodd, 1960). Since such experiments have not been repeated in gonadectomized individuals, the possibility remains that the observed effects of gonadotropin administration were extragonadal and directly on the secondary sexual characters.

LH and FSH have been identified in teleost and elasmobranch pituitary tissue as assayed in the weaver finch and in rats (Witschi, 1955), but LH seems to predominate. More recently Strahan (1962) found that hagfish and lamprey pituitaries produced an increase in uterine weight in immature mice but no noticeable ovarian response.

The fish pituitary appears to subserve all the functions of LH and FSH as described in other vertebrates and these two activities have indeed been identified in fish pituitary glands, but the nature and number of these factors remain unknown.

3. PROLACTIN

Prolactin has been identified in fish pituitary glands (Pickford, 1959) but its role in piscine reproduction is obscure, although its participation in melanogenesis is well established (Kosto et al., 1959). A curious effect of prolactin which is certain to invite speculation has recently been reported by Egami and Ishii (1962). Working with *Symphysodon discus*, a viviparous fish provided with an integument which hypertrophies after spawning and begins to secrete a mucoid substance or "discus milk" upon which the young appear to feed (Hildeman, 1959), these Japanese workers adduced preliminary evidence which suggested that prolactin administered to immature individuals of this species mimicked, at least in part, the appearance of the discus milk in normal postspawning specimens.

This hasty survey permits the conclusion that reproductive phenomena in all classes of vertebrates examined are dependent, in major fashion, upon the presence of a functional pituitary gland. While the nature, site, and mode of action of the active principles involved remain in doubt, in mammals as well as in the lower forms, their importance in gonadal and other reproductive functions is certain.

III. THE REGULATION OF THYROID FUNCTION

A. Mammals

The role of the adenohypophysis in mammalian thyroid function has been comprehensively reviewed in a number of publications (Rawson et al., 1955; Wolstenholme and Millar, 1957; Sonenberg, 1958; Pitt-Rivers and Tata, 1959; Purves and Adams, 1960; Rawson, 1960; Solomon and Dowling, 1960). The excellent summary of Pickford and Atz (1957) should also be consulted.

Hypophysectomy in a variety of mammals including man leads to a decrease in thyroid function characterized by many, and oftentimes all, of the stigmata of thyroidectomy or profound hypothyroidism. Histologically, the secretory epithelium decreases in height and assumes a low cuboidal form and the relative volume of colloid may be increased. These morphological manifestations of hypophysectomy vary in intensity from species to species, depending upon the normal appearance of the thyroid gland and its state of activity at the time of operation.

All of the intracellular functions of the thyroid gland associated with the synthesis and release of the thyroid hormones are markedly reduced in the absence of the adenohypophysis. These include the accumulation of iodide, the organic binding of iodine, the formation of the iodotyrosines and thyroxine, and the secretion of the thyroid hormones into the circulation (see Pitt-Rivers and Tata, 1959).

The administration of pituitary extracts to hypophysectomized animals re-establishes normal thyroid function. The active adenohypophyseal principle involved, the thyroid stimulating hormone (TSH), is specific in this regard and has been obtained in a relatively purified form from mammalian pituitary tissue although its exact chemical nature is still in doubt (see Chapter 12).

The reciprocal interrelationship between TSH secretion by the pituitary and the circulating levels of thyroid hormone is well established. In general, procedures which reduce effective plasma concentrations of thyroid hormone increase TSH release by the pituitary, whereas increased circulating levels of thyroxine inhibit TSH secretion. This negative feedback mechanism resides both at the level of the pituitary gland and of a hypothalamic "TSH releasing center" (see Solomon and Dowling, 1960, for review). The influence of sudden exposure to cold, stress, and other environmental factors are, for the most part, mediated by neural pathways which are discussed elsewhere in this volume.

It must be emphasized that, at least in the rat, the thyroid gland functions, albeit at an extremely low level, in the absence of the pituitary gland. Furthermore, the thyroid gland, independently of pituitary TSH release, has a modicum of autoregulation in response to variations in iodide supply and hormonal iodine stores (see Solomon and Dowling, 1960).

The most widely studied extrathyroidal action of TSH has been its relation to the exophthalmos of Graves' disease in man. While the suggestion has often been made that these orbital changes represent a direct action of TSH, the administration of this hormone to human subjects does not produce exophthalmos. Nevertheless, the administration of pituitary extracts rich in TSH can produce exophthalmos in thyroidectomized and hypophysectomized guinea pigs (see Sonenberg, 1958). The question of the identity of the exophthalmic factor in the mammalian pituitary must, however, remain open until pure TSH becomes available for study.

B. Birds

The avian thyroid gland, like the mammalian, is under adenohypophyseal control. Hypophysectomy in the growing chick (Nalbandov and Card, 1943) leads to an atrophy of the thyroid gland, which assumes a flat and bandlike structure so small that it is extremely difficult to locate after prolonged pituitary deprivation. Histologically, the number and size of follicles are greatly reduced and the secretory epithelium becomes flattened and appears inactive. Similar observations were made by Baum and Meyer (1956), who further noted the lethargic behavior, reduced appetite, and abnormal feather structure characteristic of hypothyroidism. A 50% reduction in thyroid size was recorded in the hypophysectomized pigeon by Schooley *et al.* (1941). More recently Newcomer and Hurst (1962) studied the effects of hypophysectomy on thyroid function in 6-week-old cockerels and observed a decrease in I^{131} uptake and in the formation of the iodinated tyrosines, as well as a reduction in thyroxine and triiodothyronine synthesis. These results are qualitatively similar to those observed in the rat thyroid following pituitary ablation.

Despite the extensive use of the chick as an assay animal for TSH there is relatively little available information dealing with the physiological actions of avian TSH in birds. TSH activity has been detected in the hypophysis of the chicken (Gorbman, 1946) and the turkey (Riley *et al.*, 1937), but according to Fontaine (1954) the sea gull pituitary is devoid of TSH activity when assayed in the guinea pig. There is little doubt that zoological specificity plays a role in such discrepant results, especially in view of the notoriously active immunological mechanisms in the guinea pig.

The effects of mammalian TSH preparations on the morphology of the thyroid have been described in the duck (Schockaert, 1931), in sparrows (Miller, 1938, 1939), in canaries (Witschi and Riley, 1940), and in chicks (Keating *et al.*, 1945). The familiar thyroidal hypertrophy and hyperplasia, increase in follicle cell height, increased mitotic activity, and loss of follicular colloid were noted in all instances. Schockaert (1931) also observed, following several weeks of treatment, exophthalmos, shedding of the feathers, and hypertrophy of the heart in the duck. As in mammals, the injection of thyroxine depresses thyroid function, presumably by inhibiting endogenous TSH secretion (see Benoit, 1950).

The action of mammalian TSH on the various aspects of intrathyroidal iodine metabolism has been described in detail in the chick by Keating and co-workers (1945) and by Wahlberg (1955), and in the white Leghorn hen by Tanabe *et al.* (1957). Both iodide uptake and release were markedly stimulated.

Extracts of mammalian pituitary glands rich in TSH activity were found to increase the basal metabolic rate of pigeons (Riddle *et al.*, 1936) and of sparrows (Miller, 1939).

The seasonal variations in the size of the thyroid gland in various birds (Benoit, 1950) have been ascribed to variations in adenohypophyseal TSH release, but this conclusion is inferred although probably justified. The observation that in the duck and cock testicular androgens inhibit thyroid function (see Benoit, 1950) can probably also be ascribed to an inhibition of TSH secretion.

The goitrogenic effect of antithyroid drugs in the chick can be considered in terms of a negative feedback mechanism wherein reduced circulating levels of thyroid hormone call forth an increase in TSH secretion by the pituitary (Mixner et al., 1944; D'Angelo et al., 1947).

In summary, it may be suggested that the avian pituitary secretes a TSH and that it serves essentially the same functions and is subject to the same regulatory factors as in mammals.

C. Reptiles

In this class as in other cold-blooded vertebrates adenohypophyseal–thyroid relationships are complicated by the effects of ambient temperature on the activity of the pituitary-thyroid axis as well as on the responsiveness of the thyroid gland to exogenous TSH preparations. Nevertheless, clear evidence for the dependence of normal thyroid function on the pituitary gland in reptiles has been obtained.

The effects of hypophysectomy on the thyroid gland have been investigated in the garter snakes (*Thamnophis radix* and *Thamnophis sirtalis*) by Schaefer (1933) and by Hellbaum (1936). The operation decreased the cell height of the secretory epithelium of the thyroid follicles and 28 days after hypophysectomy the follicles became large and filled with colloid. Hypophyseal ablation also entrained an acceleration of periodic molting (Schaefer, 1933; Bragdon, 1951), a phenomenon associated with thyroidal hypofunction which could be prevented by the feeding of desiccated thyroid tissue.

The regressive changes observed in the thyroid glands in the above species were reversed by homopituitary implants (Schaefer, 1933). The administration of sheep pituitary extracts to normal and hypophysectomized specimens of *Thamnophis* by Hellbaum (1936) resulted in a stimulation of the thyroids which was dose dependent. The thyroids of the turtle *Chrysemys picta*, which are in a relatively inactive state during the winter months, responded to treatment with bovine pituitary extract by an increase in the height of the follicular epithelium and a loss of colloid from the follicles (Evans and Hegré, 1940).

A careful study of the actions of mammalian TSH on thyroidal iodide uptake in turtles (*Terrapene carolina* and *Pseudemys floridanus*) has been reported by Shellabarger et al. (1956). When the hormone was given at a warm ambient temperature, I^{131} uptake by the thyroid was significantly increased, but this was not the case when the environmental temperature was reduced to 2–3°C. The authors concluded that thyroid function and its response to TSH may be directly related to the temperature of the thyroid gland. A similar dependence of the response to TSH has been described in fish (see Section E).

The effect of mammalian TSH on oxygen consumption has been studied in the lizard (*Anolis carolinensis*) by Maher and Levedahl (1959). Again, while TSH or thyroxine administration produced an increase in oxygen consumption at 30°C such treatment was ineffective at 21–24°C. Viewed in this light the increase in thyroid activity noted in the lizard *Sceloporus occidentalis* by Wilhoft (1958) at elevated environmental temperatures may be ascribed in part to a greater response to circulating TSH. One may suppose, however, that at low temperatures all metabolic processes are decelerated, including the secretion of TSH and the response of peripheral tissues to thyroxine, a situation reversed by rising temperatures.

That a reciprocal interrelationship between TSH secretion and thyroidal activity is operative in reptiles can be inferred from the goitrogenic effect of thyroid-blocking drugs in *Anolis carolinensis* (Adams and Craig, 1949) and in the turtle *Chrysamys picta* (Adams and Craig, 1950).

D. Amphibia

The prevention of metamorphosis of the anuran tadpole by pituitary extirpation, as first reported by Smith (1916) and later confirmed and extended by generations of subsequent workers, provides a dramatic demonstration of thyroidal dependence on the hypophysis in amphibia. Other evidence abounds in a voluminous literature. The early observations of Smith (1916) that hypophysectomy of larvae of *Rana boylei* results in a regression of thyroid size, a loss of cytoplasm in the secretory cells, and an accumulation of colloid by the follicles have been confirmed in a number of other amphibia. The morphological sequelae of hypophysectomy in the thyroid are slow to develop, as illustrated by the studies of Tuchmann-Duplessis (1944) in the newt of *Triton alpestris*. In this species, the first signs of thyroidal regression did not occur before the third week following operation and reached maximal expression 4 to 5 weeks later. The functional activity of the thyroid, in *Bufo arenarum* at least, is affected quite rapidly, however. Donoso and Trivelloni (1958) have reported that in this species I^{131} uptake is markedly reduced 7 days after hypophysectomy.

Implantation of *Rana pipiens* pituitaries in larvae of *Rana clamitans* stimulated the thyroidal secretory epithelium of the recipients and caused a loss of colloid from the follicles. These morphological changes may be taken as evidence for increased thyroxine secretion since metamorphosis was markedly accelerated (Ingram, 1929). Similar findings have been reported following the administration of mammalian TSH preparations to hypophysectomized toads (Houssay, 1949), hypophysectomized *Rana boylei* (Smith and Smith, 1923), hypophysectomized larvae of *Rana pipiens* and *Rana sylvatica* (Atwell, 1935), hypophysectomized newts and adults of *Triturus viridescens* (Adams, 1934, 1936), and tadpoles of *Rana temporaria* (Fabré and Marescaux, 1960), to mention but a few. These morphological changes in response to TSH administration have been correlated with thyroidal I^{131} and P^{32} uptake by D'Angelo (1956) in tadpoles of *Rana clamitans* and by Donoso and Trivelloni (1958) in *Bufo arenarum*.

The presence of TSH activity in the pituitaries of many amphibia has been amply demonstrated in a variety of assay systems employing amphibia and representatives of other classes (see Adams, 1946; Gorbman, 1941). More recently Y. A. Fontaine [quoted in Fontaine and Fontaine (1962)] reported a significant increase in I^{131} uptake of thyroids of mice treated with pituitary extracts of *Rana*.

Inhibition of thyroidal iodide uptake following thiouracil treatment has been reported by Matthews (1950) in *Rana pipiens,* confirming earlier studies demonstrating a goitrogenic effect of antithyroid compounds in various amphibia and suggesting a negative feedback relationship between thyroid and adenohypophysis in this group.

As in the turtle, the stimulatory effects of mammalian TSH are enhanced in *Rana esculenta* when the environmental temperature is raised, suggesting a temperature dependence of thyroidal response to TSH (Flatin and Delsol, 1959).

E. Fish

The exhaustive and critical survey of the literature relating to hypophyseal regulation of thyroid structure and function in teleosts, elasmobranchs, and cyclostomes by Pickford and Atz (1957) obviates the necessity for detailed discussion here.

The concensus among workers in the field is that hypophysectomy in teleost fishes leads to a reduction in thyroid function as evidenced by regressive morphological changes in the gland and a decrease in radioiodine uptake. The rapidity of these effects varies from species to species and appears to be accelerated at higher ambient temperatures. Implants or injections of pituitary preparations derived from a variety of teleosts stimulate the thyroids of normal and hypophysectomized teleostean and amphibian recipients as adjudged by morphological and functional criteria. However, attempts to elicit thyrotropic effects in higher forms, particularly mammals, with extract of teleostean pituitary glands have been generally unsuccessful although, as a rule, teleosts are quite responsive to mammalian TSH preparations. As in some other poikilotherms, however, the response to mammalian TSH is inhibited at low environmental temperatures. Approaches to these problems using highly quantitative and well-controlled assay procedures in trout and mice have recently been summarized by Fontaine and Fontaine (1962). They report appreciable TSH activity as assayed in the trout in the pituitaries of a number of teleosts with considerable variation from species to species, variations which could not be related to habitat, behavior, or systematic position. The TSH activity of the eel (*Anguilla*) pituitary was uniformly high, whereas that of a number of Salmonidae was extremely low. In this connection the authors call attention to the fact that the circulating levels of 17-hydroxycorticoids are very high in *Salmo salar* and low in *Anguilla anguilla*, and point out a similar inverse relationship between pituitary TSH content and plasma corticoid level in the rat and the guinea pig. The physiological significance of this relationship, however, remains obscure.

Comparing the thyrotropic activities of mammalian as well as teleostean (eel) pituitary preparations in mice and in trout, Fontaine and Fontaine (1962) confirmed earlier observations by demonstrating that, while mammalian and teleost preparations were equally active in promoting thyroidal radioiodine uptake in trout, only mammalian TSH was effective in the mouse, eel pituitaries evoking no notable response. Similar effects were obtained when purified TSH preparations derived from eel pituitaries were employed, leading the authors to minimize the possibility of an inhibitor present in the teleostean pituitary which would interfere in the mammalian but not in the trout assay. These observations, along with their finding that the pituitary of the dipnoan *Protopterus annectens*, a species considered to be closely related phylogenetically to the first tetrapods, was as active in the mouse assay as amphibian or mammalian TSH, led the authors to support the concept of the zoological or phylogenetic specificity of TSH (see Pickford and Atz, 1957). It should be kept in mind, however, that the adenohypophyseal hormones are highly complex proteins and that the "active sites" responsible for physiological activity probably represent but a small fraction of the molecule. The possibility must be considered, therefore, that the molecular configurations responsible for TSH activity could be the same in teleosts and higher vertebrates, but that the difference resides in the remainder of the molecule and that fish TSH may be so rapidly metabolized in the mouse that its potential effect on thyroid function in this species may not be expressed. That the biological half-life of various mammalian gonadotropins may profoundly influence their assay in different mammalian systems has been suggested by the work of Parlow (1961). Similarly, the finding that mammalian TSH is more active on the teleostean thyroid at high than at low ambient temperatures while eel pituitary preparations are equally effective under both circumstances (Fontaine and Fontaine, 1962) could perhaps be interpreted in terms of an enzymatic modification of the mammalian molecule by the piscine tissues revealing the active site, a reaction which could progress more rapidly at the elevated temperatures and be inhibited at the lower.

In adult elasmobranchs, the existence of pituitary regulation of thyroid function has been difficult to demonstrate although the evidence for a pituitary-thyroid relationship is quite clear in the embryo (see Pickford and Atz, 1957). More recently Dent and Dodd (1961) reported a marked effect of mammalian TSH on radioiodine fixation by thyroids of newly hatched *Scylliorhinus caniculus*, which was temperature dependent. TSH activity has been detected in the pituitary of this species as assayed in the teleost (Fontaine and Fontaine, 1962).

The problem in the cyclostomes is in a most obscure state at the present time and available evidence does not warrant a conclusion regarding the existence of TSH in the pituitary or the dependence of the thyroid or the endostyle on pituitary function in this group (see Pickford and Atz, 1957; Olivereau, 1957; Barrington, 1960).

IV. THE REGULATION OF ADRENAL CORTICAL FUNCTION

The following section will be limited to a consideration of the direct actions of adenocorticotropic substances on adrenal cortical or interrenal tissue, and will not endeavor to discuss the regulation of adrenocorticotropic hormone (ACTH) secretion or the extra-adrenal effects of the hormone since these are dealt with elsewhere in this volume. For a more complete analysis of the comparative aspects of the problem the reader is referred to the excellent monograph by Chester Jones (1957) and the comprehensive summary by Pickford and Atz (1957).

A. Mammals

The interrelationship between adrenal and adenohypophyseal function in mammals has been the subject of intense investigation for a number of years and has been repeatedly reviewed, most recently by Sayers *et al.* (1958), Sayers and Royce (1960), Ganong and Forsham (1960), Fortier (1962), and Yates and Urquhart (1962). In brief summary, hypophysectomy in a variety of mammals including man results in an atrophy of the adrenal cortex and a profound reduction in the secretion of the glucocorticoids, cortisol and corticosterone. Aldosterone secretion is also reduced, but to a much lesser extent, and is produced in sufficient quantities in the absence of the pituitary to maintain normal or nearly normal electrolyte metabolism (see Knobil and Greep, 1958; Farrell, 1958). The other

manifestations of adrenal cortical insufficiency, however, are clearly evident in hypophysectomized individuals.

The administration of ACTH, to normal or hypophysectomized animals,
leads to a hypertrophy and hyperplasia of the adrenal cortex, which is
generally limited to the zona reticularis and fasciculata (see Knobil *et al.*,
1954), and an increased secretion of cortisol and corticosterone into the
adrenal venous effluent. These effects of ACTH are accompanied by a loss
of stainable lipid from adrenal cortical cells, a decrease in adrenal cholesterol
concentration, and a discharge of ascorbic acid from the gland. Again,
aldosterone secretion, while increased by exogenous ACTH treatment,
does not seem to be primarily dependent on pituitary function (see Farrell,
1958) and, like the zona glomerulosa from which it is secreted, is currently
thought to be under the immediate control of extrapituitary factors (see
Davis, 1961; Farrell and Taylor, 1962). Adrenal cortical vascularity, blood
flow, and general metabolism are also stimulated by ACTH.

The action of ACTH on adrenal cortical secretion, in *in vivo* and *in
vitro* systems, is rapid and can be demonstrated with extremely small
quantities of the hormone, especially in hypophysectomized preparations.
The site and mechanism of action of ACTH in the biosynthesis of adrenal
cortical hormones have not been fully elucidated and continue to be the
subject of intensive study (see Fortier, 1962, for review).

A reciprocal interrelation or negative feedback mechanism between
ACTH release by the adenohypophysis and circulating levels of cortisol
and corticosterone has been amply demonstrated. In the absence of stressful
stimuli, the secretion of ACTH appears to be inversely related to the
circulating levels of corticosteroids, the latter being able to completely
suppress ACTH release when administered in sufficient quantities. Conversely, ACTH levels in the blood rise when the adrenals are removed or
steroid secretion is inhibited by pharmacological means (see Munson,
1961). Available evidence strongly suggests that the regulation of ACTH
release by circulating steroids is mediated at the level of the central nervous
system as are exogenous stimuli which stimulate ACTH secretion (see
Ganong, 1959; Yates and Urquhart, 1962, and Chapter 1 by Fortier).

That ACTH may stimulate the secretion of adrenal androgens under
nonpathological circumstances has been reported (see Nelson, 1961) and
there is good evidence in support of the view that androgen secretion by
the adrenal cortex of the mouse may be influenced by gonadotropic preparations (Chester Jones, 1957). It may be concluded with confidence that
in mammals the morphological and functional integrity of the inner two
zones of the adrenal cortex is dependent on adenohypophyseal ACTH and
that this hormone mediates the physiological alterations in the secretion of
adrenal corticoids, with the probable exception of aldosterone.

B. Birds

The earlier literature dealing with the effects of hypophysectomy and ACTH-containing pituitary extracts in birds has been reviewed by Chester Jones (1957).

That hypophysectomy can lead to a reduction in adrenal weight accompanied by characteristic histological changes in adrenal cortical cells has been reported in the pigeon (Schooley et al., 1941; Miller and Riddle, 1942), the duck (Benoit and Assenmacher, 1953), and the chicken (Nalbandov and Card, 1943). Some authors, however, find only minimal decreases in adrenal weight following hypophysectomy in the domestic fowl (Baum and Meyer, 1956; Brown et al., 1958; Newcomer, 1959). Newcomer (1959) also failed to find any effect of hypophysectomy on the adrenal content of ascorbid acid, cholesterol, and Δ^4-3-ketosteroids in the chick. Nevertheless, Meyer (1962) observed that hypophysectomy in male pheasants and chickens results in a marked depression of corticoid secretion into the adrenal venous effluent and concluded that the biosynthesis of adrenal corticosteroids is pituitary dependent.

Conversely, it has been reported that the administration of mammalian pituitary extracts to hypophysectomized pigeons repaired the atrophic changes produced by hypophysectomy or effected hypertrophy in adrenal cortical cells of hypophysectomized and normal birds (Schooley et al., 1941; Miller and Riddle, 1942). Significant increases in adrenal weight following mammalian ACTH administration have also been observed in the chick by Jailer and Boas (1950), in cockerels by Brown et al. (1958), and in the quail by Zarrow and Baldini (1952). That adrenal weight increase may be a relatively insensitive index of administered or endogenous ACTH activity in birds has, however, been suggested by a number of studies (Brown et al., 1958; Flickinger, 1959; Garren et al., 1961; Zarrow et al., 1962).

A somewhat controversial area has been the effect of ACTH administration on adrenal ascorbic acid concentration. Large doses of mammalian ACTH have failed, in contrast to their action in mammals, to produce a depletion of adrenal ascorbic acid in several avian species (Jailer and Boas, 1950; Zarrow and Zarrow, 1950; Zarrow and Baldini, 1952; Elton et al., 1959). Perek and Eckstein (1959), on the other hand, reported an effect of ACTH on adrenal ascorbic acid depletion in mature hens which they were unable to demonstrate in 3-month-old pullets, leading them to the conclusion that the age of the bird was a determinant factor in the response. The studies of Elton et al. (1959), however, were conducted on sexually mature birds.

Mammalian ACTH, when administered to birds, entrains many of the physiological changes attributable to increased secretion of adrenal corticosteroids (see, for example, Brown *et al.*, 1958). More recently Nagra *et al.* (1960) have reported that mammalian ACTH administration to fowl and pheasants produces a marked rise in the secretion of corticosterone by the adrenal gland, supporting the *in vitro* observation of de Roos (1961) that ACTH increases the production of corticosterone by the avian adrenal but has no detectable effect on aldosterone formation. This latter point is of interest in view of the finding that the peripheral zone of the avian adrenal cortex is less affected by hypophysectomy and could perhaps be considered a homologue of the zona glomerulosa in mammals (Chester Jones, 1957), which, as noted earlier, secretes aldosterone relatively independently of ACTH.

Direct evidence for the presence of ACTH in the avian pituitary is poorly documented although attempts to demonstrate ACTH activity in extracts of turkey and chicken adenohypophyseal tissue in various test animals are suggestive (Riley *et al.*, 1937; Meyer *et al.*, 1939; Moszkowska, 1949).

The compensatory hypertrophy of the remaining adrenal which follows unilateral adrenalectomy in the pigeon (Miller and Riddle, 1942) and the adrenal hypertrophy following stress (Brown *et al.*, 1958) suggest an endogenous release of ACTH regulated by mechanisms demonstrated in mammals.

Virtually nothing, however, is known of the nature of avian corticotropin and of its actions in avian recipients.

C. Reptiles

Little is known of adrenal cortical function in this class although the dependence of normal adrenal morphology on the presence of the pituitary and the existence of a reciprocal pituitary-adrenal interrelationship are relatively well established on morphological grounds (see Chester Jones, 1957). Hypophysectomy in the snakes *Thamnophis sirtalis*, *Thamnophis radix* (Schaefer, 1933), and *Natrix natrix* (Wright and Chester Jones, 1957) resulted in a reduction in adrenal size and degenerative changes in the cortical cells. Groups of these, however, retained their normal appearance. Similar observations have been made in the lizards *Xantusia vigilis* (Miller, 1952) and *Agama agama* (Wright and Chester Jones, 1957). These rather profound sequelae of hypophysectomy were not accompanied by notable changes in tissue electrolyte distribution, suggesting that the nests of normal cells remaining in the adrenal after the operation may continue to secrete since adrenalectomy does cause derangements in this regard (Wright and Chester Jones, 1957).

The reptilian forms so far studied respond to the administration of mammalian ACTH. Miller (1952) found marked lipid depletion in the adrenal cortical cells of *Xantusia* following the injection of moderate doses of the hormone while larger doses seemed to result in degenerative changes. Wright and Chester Jones (1957) maintained the adrenals of hypophysectomized *Natrix* with mammalian ACTH, but similar treatment in normal snakes, possessing adrenals which appeared hyperactive, failed to respond. Injection of ACTH to normal or hypophysectomized lizards (*Agama*) induced degenerative adrenal changes which the authors attributed to overstimulation.

Of particular interest are the findings of compensatory adrenal hypertrophy following unilateral adrenalectomy in *Natrix* and of compensatory atrophy comparable to that seen after hypophysectomy in this species and in *Xantusia* (Wright and Chester Jones, 1957; Miller, 1952) following the administration of adrenal steroids, suggesting a regulation of endogenous pituitary ACTH secretion by circulating levels of adrenal corticoids.

The only direct evidence that the reptilian pituitary does in fact contain an ACTH is the observation of Schaefer (1933) that homoimplants of pituitary tissue to hypophysectomized snakes restored their atropic adrenals to a normal appearance.

Nothing can be said at present of the actions of reptilian or mammalian ACTH on the secretory function of the reptilian adrenal.

D. Amphibia

Definitive information regarding adenohypophyseal-adrenocortical interrelationships in amphibia is scarcely more abundant than in the reptiles.

Either adenohypophysectomy or total hypophysectomy is followed by adrenal atrophy or some form of degeneration in all species studied. The extent and duration of these changes vary with the state of the adrenal at the time of operation, which in turn is dependent upon the season of the year, but exceptions to this generalization have been noted (see Chester Jones, 1957, for review).

Injections of pituitary extracts or purified mammalian ACTH stimulate, in morphological terms, the adrenals of normal and hypophysectomized representatives of the amphibia, although in some instances restoration of the adrenal cortical cells to normal appearance could not be achieved if ACTH treatment following hypophysectomy was long delayed. These manifestations of ACTH administration have been reviewed by Chester Jones (1957).

Attempts to induce adrenal ascorbic acid depletion in frogs and toads with mammalian ACTH have been unsuccessful (Elton and Zarrow, 1955; Elton *et al.* 1959), but *in vitro* stimulation of adrenocortical secretion by mammalian ACTH has been shown in the bullfrog *Rana catesbeiana* (Carstensen *et al.*, 1961), a finding strongly suggesting that the morphological effects of this hormone have physiological significance.

The presence of ACTH activity in the amphibian pituitary has been adduced by administering amphibian pituitary suspensions to hypophysectomized rats and observing an adrenal weight increase (Foglia, 1941) and by the *in vitro* steroidogenic effect of *Rana catesbeiana* pituitary tissue on the adrenal of the same species (Carstensen *et al.*, 1961). In the latter study it was noted that frog or mammalian ACTH had a greater effect on the production of aldosterone than on that of corticosterone, the only two Δ^4-3-keto compounds found.

E. Fish

Once again this problem has been thoroughly reviewed by Pickford and Atz (1957) and by Chester Jones (1957). A briefer review by Pickford (1959) has also appeared. In the teleosts the actions of hypophysectomy and of ACTH administration appear to be limited to the anterior interrenal cortical tissue.

With the exception of *Fundulus heteroclitus*, hypophysectomy in the other forms studied (*Anguilla*, *Carassius*) led to atrophic changes in the interrenal tissue. Conversely, teleostean pituitary extracts and mammalian ACTH have been shown to induce hypertrophic changes in anterior interrenal tissue in a number of teleosts, both normal and hypophysectomized, including *Fundulus*. Of additional interest is the remarkable observation that in hypophysectomized *Anguilla* a restoration of the atrophic adrenal to normal weight was achieved within 1 hour after mammalian ACTH administration (see Pickford and Atz, 1957).

ACTH activity has been unequivocally demonstrated by Rinfret and Hane (1955) in acidic extracts and purified fractions of the Pacific Salmon (*Oncorhynchus keta*) pituitary and by Woodhead (1960) in the pituitaries of *Gadus morruha*, using adrenal ascorbic acid depletion and adrenal weight maintenance in hypophysectomized rats as bioassays.

Evidence based largely on secondary effects attributable to adrenal secretion indicates that stressful situations may result in ACTH release from the teleostean pituitary (see Pickford and Atz, 1957), but more suggestive is the finding that in migrating fish the plasma 17-hydroxycorticoid concentration is considerably higher than in nonmigrating specimens of the same species (Chester Jones and Phillips, 1960).

In elasmobranchs, pituitary-adrenal relationships have been studied principally in *Torpedo*. In this group, hypophysectomy led to atrophic changes in the interrenal gland and treatment with mammalian ACTH stimulated it in both normal and hypophysectomized animals (Dittus, 1940). Mammalian ACTH appears to increase steroid production *in vitro* by interrenal tissue of *Raia erinacea* (Macchi and Rizzo, 1962).

That the plasma of cyclostomes contains appreciable quantities of adrenal cortical steroids has recently been reported by Chester Jones and Phillips (1960) and by Chester Jones *et al.* (1962). The latter workers quote Sterba as having shown that mammalian ACTH stimulates the adrenal cortical cells of *Petromyzon*, and in addition provide evidence, albeit indirect, that *Myxine* pituitaries possess ACTH activity as assayed in this species and that the administration of mammalian ACTH exerted an effect on electrolyte distribution. In the discussion of the paper by Chester Jones and his colleagues (1962) Strahan reported a corticotropic effect of hagfish and lamprey pituitaries in immature mice, but unfortunately the assay animals were not stated to be hypophysectomized and the results can therefore not be evaluated with confidence.

V. THE REGULATION OF GROWTH

A wide variety of endocrine and environmental factors influences the growth of vertebrates. The secretions of the thyroid gland, gonads, and adrenal cortex are of cardinal import in this regard and the significance of nutrition scarcely requires emphasis. Limitations of space, however, do not permit a consideration of the complex interplay of these factors as they impinge on the accretion in body size, and the following discussion will be limited to the role of the pituitary growth or somatotropic hormone (STH).

A. Mammals

The observation, that hypophysectomy arrests while extracts of adeno-hypophyseal tissue stimulate growth in hypophysectomized and intact animals, has led to the isolation and purification from such extracts of a protein which specifically accelerates growth without having major influences on the "target" glands of the pituitary (see Chapter 12 by Li). The actions of this hormone on growth and attendant metabolic changes in several mammalian species including man have been extensively reviewed (Simpson *et al.*, 1950; Smith *et al.*, 1955; de Bodo and Altszuler, 1957, 1958; Ketterer *et al.*, 1957; Russell and Wilhelmi, 1958; Knobil and Greep, 1959; Raben, 1959; Beck *et al.* 1960; Knobil, 1961). The reader is also referred to the typically excellent summary of the earlier literature by Pickford (Pickford and Atz, 1957).

The essentiality of the pituitary growth hormone for normal growth only becomes evident sometime after birth (30 days in the rat; Asling et al., 1950), since the exceedingly rapid rate of growth exhibited by the fetus and the neonate is not remarkably diminished after hypophysectomy (Jost, 1953). Similarly, removal of the maternal pituitary gland during pregnancy does not appreciably retard the growth of the fetus (see Knobil, 1961). These observations suggest that the growth processes of the fetus and the neonatal animal are independent of pituitary control but at some critical state in postnatal development the pituitary growth hormone assumes the functions which heretofore were exercised by more primitive regulatory mechanisms. It is of interest in this regard that the guinea pig continues to grow, albeit at a somewhat reduced rate, following hypophysectomy (Knobil and Greep, 1959; Clayton and Worden, 1960). A few cells, resembling those of the pars tuberalis, remain attached to the hypothalamus and to the pituitary stalk after hypophysectomy, raising the possibility that these cells may secrete adequate quantities of growth hormone. Similar remnants, however, are easily demonstrable in hypophysectomized rats and monkeys, animals which show a complete arrest of growth. That incompleteness of the operation is not an important factor in this peculiar behavior of the hypophysectomized guinea pig is further suggested by the finding that these animals show the characteristic loss of thyrotropic, gonadotropic, and corticotropic functions (Knobil and Greep, 1959). An acceptable explanation of the true growth (rather than the deposition of fat) of the hypophysectomized guinea pig, in contrast to other mammals studied to date, is not yet available. One is tempted to consider the possibility, however, that the guinea pig may represent an "adult fetus" and that in this species, the pituitary-independent fetal growth processes may remain functional long after birth.

The administration of small quantities of growth hormone to normal and hypophysectomized rats produces striking increases in body weight and size attributable to an elongation and widening of the long bones, an enlargement of the skull, an increase in the size and weight of the non-endocrine viscera, as well as a marked hypertrophy of the musculature, skin, and connective tissue. The growth of the central nervous system and its derivatives appears to be relatively independent of the action of growth hormone (Asling et al., 1952), as is that of the thyroid, adrenals, gonads, and accessory organs of reproduction, structures dependent on other, more specific hormonal stimuli.

The deposition of new tissue in response to growth hormone administration is accompanied by an increased retention of nitrogen and of other protoplasmic constituents including water, sodium, and potassium (see Knobil and Greep, 1959; Beck et al., 1960). This anabolic action of growth hormone appears to be a direct one on peripheral tissues since its addition to muscle tissue in vitro increases amino acid transport into cells and amino acid incorporation into protein (see Knobil, 1961).

Characteristically, also, growth hormone increases fatty acid mobilization from adipose tissue but appears to have no major influence on fat oxidation as was previously supposed, although the respiratory quotient of growth hormone treated animals is depressed. The latter observation is probably best explained by the inhibitory effect of growth hormone on fat synthesis (de Bodo and Altszuler, 1957; Knobil, 1961).

The effects of growth hormone on carbohydrate metabolism have been under intensive study since the classic observations of Houssay and his school (Houssay, 1931) that hypophysectomy alleviates diabetes in the dog while the chronic administration of pituitary extracts exacerbates it and can render intact animals diabetic. It is now generally agreed that the diabetogenic or hyperglycemic principle of the adenohypophysis is indeed growth hormone and that its principal mode of action is the inhibition of peripheral glucose utilization (Morgan et al., 1961), although additional mechanisms undoubtedly come into play (see de Bodo and Altszuler, 1958). Conversely, hypophysectomy increases sensitivity to insulin and leads to profound hypoglycemia upon food deprivation (see Knobil and Greep, 1959).

In contrast to the anti-insulin effect of growth hormone just mentioned, acute injections of the hormone or its addition to muscle tissue in vitro accelerates glucose utilization and produces an insulinlike response (see de Bodo and Altszuler, 1958; Knobil and Greep, 1959, Morgan et al., 1961). The explanation for this biphasic effect of growth hormone on carbohydrate metabolism is not yet apparent.

Growth hormone shares some of the physiological activities of prolactin, and vice versa, but in preparations obtained from human pituitary glands this overlap is almost complete, suggesting that these activities may be resident in the same molecule (Hayashida, 1962). This view is supported by immunochemical evidence which is discussed in the chapter by Li.

A complete species specificity of growth hormone action has been demonstrated within the Mammalia (see Knobil and Greep, 1959; Knobil, 1961). Only growth hormone of primate origin has physiological activity in primates, that from all other mammalian species tested being completely ineffective. Primate growth hormone, however, is fully effective in the rat.

Primate, bovine, and porcine growth hormones do not stimulate growth in intact or hypophysectomized guinea pigs but do elicit the expected acute effects, suggesting the production of neutralizing antibodies in this species, a phenomenon which cannot account, however, for the ineffectiveness of the latter two preparations in primates (Knobil, 1961).

Immunologically, primate growth hormone preparations cross-react only with each other, and do not do so with rat pituitary extracts, although they are physiologically active in this species. Similarly, bovine growth hormone, which is effective in the rat, does not cross-react with rat pituitary extract (Li *et al.*, 1962), suggesting that immunological specificity alone cannot account for the refractoriness of primates to nonprimate preparations.

The factors normally regulating the secretion of growth hormone by the adenohypophysis are currently unknown and convincing evidence to support the view that plasma levels of growth hormone in adults are significantly lower than that in young, growing individuals is not presently available. Much progress in the elucidation of these problems can be expected from the current development of sensitive and specific immunochemical assay methods for circulating growth hormone (Knobil and Greep, 1961; Wolstenholme and Cameron, 1962).

B. Birds

Although body weight gain may not necessarily be altered following hypophysectomy in birds, due to the increased deposition of fat (Newcomer, 1959), growth as measured by the length of the long bones is generally reduced. This has been observed in the domestic fowl by Nalbandov and Card (1943), who also found a reduction in the size of the viscera, as had Schooley *et al.* (1941), in hypophysectomized pigeons.

In contrast to the usual observation in hypophysectomized fasting mammals, Riddle and Dotti (1947) observed decreased glucose tolerance in the hypophysectomized pigeon, but an increased glucose tolerance was found in the pancreatectomized duck following the operation, a finding consonant with the effects of this procedure in the dog (Mialhe, 1957).

The effects of mammalian (bovine and porcine) growth hormone preparations in birds have, for the most part, been disappointing and are reminiscent of the negative results obtained with those preparations in primates (see Knobil and Greep, 1959). Injections of these preparations into immature, as well as mature, chickens was without effect on body weight gain, blood glucose concentration, and nitrogen balance (Carter *et al.*, 1955; Eaton *et al.*, 1955; Libby *et al.*, 1955; Glick, 1960; Sell and Balloun, 1960, 1961).

The report by Hsieh *et al.* (1952) that mammalian growth hormone administration to 13-day-old chick embryos led to an increase in size and blood sugar levels on hatching was not confirmed by Libby and co-workers (1955). Mialhe (1955), however, found a marked diabetogenic effect of bovine growth hormone in partially pancreatectomized ducks, but this could not be elicited in the intact bird.

While the evidence indicates that the chicken is, in all probability, not responsive to mammalian growth hormone, the possibility remains that other avian species are. The findings in the duck, for example, are suggestive. Similarly, the administration of various mammalian growth hormone preparations to parakeets (Rudolph and Pehrson, 1961) duplicates, at least in part, the actions of a growth-hormone-secreting pituitary tumor which occurs in these birds (Schlumberger and Rudolph, 1959). These tumors contain appreciable quantities of growth hormone activity as assayed in the rat but little, if any, ACTH and prolactin. The tumor-bearing birds become obese, hyperlipemic, and hyperglycemic and the concentration of plasma albumin is increased. These animals also have a tendency to become larger than their normal controls. Whether these effects can be interpreted solely in terms of endogenous avian growth hormone secretion remains to be determined.

That avian pituitary extracts have growth hormone activity as assayed in the rat has also been demonstrated for the chicken by Moudgal and Li (1961) and by Hazelwood and Hazelwood (1961). The potency of the chicken pituitary, however, was low when compared to the rat pituitary in the rat assay system and relatively large doses were required to elicit a growth promoting effect.

A hyperglycemic effect of chicken pituitaries has been observed in the hypophysectomized-pancreatectomized toad and in similarly operated dogs (Houssay and Biasotti, 1931; Houssay et al., 1942), animals which respond in like manner to mammalian growth hormone preparations.

Clearly, much work remains to be done before the physiology of growth hormone in birds can be properly evaluated. The available information, while permitting the conclusion that a growth hormonelike factor, as assayed in the rat and toad, is present in the chicken pituitary and in pituitary tumors of parakeets, does not allow further generalization regarding the action of this substance in birds.

C. Reptiles

Information regarding the dependence of normal growth on the pituitary is virtually nonexistent.

Weight loss after hypophysectomy has been reported in *Natrix* when the operation was performed in summer, but in winter snakes and in the lizard

Agama hypophysectomy was without effect (Wright and Chester Jones, 1957). These findings confirmed an earlier report of Bragdon (1951) in the common garter snake. This weight loss, of course, could be the result of a decreased food intake.

Somewhat more convincing are the observations of Foglia *et al.* (1955) and of Miller and Wurster (1958) that hypophysectomy of diabetic turtles (*Chrysemys* and *Phrynops*) and otherwise normal lizards (*Eumeces*) reduced blood sugar levels, a phenomenon which could be attributed to the loss of the anti-insulin action of growth hormone but which cannot be considered specific in this regard. Conversely, bovine growth hormone has been reported to have a hyperglycemic effect in subtotally pancreatectomized turtles (*Phrynops*), but this was transient despite continued administration (Marques, 1955).

D. Amphibia

P. E. Smith's classic experiments (Smith, 1916) in which he demonstrated that hypophysectomy in larvae of *Rana boylei* resulted in a retardation of growth have been widely confirmed in a variety of amphibia. This operation, as in mammals, seems to inhibit the loss of depot fat during fasting since large fat bodies persist in hypophysectomized tadpoles (Smith and Smith, 1923) and in larvae of *Ambystoma tigrinum* (Burns and Buyse, 1932) subjected to prolonged food deprivation. In this species, however, hypophysectomy of the larva, while resulting in the expected regressive changes in the pituitary target glands, does not markedly inhibit growth, such animals reaching adult size within a year after operation (Greenwood, 1924; Burns and Buyse, 1932), a situation strongly reminiscent of that observed in the guinea pig.

Hypophysectomy in the toad has been reported by Houssay (Houssay *et al.*, 1933, Houssay, 1936, 1949) to produce a hypoglycemia, increased insulin sensitivity, and a loss of liver glycogen during fasting, as well as a reduction in nitrogen excretion. Kepinov (1946), on the other hand, observed a stimulation of glycogen deposition in the liver and an inhibition of glycogenolysis by hypophysectomy in the common frog.

That the implantation of adult amphibian pituitaries into hypophysectomized and intact larvae of frogs and salamanders can stimulate their growth was clearly demonstrated by the early studies of Allen (1920) and Burns (1930). On the other hand, homotransplantation of the hypophyseal primordium in the larva of *Rana aurora* produced no growth stimulatory effect (Allen, 1929), retarded the growth of *Ambystoma punctatum* and *Ambystoma mexicanum* larvae (Blount, 1935), and accelerated growth and produced postmetamorphic gigantism in *Rana pipiens* (Etkin and Lehrer, 1960).

The growth promoting effect of mammalian adenohypophyseal extracts in hypophysectomized frogs is well established (Smith and Smith, 1923) as is the diabetogenic action of mammalian growth hormone preparations in pancreatectomized-hypophysectomized toads (Houssay *et al.*, 1955). Conversely, the growth promoting activity of amphibian (frog) pituitaries can be demonstrated in hypophysectomized rats (Foglia, 1941; Solomon and Greep, 1959; Moudgal and Li, 1961). Similarly, extracts of toad pituitaries have been found to be diabetogenic in the hypophysectomized-pancreatectomized dog (Foglia, 1941; Houssay *et al.*, 1942) as well as in toads subjected to the same operation (Houssay *et al.*, 1942).

E. Fish

Pickford has recently reviewed her extensive studies on the physiology of growth hormone in fish as well as the investigations of other workers in this field (Pickford and Atz, 1957; Pickford, 1959) and the reader is referred to these papers for detailed and critical discussions of the subject. Suffice it to say, in this briefest of summaries, that the teleosts so far studied in some detail are dependent on their pituitaries for normal growth. Linear growth ceases in hypophysectomized fish and can be re-established by the administration of purified growth hormone preparations from mammalian and fish pituitary glands. Curiously, primate growth hormone is less effective in this regard than bovine material although these preparations are roughly equipotent in the rat (Pickford *et al.*, 1959). Fish growth hormone preparations and pituitary extracts have, however, been uniformly ineffective in significantly promoting growth in the hypophysectomized rat (Wilhelmi, 1955; Pickford *et al.*, 1959; Solomon and Greep, 1959; Hazelwood and Hazelwood, 1961; Mougdal and Li, 1961).

Little is known regarding the adenohypophyseal regulation of growth in elasmobranchs beyond the observation by Vivien (1941) that hypophysectomy in the dogfish *Scylliorhinus caniculus* reduced the rate of growth, a response which cannot be interpreted solely in terms of the loss of a growth hormone. Orias (1932) and Abramowitz *et al.* (1940) were able to show an amelioration of the diabetes in pancreatectomized dogfish following hypophysectomy, but replacement therapy was not attempted and further analysis of these experiments is conjectural.

The only information possibly relating to growth hormone in the cyclostomes is the recent report by Enemar and von Mecklenburg (1962) that pituitaries of the marine lamprey *Petromyzon marinus* did not stimulate growth when implanted into larval frogs.

The interesting and varied species specificities regarding the physiological activity of growth hormone preparations from different sources in different recipients seem to be more pronounced than in other pituitary hormones. Clear phylogenetic relationships as a basis for this functional specificity are far from obvious, however, and probably are not a major component of the problem.

References

Abramowitz, A. A., Hisaw, F. L., Boettiger, E., and Papandrea, D. N. (1940). *Biol. Bull.* **78**, 189–201.

Adams, A. E. (1934). *Anat. Record* **59**, 349-358.

Adams, A. E. (1936). *Anat. Record* **65**, 319-331.

Adams, A. E. (1946). *Quart. Rev. Biol.* **21**, 1–32.

Adams, A. E., and Craig, M. (1949). *Anat. Record* **103**, 565.

Adams, A. E., and Craig, M. (1950). *Anat. Record* **108**, 594.

Adams, A. E., and Tukey, G. R. (1937). *Anat. Record* **67**, Suppl. 3, 2.

Allen, B. M. (1920). *Science* **52**, 274–276.

Allen, B. M. (1929). *Anat. Record* **44**, 207.

Asling, C. W., Walker, D. G., Simpson, M. E., and Evans, H. M. (1950). *Anat. Record* **106**, 555–569.

Asling, C. W., Walker, D. G., Simpson, M. E., Li, C. H., and Evans, H. M. (1952). *Anat. Record* **114**, 49–65.

Atwell, W. J. (1935). *Anat. Record* **62**, 361–379.

Ball, J. N. (1960). *In* "Symposia of the Zoological Society of London" (I. Chester Jones, ed.), No. 1, pp. 105–135. Zoological Society, London.

Barrington, E. J. W. (1960). *In* "Symposia of the Zoological Society of London" (E. J. W. Barrington, ed.), No. 2, pp. 69–85. Zoological Society, London.

Baum, G. J., and Meyer, R. K. (1956). *Endocrinology* **58**, 338–346.

Beck, J. C., McGarry, E. E., Dyrenfurth, I., Morgen, R. O., Bird, E. D., and Venning, E. H. (1960). *Metabolism Clin. and Exptl.* **9**, 699–737.

Benoit, J. (1950). *In* "Traite de Zoologie" (P. P. Grasse, ed.), Vol. 15, pp. 341–377. Masson, Paris.

Benoit, J. (1961). *Yale J. Biol. and Med.* **34**, 97–116.

Benoit, J. (1962). *Gen. Comp. Endocrinol. Suppl. No.* **1**, 254–274.

Benoit, J., and Assenmacher, I. (1953). *Arch. anat. microscop. et. morphol. exptl.* **42**, 334–386.

Blount, R. F. (1935). *J. Exptl. Zool.* **70**, 131–185.

Bragdon, D. E. (1951). *J. Exptl. Zool.* **118**, 419–435.

Bragdon, D. E. (1952). *J. Morphol.* **91**, 413–445.

Breneman, W. R. (1955). *Mem. Soc. Endocrinol. No.* **4**, 94–113.

Brown, K. I., Brown, D. J., and Meyer, R. K. (1958). *Am. J. Physiol.* **192**, 43–50.

Burgers, A. C. J., and Li, C. H. (1960). *Endocrinology* **66**, 255–259.

Burgos, M. H. (1950). *Compt. rend. soc. biol.* **144**, 420–421.

Burgos, M. H., and Ladman, A. J. (1955). *Proc. Soc. Exptl. Biol. Med.* **88**, 484–487.

Burgos, M. H., and Ladman, A. J. (1957). *Endocrinology* **61**, 20–34.

Burns, R. K. (1930). *Proc. Soc. Exptl. Biol. Med.* **27**, 836–838.

Burns, R. K. (1932). *J. Exptl. Zool.* **63**, 309–327.

Burns, R. K., and Buyse, A. (1932). *Anat. Record* **51**, 333–359.

Carlisle, D. B. (1954). *J. Marine Biol. Assoc. United Kingdom* **33**, 65–68.

Carstensen, H., Burgers, A. C. J., and Li, C. H. (1961). *Gen. Comp. Endocrinol.* **1**, 37–50.

Carter, R. D., Risner, R. N., and Yacowitz, H. (1955). *Poultry Sci.* **34**, 1407–1414.

Carter, F., Woods, M. C., and Simpson, M. E. (1961). *In* "Control of Ovulation" (C. A. Villee, ed.), pp. 1–23. Pergamon Press, New York.

Chester Jones, I. (1957). "The Adrenal Cortex." Cambridge Univ. Press, London and New York.

Chester Jones, I., and Phillips, J. G. (1960). *In* "Symposia of the Zoological Society of London" (I. Chester Jones, ed.), No. 1, pp. 17–32. Zoological Society, London.

Chester Jones, I., Phillips, J. G., and Bellamy, D. (1962). *Gen. Comp. Endocrinol. Suppl.* **1**, 36–47.

Cieslak, E. S. (1945). *Physiol. Zoöl.* **18**, 299–329.

Clausen, H. J. (1940). *Endocrinology* **27**, 700–704.

Clayton, B. E., and Worden, J. M. (1960). *J. Endocrinol.* **20**, 36–47.

Combescot, C. (1955). *Compt. rend. soc. biol.* **149**, 1969–1971.

Combescot, C. (1958). *Compt. rend. soc. biol.* **152**, 1077–1079.

Coombs, C. J. F., and Marshall, A. J. (1956). *J. Endocrinol.* **13**, 107–111.

Cowie, A. T. (1961). *In* "Milk: The Mammary Gland and its Secretion" (S. K. Kon and A. T. Cowie, eds.), Vol. 1, pp. 163–203. Academic Press, New York.

Cowie, A. T., and Folley, S. J. (1955). *In* "The Hormones" (G. Pincus and K. V. Thiman, eds.), Vol. 3, pp. 309–387. Academic Press, New York.

Creaser, C. W., and Gorbman, A. (1939). *Quart. Rev. Biol.* **14**, 311–331.

D'Angelo, S. A. (1956). *Proc. Soc. Exptl. Biol. Med.* **92**, 693–698.

D'Angelo, S. A., Gordon, A. S., and Charipper, H. A. (1947). *Anat. Record* **99**, 663–664.

Das, B. C., and Nalbandov, A. V. (1955). *Endocrinology* **57**, 705–710.

Davis, J. O. (1961). *Recent Progr. in Hormone Research* **17**, 293–352.

de Bodo, R. C., and Altszuler, N. (1957). *Vitamins and Hormones* **15**, 205–258.

de Bodo, R. C., and Altszuler, N. (1958). *Physiol Revs.* **38**, 389–445.

Delsol, M., and Blond-Fayolle, M. (1961). *Ann. endocrinol. (Paris)* **22**, 561–565.

Dent, J. N., and Dodd, J. M. (1961). *J. Endocrinol.* **22**, 395–402.

de Roos, R. (1961). *Gen. Comp. Endocrinol.* **1**, 494–512.

Dittus, P. (1940). *Z. wiss. Zoöl.* **154**, 40–124.

Dodd, J. M. (1955). *Mem. Soc. Endocrinol. No. 4*, 166–187.

Dodd, J. M. (1960). *In* "Marshall's Physiology of Reproduction" (A. S. Parkes, ed.), Vol. 1, Part 2, pp. 417–582. Longmans, Green, New York.

Dodd, J. M., Evennett, P. J., and Goddard, C. K. (1960). *In* "Symposia of the Zoological Society of London" (I. Chester Jones, ed.), No. 1, pp. 77–103. Zoological Society, London.

Donoso, A. O., and Trivelloni, J. C. (1958). *Compt. rend. soc. biol.* **152,** 1399–1401.

Eaton, R. C., Nalbandov, A. V., and Forbes, R. M. (1955). *Poultry Sci.* **34,** 1191–1192.

Egami, N., and Ishii, S. (1962). *Gen. Comp. Endocrinol. Suppl* **1,** 248–253.

Elton, R. L., and Zarrow, M. X. (1955). *Anat. Record* **122,** 473–474.

Elton, R. L., Zarrow, I. G., and Zarrow, M. X. (1959). *Endocrinology* **65,** 152–157.

Enemar, A., and von Mecklenburg, C. (1962). *Gen. Comp. Endocrinol.* **2,** 273–278.

Etkin, W., and Lehrer, R. (1960). *Endocrinology* **67,** 457–466.

Evans, L. T. (1935a). *Anat. Record* **62,** 213–221.

Evans, L. T. (1935b). *Biol. Bull.* **68,** 355–359.

Evans, L. T., and Hegré, E. (1940). *Endocrinology* **27,** 144–148.

Fabré, M., and Marescaux, J. (1960). *Compt. rend. soc. biol.* **154,** 1625–1628.

Farrell, G. (1958). *Physiol. Revs.* **38,** 709–728.

Farrell, G., and Taylor, A. N. (1962). *Ann. Rev. Physiol.* **24,** 471–490.

Flatin, J., and Delsol, M. (1959). *Ann. endocrinol. (Paris)* **20,** 761–675.

Flickinger, D. D. (1959). *Proc. Soc. Exptl. Biol. Med.* **100,** 23–25.

Foglia, V. G. (1940). *Rev. soc. arg. biol.* **16,** 559–562.

Foglia, V. G. (1941). *Endocrinology* **29,** 503–513.

Foglia, V. G., Wagner, E. M., De Barros, M., and Marques, M. (1955). *Rev. soc. arg. biol.* **31,** 87–95.

Fontaine, Y. A. (1954). *Compt. rend. acad. sci.* **239,** 1684–1686.

Fontaine, M., and Fontaine, Y. A. (1962). *Gen. Comp. Endocrinol. Suppl.* **1,** 63–74.

Forbes, T. R. (1937). *Anat. Record* **70,** 113–137.

Fortier, C. (1962). *Ann. Rev. Physiol.* **24,** 223–258.

Fraps, R. M. (1961). *In* "Control of Ovulation" (C. A. Villee, ed.), pp. 133–162. Pergamon Press, New York.

Galli Mainini, C. (1950). *Rev. soc. arg. biol.* **26,** 166–178.

Galli Mainini, C. (1951). *Compt. rend. soc. biol.* **145,** 131–133.

Ganong, W. F. (1959). *In* "Comparative Endocrinology" (A. Gorbman, ed.), pp. 187–201. Wiley, New York.

Ganong, W. F., and Forsham, P. H. (1960). *Ann. Rev. Physiol.* **22,** 579–614.

Garren, H. W., Hill, C. H., and Carter, M. W. (1961). *Poultry Sci.* **40,** 446–453.

Glick, B. (1960). *Poultry Sci.* **39,** 1527–1533.

Gorbman, A. (1941). *Quart. Rev. Biol.* **16,** 294–310.

Gorbman, A. (1946). *Univ. Calif. (Berkeley) Publs. Zoöl.* **51,** 229–243.

Godfrey, E. F., and Jaap, R. G. (1950). *Poultry Sci.* **29,** 356–361.

Grant, C. W. (1959). *Endocrinology* **64,** 839–841.

Grant, C. W., and Grant, J. A. (1958). *Biol. Bull.* **114,** 1–9.

Greenwood, A. W. (1924). *J. Exptl. Biol.* **2,** 75–78.

Greep, R. O. (1961). *In* "Sex and Internal Secretions" (W. C. Young, ed.), Vol. 1, pp. 240–301. Williams & Wilkins, Baltimore, Maryland.

Greep, R. O., Van Dyke, H. B., and Chow, B. F. (1942). *Endocrinology* **30,** 635–649.

Hayashida, T. (1962). CIBA *Foundation Colloq. on Endocrinol.* **14,** 338–372.

Hazelwood, R. L., and Hazelwood, B. S. (1961). *Proc. Soc. Exptl. Biol. Med.* **108,** 10–12.

Hellbaum, H. W. (1936). *Anat. Record* **67**, 53–67.

Hildeman, W. H. (1959). *Am. Naturalist* **93**, 27–34.

Hisaw, F. L. (1947). *Physiol. Revs.* **27**, 95–119.

Hisaw, F. L., and Abramowitz, A. A. (1938). *Rept. Woods Hole Oceanog. Inst. 1937*, pp. 21–22.

Hisaw, F. L., and Abramowitz, A. A. (1939). *Rept. Woods Hole Oceanog. Inst., 1938*, p. 22.

Hoar, W. S. (1955). *Mem. Soc. Endocrinol. No.* **4**, 5–24.

Houssay, B. A. (1931). *Compt. rend. soc. biol.* **106**, 377–378.

Houssay, B. A. (1936). *New Engl. J. Med.* **214**, 913–926.

Houssay, B. A. (1949). *Quart. Rev. Biol.* **24**, 1–27.

Houssay, B. A., and Biasotti, A. (1931). *Compt. rend. soc. biol.* **107**, 733–735.

Houssay, B. A., Giusti, L., and Lascano-Gonzalez, J. M. (1929). *Compt. rend. soc. biol.* **102**, 864–866.

Houssay, B. A., Di Benedetto, E., and Mazzocco, P. (1933). *Compt. rend. soc. biol.* **113**, 465–467.

Houssay, B. A. Smyth, F. S., Foglia, V. G., and Houssay, A. B. (1942). *J. Exptl. Med.* **75**, 93–106.

Houssay, B. A., Anderson, E., Bates, R. W., and Li, C. H. (1955). *Endocrinology* **57**, 55–63.

Hsieh, K., Wang, T., and Blumenthal, H. (1952). *Endocrinology* **51**, 298–302.

Ingram, W. R. (1929). *J. Exptl. Zool.* **53**, 387–409.

Jailer, J. W., and Boas, N. F. (1950). *Endocrinology* **46**, 314–318.

Jost, A. (1953). *In Recent Progr. in Hormone Research* **8**, 379–418.

Kawakami, M., and Sawyer, C. H. (1959). *Endocrinology* **65**, 631–643.

Keating, F. R., Rawson, R. W., Peacock, W., and Evans, R. D. (1945). *Endocrinology* **36**, 137–169.

Keaty, C., and Stanley, A. J. (1940). *Anat. Record* **78**, Suppl., p. 140.

Kehl, R., and Combescot, C. (1955). *Mem. Soc. Endocrinol. No.* **4**, 57–74.

Kepinov, L. (1946). *Bull. soc. chim. biol.* **28**, 813–822.

Ketterer, B., Randle, P. J., and Young, F. G. (1957). *Ergeb. Physiol. biol. Chem. u. exptl. Parmakol.* **49**, 127–211.

Knobil, E. (1961). *In* "Growth in Living Systems" (M. X. Zarrow, ed.), pp. 353–381. Basic Books, New York.

Knobil, E., and Greep, R. O. (1958). *Endocrinology* **62**, 61–63.

Knobil, E., and Greep, R. O. (1959). *Recent Progr. in Hormone Research* **15**, 1–69.

Knobil, E., and Greep, R. O. (1961). *In* "Hormones in Human Plasma" (H. N. Antoniades, ed.), pp. 141–148. Little, Brown, Boston, Massachusetts.

Knobil, E., and Josimovich, J. B. (1961). *Endocrinology* **69**, 139–151.

Knobil, E., Morse, A., Hofmann, F. G., and Greep, R. O. (1954). *Acta Endocrinol.* **17**, 229–238.

Knobil, E., Kostyo, J. L., and Greep, R. O. (1959). *Endocrinology* **65**, 487–493.

Kosto, B., Pickford, G. E., and Foster, M. (1959). *Endocrinology* **65**, 869–881.

Leblond, C. P., and Noble, G. K. (1937). *Proc. Soc. Exptl. Biol. Med.* **36**, 517–518.

488 E. KNOBIL AND R. SANDLER

Lehrman, D. S., and Brody, P. (1961). *J. Endocrinol.* **22,** 269–275.

Li, C. H., Moudgal, N. R., Trenkle, A., Bourdel, G., and Sadri, K. (1962). *CIBA Foundation Colloq. on Endocrinol.* **14,** 20–44.

Libby, D. A. Meites, J., and Schaible, P. J. (1955). *Poultry Sci.* **34,** 1329–1331.

Lofts, B. (1961). *Gen. Comp. Endocrinol.* **1,** 179–189.

Lofts, B., and Marshall, A. J. (1958). *J. Endocrinol.* **17,** 91–98.

Lopez-Wille, G. (1959). *Ann. endocrinol. (Paris)* **20,** 897–901.

Macchi, I. A., and Rizzo, F. (1962). *Proc. Soc. Exptl. Biol. Med.* **110,** 433–436.

Maher, M. J., and Levedahl, B. H. (1959). *J. Exptl. Zool.* **140,** 169–189.

Marshall, A. J. (1955). *Mem. Soc. Endocrinol. No.* **4,** 75–93.

Marshall, A. J., ed. (1961). *In* "Biology and Comparative Physiology of Birds." Academic Press, New York.

Marques, M. (1955). *Rev. soc. arg. biol.* **31,** 177–183.

Matthews, S. A. (1950). *Am. J. Physiol.* **162,** 590–597.

Mayo, V. (1937). *Biol. Bull.* **73,** 373.

Meites, J. (1959). *In* "Reproduction in Domestic Animals" (H. H. Cole and P. T. Cupps, eds.), Vol. 1, pp. 539–593. Academic Press, New York.

Mellish, C. R. (1936). *Anat. Record* **67,** 23–33.

Mellish, C. R., and Meyer, R. K. (1937). *Anat. Record* **69,** 179–189.

Meyer, R. K. (1962). Discussion of paper by Benoit, J. (1962). *Gen. Comp. Endocrinol. Suppl.* **1,** 273.

Meyer, R. K., Mellish, C. R., and Kupperman, H. S. (1939). *J. Pharmacol. Exptl. Therap.* **65,** 104–114.

Mialhe, P. (1955). *Compt. rend. ac. sci.* **241,** 1500–1503.

Mialhe, P. (1957). *J. physiol. (Paris)* **49,** 312–314.

Miller, D. S. (1938). *Proc. Soc. Exptl. Biol. Med.* **38,** 453–455.

Miller, D. S. (1939). *J. Exptl. Zool.* **80,** 259–285.

Miller, M. R. (1952). *Anat. Record* **113,** 309–321.

Miller, M. R., and Wurster, D. H. (1958). *Endocrinology* **63,** 191–200.

Miller, R. A., and Riddle, O. (1942). *Am. J. Anat.* **71,** 311–323.

Mixner, J. P. Reineke, E. P., and Turner, C. W. (1944). *Endocrinology* **34,** 168–174.

Morgan, H. E., Regen, D. M., Henderson, M. J., Sawyer, T. K., and Park, C. R. (1961). *J. Biol. Chem.* **236,** 2162–2168.

Moudgal, N. R., and Li, C. H. (1961). *Arch. Biochem. Biophys.* **93,** 122–127.

Moszkowska, A. (1949). *Compt. rend. soc. biol.* **143,** 1332–1333.

Munson, P. L. (1961). *In* "Hormones in Human Plasma" (H. N. Antioniades, ed.), pp. 149–190. Little, Brown, Boston, Massachusetts.

Nagra, C. L., Baum, G. J., and Meyer, R. K. (1960). *Proc. Soc. Exptl. Biol. Med.* **105,** 68–70.

Nalbandov, A. V. (1945). *Endocrinology* **36,** 251–258.

Nalbandov, A. V. (1953). *Poultry Sci.* **32,** 88–103.

Nalbandov, A. V. (1959). *In* "Comparative Endocrinology" (A. Gorbman, ed.), pp. 161–173. Wiley, New York.

Nalbandov, A. V. (1961). *In* "Control of Ovulation" (C. A. Villee, ed.), pp. 122–131. Pergamon Press, New York.

Nalbandov, A. V., and Card, L. E. (1943). *J. Exptl. Zool.* **94**, 387–413.

Nalbandov, A. V., and Card, L. E. (1946). *Endocrinology* **38**, 71–78.

Nalbandov, A. V., Meyer, R. K., and McShan, W. H. (1951). *Anat. Record* **110**, 475–493.

Nelson, D. H. (1961). *In* "Hormones in Human Plasma" (H. N. Antoniades, ed.), pp. 335–350. Little, Brown, Boston, Massachusetts.

Newcomer, W. S. (1959). *Endocrinology* **65**, 133–135.

Newcomer, W. S., and Hurst, J. G. (1962). *Federation Proc.* **21**, 217.

Olivereau, M. (1957). *Compt. rend. assoc. anat.* **43**, 636–657.

Opel, H., and Nalbandov, A. V. (1961). *Endocrinology* **69**, 1016–1028.

Orias, O. (1932). *Biol. Bull.* **63**, 477–483.

Panigel, M. (1956). *Ann. sci. nat. Zool. et biol. animale* **18**, 569–668.

Parlow, A. F. (1961). *In* "Human Pituitary Gonadotropins" (A. Albert, ed.), pp. 319–322. C. C. Thomas, Springfield, Illinois.

Perek, M., and Eckstein, B. (1959). *Poultry Sci.* **38**, 996–999.

Pickford, G. E. (1959). *In* "Comparative Endocrinology" (A. Gorbman, ed.), pp. 404–420. Wiley, New York.

Pickford, G. E., and Atz, J. W. (1957). "The Physiology of the Pituitary Gland of Fishes." New York Zoological Society, New York.

Pickford, G. E., Wilhelmi, A. E., and Nussbaum, N. (1959). *Anat. Record* **134**, 624–625.

Pitt-Rivers, R., and Tata, J. R. (1959). "The Thyroid Hormones." Pergamon Press, New York.

Purves, H. D., and Adams, D. D. (1960). *Brit. Med. Bull.* **16**, 128–132.

Raben, M. S. (1959). *Recent Progr. in Hormone Research* **15**, 71–114.

Ralph, C. L., and Fraps, R. M. (1960). *Endocrinology* **66**, 269–272.

Rawson, R. W. (1960). *Ann. N. Y. Acad. Sci.* **86**, 311–676.

Rawson, R. W., Rall, J. E., and Sonenberg, M. (1955). *In* "The Hormones" (G. Pincus and K. V. Thimann, eds.), Vol. 3, pp. 433–520. Academic Press, New York.

Riddle, O., and Braucher, P. F. (1931). *Am. J. Physiol.* **97**, 617–625.

Riddle, O., and Dotti, L. B. (1947). *Carnegie Inst. Wash. Publ. No.* **569**, 1–128.

Riddle, O., Bates, R. W., and Dykshorn, S. W. (1932). *Proc. Soc. Exptl. Biol. Med.* **29**, 1211–1212.

Riddle, O., Bates, R. W., and Dykshorn, S. W. (1933). *Am. J. Physiol.* **105**, 191–216.

Riddle, O., Smith, G. C., Bates, R. W., Moran, C. S., and Lahr, E. L. (1936). *Endocrinology* **20**, 1–16.

Riley, G. M., Stanley, A. J., and Witschi, E. (1937). *Anat. Record* **70**, Suppl. 1, 92.

Rinfret, A. P., and Hane, S. (1955). *Proc. Soc. Exptl. Biol. Med.* **90**, 508–510.

Rothschild, I., and Fraps, R. M. (1949). *Endocrinology* **44**, 141–149.

Rudolph, H. J., and Pehrson, N. C. (1961). *Endocrinology* **69**, 661–663.

Rugh, R. (1935) *J. Exptl. Zool.* **71**, 149–162.

Russell, J. A., and Wilhelmi, A. E. (1958). *Ann. Rev. Physiol.* **20**, 43–66.

Sayers, G., and Royce, P. C. (1960). *In* "Clinical Endocrinology" (E. B. Astwood, ed.). Vol. I, pp. 323–343. Grune and Stratton, New York.

Sayers, G., Redgate, E. S., and Royce, P. C. (1958). *Ann. Rev. Physiol.* **20**, 243–274.

Schaefer, W. H. (1933). *Proc. Soc. Exptl. Biol. Med.* **30**, 1363–1365.

Schlumberger, H. G., and Rudolph, H. J. (1959). *Endocrinology* **65**, 902–908.

Schockaert, J. A. (1931). *Proc. Soc. Exptl. Biol. Med.* **29**, 306–308.

Schooley, J. P., Riddle, O., and Bates, R. W. (1941). *Am. J. Anat.* **69**, 123–154.

Sell, J. L., and Balloun, S. L. (1960). *Poultry Sci.* **39**, 1292.

Sell, J. L., and Balloun, S. L. (1961). *Poultry Sci.* **40**, 1118–1129.

Shellabarger, C. J., Gorbman, A., Schatzlein, F. C., and McGill, D. (1956). *Endocrinology* **59**, 331–339.

Simpson, M. E. (1959). *In* "Reproduction in Domestic Animals" (H. H. Cole and P. T. Cupps, eds.), Vol. 1, pp. 59–110. Academic Press, New York.

Simpson, M. E., Asling, C. W., and Evans, H. M. (1950). *Yale J. Biol. and Med.* **23**, 1–27.

Smith, C. L. (1955). *Mem. Soc. Endocrinol. No.* **4**, 39–56.

Smith, P. E. (1916). *Anat. Record* **11**, 57–64.

Smith, P. E. (1927). *J. Am. Med. Assoc.* **88**, 158–161.

Smith, P. E., and Smith, I. B. (1923). *Endocrinology* **7**, 579–590.

Smith, R. W., Jr., Gaebler, O. H., and Long, C. N. H., eds. (1955) *In* "The Hypophyseal Growth Hormone, Nature and Actions." McGraw-Hill, New York.

Solomon, D. H., and Dowling, J. T. (1960). *Ann. Rev. Physiol.* **22**, 615–650.

Solomon, J., and Greep, R. O. (1959). *Endocrinology* **65**, 334–336.

Sonenberg, M. (1958). *Vitamins and Hormones* **16**, 206–261.

Stefan, Y. (1961). *Compt. rend. soc. biol.* **155**, 638–641.

Strahan, R. (1962). Discussion of Chester Jones, I., Phillips, J. G., and Bellamy, D. (1962). *Gen. Comp. Endocrinol. Suppl.* **1**, 36–47.

Sturkie, P. D. (1954). "Avian Physiology." Comstock (Cornell Univ. Press), Ithaca, New York.

Taber, E., Claytor, M., Knight, J., Gambrell, D., Flowers, J., and Ayers, C. (1958). *Endocrinology* **62**, 84–89.

Tanabe, Y., Himeno, K., and Nazaki, H. (1957). *Endocrinology* **61**, 661–666.

Tuchmann-Duplessis, H. (1944). *Bull. histol. appl. physiol. et pathol. et tech. microscop.* **22**, 17–25.

Turner, C. D. (1935). *Biol. Bull.* **69**, 143–158.

van Oordt, G. J., and van Oordt, P. G. W. J. (1955). *Mem. Soc. Endocrinol. No.* **4**, 25–58.

van Oordt, G. J., Sluiter, J. W., and van Oordt, P. G. W. J. (1951). *Acta Endocrinol.* **7**, 257–269.

van Oordt, P. G. W. J.(1960). *In* "Symposia of the Zoological Society of London" (E. J. W. Barrington, ed.), No. 2, pp. 29–52, Zoological Society, London.

Vivien, J. H. (1941). *Bull. biol. France et Belg.* **74**, 257–309.

Wahlberg, P. (1955). *Acta Endocrinol. Suppl.* **23**, 1–79.

Wilhelmi, A. E. (1955). *In* "Hypophyseal Growth Hormone, Nature and Actions" (R. W. Smith, Jr., O. H. Gaebler and C. N. H. Long, eds.), pp. 59–104. McGraw-Hill, New York.

Wilhoft, D. C. (1958). *Copeia No.* **4**, 265–276.

Witschi, E. (1937). *Cold Spring Harbor Symposia Quant. Biol.* **5,** 180–190.

Witschi, E. (1955). *Mem. Soc. Endocrinol. No.* **4,** 149–165.

Witschi, E., and Chang, C. Y. (1959). *In* "Comparative Endocrinology" (A. Gorbman, ed.), pp. 149–160. Wiley, New York.

Witschi, E., and Riley, G. M. (1940). *Endocrinology* **26,** 565–576.

Wolstenholme, G. E. W., and Cameron, M. P., eds. (1962). *CIBA Foundation Colloq. on Endocrinol.* **14,**

Wolstenholme, G. E. W., and Millar, E. C. P., eds. (1957). *CIBA Foundation Colloq. on Endocrinol.* **11,**

Woodhead, A. D. (1960). *J. Endocrinol.* **21,** 295–301.

Woods, M. C., and Simpson, M. E. (1961). *Endocrinology* **69,** 91–125.

Wright, A., and Chester Jones, I. (1957). *J. Endocrinol.* **15,** 83–99.

Wright, P. A., and Hisaw, F. L. (1946). *Endocrinology* **39,** 247–255.

Yates, F. E., and Urquhart, J. (1962). *Physiol. Revs.* **42,** 359–443.

Young, W. C., ed. (1961). *In* "Sex and Internal Secretions," Vol. 1, pp. 449–496. Williams & Wilkins, Baltimore, Maryland.

Zarrow, M. X., and Baldini, J. T. (1952). *Endocrinology* **50,** 555–561.

Zarrow, M. X., and Zarrow, I. G. (1950). *Anat. Record* **108,** 600–601.

Zarrow, M. X., Greeman, D. L., Kollias, J., and Dalrymple, D. (1962). *Gen. Comp. Endocrinol.* **2,** 177–180.

Author Index

Numbers in italics indicate the pages on which the complete references are listed.

493

du Vigneaud, V., 27, 29, 30, 31, 32, 33, 34,
    35, 37, 38, 43, 44, 61, 72, 74, 75, 77,
    78, 80
Dye, J. A., 384, 403, 406
Dyer, H. M., 29, 74
Dykshorn, S. W., 451, 456, 489
Dyrenfurth, I., 228, 229, 249, 254, 477,
    479, 484

Eade, N. R., 279, 286
Eakin, R. M., 304, 310, 318, 323
Earle, D. P., 414, 426
Eartly, H., 305, 318
Eaton, R. C., 480, 486
Ebling, F. J., 177, 200
Ecker, A., 332, 368
Eckles, N. E., 18, 20
Eckstein, B., 473, 489
Eckstein, P., 116, 119, 120, 151
Edgar, D. G., 116, 118, 119, 146
Edgren, R. A., 88, 106, 140, 146, 180, 200
Edson, M., 131, 145
Egami, N., 160, 162, 200, 202, 464, 486
Egdahl, R. H., 10, 20, 226, 251
Eggert, B., 309, 310, 318
Eggleton, M. G., 32, 52, 74
Ehni, G., 18, 20
Ehrlén, I., 265, 286
Eigner, E. A., 436, 445
Eik-Nes, K. B., 114, 130, 146, 150
Eisenberg, E., 176, 205
Eisentraut, A. M., 412, 426
El Attar, T., 131, 133, 146
Elgart, S., 383, 386, 407
Eliot, T. S., 166, 200
Ellis, J. T., 312, 426
Ellis, R. M., 416, 425
Ellis, S., 282, 286, 419, 424, 430, 444
Elrick, H., 414, 424, 426
Elterich, C. F., 298, 318
Elton, R. L., 473, 476, 486
Elwers, M., 17, 20
Elwers-Bar-Sela, M., 17, 20
Elwyn, D., 242, 245, 254
Emmens, C. W., 124, 140, 150, 182, 204
Emmerson, M. A., 126, 149
Enami, M., 87, 106
Endahl, B. R., 247, 251
Enemar, A., 40, 75, 483, 486

Eness, P. G., 126, 149
Engel, F. L., 242, 251, 437, 445
Engel, H. R., 416, 425
Engel, L. L., 114, 115, 134, 136, 144, 146,
    150, 231, 256
Engel, S. L., 32, 41, 42, 43, 44, 72, 80
Entenman, C., 140, 149
Epstein, A. A., 383, 404
Epstein, E., 383, 404
Epstein, M., 187, 203
Eränkö, O., 270, 271, 274, 275, 286
Erb, R. E., 118, 128, 130, 147, 151
Erichsen, S., 136, 146, 152
Ernster, L., 307, 324
Erspamer, V., 276, 289
Erving, H. W., 142, 149
Erwin, H. L., 7, 11, 22
Eschbach, J., 87, 106
Essex, H. E., 63, 79
Etkin, W., 87, 106, 301, 311, 316, 318, 319,
    483, 486
Etkin, W. N., 319
Etkin, W. R., 316, 323
Eton, B., 120, 144, 151
Euler, C. von (see von Euler, C.)
Euler, Chr. von (see von Euler, Chr.)
Euler, U. S. von (see von Euler, U.S.)
Evans, H. M., 231, 253, 306, 323, 433,
    442, 444, 445, 447, 478, 484, 490
Evans, J. D., 309, 319
Evans, L. T., 163, 178, 200, 299, 319, 458,
    467, 486
Evans, R. O., 466, 487
Evennett, P. J., 156, 200, 461, 462, 485
Everett, G. M., 316, 323
Everett, J. W., 7, 16, 17, 18, 19, 20, 21, 23
Eversole, E., 160, 200
Eviatar, A., 86, 109
Ewer, R. F., 63, 69, 70, 75
Eycleshymer, A., 332, 368
Ezrin, C., 416, 418, 426

Fabiani, G., 356, 357, 359, 367
Fabré, M., 469, 486
Fänge, R., 237, 251, 261, 276, 283, 284,
    285, 286, 287
Fagerlund, U. H. M., 217, 253
Fajans, S-S., 245, 251
Falck, B., 261, 263, 264, 285, 287

Index of Species

References to tables are marked by a T in parentheses after the page number and references to figures by an F in parentheses after the page number.

Subject Index

Arginine vasopressin, 31
  in Artiodactyla, 46
  chromatography of, 31
Artiodactyla, neurohypophyseal hormones
    in, 46
Ascidians, cerebral ganglion of, 26
Ascorbic acid, adrenal
  action of ACTH on, 437
  depletion of, 8, 9, 11
Aves, *see* Birds.

β-Cells in pancreas, damage to, 378–379
Birds
  adrenocorticosteroids of, 213, 215
  effects of androgens on, 163
    of light on testicular function of, 189
    of neurohypophyseal hormones on,
      71–72
  nasal gland of, 237–238
  neurohypophyseal hormones of, 63–65
  stimulatory action of ACTH in, 230
Bladder, urinary
  effect of neurohypophyseal hormones on
    amphibian, 69
β-MSH,
  see also Melanophore stimulating hor-
    mone
  antagonism to chlorpromazine, 104
  chemical structure, 94–95
  effect on human skin, 102
    on melanogenesis in guinea pig skin,
      102
    on spinal cord, 103
  isolation of, 92–93
  potency, 98

Carbohydrate metabolism
  effects of corticosteroids on, 240–242
Castration,
  effects on accessory sex organs of mam-
      mals, 170, 173
    in amphibians, 162
    on antlers, 168–169
    in birds, 157–165
    on frogs, 155
    on hair color, 168
    on plumage, 166
    in rats, 155
Castration cells, in adenohypophysis, 174
Catecholamines, 258–285
  actions, 281–284
  assay, 264–266

biosynthesis, 278, 279
concentration in plasma, 281
differential release from adrenal medulla,
    281
distribution, 267–276
formation, 278–279
inactivation, 281
metabolism, 278–281
release, 280–281
storage in granules, 279
Chlorpromazine, antagonism to β-MSH,
    104
Choanichthyes,
  see also Dipnoi
  lungfish, 58, 61
Cholesterol, 113
  as precursor of gonadal hormones,
    114–115
Chromaffin cells, 258–285
  distribution, 260–264
  in carotid body, 273
  in cyclostome heart, 261–262, 276
  in ganglia, 273
  in prostate, 273
  morphology, 261–262
  staining methods, 259
Chromaffin cell tumors, 273–274
Chromatophores, 82–105
Cock-feathered breeds, testes of, 181
Cold,
  effect on hypothalamo-adenohypophy-
      seal complex, 14
    on thyroid, 307
Cold-blooded vertebrates, color changes in,
    81
Color changes,
  in cold-blooded vertebrates, 81
  morphological, 99
  physiological, 98
Corpus luteum,
  formation of, 15
Corpuscles of Stannius, 212
Cortecin, 194
Corticosteroid-binding protein, 225
Corticosteroids, *see* Adrenocorticosteroids
Corticosterone,
  in amphibians, 217
  in Myxinoidea, 225
  production by subeutherian vertebrates,
    209